D0936165

COMPARATIVE BIOCHEMISTRY

VOLUME VII: SUPPLEMENTARY VOLUME

COMPARATIVE BIOCHEMISTRY

A Comprehensive Treatise

Volume I: Sources of Free Energy

Volume II: Free Energy and Biological Function

Volume III: Constituents of Life—Part A

Volume IV: Constituents of Life—Part B

Volume V: Constituents of Life—Part C

Volume VI: Cells and Organisms

Volume VII: Supplementary Volume

COMPARATIVE BIOCHEMISTRY

A Comprehensive Treatise

Edited by

Marcel Florkin
Department of Biochemistry
University of Liège
Liège, Belgium

Howard S. Mason
University of Oregon Medical School
Portland, Oregon

Volume VII

SUPPLEMENTARY VOLUME

1964

ACADEMIC PRESS • New York and London

ACADEMIC PRESS INC.
111 FIFTH AVENUE
NEW YORK, NEW YORK 10003

United Kingdom Edition
Published by
ACADEMIC PRESS INC. (LONDON) LTD.
BERKELEY SQUARE, LONDON W. 1

Library of Congress Catalog Card Number 59–13830

PRINTED IN THE UNITED STATES OF AMERICA

CONTRIBUTORS TO VOLUME VII

P. W. KENT, *Department of Biochemistry, University of Oxford, Oxford, England*

N. G. PON, *Department of Biochemistry, University of California, Riverside, California*

ERNEST SCHOFFENIELS, *Institut Léon Frédéricq, University of Liège, Liège, Belgium*

MAURICE WELSCH, *Laboratory of General and Medical Microbiology, University of Liège, and C.N.P.E.M., Liège, Belgium*

WILLIAM C. YOUNG, *Oregon Regional Primate Research Center, Beaverton, Oregon, and Department of Anatomy, University of Oregon Medical School, Portland, Oregon*

PREFACE

The previous volumes of this treatise have been arranged to survey the field of comparative biochemistry within a comprehensive framework. The energetic aspect of living organisms was described in Volumes I and II. The composition of living organisms, and the transformations of the constituents were described in Volumes III to V. Volumes VI and VII are concerned primarily with comparative biochemistry at levels of organization higher than the molecular. The present volume includes, in addition, two chapters relating to molecular biochemistry which, for reasons beyond the control of the editors, could not be included in the appropriate volume. Volume VII also includes a comprehensive topical index to the whole treatise.

With this volume we finish a task begun in 1955, the organizing and editing of a comprehensive treatise. The authors contributing to this treatise have pioneered in difficult areas of biochemistry and have helped to produce a work which we believe to be of enduring value whatever the future shape of the field. Once again, we wish to record our gratitude to our publisher, Academic Press, and its staff, for exceedingly competent professional assistance throughout the preparation of the treatise.

MARCEL FLORKIN
Liège, Belgium

HOWARD S. MASON
Portland, Oregon

April, 1964

CONTENTS

COMPARATIVE BIOCHEMISTRY

A Comprehensive Treatise

Volume I: Sources of Free Energy

Volume II: Free Energy and Biological Function

Volume III: Constituents of Life—Part A

Volume IV: Constituents of Life—Part B

Volume V: Constituents of Life—Part C

Volume VI: Cells and Organisms

---

* Most of the names refer to phyla, except in a few cases where some of the smaller taxonomic groups are shown. Capitalized names written across lines are groups including all forms above the name.

NOTE: Charts I, II, and III were prepared by Helen A. Stafford, Reed College, Portland, Oregon. For further information see "A Guide to the Nomenclature and Classification of Organisms," by Dr. Stafford, in Vol. I of this treatise.

CHART I
HYPOTHETICAL PHYLOGENETIC RELATIONSHIPS BETWEEN EXTANT MAJOR GROUPS OF ORGANISMS*

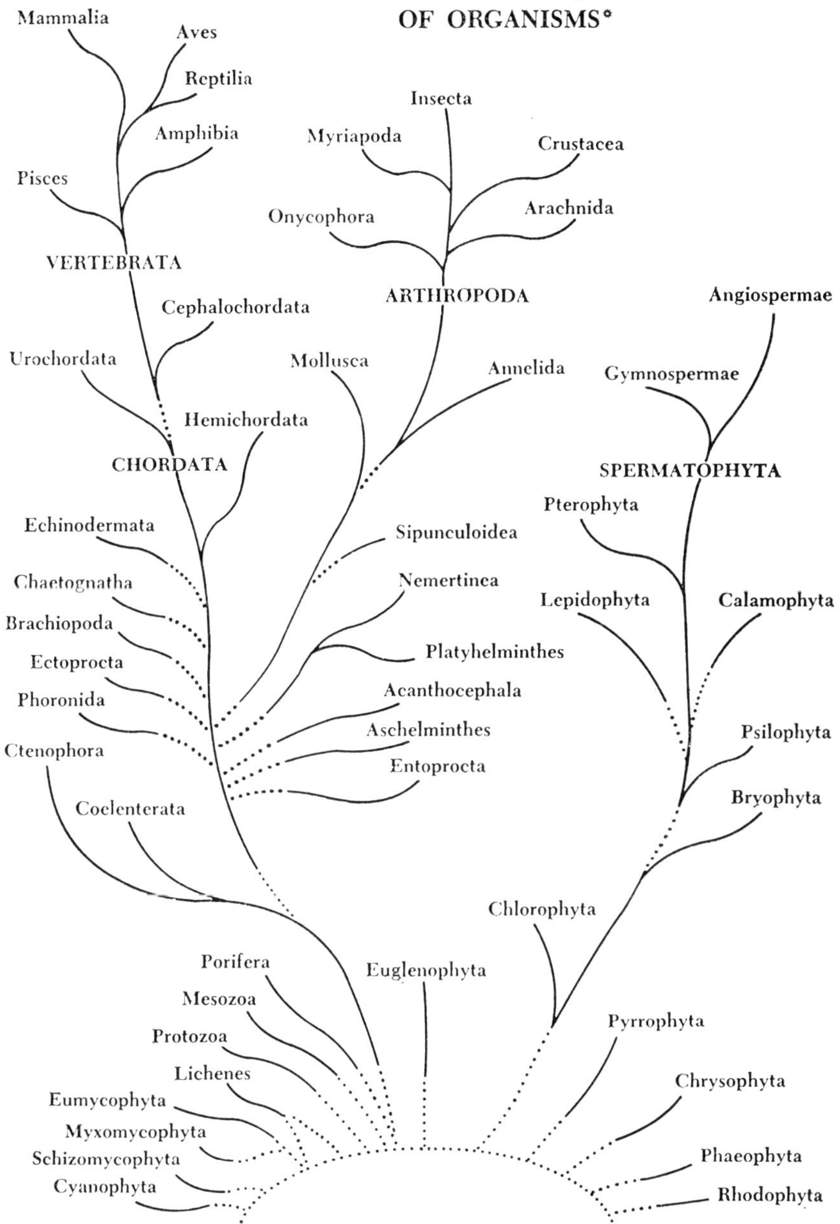

CHART II: ANIMAL KINGDOM

Divisions	Estimated Number of Species[d]	Taxonomic Classifications			
Protozoa (acellular animals)	15,000				
Mesozoa	—				
Porifera (sponges)	5,000				
Coelenterata (coelenterates)	10,000				Radiata
Ctenophora (comb jellies)	100				Radiata
Platyhelminthes (flat worms)	6,000	Acoelomates		Protostomia	Bilateria
Nemertinea (nemertine worms)	500	Acoelomates		Protostomia	Bilateria
Aschelminthes[a], Acanthocephala[a]	7,000	Pseudocoelomates		Protostomia	Bilateria
Entoprocta[b], Ectoprocta[b] (moss animals)	3,000	Pseudocoelomates / Eucoelomates	Schizocoela	Protostomia	Bilateria
Phoronida	15	Eucoelomates	Schizocoela	Protostomia	Bilateria
Brachiopoda (lamp shells)	120	Eucoelomates	Schizocoela	Protostomia	Bilateria
Mollusca (mollusks)	70,000	Eucoelomates	Schizocoela	Protostomia	Bilateria
Sipunculoidea	—	Eucoelomates	Schizocoela	Protostomia	Bilateria
Annelida[c] (segmented worms)	6,500	Eucoelomates	Schizocoela	Protostomia	Bilateria
Arthropoda (arthropods)	750,000	Eucoelomates	Schizocoela	Protostomia	Bilateria
Chaetognatha (arrow worms)	30	Eucoelomates	Enterocoela	Deuterostomia	Bilateria
Echinodermata (echinoderms)	5,000	Eucoelomates	Enterocoela	Deuterostomia	Bilateria
Hemichordata, Chordata (including vertebrates)	60,000	Eucoelomates	Enterocoela	Deuterostomia	Bilateria

[a] Includes Rotifera, Gastrotricha, Kinorhyncha, Nematoda, Nematomorpha, Priapuloidea. Formerly called Nemathelminthes.

[b] Formerly in Bryozoa.

[c] Includes Echiuroidea.

[d] Taken from "Handbook of Biological Data" (*4*), p. 533.

CHART III: PLANT KINGDOM

Divisions	Estimated Number of Species[d]	Major Synonymous Terms		
Euglenophyta (euglenoids)	340	Algae	Thallophyta	Cryptogamia
Chlorophyta (green algae)	5,700	Algae	Thallophyta	Cryptogamia
Pyrrophyta (cryptomonads, dinoflagellates)	1,000	Algae	Thallophyta	Cryptogamia
Chrysophyta (yellow green algae, diatoms)	5,700	Algae	Thallophyta	Cryptogamia
Phaeophyta (brown algae)	900	Algae	Thallophyta	Cryptogamia
Rhodophyta (red algae)	2,500	Algae	Thallophyta	Cryptogamia
Cyanophyta[a] (blue-green algae)	1,400	Algae	Thallophyta	Cryptogamia
Schizomycophyta[a] (bacteria)	1,300[e]	Fungi	Thallophyta	Cryptogamia
Myxomycophyta (slime molds)	430	Fungi	Thallophyta	Cryptogamia
Eumycophyta (true fungi)	74,000	Fungi	Thallophyta	Cryptogamia
Lichenes (lichens)	15,500		Thallophyta	Cryptogamia
Bryophyta (mosses and liverworts)	23,800		Bryophyta	Cryptogamia
Psilophyta[b] (whisk ferns)	3	Psilopsida	Tracheophyta	Cryptogamia
Calamophyta[b] (horsetails)	30	Sphenopsida	Tracheophyta	Cryptogamia
Lepidophyta[b] (lycopods)	1,300	Lycopsida	Tracheophyta	Cryptogamia
Pterophyta[b, c] (ferns)	10,000	Pteropsida	Tracheophyta	Cryptogamia
Spermatophyta (seed plants)	201,000	Pteropsida	Tracheophyta	Phanerogamia

[a] Sometimes grouped as Schizophyta.

[b] Formerly classed as Pteridophyta.

[c] Formerly classed as Filicineae in Pteropsida.

[d] Taken from "Handbook of Biological Data" (*4*), p. 533.

[e] There is much disagreement concerning designation of species here.

CHAPTER 1

Expressions of the Pentose Phosphate Cycle*

N. G. Pon

Department of Biochemistry, University of California, Riverside, California

* The work described in this paper was supported, in part, by the United States Atomic Energy Commission, Lawrence Radiation Laboratory, Berkeley, California.

I. General Considerations

Without exception, all living things require energy to support life. They derive this energy either from photosynthesis or from the oxidation of inorganic or organic compounds. Those organisms which oxidize organic compounds often utilize glucose as the source of energy, and they generally oxidize glucose via glycolysis (*1*). [The term glycolysis is used here to describe the Embden-Meyerhof-Parnas (EMP) pathway, although the original meaning of glycolysis is simply the breakdown of glucose (*2*).] There are, however, certain organisms which degrade glucose by alternate pathways, or which, under certain conditions, have to call upon alternate pathways for the metabolism of glucose. One such alternate pathway is the pentose phosphate cycle. To complicate matters further, there exist at least two types of pentose phosphate cycles. The one referred to above is the oxidative pentose phosphate cycle and is a catabolic pathway. The other cycle is a synthetic pathway and is sometimes called the reductive pentose phosphate cycle. Both cycles are still being actively studied, as is evident from the enormous mass of literature accumulated to date. Fortunately, a number of excellent reviews over the past decade have been made available by Horecker and Mehler (*3*), Racker (*4*), Axelrod and Beevers (*5*), Gibbs (*6*), and many others.

II. Description of the Pentose Phosphate Cycle

The oxidative pentose phosphate cycle (*7*) comes under the guise of many aliases. Notable among them are such names as the hexose monophosphate shunt, the phosphogluconate oxidative pathway, the Warburg-Lipmann-Dickens pathway, the direct oxidative pathway (*8*). These names, however, do not describe the operation of this cycle completely. In brief, the operation is as follows: A hexose molecule enters the pathway in the form of its monophosphate. The latter is oxidized to an aldonolactone, which is then decarboxylated oxidatively to a pentose phosphate. The pentose phosphate rearranges and condenses with another pentose phosphate to form a heptulose monophosphate and a triose phosphate. These two compounds eventually are reconverted to a hexose monophosphate and a tetrose phosphate. The pathway is shown in detail in Fig. 1. Noteworthy is the production of reduced pyridine nucleotides during the operation of the cycle.

The reductive pentose phosphate cycle (*9*) is also a cycle of many names, two of them being the photosynthetic carbon reduction cycle (*10*) and the Calvin cycle (*11*). [A slight difference between the reductive pentose phosphate cycle and the carbon reduction cycle of photosynthesis has been noted by Krebs and Kornberg (*12*). This difference will be discussed later.] This cycle (Fig. 2) starts with the reaction of carbon dioxide with a pentose diphosphate to form three-carbon phosphorylated acids. This three-carbon compound is subsequently reduced to triose phosphate, which then condenses with another molecule of

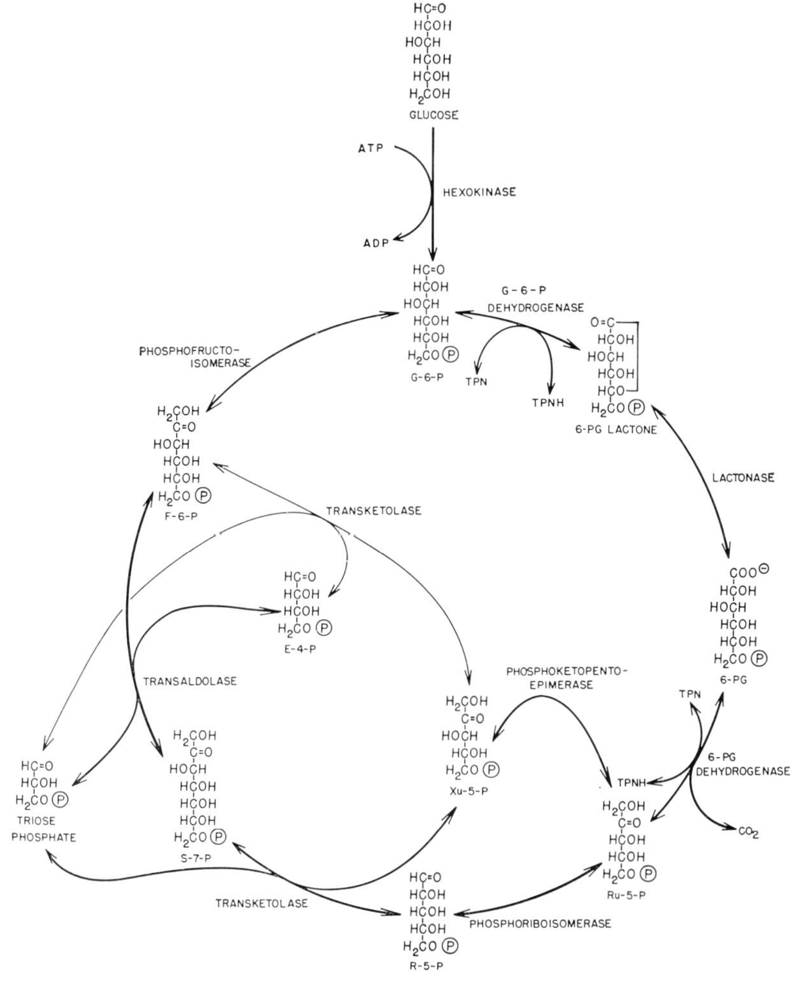

FIG. 1. The oxidative pentose phosphate cycle.

triose phosphate to form a hexose diphosphate. The latter undergoes a series of rearrangements and transformations to form, finally, the carbon dioxide acceptor ribulose-1,5-diphosphate. In the course of this cycle, adenosine triphosphate (ATP) and reduced triphosphopyridine nucleotide (TPNH) are consumed.

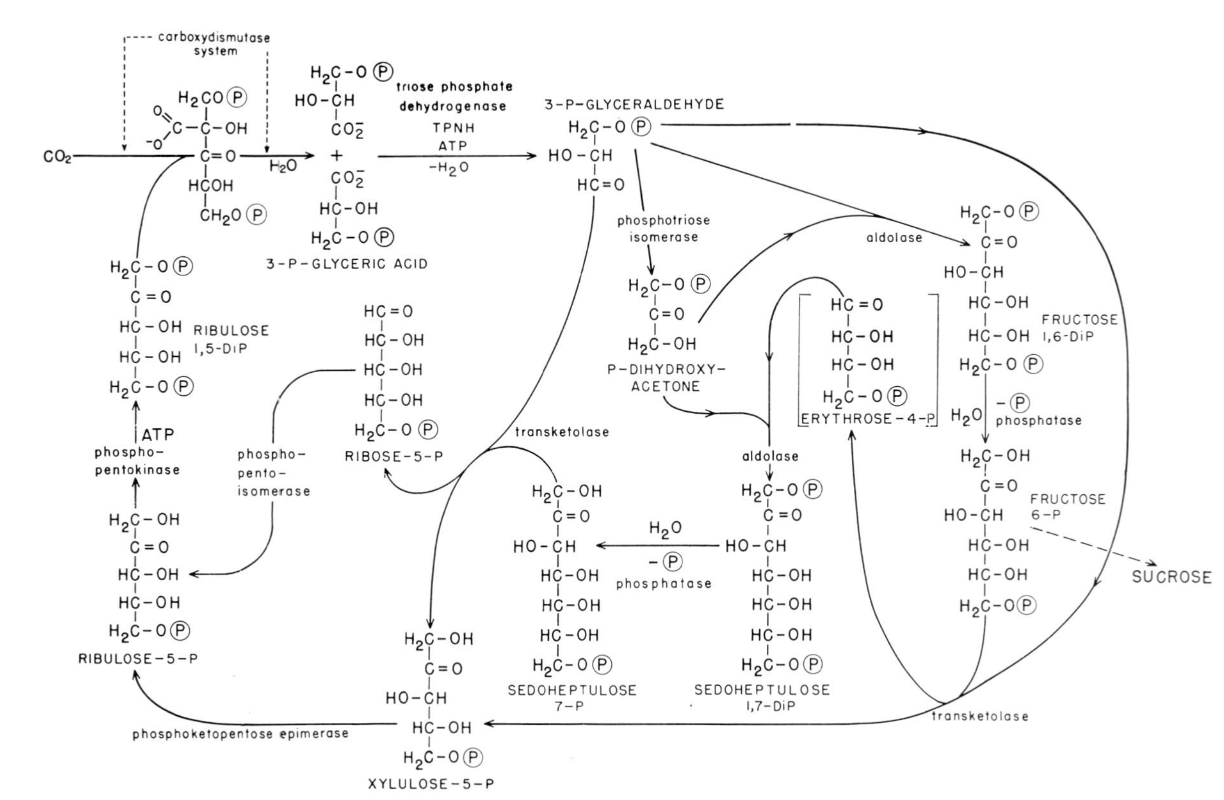

FIG. 2. The photosynthetic carbon reduction cycle or the reductive pentose phosphate cycle.

III. Role of the Pentose Phosphate Cycle

The pentose phosphate cycle serves three purposes—the furnishing of intermediates, reduced pyridine nucleotides, and, perhaps, energy. Triose phosphate may be used for carbohydrate synthesis as in the case of the carbon reduction cycle (*10*), pentose phosphates for the synthesis of nucleic acids (*13*), tetrose phosphate for the synthesis of aromatic amino acids via shikimic acid (*14*), and phosphogluconate for L-ascorbate synthesis in plants (*15*). Since fatty acid synthesis is dependent on the level of TPNH (*16*), the formation of fatty acids may be linked to the oxidative pentose phosphate pathway through this mechanism (*17*). In lactating mammary glands, however, fatty acid synthesis appears to regulate this pentose phosphate cycle activity via the rate-limiting reoxidation of TPNH (*18*).

As an energy source, the direct oxidative pathway may play a lesser role than glycolysis. So far, there is no evidence for the direct coupling of TPNH with oxidative phosphorylation (*19*), although TPNH can transfer its hydrogen to diphosphopyridine nucleotide (DPN^+) via the transhydrogenase reaction. Other means, however, are possible for the formation of ATP: (*a*) substrate level phosphorylation of adenosine diphosphate during the oxidation of the triose phosphate; and (*b*) phosphoroclastic cleavage of either fructose-6-phosphate or xylulose-5-phosphate to form acetyl phosphate (*20*).

IV. Brief History

A. The Oxidative Pentose Phosphate Cycle

The history of the oxidative pentose phosphate cycle dates back to 1931 when Warburg and Christian discovered glucose-6-phosphate dehydrogenase in red blood cells (*21*). Actually, there was much evidence suggesting the existence of alternate pathways of glucose metabolism (*22, 23*) as well as of pentose metabolism (*24, 25*) prior to this time, but proof was not unequivocal owing to the lack of information about the exact mechanism of the Embden-Meyerhof-Parnas scheme. In the years following the discovery of this dehydrogenase, much effort was devoted to the isolation and characterization of the coenzyme of the dehydrogenase reaction, namely, triphosphopyridine nucleotide (TPN^+) (*26*). Between 1935 and 1936, a second dehydrogenase was found, this enzyme being capable of oxidizing the product of the first dehydrogenase reaction with a concomitant evolution of carbon dioxide (*26–29*). Although a pentose phosphate was suggested as the product of this second dehydrogenase reaction, proof was not forthcoming until two different laboratories isolated salts of pentonic acid phosphates (*30, 31*). Furthermore, since ribose-5-phosphate was oxidized and fermented more vigorously than other pentose phosphates, Dickens proposed that ribose phosphate originated from the oxidative decarboxylation of 6-phosphogluconate (*31, 32*). Meanwhile, Dische showed that hemolyzates of erythrocytes formed triose phosphate and fructose diphosphate from the ribose moiety of adenosine (*33*). Eight years elapsed before work was continued along this line of pentose metabolism by Schlenk and Waldvogel (*34*). They found that various nucleosides were broken down more easily than the corresponding nucleotides and that ribose-5-phosphate does not require the presence of inorganic phosphate for breakdown (as compared with an absolute requirement of inorganic phosphate when adenosine was used as substrate). The enzymes that caused the disappearance of pentoses were found in rat tissues including the liver, kidney, spleen, brain, blood (*35*). These data suggested that ribose-5-phosphate is an intermediate in the formation of triose phosphate and fructose phosphate. Moreover, these same investigators demonstrated that liver enzyme plus guanosine yielded glucose-6-phosphate (*36*). Finally, in bacterial extracts, Racker found that ribose-5-phosphate is converted to triose phosphate (*37*). These facts led to a scheme of reactions in which glucose phosphate is oxidized to phosphogluconate to pentose phosphate to triose phosphate, with a C_2 fragment not accounted for. The triose phosphate is transformed by the already well-known route of isomerization and condensation to fructose diphosphate. This diphosphate ester is dephosphorylated and is isomerized to glucose phosphate, hence completing the cycle (*38*). At just about this time, however, Horecker and his associates found that ribulose-5-phosphate was the product of the oxidative decarboxylation of 6-phosphogluconate (*39–41*) and that this product was further converted to ribose-5-phosphate via the action of an isomerase (*42, 43*). [Cohen believed that a 1,2-enediol pentose-5-phosphate is the primary decarboxylation product of 6-phosphogluconate (*38, 44*).] In spite of the accumulation of a massive amount of evidence on the pathway of glucose oxidation, the fate of the two-carbon fragment remained a thorny unsolved problem. This matter was clarified by the brilliant research performed mainly by Horecker and Racker and their co-workers, who discovered in rapid succession transketolase, transaldolase, and a pentose phosphate epimerase (*45–49*). These enzymes enable the ribulose phosphate to be converted to xylulose-5-phosphate, the true substrate for the transketolase reaction. Xylulose phosphate plus ribose phosphate then yielded sedoheptulose-7-phosphate and glyceraldehyde-3-phosphate. These two products, by the action of transaldolase, are transformed to fructose-6-phosphate and erythrose-4-phosphate. The fructose phosphate is isomerized to glucose-6-phosphate, and the tetrose phosphate served as an acceptor for another C_2 fragment from the action of transketolase on a second xylulose phosphate molecule. In the latter case, fructose phosphate is again formed.

What happens to the triose phosphate in the meantime? According to Fig. 1, this intermediate would accumulate with time if it is not diverted into other pathways. Actually, there is ample evidence that this compound is metabolized via the familiar "triose phosphate enzymes" such as aldolase, triose phosphate isomerase (in the reverse direction of the Embden-Meyerhof-Parnas scheme) or triose phosphate dehydrogenase, phosphoglycerate mutase, enolase, and pyruvate kinase in the forward direction (5).

The work described above was concerned with the pentose phosphate cycle *in vitro;* i.e., experiments with homogenates and partially purified enzymes, but the question always arises whether the sequences catalyzed by the *in vitro* enzyme systems actually occur in the whole cell. In 1951, Cohen showed that *Escherichia coli* adapted to grow in gluconate, when fed gluconate-1-C^{14}, yielded a 100% recovery of carbon atom 1 (C-1) as CO_2 for growth aerobically and for oxidation without growth (*44*). He concluded that gluconate was utilized almost completely via the oxidative pathway. A classic example of the *in vivo* operation of the oxidative pathway of glucose metabolism was demonstrated in the heterolactic fermentation of glucose-1-C^{14} and glucose-3,4-C^{14} by *Leuconostoc mesenteroides* (*50*).

B. The Reductive Pentose Phosphate Pathway

While the studies on the oxidative pentose phosphate cycle were being executed, radioactive bicarbonate was used for determining the path of carbon in photosynthesis. Benson and Calvin described the first application of $C^{14}O_2$ to the study of the effect of preillumination on the dark assimilation of CO_2 in *Chlorella pyrenoidosa* (*51*). They obtained data which suggested that phosphoglycerate (PGA) was the first stable product of CO_2 fixation. These results were confirmed by another group (*52*). With the advent of paper chromatography coupled with the detection of radioactive material by radioautography, thus permitting rapid separation and identification of many compounds simultaneously, more detailed kinetic studies were possible. These studies showed that as *Scenedesmus obliquus* was exposed to $C^{14}O_2$ in the light for shorter and shorter times, the labeled phosphoglycerate spot on the chromatogram became more and more dominant until for 5 seconds' photosynthesis, about 90% of the tracer was found in this compound with about 90% of its label in the carboxyl group (*53*). Among the earliest sugar phosphates to be detected were triose phosphate and hexose monophosphate, a finding that immediately suggested the reduction of PGA and the coupling of this reduction product, head to head, as in the reversal of the well-known Embden-Meyerhof-Parnas sequence. Degradation of these two sugar phosphates gave distribution of radioactivity which was consistent with this notion.

The relationship of the observed labeling of the pentose phosphates and of sedoheptulose phosphate remained obscure even after repeated kinetic studies (*10*). Degradation of these radioactive compounds gave a complicated and confusing picture also, even when the algae were exposed for a very short time to labeled bicarbonate. By calling on logical arithmetic, the investigators deduced that the heptulose must have originated from the hexoses and trioses by the actions of transketolase and aldolase. The sedoheptulose phosphate is converted by transketolase, with labeled triose phosphate from the pool as the acceptor, to two different pentose phosphates, which, when mixed together, had the same distribution of radiocarbon as that observed in the pentose monophosphates. Thus the pathway from PGA to hexose phosphates, to sedoheptulose phosphates, and to pentose phosphates was provided.

Despite all this progress, however, the identity of the two-carbon CO_2 acceptor posed the most difficult problem. Here a rather unusual approach was employed, involving the study of the transient changes immediately after interruption of a steady-state condition. In this method the biological sample was exposed to radioactive bicarbonate or carbon dioxide for a long period of time, until the intermediates under steady state had become uniformly labeled. If the assimilation of C^{14} from $C^{14}O_2$ into these intermediates is plotted as a function of time, this assimilation will rise from zero and level off after a certain time of exposure to radiocarbon. (The incorporation of non-steady-state intermediates does not level off with increasing time.) The specific activity of the initial $C^{14}O_2$ being known, one can calculate the concentration of each of these intermediates in the cell.

When this "steady-state" method was applied to *Scenedesmus* in $C^{14}O_2$ and in light, followed by a dark period after the photostationary state was reached, a marked change occurred (*54*). Thus with the onset of the dark period, the phosphoglycerate concentration suddenly rose while the diphosphate (mostly ribulose diphosphate) concentration decreased. These results not only confirmed that PGA was the primary product of carboxylation, but also strongly suggested that ribulose-1,5-diphosphate (RuDP) was the CO_2 acceptor.

This idea was strengthened by another experiment in which the $C^{14}O_2$ pressure was reduced suddenly from 1% to 0.003% over the algae after steady-state conditions were established (*55*). The transient changes in the PGA level and in the RuDP level were measured. The results were a decrease in the concentration of PGA and a concomitant increase in the concentration of RuDP.

These data naturally suggested a search for a cell-free extract of algae containing this type of carboxylase activity (*56*). Such a cell-free extract was obtained by sonically rupturing *Chlorella pyrenoidosa* and then centrifuging down the whole cells. To the supernatant liquid were added labeled bicarbonate and unlabeled ribulose diphosphate (isolated in a separate experiment by paper chromatography of an aqueous extract of algae). Experiments were also carried out with this cell-free extract using unlabeled bicarbonate and labeled ribulose diphosphate. In both cases, the product obtained was radioactive PGA and to a lesser extent, organic acids. Where labeled bicarbonate plus unlabeled ribulose diphosphate were used, all the tracer was located in the carboxyl group of PGA.

Meanwhile, Weissbach *et al.* found in a soluble spinach extract an enzyme system which when incubated with radioactive carbonate and ribose-5-phosphate in the presence of ATP and TPN^+, formed carboxyl-labeled PGA (*57*). Furthermore, if ribose-5-phosphate-1-C^{14} was incubated with the extract in the presence of unlabeled carbonate, over 70% of the tag was in the beta carbon of PGA, the rest being in the carboxyl carbon.

Finally, Racker (*58*) has constructed an artificial cell-free system by mixing together enzymes from various sources—enzymes necessary for the operation of the carbon reduction cycle plus ATP, hydrogenase for generating reduced pyridine nucleotide and metal ion. In the presence of CO_2, H_2, and a catalytic amount of ribose-5-phosphate, this system yielded a net synthesis of carbohydrate. One difference should be indicated: the *in vivo* scheme elaborated by Calvin and his co-workers uses aldolase to produce sedoheptulose diphosphate and then a phosphatase to form sedoheptulose monophosphate, whereas Racker's reconstructed system uses transaldolase to yield sedoheptulose monophosphate directly. This difference would not alter substantially the over-all labeling pattern and the distribution labeling in sedoheptulose.

V. Criteria for the Presence of the Pentose Phosphate Cycle

The sequences of reactions have already been defined in the beginning paragraphs of this review. It should be clearly stated, however, that it is not the author's intent to stipulate what are the standards for justifying the existence of any given pathway. Rather, it should be noted that different investigators use different indicators for suggesting the operation of a particular pathway in a tissue, but any definite conclusion must take into account the criticism and restrictions inherent in the method.

Axelrod and Beevers (*5*) have indicated, in their review article of

1956, that there are at least six different ways of indicating the presence of the oxidative pentose phosphate cycle. These are: (*a*) experiments with inhibitors; (*b*) the presence of pentose phosphate cycle intermediates in the tissues; (*c*) the use of these intermediates as substrates for respiration; (*d*) the transformation of these intermediates to others; (*e*) the presence of pentose phosphate pathway enzymes; and (*f*) experiments with specifically labeled substrates for respiration. These criteria apply as well for the reductive pentose phosphate cycle.

A. Inhibitors as Indicators of Alternate Pathways of Metabolism

The classic case of the use of such substances is that of iodoacetic acid or iodoacetamide. An early example is the work of Lundsgaard in which he showed that respiration continued uninterrupted under conditions where the iodoacetate concentration was sufficiently high to poison the process of fermentation (*59*). He further demonstrated that oxidation of hexose occurs in yeast which is inhibited by this same chemical. Essentially the same technique was applied to the study of the aerobic and anaerobic formation of acids using iodoacetate and cyanide as inhibitors in the fertilized egg of sea urchins (*60*). Iodoacetic acid also affects carbohydrate metabolism in a variety of isolated mammalian tissues such as cat brain cortex, smooth muscle and heart muscle tissues, and also in dog skeletal muscle and heart muscle tissues (*61*). Thus anaerobic glycolysis is inhibited to the extent of 90–100% as measured by lactate production or CO_2 evolution (acid formation) whereas respiration continues unaffected. To this type of experiment, however, Racker raised the following objections (*4*): In muscle tissues, the activity of alternate pathways of glucose oxidation is very low, but the effect of iodoacetate is pronounced, although glucose oxidation is not affected. Furthermore, in a system where the formation of ATP is limiting, a slight inhibition of the triose phosphate dehydrogenase system markedly affects the ATP level. This condition would lead to a large decrease in hexose phosphorylation and thus to a large decrease in glucose uptake. Finally, it should be mentioned that this approach of using inhibitors for the determination of alternate pathways of metabolism does not pinpoint exactly what type of pathway is involved since, most certainly, many organisms contain pathways that are as yet unknown.

B. Presence of Pentose Phosphate Cycle Intermediates in Tissues

It is not enough to show that a particular intermediate is present in the tissue or that its concentration varies under changes of conditions such as from aerobic to anaerobic conditions. Moreover, the formation of this intermediate from precursors must be followed with studies of the fate of this intermediate further down the line of the metabolic pathway. A prime example of this pitfall is the presence of 6-phosphogluconate arising from glucose-6-phosphate, say, in extracts of certain bacteria. The point of departure from the oxidative pentose phosphate cycle is in the step where the phosphogluconate is dehydrated to 2-keto-3-deoxy-6-phosphogluconate. The sequence of reactions is shown in Fig. 3 and is

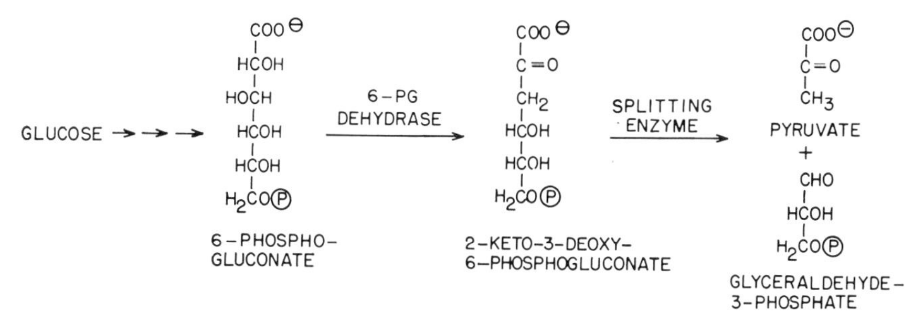

FIG. 3. The Entner-Doudoroff Pathway.

known as the Entner-Doudoroff pathway (*62, 63*). This pathway is limited to bacteria.

Even the most stalwart indicators of the pentose phosphate cycle, such as the pentose phosphates themselves, or sedoheptulose-7-phosphate, may arise from the nonoxidative portion of the oxidative pentose phosphate cycle (cf., e.g., the counterclockwise sequence of Fig. 1). Brenneman *et al.* showed that in *Alcaligenes faecalis*, ribose-5-phosphate is synthesized from fructose-6-phosphate not via the oxidative shunt mechanism, but from the action of transketolase, transaldolase, isomerase, and epimerase. Both glucose-6-phosphate dehydrogenase and 6-phosphogluconate dehydrogenase are absent in extracts of this organism (*64*). Even triose phosphate need not be present for the fructose-6-phosphate to be transformed to sedoheptulose-7-phosphate; all that is required is the simultaneous action of both transaldolase and transketolase (*65*). The mechanism involves the coupled action of these two enzymes on two moles of fructose phosphate, yielding one pentose phosphate and one sedoheptulose monophosphate.

C. PENTOSE PHOSPHATE PATHWAY INTERMEDIATES AS SUBSTRATES FOR RESPIRATION

A decision can be made as to whether a compound is an intermediate of the pentose phosphate cycle by feeding it to a tissue and observing whether it is rapidly metabolized to CO_2 or whether it stimulates oxygen uptake. A number of examples of the former case (i.e., rapid formation of CO_2) is cited in the review article by Axelrod and Beevers (*5*). A recent example of the latter case is an experiment with homogenates of lobster hepatopancreas to which addition of 6-phosphogluconate and ribose-5-phosphate stimulated oxygen uptake (*66*).

One serious drawback of this approach is that all the intermediates of the pentose phosphate cycle are phosphorylated compounds and therefore are impermeable to the intact cells. This property of these substances requires working with either cell-free homogenates or tissue slices or minces, which makes the problem fall within the realm of enzymology, the pitfalls of which are described below. Alternatively, unphosphorylated precursors of these cycle intermediates may be supplied to the intact tissue; however, assumptions have to be made that the cell utilizes the supplied substance subsequently in the form of its phosphate ester.

D. Transformation of Pentose Phosphate Cycle Intermediates

Here again we are faced with the same problem as above, namely, that of getting these intermediates into the cell, because of the impermeable nature of these compounds. The basic idea behind this whole approach is to study the formation of compounds derived from an intermediate of the pentose phosphate cycle. If these compounds are also pentose phosphate intermediates, then it is probable that the cycle is in operation under the conditions of the experiment. One early example of this type of approach was the study of the metabolism of sedoheptulose-C^{14} in beet, barley, and tobacco leaves (*67*). The labeled compounds formed varied considerably depending on the conditions; i.e., whether in the light or in the dark or whether under nitrogen or under air. Some of the radioactive phosphorylated esters obtained in light under nitrogen were those of ribulose, ribose, and fructose. These compounds are characteristic of the operation of both the oxidative pentose phosphate cycle and the photosynthetic carbon reduction cycle. Later, as more refined techniques became available, kinetic analyses of shorter and shorter time of incorporation of C^{14} from labeled substrates were possible. The classic example of the use of this method is the study of CO_2 fixation during photosynthesis using $C^{14}O_2$ as substrate; it has been described elsewhere in this review (cf. brief history section on the reductive pentose phosphate cycle, Section IV, B). The same methods have been applied on nonphotosynthetic organisms. In one case, using glucose-C^{14}, Moses demonstrated the presence of the oxidative pentose phosphate cycle in *Zygorhynchus moelleri* (*68*), and in the other case, using $C^{14}O_2$, Aubert *et al.* showed that the reductive pentose phosphate cycle was operating in *Thiobacillus denitrificans* (*69*).

E. Presence of Enzymes of the Pentose Phosphate Pathway

This method involves the assay of one or more of the pentose phosphate pathway enzymes by adding the required substrate(s) to a crude extract or a purified fraction from the tissue. Control experiments have to be performed in order to ensure that there are no inhibitors of the enzyme in the crude extract. The latter experiments are done by adding the fraction to be tested to a purified enzyme preparation from another organism. If the activity of this enzyme is not affected by this addition, then the test fraction does not contain an inhibitor of the enzyme. Such an approach was used by Richter (*70*) in his studies of carbohydrate-metabolizing enzymes in two photosynthetic algae.

The interpretation of this method is fraught with many reservations. Even when an enzyme is found to be present, this does not necessarily mean that the organism is using the pentose phosphate cycle for the catabolism of carbohydrates. There are already a number of cases where enzymes of the pentose phosphate cycle are found in extracts of the organism, but where the main pathway in operation (greater than 90%) is the Embden-Meyerhof-Parnas sequence. Among the many examples that contain shunt enzymes, but metabolize glucose chiefly via glycolysis, are *Avena* coleoptiles (*71*), Ehrlich ascites mouse tumors (*72*), and yeast (*73, 74*).

Even if we grant that glucose is not metabolized mainly by the Embden-Meyerhof-Parnas route, and assuming that we find one or two enzymes normally associated with the pentose phosphate pathway, we are still uncertain as to the interpretation of the results. As already pointed out by Axelrod (*75*), the assignment of a given enzyme to a particular pathway of metabolism is purely arbitrary and, to add to the confusion, some enzymes initially thought to belong to the glycolytic pathway were later found to belong also to the oxidative pathway (as well as to the reductive cycle). These enzymes are aldolase, triose phosphate isomerase, triose phosphate dehydrogenase, and others. It should be noted that some differences exist between triose phosphate dehydrogenase derived from plants and animals. In contrast to the DPN-linked dehydrogenase from animal tissues, the corresponding plant enzymes are of three types: (*a*) DPN-linked (*76, 77*), (*b*) TPN-linked (*77–80*), and (*c*) TPN-linked, but not coupled with phosphorylation (*81, 82*).

In spite of the reservations mentioned above, it is nevertheless useful to obtain information as to whether a tissue or organism has a particular "indicator" enzyme of the pentose phosphate cycle. Most prevalently used are glucose-6-phosphate dehydrogenase, transketolase, transaldolase, and carboxydismutase. The presence of one or two of these enzymes in extracts of the tissue, however, does not necessarily mean that the whole cycle is operating. For example, glucose-6-phosphate dehydrogenase can be present without pentose phosphate formation, i.e., via the Entner-Doudoroff pathway. Similarly, both transketolase and transaldolase may be present without having the oxidative portion of the pentose phosphate cycle, as indicated previously in ribose synthesis by *Alcaligenes faecalis* (*64*). The presence of carboxydismutase in several blue-green algae, which contain no aldolase (*83*), strongly suggests that the formation of hexose from photosynthesis in these organisms may well have to be via a pathway other than the reductive pentose phosphate cycle.

When no enzyme of a particular pathway is found in extracts of the tissue, can we say that this enzyme is really absent? Probably not; perhaps the proper conditions either for the preservation of its activity or for its activation have not been found. Marks *et al.* (*84*) found that glucose-6-phosphate dehydrogenase from normal individuals is activated to a greater degree under certain conditions than the corresponding enzyme from individuals who have a genetic deficiency of this enzyme. However, with proper precautions and cautious interpretation of the data, the lack of an enzyme in a given preparation might actually be significant. One other fact might be considered: The lack of a given enzyme does not eliminate the possibility that another enzyme having slightly different specificities is present.

If one or two indicator enzymes can serve for the prediction of a route of glucose metabolism, then it would seem reasonable that a map or profile of all the enzymes of the pathway would be even more helpful. Studies of this kind were performed on several photosynthetic organisms (*70, 85*), the two-spotted spider mite (*86*), photosynthetic purple bacteria (*87*), and several photosynthetic green tissues (*88*). In spite of the presence of all the enzymes of a given pathway, there is still some doubt as to whether all these enzymes are located in a common pool. It may be argued, however, that the pentose phosphate cycle enzymes are generally found in the soluble fraction of the cell, but recent work has shown that the particulate fraction of male guinea pig brain contains at least 10% of the glucose-6-phosphate and 6-phosphogluconate dehydrogenases (*89*). The unusual feature of this finding arose because these enzymatic activities manifested themselves only when the particulate fractions were first treated with a detergent and then separated from the solubilized enzymes. Care should be exercised to ensure that the enzymes in question are not absorbed on the particles during their preparation as in the case of the absorption of lactate dehydrogenase by microsomes from a medium of low ionic strength (*90*). This enzyme could subsequently be released from these particles upon addition of salt.

The problem posed by the compartmentalization of the enzymes has in part been solved. Progress toward this end was first achieved by Arnon and his co-workers, who showed that chloroplasts contain the enzymes necessary to fix carbon dioxide (*91*). Whether all these enzymes are located entirely in the chloroplasts or some in the cytoplasm was not certain. However, a novel method was independently elaborated by two investigators (*92, 93*), who obtained chloroplasts from lyophilized leaves, ground and fractionated in a nonaqueous medium. One of them (*93*) showed that aldolase normally thought to be associated with the cytoplasm (i.e., to exist in low concentrations within the chloroplasts), was in fact localized predominantly in the chloroplasts. Later, Smillie and Fuller showed that there is a parallel relationship between the percentage distribution of carboxydismutase and the percentage distribution of chlorophyll in chloroplast-containing fractions derived by the nonaqueous method (*94*). Finally, Heber *et al.* (*95*), using the same type of chloroplasts, showed that all the carboxydismutase and the TPN-dependent triose phosphate dehydrogenase is located in the chloroplasts, whereas the DPN-linked triose phosphate dehydrogenase is distributed between both the chloroplasts and the cytoplasm.

F. Metabolism of C^{14}-Labeled Substrates

A specifically labeled substrate is incubated with the tissue or organism, and the distribution of the label in the products and/or the specific activities of the products are measured. An application of this method is the study of the heterolactic fermentation of glucose-1-C^{14} and glucose-3,4-C^{14} by *Leuconostoc mesenteroides* (*50*). The products, lactate, carbon dioxide, and ethanol, were degraded chemically. The label was found to be in the carboxyl group of lactate, in CO_2, and in the C-1 of ethanol, indicating that a new pathway is in operation. Another pioneering work was done by Bloom *et al.* (*96*), who determined the catabolic routes of glucose in mammalian tissues. They fed glucose-1-C^{14} and glucose-6-C^{14} and specifically labeled lactate to these tissues and then measured the C^{14} incorporated into the CO_2. The assumption underlying this procedure is that the pentose phosphate cycle would yield $C^{14}O_2$ from glucose carbon atom 1 at a greater rate than that from carbon atom 6, whereas glycolysis plus the operation of the Krebs cycle would yield carbon dioxide derived from carbon atoms 1 and 6 at the same rate. The ratio of the $C^{14}O_2$ derived from glucose-6-C^{14} to the $C^{14}O_2$ derived from glucose-1-C^{14} would be a measure of relative participation of the two pathways (*97*). Abraham *et al.* used these same radioactive substrates, and although they found that the so-called C-6:C-1 ratio was indicative of the operation of the pentose cycle in rat mammary glands, they used the amount of fatty acid-C^{14} recovered from these substrates to evaluate the relative contribution of the pentose cycle toward the metabolism of glucose (*98*).

Other workers varied the type of labeled substrates used; for example, Heath and Koffler measured the preferential oxidation of the C-1 position of glucose by comparing the utilization of glucose-1-C^{14} and glucose-U-C^{14} (uniformly labeled) (*99*). Some investigators measured the specific activities of the lactate, or acetate (*100*), or pyruvate (*100, 101*). In some cases, lactate formed from the labeled glucose was degraded (*102, 103*). One of the latest methods is the radiorespirometric method of Wang (*104*), which, in essence, is a measurement of the rate of $C^{14}O_2$ evolved as a function of incubation time using variously labeled glucose. It is beyond the scope of this review to discuss the merits of the various methods. Several critiques have been published (*105–107*), and a study of them should allow the reader a more accurate appraisal of these methods. Generally, many investigators now believe that the use of the "C-6:C-1" ratio alone is not sufficient for determining the relative participation of the pentose phosphate pathway.

Radioactive bicarbonate has been used for studying the pathway of metabolism of glucose also (*108, 109*). In these cases, labeled glycogen was obtained with C^{14} being incorporated mainly in carbon atoms 3 and 4. A minor, but reproducible, amount of radioactivity resided in the rest of the carbon atoms of the glycogen glucose molecule, indicating that a nonglycolytic pathway is operating during glycogenesis.

The most famous case of the use of $C^{14}O_2$ for studying the pathway of metabolism is the elucidation of the path of carbon in photosynthesis (*10*). These studies date back to about 1948 and have been discussed earlier in this paper. The point to be reemphasized here is that the labeling pattern was studied as a function of the time of exposure $C^{14}O_2$. The labeling pattern, in this case, means both the compounds which became labeled and the distribution of the label within each compound.

It is interesting to note that Gibbs and Kandler, using this method with more refined methods of degrading the hexose (with *L. mesenteroides*), found that the distribution of the label in starch glucose after short time photosynthesis with $C^{14}O_2$ was asymmetric (*110*). They therefore suggested that there may be an alternative pathway of carbon in photosynthesis. However, Bassham and Calvin have explained the asymmetric distribution of the radiocarbon via equilibration of the triose phosphate with a large unlabeled pool and via transketolase exchange reactions (*10*).

VI. Chordates

A. Mammals

Almost half of all the studies on the pentose phosphate cycle have been carried out on mammalian systems. An excellent survey of the occurrence of this pathway in mammal tissues has been written by Katz (*111*). Several problems arise, however, because of the complexity of a living system. For example, we are faced with a study of metabolic pathways in a biological organization which ranges from the most complicated form, the intact animal, to the tissues, to the cellular level, to the organelles, and ultimately to the simplest form, the enzymes (*112*). Even with these classifications clearly outlined, there remain the factors that may influence the activity of the pentose phosphate cycle. Some examples of these modifying factors are the physiological and pathological conditions of the animal, its growth stage, the ionic environment in which tissues are suspended, diet, hormonal regulation, genetic effects, and many others.

1. *Intact Animal*

Research of this type has been conducted mainly on humans, rats, mice, and lactating cows. Labeled substrates were administered to the animal, and the pattern of labeling in the product was thus determined. Thus in the study of the pentose phosphate cycle in humans, in one case, radioactive acetate was injected and the distribution of label in blood glucose was measured (*113*). In two other cases, variously labeled glucose was administered and the labeling pattern of the ribose in the urine (*114*) as well as the recovery of $C^{14}O_2$ (*115*) were determined. With rats the method was essentially similar (*116–118*); however, in some instances (with mice also) the incorporation of the tracer in liver glycogen was used as a measure of the operation of pentose cycle (*119, 120*). Labeled alanine isolated from the proteins of internal organs of rats, such as heart, lungs, spleen, reproductive organs, and kidney, also served as an index of pentose phosphate cycle activity (*121*). *In vivo* studies in cows have been concentrated on the incorporation of label in the constituents of the milk (*122*), and the respired CO_2 (*123*). In general the different investigators concluded that glucose is metabolized mainly, i.e., greater than 90%, via the Embden-Meyerhof-Parnas sequence; that gluconate is catabolized by the oxidative portion of the pentose phosphate cycle, and that ribose is formed mostly by the transketolase-transaldolase sequence of reactions and partly by the oxidative pathway. A small contribution toward pentose formation is by way of the glucuronate pathway (*15, 114*). Results from experiments with lactating cows will be discussed under mammary glands (Section VI,A,12). That any of the above conclusions can be reached is indeed remarkable in view of the facts that the resultant expired CO_2, the blood glucose, and the urinary ribose may be a reflection of the over-all metabolism of the intact animal. Furthermore, Katz (*111*) has repeatedly emphasized that the ratios of CO_2 respired from feeding experiments with labeled glucose may be a measure only of the metabolic fate of the triose phosphate that is formed. Nevertheless he has recently conceded that, under certain conditions, use can be made of the specific yields of $C^{14}O_2$ from glucose-1-C^{14} and from glucose-6-C^{14} (*124*) to estimate the relative participation of the EMP and the pentose phosphate pathways.

2. *Adipose Tissue*

There is no doubt that the oxidative pentose phosphate cycle occurs in the adipose tissue, as shown by experiments with variously labeled glucose and by measuring the incorporation of the radioactive carbon into the expired CO_2, long-chain fatty acids, glyceride glycerol, and free fatty acids (*125*). Moreover, Weber *et al.* have shown that both glucose-6-phosphate and 6-phosphogluconate dehydrogenases are present in extracts of rat fatty tissue (*126*). The question is, What is the relative contribution of this pathway toward the metabolism of glucose? Using the data supplied by Cahill *et al.*, Katz has recalculated this contribution and obtained a range of 10–15% for the relative contribution of the pentose cycle to the triose pathway (*111*).

So far, only adipose tissue from rats and mice have been investigated; therefore, the comparative biochemistry of pentose phosphate metabolism is reduced to a study of the *in vivo* and *in vitro* disturbances of substances on these tissues. Because most of the synthesis and degradation of body fat takes place in the adipose tissue, one might expect that hormones would regulate carbohydrate and lipid metabolism in these tissues. Table I summarizes the effect of some hormones added *in vitro* to epididymal fat pads of rats on the oxidative pentose phosphate pathway. Both insulin and prolactin stimulate the activity of the pentose phosphate cycle, the former to an extent between 15 and 20% of the relative participation of the two major pathways of glucose metabolism (*111*). Although both insulin and prolactin increase the CO_2 yield and fatty acid synthesis, the resemblance ends here in that prolactin fails to correct the defect in fatty acid synthesis found in adipose tissues of alloxan-treated rats (*127*).

Other hormones showed no effect on the activity of the pentose phosphate cycle; however, they do affect the activities of some other paths of carbohydrate metabolism, such as increasing the activities of the EMP pathway and the tricarboxylic acid (TCA) cycle (*128*) and possibly the uronic pathway (*129*). The net effect, therefore, is a decrease in the relative contribution of the pentose phosphate cycle for the oxidation of glucose.

TABLE I
EFFECT OF HORMONES IN RAT ADIPOSE TISSUE, *in Vitro*, ON THE OXIDATIVE PENTOSE PHOSPHATE CYCLE ACTIVITY

Hormone added	Effect on the pentose cycle	Reference
None	—	(*125*)
Insulin	Stimulation	(*125*)
Prolactin	Stimulation	(*127*)
ACTH	No effect	(*128*)
Growth hormone	No effect	(*129*)
Glucagon	No effect	(*130*)
Epinephrine	No effect	(*125*)

It should be emphasized that the yardstick for the relative contribution of the pathways for glucose metabolism is based chiefly on incorporation of radioactive carbon into the respired CO_2 from variously labeled glucose. Thus the interpretations of the many investigators suffer from numerous uncertainties. To complicate matters further, Jeanrenaud and Renold performed experiments in which they varied either the insulin or the glucose concentrations while keeping the concentration of the other component fixed in the incubation mixture containing the adipose tissue. In either case, when one of the concentrations was increased and the other held fixed, the $C_1:C_6$ ratio in the respired CO_2 increased while that incorporated into fatty acids remained more or less constant (*131*). The results seemed to them not reconcilable with the effect of insulin on the metabolic pathways, but rather, they proposed a new unifocal hypothesis involving translocation or phosphorylation of glucose.

Other factors affecting the pattern of metabolism in adipose tissues (epididymal fat pads) have been reported: Drugs used to treat cases of diabetes mellitus, such as the arylsulfonyl ureas, tolbutamide, and chlorpropamide, when added *in vitro* to adipose tissues, inhibit lipogenesis and enhance glucose oxidation (*132*). The researchers reasoned that the pentose phosphate cycle is affected via interference of the transfer of hydrogen via the pyridine nucleotides. A high level of glucose or a sudden load of carbohydrate in the diet of a rat also increases the glucose-6-phosphate and the 6-phosphogluconate dehydrogenase levels in extracts of epididymal fat pads (*133*). This and other experiments with homogenates of fat pads from fasted rats led to the conclusion that the activation of the dehydrogenases following ingestion of a sudden load of carbohydrate results in the synthesis of the enzymes, not in the activation of inactive preformed enzymes.

Experiments with adipose tissues of normal and obese mice, in the presence and absence of insulin and/or growth hormone, gave essentially the same results as those with rats (*134*). On the other hand, adipose tissue of tumor-bearing mice has a relatively depressed pentose phosphate cycle activity (*135*). One final note; the interscapular brown fat of the rat also seems to contain pentose phosphate cycle enzymes, as shown by experiments with homogenates and variously labeled glucose in the presence and absence of DPN^+, ATP, and TPN^+ (*136*).

3. *Adrenals*

Glock and McLean have shown that adrenal cortex contains a high level of the oxidative enzymes of the pentose phosphate cycle (*137*). They have also demonstrated that the adrenal medulla contains much less of these enzymes, which was confirmed by the work of Kelley *et al.* (*138*). Other investigators have gone further by showing that both dehydrogenases are localized within the adrenal cortex, with maximum levels in the zona fasciculata (an inner zone of the cortex) (*139*). *In vivo* administration of ACTH causes the glucose-6-phosphate and 6-phosphogluconate dehydrogenases to shift toward the medulla, to a section between the fasciculata and the reticularis. The latter enzyme, however, is activated throughout the cortex. In contrast to these studies are those of glucose-6-phosphate dehydrogenase in the glomerulosa, the subcapsular region nearest the periphery of the adrenal cortex (*140, 141*). In tissues from sodium-depleted rats (fed a salt-poor diet), the normally narrow zone widens and the dehydrogenase level increases markedly. The high enzymatic activity is concentrated in the peripheral glomerulosa, the inner portion becoming relatively poor in dehydrogenase activity. The conclusion is that the glomerulosa are composed of two types of cells that respond to sodium-depletion. Glucose phosphate dehydrogenase may be required for energy production and TPNH formation, possibly for synthesis of aldosterone, since the dehydrogenase activity is highest in the region where lipid concentration is lowest.

As in the case of adipose tissues, a variety of conditions can affect the pentose phosphate cycle activity in the adrenal glands. Thus dehydroepiandrosterone, when added *in vitro* to a homogenate of adrenals in the presence of glucose and TPN^+, has two effects. If the TPN^+ level is not limiting, the hormone decreases the formation of CO_2 and the production of TPNH; however, if the level is limiting, then the steroid stimulates the production of CO_2 (*142*). Most likely, steroid is in the meantime being reduced to the corresponding cortisol, as in the case of progesterone added *in vitro* to a similar system (*143*). *In vitro* addition of thioperazine inhibits both dehydrogenases of the pentose cycle—glucose phosphate enzyme noncompetitively, and phosphogluconate enzyme competitively (*144*). On the other hand, ACTH administered either *in vivo* (*145, 146*) or *in vitro* (*147*) had no effect on the dehydrogenase systems, but instead decreased the specific activity and total activity of glucose-6-phosphatase (*145, 146*). Finally, the levels of glucose-6-phosphate dehydrogenase, transketolase, and transaldolase were not modified by pregnancy (*148*). Thus far, adrenals from human fetuses, rats, oxen, calfs, guinea pigs, and mice have been examined.

4. *Brain and the Nervous System*

Experiments with variously labeled glucose led to the conclusion that in cerebral cortex slices, the EMP pathway is almost totally operative in the catabolism of glucose (*149–151*). Nevertheless, enzymes of the pentose phosphate cycle, such as transketolase, and the dehydrogenases do exist in homogenates of the brains from various sources (*137, 152–155*). The oxidation of pentose phosphate cycle intermediates and of labeled glucose is stimulated by addition of TPN^+ *in vitro* (*151, 156, 157*). Higgins (*149*) surmised that the dehydrogenases were carried over from the young stage where cholesterol and lipid synthesis occur *in situ*, thereby oxidizing TPNH without the presence of oxygen. On the other hand, Hotta (*157*) feels that a considerable amount of TPN^+ is lost during the preparation of the tissues for the experiments. That oxidized glutathione also accelerates the oxidation of glucose-1-C^{14} to $C^{14}O_2$ but not that of glucose-6-C^{14} suggests that the pentose phosphate pathway is responsible for the reduction of oxidized glutathione, the reduced form being necessary for the protection of the integrity of the cells.

A study of the distribution of glucose-6-phosphate dehydrogenase and of transketolase in the brain and the spinal cord showed that these enzymes are found in both regions (*152, 154, 155*). Levels of these enzymes are higher in the spinal cord than in the brain. Moreover, the white matter of the central nervous system tends to be more active than the gray matter, indicating that perhaps the pentose phosphate cycle may be connected with the initial development and subsequent maintenance of the normal myelin sheath. Indeed, the heavily myelinated tract with the highest lipid content as well as the highest glucose-6-phosphate dehydrogenase activity is the dorsal column (*155*).

The intracellular localization of the dehydrogenases has been discussed elsewhere (see Section V,E on criteria for the presence of the pentose phosphate cycles; also cf. ref. *89*). In essence, 10% of the total glucose phosphate and the phosphogluconate dehydrogenases are located in the particulate fractions of the brain.

Both arsenite and Synkavite, a derivative of menadione, seem to alter the normal metabolic pattern of glucose oxidation (*158*). The former inhibitor, however, not only decreases the production of $C^{14}O_2$ from glucose-6-C^{14}, but also the oxygen uptake, so that with the increased $C^{14}O_2$ yield from glucose-1-C^{14} the net result may be a combination of two effects: the inhibition of the TCA cycle and the stimulation of the pentose phosphate pathway. Synkavite, on the other hand, operates differently, by activating the oxidation of C-1 by threefold without affecting that of C-6 or the oxygen uptake. It should be mentioned that the investigations described above (and others not mentioned) were carried out on a number of nervous systems from many sources, among them the rat (*149*), the rabbit (*155*), the guinea pig (*158*), the monkey *Macaca mulatta* (*153, 159*), and the cat (*160*).

5. *Cardiac, Arterial, and Venous Tissues*

Source materials for studies described below were the following: female breeder rats with signs of arteriosclerosis (*161*), normal rats (*162*), mongrel dogs (*163*), guinea pigs (*164*), bovine (*165*), humans (*166*), adult and fetal pigs (*167*). In general, one can say that heart muscle in the form of a homogenate (*162*) or as ventricle strips (*163*) metabolizes glucose chiefly by glycolysis and the oxidation of pyruvate. This applies even when the ventricle strips are electrically contracted and are placed in a medium containing arsenate (*168*). To be sure, homogenates of adult heart contain the enzymes necessary for the reduction of TPN^+ when the pentose phosphate cycle intermediates are added (*167*). More specifically, Glock and McLean showed that both glucose-6-phosphate dehydrogenase and 6-phosphogluconate dehydrogenase are present in rat cardiac muscle, although at relatively low levels (*137*). Thus cardiac tissues have the potential to oxidize glucose via an alternate pathway. In this regard, Jolly *et al.* concluded from experiments with variously labeled sugars added to homogenates of fetal pig and adult pig heart, in the presence and absence of TPN^+, that the pentose phosphate cycle in the soluble enzymes of the fetal heart is 4 times greater than those of the adult heart (*167*). The pentose phosphate pathway in arterial tissues is operative, as is evident from a large C-1:C-6 ratio from the respectively labeled glucose (*163–165*), and from enzymological studies (*161, 166*). Furthermore, aortic tissues without arteriosclerosis have higher glucose-6-phosphate dehydrogenase activity than those with this disease (*161, 166*). In fact, the levels of this enzyme decrease with increasing severity of arteriosclerosis whereas the level of phosphogluconate dehydrogenase remains more or less constant (*161*).

6. *Other Endocrine Tissues and Related Material*

Slices of almost all endocrine glands can oxidize carbon atom 1 of glucose to CO_2 in preference to carbon atom 6 (*147*). Among the tissues examined were ovaries of calf and human. In agreement with these results are the findings by Glock and McLean that enzymes of the oxidative pathway are present in the ovaries of cows (*137*). However, in slices of luteinized rat ovaries, very little glucose is metabolized via the hexose monophosphate shunt (*169*). This phenomenon applies whether the glucose uptake by ovaries is stimulated by *in vivo* injection of luteinizing hormone or not. (Luteinizing hormone, administered to the rat *in vivo*, increases the uptake of glucose by the ovaries accompanied by a less pronounced increase in the production of $C^{14}O_2$ and of C^{14}-lipids from glucose-1-C^{14} and glucose-6-C^{14}. The rate of incorporation of the C^{14} both into CO_2 and lipids from these two labeled substrates, however, is the same.) The discrepancy between the two conflicting results was attributed either to a difference in the proportion of luteal tissues or to the inactivation of enzymes in the samples studied (*169*).

In contrast to these studies, experiments with fertilized ovum of a rabbit using specifically labeled glucose suggested that up to the fourth day of development (before the blastocyst stage) glucose is mainly oxidized via the pentose phosphate cycle (*170*). After this stage, the principal pathways are the EMP pathway and TCA cycle. Methylene blue, however, seemed to stimulate the activity of the pentose phosphate cycle at this stage.

Histochemical analyses of rabbit pancreas slices showed that glucose-6-phosphate dehydrogenase activity is most marked in the beta cells of islets and in the ductular epithelium (*171*). The authors concluded from these studies that glucose-6-phosphate is oxidized predominantly via the oxidative pathway while the EMP route plays a secondary role. The role of the pentose phosphate pathway is to furnish TPNH, thus making available reduced glutathione or free sulfhydryls in enzymes, which in turn may possibly be connected with the control of insulin output by the beta cells.

Other workers have shown, also in rabbit pancreas and by histochemical means, that both glucose-6-phosphate dehydrogenase and 6-phosphogluconate dehydrogenase exist in the islet and acinar tissues (*172*). The glucose-6-phosphate dehydrogenase is present in equal amounts in islets and acini from pancreas of normal rabbit, but the

6-phosphogluconate dehydrogenase activity is higher in the islets than in the acini. On the other hand, hyperglycemic rabbits have increased levels of glucose-6-phosphate dehydrogenase in both tissues. The islets having greater vascularity than the acini, this suggests that the islets have greater capacity for aerobic metabolism than the acini. The investigators concluded from these experiments that the pentose phosphate cycle seems to be utilized in the metabolism of large amounts of exogenously administered glucose.

Evidence was also obtained for the operation of the pentose cycle in the insulin-producing tumors of human pancreas composed only of beta cells (*173*). Addition, *in vitro,* of alloxan did not alter the rate of conversion of glucose to CO_2. The role of the pentose phosphate pathway, in this case, may be for protein synthesis via the generation of TPNH.

Slices of beef and calf pituitaries have been examined for pentose phosphate cycle activity (*137, 174, 175*). In both cases the results were positive as determined by the use of variously labeled glucose (*174, 175*) as well as by enzymatic assays (*137*). Insulin added to the incubation mixture increased a number of parameters, but did not change the C-1:C-6 ratio (*175*). Using a number of assumptions, Dumont estimated "grossly" that 25% of the CO_2 from glucose comes by way of the hexose monophosphate shunt (*174*).

There is ample evidence to indicate that the pentose phosphate cycle is operative in the thyroid glands. In Table II are listed the mammalian

TABLE II
SOURCES OF THYROIDS AND EFFECTS OF SUBSTANCES ADDED *in Vitro* ON THE PENTOSE PHOSPHATE CYCLE ACTIVITY

Source	Substance added	Effect	Reference
Sheep	Synkavite, monoiodotyrosine, diiodotyrosine	Increase	(*176*)
Beef	Thyroid-stimulating hormone	Increase	(*177*)
Rat, fed	Thyroxine	Increase	(*178*)
Rat, fasted	Thyroxine	No effect	(*178*)
Rat	Propylthiouracil, small dose	Decrease	(*179*)
	thyroid-stimulating hormone	Increase	(*179*)
Dog	Acetylcholine	No effect	(*180*)
Calf and dog	Epinephrine	Increase	(*181*)
Beef, pig, and dog	Serotonin, tryptamine, 5-methoxytryptamine	Increase	(*182*)

sources of the thyroid and the substances that affect the pentose phosphate activity in this tissue. Conclusions are based mainly on a measure of the C-1:C-6 ratio of CO_2 from the oxidation of glucose labeled in the respective positions, but, in the case of the thyroxine studies, the activities of glucose-6-phosphate and 6-phosphogluconate dehydrogenases were assayed.

Of interest is the action of epinephrine on the thyroid system. Apparently, the epinephrine in the incubation mixture turns pink, a finding which suggested to the workers that adrenochrome is formed (*181*). Accordingly, adrenochrome was tested and found to stimulate the oxidation of glucose in even lesser amounts than epinephrine. Thus epinephrine may act after its conversion to adrenochrome. Both these compounds catalytically accelerate the oxidation of TPNH and DPNH by a thyroid mitochondrial-microsomal preparation. The conclusion is that a rise in the TPN^+ level seems to be responsible for the increased oxidation of glucose-1-C^{14}, although the reason for the increase of glucose-6-C^{14} oxidation remains obscure. These observations are consistent with the findings of experiments with *in vitro* addition of serotonin (*182*), thyroid-stimulating hormone (*183*), and the artificial electron acceptor Synkavite (*176*) to slices of thyroid gland. In all cases, the level of TPN^+ seems to be rate limiting.

Thyroxine, administered *in vitro* (*178*), increased the activity of the dehydrogenases of the pentose phosphate cycle. However, the response of these enzymes to thyroxine does not occur in the fasted rat.

Propylthiouracil is a drug that affects the uptake of radioactive iodine and of oxygen as well as the formation of diiodotyrosine by thyroid slices. Its effect on the oxidation of glucose is concentration dependent, a small dose (10^{-8} *M*) inhibiting slightly the oxidation of C-1 while augmenting that of C-6, whereas a large dose (10^{-3} *M*) significantly decreasing the oxidation of both carbons (*179*).

Tremblay and Pearse have examined by histochemical techniques slices of monkey (*Macaca irus*) and human parathyroids (*184*). They found that oxyphile cells contain a high activity of DPNH and TPNH diaphorases and dehydrogenases including those of succinate, β-hydroxybutyrate, and glucose-6-phosphate. The principal cells, on the other hand, are weak in these enzymes. They concluded, therefore, that the oxyphile cells, which are normally considered to be degenerate, are in fact active secretory elements of the parathyroid glands. In connection with glucose metabolism in this tissue, parathyroid adenoma slices gave large C-1:C-6 ratios when incubated with the corresponding labeled glucose (*147*).

Human, rabbit, and calf testes also gave very high C-1:C-6 ratios of CO_2 from labeled glucose (*147*). *In vitro* treatment of these tissues with follicle-stimulating hormone, luteinizing hormone, or chorionic gonadotropin did not affect this ratio. Using cytochemical methods,

Niemi and Ikonen showed that among other oxidative enzymes present in the Leydig cells of rat testis is glucose-6-phosphate dehydrogenase (*185*). These cells, which are the producer of testosterone, contain less of this dehydrogenase after hypophysectomy of the rat. These workers were also unable to demonstrate any *in vivo* effect of the above-mentioned pituitary hormones on the hexose monophosphate shunt.

There was no evidence of the pentose-shunt activity in ram, bull, dog, or fowl spermatozoa as measured by incubating them with variously labeled glucose (*186*). In all these cases the C-1:C-6 ratios were close to unity. Sperm cells from different locations, however, seem to use different metabolic routes for oxidizing glucose. Thus, ram and bull epididymal spermatozoa oxidize glucose-1-C^{14} and glucose-6-C^{14} to yield CO_2 with a C-1:C-6 ratio of about 1, whereas testicular sperm cells gave a ratio which indicated preferential oxidation of C-1 (*187*). The ratio of TPN^+ to DPN^+ may be the controlling factor in this case.

7. *Erythrocytes, Genetically Determined Glucose-6-phosphate Dehydrogenase Deficiency and Leukocytes*

Rather than cope with the already enormous mass of literature dealing with the pentose phosphate cycle in erythrocytes, this reviewer recommends to the reader recent and more complete coverage of this subject by Schweiger (*188*). For the sake of convenience, however, some highlights are reported here.

Apparently, the often cited experiments of Barron and Harrop started the whole line of investigation on the alternate pathway of carbohydrate metabolism in erythrocytes (*23*) when they showed that methylene blue stimulates oxygen uptake of rabbit erythrocytes twentyfold. With the discovery of glucose-6-phosphate dehydrogenase in erythrocytes by Warburg and Christian (*21*), the concept of a new route of glucose metabolism became well entrenched. Since those historic times, many studies have been carried out on erythrocytes from all sources using mainly three methods: measuring $C^{14}O_2$ production from labeled glucose, assaying enzymes, and determining the pattern of products formed from various substrates.

Examples of studies using labeled glucose in erythrocytes are described below: Brin and Yonemoto studied the effect of methylene blue on CO_2 production and O_2 consumption by human erythrocytes (*189*). Murphy used uniformly labeled glucose to evaluate the relative contribution of the pentose phosphate pathway in glucose metabolism (*190*). Redding and Johnson investigated the effect of the state of the thyroid on glucose metabolism by blood (*191*). Strömme and Eldjarn determined the role of the pentose phosphate cycle in the reduction of methemoglobin, also using uniformly labeled glucose (*192*).

Experiments using enzymatic assays for measuring the role of the pentose cycle in erythrocytic metabolism of glucose are far too numerous to mention. Of all the enzymes, glucose-6-phosphate dehydrogenase appears to be the most frequently studied although attention has been focused on other enzymes of the pentose cycle. Some relatively recent results have been derived from experiments on the effect of steroids on glucose-6-phosphate and 6-phosphogluconate dehydrogenase activity (*193*), monkey erythrocytic glucose-6-phosphate dehydrogenase (*194*), and the nonoxidative enzymes of the pentose phosphate cycle in the human erythrocyte (*195–197*).

Products formed in various substrates have been studied extensively also. Late examples of these investigations have been documented by Bucolo and Bartlett (*198*), Dische and Igals (*199*), Lionetti *et al.* (*200*), Golovatsky (*201*), and Shafer and Bartlett (*202*). In general, either ribose in the form of nucleosides or as the phosphate was added to erythrocytes, their ghosts, or hemolyzates. Products were examined colorimetrically, enzymatically, and chromatographically.

Most of the research on glucose metabolism has been performed on red blood cells from humans. Other animals, however, have served as sources; e.g., cows (*201*), sheep (*201*), monkeys (*194*), cats (*194*), horses (*21*), rabbits (*201, 203*), and rats (*204*). The extent of oxidation of glucose via the pentose phosphate pathway is of the order of 10% as calculated by Murphy (*190*) and by Katz (*111*), who used the data of Brin and Yonemoto (*189*). This contribution by the shunt mechanism, however, is dependent on the presence or absence of methylene blue (*189*), on the pH of the suspending medium (*190*), on the oxygen tension (*190*), and on the age of the erythrocytes (*205*). In connection with this last item, aged erythrocytes have lower activities of glucose-6-phosphate and 6-phosphogluconate dehydrogenases than young cells. Also related to this problem are the findings by Rubenstein *et al.*, that the reticulocyte, the presumed nucleated precursor of the erythrocyte in hemopoiesis, has about the same level of glucose-6-phosphate dehydrogenase as the mature erythrocyte (*203*).

Besides the two dehydrogenases, the nonoxidative enzymes have been found in erythrocytes and characterized. Phosphoribose isomerase has been shown to exist in human erythrocytes (*195*) and in a whole gamut of erythrocytes of different species (*206*), which include the enzyme, in decreasing order of activity, from cats, dogs, horses, pigs, bovines, mice (whole blood in this case), rats, sheep, guinea pigs, and fowl. Human erythrocyte phosphoriboisomerase was the most active. Bruns *et al.* (*206*) also showed that phosphoriboisomerase of mouse erythrocytes has the highest activity as compared with that of heart muscle, skeletal muscle, liver, or kidney. Pig hemolyzates possess a complete pentose phosphate cycle, the ketopentoses being formed at a greater rate than triose phosphate and sedoheptulose-7-phosphate followed by fructose-6-phosphate and glucose-6-phosphate. These results are in contrast to those obtained by Schneider and Wagner, who were unable to demonstrate the presence of glucose-6-phosphate dehydrogenase in pig erythrocytes (*188*).

Transketolase in pentose metabolism has been implicated by experiments with thiamine-deficient rat erythrocytes (*204*). In these erythrocytes, in the presence of methylene blue, pentose accumulates to levels greater than normal and the oxidation of glucose-2-C^{14} to $C^{14}O_2$ is strikingly depressed below normal. This latter fact indicates that recycling of glucose is hindered by the thiamine deficiency. Thiamine therapy, on the other hand, decreases the pentose level in human red blood cells (*207*). Because the action of transketolase is mediated by thiamine pyrophosphate (*208*) one should expect to find this enzyme in erythrocytes, and indeed it is present (*196, 209*).

When intact erythrocytes are incubated with inosine, the product is sedoheptulose-1,7-diphosphate. This product is probably formed by an aldolase reaction of dihydroxyacetone phosphate and erythrose-4-phosphate (*198*). Furthermore, in the conversion of ribose-5-phosphate to hexose-6-phosphate by human hemolyzates, sedoheptulose and triose phosphates are intermediates (*210*).

The fact that the tetrose phosphate has to be present for the synthesis of sedoheptulose-1,7-diphosphate indicates that transaldolase occurs in the red blood cell. This has been demonstrated by experiments with stroma-free hemolyzates of human erythrocytes (*196*).

Several factors that influence the pentose phosphate cycle in red blood cells have already been mentioned, such as the presence of methylene blue, the age of the erythrocytes, and the effect of thiamine. Blood of individuals with hyperthyroid conditions and subjects with experimentally induced (by treatment with triiodothyronine) hyperthyroidism, gave a decrease in the early $C^{14}O_2$ production from glucose-1-C^{14} in the presence of methylene blue (*191*). The reason for this phenomenon is obscure because the levels of both glucose-6-phosphate and 6-phosphogluconate dehydrogenases are actually raised in thyrotoxic cases (*211, 212*). Some explanations were forwarded: There may be a net decrease in both TPN^+ and TPNH levels; other enzymes of the pentose phosphate cycle may have diminished; and/or the methylene blue added to the blood for these studies may have been inadequate for the thyrotoxic blood.

Glucose-6-phosphate dehydrogenase, being a key enzyme of the oxidative portion of the pentose phosphate cycle, has borne the brunt of attack from innumerable researchers. A comprehensive review of this enzyme, as well as of 6-phosphogluconate dehydrogenase, has now been made available (*213*). Since glucose-6-phosphate dehydrogenase is a TPN^+-linked enzyme, it is not surprising that this coenzyme has the greatest effect on the activity of the enzyme. However, TPNH also stimulates the metabolism of glucose-1-C^{14} to $C^{14}O_2$, whereas DPN^+ and DPNH are only mildly stimulatory (*214*). The activation of TPNH may be due to the action of a transhydrogenase. The resulting DPNH is reconverted to DPN^+ by the lactate dehydrogenase reaction. Glucose-6-phosphate dehydrogenase from normal human erythrocytes apparently can exist in a partially active state or an almost totally inactive state (*215, 216*). In the presence of TPN^+, the enzyme is reactivated and there are accompanying changes in sedimentation properties and antigenic activity.

As noted before, the effects of steroids on dehydrogenase activity have been studied (*193*). Very low concentrations ($<10^{-6}\,M$) inhibit glucose-6-phosphate dehydrogenase from mammalian tissues including human erythrocytes; that from yeast or spinach is not affected. Even mammalian 6-phosphogluconate dehydrogenase remains uninhibited. Furthermore, only steroids possessing a ketone group in the C-17 or C-20 positions are effective; e.g., dehydroisoandrosterone or pregnenolone. Steroids such as estrogens, testosterone, corticosteroids, and progesterone were ineffective as inhibitors in concentrations up to $4 \times 10^{-5}\,M$.

Other chemicals that apparently affect the oxidative enzymes of the pentose phosphate cycle are cysteine, ascorbate, pyruvate, and a number of hemolytic anemia-inducing drugs such as acetylphenylhydrazine, nitrofurantoin, α- and β-naphthol, primaquine phosphate, and fava bean extract (*217*). Addition of any one of these substances to red blood cells of normal human subjects enhances the oxidation rate of glucose-1-C^{14} to $C^{14}O_2$, but does not increase the rate of conversion of glucose to lactate. The stimulatory effect is due not to the direct action on glucose-6-phosphate dehydrogenase, but to the oxidation of TPNH in the presence of diaphorase and the substance added. In fact, α-naphthol and nitrofurantoin both inhibit glucose-6-phosphate dehydrogenase. The increased rate of reoxidation of TPNH may be a factor in the mechanism by which these substances destroy aged red blood cells.

Certain pathological conditions also affect the levels of the oxidative enzymes of the shunt. Thus reticulocytosis as a consequence of acquired and congenital hemolytic anemias, blood loss, pernicious anemia, sprue, and neoplastic diseases results in higher than normal activities of both dehydrogenases (*205*), although purine nucleoside phosphorylase activity remains the same. Full-term infants also show a higher level of glucose-6-phosphate dehydrogenase in the umbilical cord blood than do premature infants (*218*). The latter are frequently susceptible to anemic tendencies. Since glutathione and stability of glutathione are not significantly different in cord blood of full-term babies and of premature babies, conclusions could not be made as to what factors are responsible for shortening the life span of the erythrocytes in premature infants. Perhaps both rapid destruction of red blood cells and poor erythropoiesis in the bone marrow occur.

One of the most intensive phases of study on glucose-6-phosphate dehydrogenase (G-6-P DH) is the hemolytic anemia resulting from a lack or deficiency of this enzyme. Bruns and Werners (*213*) state that, in a United Fruit Company Annual Report in 1926, W. Cordes described the discovery of cases of hemolysis in Negroes who were given pamaquine for treatment of malaria. Since then much research has been carried out to determine the mechanism of this type of hemolysis. The facts can be outlined as follows:

Certain exogenous agents, when ingested, cause acute hemolytic anemia in subjects who have a deficiency in reduced glutathione (GSH) and G-6-P DH in the red blood cells. Some of these agents are pamaquine (*219*), primaquine (*219*), nitrofurantoin (*220*), naphthalene (*220*), aniline derivatives (*219*), and *Vicia faba* beans (*220, 221*). The hemolysis appears to be associated with the GSH level, the latter being needed, somehow, for maintaining the integrity of the erythrocytes (*222*). GSH is linked to G-6-P DH through TPN^+, the latter becoming TPNH while glucose-6-phosphate is being oxidized. In turn, TPNH reacts with oxidized glutathione (GSSG) catalyzed by glutathione reductase, to yield GSH, thereby regenerating TPN^+. Although primaquine-sensitive individuals have a deficiency in the blood G-6-P DH level, glutathione reductase activity of their hemolyzates is increased, as if to compensate partially for the deficiency of the former enzyme (*223*). Nevertheless, GSH level in erythrocytes of primaquin-sensitive subjects is decreased (*222*). The critical factor thus seems to be the level of TPNH. Old erythrocytes are hemolyzed by the drug, but after this first attack there is a period of several weeks during which more primaquine has no further effect (*224*). The younger red blood cell population, however, contains higher G-6-P DH activity than the old cells, although not normal. Therefore the younger cells are able to maintain a high enough level of reduced glutathione to protect the cells.

The mechanism for drug-induced hemolysis was suggested by Beutler (*219*) and by Tarlov *et al.* (*225*). When the drug is administered to an individual, the hemoglobin in the erythrocytes is oxidized. The oxidized hemoglobin returns to the original state by converting GSH to GSSG. This occurs only if the activity of G-6-P DH is sufficiently high, as in the case of nonsensitive (normal) individuals. The drug-sensitive person, on the other hand, lacks this dehydrogenase and consequently the supply of GSH will be exhausted. Following this the oxidized hemoglobin becomes denatured and simultaneously forms Heinz bodies. Intervasal hemolysis thus ensues. Akin to this problem are the findings that human erythrocytes which are deficient in G-6-P DH cannot maintain their levels of GSH in the presence of low level steady state concentrations of hydrogen peroxide (*226*). It was suggested that this low level H_2O_2, resulting from the autoxidation of the drug (or intermediates therefrom), causes in part the oxidative damage to the red blood cells.

The deficiency in the level of G-6-P DH may be due to at least several factors (*227*): there is a real lack of the enzyme, there is an inhibitor present, or there is a deficiency of an activator. Thus stromata in hemolyzates of primaquine-sensitive and nonsensitive erythrocytes inactivate G-6-P DH (*228*). In contrast to these results, Ramot *et al.* showed that a factor existing in normal erythrocyte stroma can activate the dehydrogenase of drug-sensitive red blood cells (*229*). To confuse the picture further, Kidson and Gorman demonstrated that although there is indeed a stromal activating factor, this factor failed to activate the dehydrogenase in 20% of the cases (*230*). Hence there seems to be a definite heterogeneity of response to stromal activation of G-6-P DH, at least in erythrocytes of Melanesians.

The hemolytic activity of primaquine and primaquine-like drugs has been clearly demonstrated in American Negroes with an incidence of the order of 10%, in contrast to that in Caucasians with less than 1% (*213, 219*). Among the Jewish population the affliction was found in 20% of the non-Ashkenazic Jews from Iraq and Persia, in 5% from Yemen and Turkey, and in 2% from North Africa; 3% of the Arabs in Israel also showed sensitivity to these drugs (*231*). The Mediterranean population also has its share of this affliction, Sardinians (*232*), and Greeks (*233*) having the usual symptoms along with sensitivity toward fava beans. The enzyme deficiency trait is also common among East Africans (*234*) and West Africans (*235, 236*). [It is interesting to note that among these people difficulty may be encountered in blood sampling so that other methods of sampling had to be devised. Tests showed that the G-6-P DH levels in the saliva and skin of drug-sensitive subjects are markedly lower in activity, 0.54 units, than those of the nonsensitive cases, 8 units (*237*).]

Finally, some Chinese in Singapore (*238*), Indians (*219*), and Papuans (*239, 240*) show a deficiency in the dehydrogenase level. Quantitative differences have also been shown to exist between the dehydrogenase levels in whole erythrocyte population, young red blood cells, and leukocytes of affected Caucasians and Negroes (*241*).

The lack of G-6-P DH thus appears to be an inheritable trait, as judged from the descriptions in the preceding paragraphs. In fact the mode of inheritance is sex linked and is controlled by a gene of intermediate dominance (*220, 241a*) giving a full expression in the hemizygous males and homozygous females and partial expression heterozygous females. Comparison of families having color-blind sons with G-6-P DH deficiency shows a fairly close linkage between the sex-linked color-blind locus and the enzyme-deficiency locus (*242, 243*).

The distribution of G-6-P DH deficiency in certain geographical localities among East Africans and among Sardinians raises several interesting questions: Is there any relationship between enzyme deficiency and malaria? In view of the high incidence of thalassemia (a hypochromic microcytic anemia commonly found in the Mediterranean area) in Sardinia, is there a connection of this disease with enzyme deficiency? Siniscalco *et al.* (*232*) made such an analysis in Sardinia and found positive correlations between thalassemia and frequency of the gene for enzyme deficiency as well as between past malarial incidence and G-6-P DH deficiency. Moreover, there was an inverse relationship between enzyme deficiency and altitude. Allison (*234*), while studying the geographical distribution of enzyme deficiency in East Africa, found that the incidence of this affliction is high in tribes near the coast and around Lake Victoria, whereas the incidence is low in the intermediate highlands. All other populations with a high frequency of this trait reside in the malarial region or where malaria was until recently holoendemic. The possibility is considered then, that there is less multiplication of malarial parasites in cells deficient in the enzyme than in normal cells, because GSH is required for the propagation of the parasite. Indeed, young malaria-susceptible East African children, in a region where *Plasmodium falciparum* malaria is holoendemic, showed lower parasite counts in the G-6-P DH deficient erythrocytes than in normal red blood cells.

Both these concepts have been challenged on the grounds that only 3 out of 6 patients with thalassemia had a lack of the enzyme whereas others with abnormal hemoglobin were not deficient at all (*244*). Furthermore, a close examination of the distribution pattern of the enzyme-deficiency trait among various linguistic groups in New Guinea and New Britain showed that there are extreme differences in the enzyme-deficiency gene even though these culturally distinct groups are living close to where the *P. falciparum* malaria is prevalent (*245*). In two cases of the highland linguistic group, the frequency of the enzyme-deficiency gene was greater than that of the lowland. Thalassemia was also found to be dissociated from enzyme deficiency in that the former yielded a consistent high incidence in the coastal regions, rapidly diminishing with altitude. On the other hand, the enzyme deficiency gave erratic frequencies in the various linguistic groups examined.

How does the G-6-P DH deficiency affect the pentose phosphate cycle? We would expect a decrease in the level of 6-phosphogluconate, and hence less pentose phosphates via the oxidative pathway. [Primaquine-sensitive erythrocytes possess a fully active 6-phosphogluconate dehydrogenase (*246*).] In order to compensate for a low level of pentose phosphates synthesis, more active transketolase and transaldolase are required. This is indeed the case (*247*).

By comparison with the literature dealing with erythrocyte metabolism, that of leukocytic carbohydrate metabolism seems meager. The operation of the oxidative pathway was demonstrated first in the white cells from the peripheral blood of cats, rabbits, and dogs (*248*). The metabolism of glucose via the oxidative pentose phosphate cycle is quantitatively very small (*111, 249*) in normal human leukocytes. Less than 10% of the glucose catabolized is via this pathway although somewhat higher values are obtained for myelocytic leukemia and for lymphocytic leukemia. These values were estimated from the radioactive carbon dioxide formed from specifically labeled glucose as well as from the specific activity of the labeled lactate. Transketolase and transaldolase were also found in both normal and leukemic cells. Levels of other enzymes, including G-6-P DH, 6-PG DH, and pentose phosphate isomerase were also studied to determine the factors controlling the rate behavior in the multienzyme systems of normal and leukemic leukocytes (*250*). The activities of the two dehydrogenases along with the glycolytic enzymes approximately parallel the over-all aerobic glycolysis as measured by lactate production, but that of pentose phosphate isomerase remained constant in both normal and leukemic cells alike. Further experiments in the presence and absence of ADP, ATPase, and glucose-6-phosphate indicate that hexokinase is rate limiting. It may well be that the increase in flow of glucose through the shunt mechanism is indirectly controlled by this enzyme and that the higher percentage participation of the pentose cycle in leukemia is due to a deficiency of hexokinase. Specific activity of G-6-P DH based on units per cell could be misleading, however (*251*). Thus if the enzyme levels in myeloid leukemic cells (granulocytes) were compared with the granulocytes in the normal cells, and if the lymphatic leukemic cells were compared with lymphocytes, the activity of G-6-P DH in the granulocytes of myeloid leukemia was found to increase to three times that of normal granulocytes while that of lymphatic leukemia decreased to one-third that of the normal leukocytes.

Further evidence for the presence of transketolase and transaldolase in rabbit polymorphonuclear leukocytes is derived from experiments with labeled pentoses (*252*) and labeled hexoses (*253*). The incorporation of labeled bicarbonate was also investigated (*254*), but the percentage of incorporation was extremely low. Nevertheless, enough labeled products were obtained for degradation, which showed a distribution pattern explainable only by a slow reversal of the 6-PG DH reaction superimposed on a transaldolase exchange reaction.

Another type of regulation of the flow of glucose through the pentose phosphate pathway occurs when human and guinea pig leukocytes are allowed to metabolize the exogenous glucose in the presence of bicarbonate. In this case the respiration is completely insensitive to added cyanide (*255*), whereas in phosphate medium respiration is inhibited by this ion in the presence of glucose. A mechanism was proposed involving the dicarboxylic acid shuttle and transhydrogenase or DPN-oxidase to provide the necessary cofactors, TPN^+ and DPN^+, for glucose catabolism via glycolysis and the pentose phosphate cycle.

When foreign bodies are ingested by certain types of leukocytes, for example, guinea pig neutrophilic granulocytes, glycolysis is stimulated (*256*). Furthermore, oxygen uptake and the preferential conversion of glucose-1-C^{14} to $C^{14}O_2$ are increased (*257*). Since a TPN-linked lactate dehydrogenase was found in these leukocytes, Evans and Karnovsky suggested that the following mechanism can account for the observations above (*258*): Phagocytosis yields a decrease in the intracellular pH because of the increased lactate production due to a stimulated glycolysis. This lowered pH, in turn, activates both DPNH oxidase and the TPN-linked lactate dehydrogenase since these enzymes have optimal activities around pH 5. The regeneration of oxidized pyridine nucleotides thus increases the rate of glycolysis as well as of the oxidative pentose phosphate cycle.

Some final words should be said about ribonucleic acid pentose metabolism. Lymphatic leukemic cells and Gardner lymphosarcoma cells (as well as rat thymus, mouse spleen, rabbit appendix) were incubated with variously labeled glucose, and the distribution pattern in the ribose of the RNA-purine nucleotides was determined along with that in some of the free amino acids (*259*). The results indicate that both the transketolase-transaldolase pathway and the direct oxidative pathway are of importance for the synthesis of the ribose moiety of RNA by lymphatic tissues and tumor.

8. *Eyes*

Studies of the pentose phosphate cycle in the eye have been concentrated on the cornea, lens, and retina. Source material for these tissues were the rat, bovine, monkey, human, and rabbit. Most of the work on the pathways of glucose metabolism in bovine corneal epithelium have been done by Kinoshita and his co-workers. They showed that both G-6-P DH and 6-PG DH were present in the homogenate of corneal epithelium and that pentose phosphate can be converted to sedoheptulose-7-phosphate, from which hexose monophosphate is formed (*260*). Using specifically labeled glucose, von Holt *et al.* concluded that CO_2 production comes almost exclusively via the pentose phosphate cycle (*261*), although calculations using the ratio of radioactive lactate from glucose-1-C^{14} and from glucose-6-C^{14} (*262*) gave a value of 15% for the relative participation of this pathway for the metabolism of glucose (*111*). Pyruvate, added *in vitro* to corneal epithelium, stimulates the preferential oxidation of C-1 of glucose to CO_2 (*263*). The mechanism of this stimulation appears to be due to the presence of a TPN-linked lactate dehydrogenase, thereby coupling the oxidation of glucose with the anaerobic utilization of pyruvate via the pentose phosphate cycle. Although the TCA cycle is functioning in the corneal epithelium, the hexose monophosphate shunt appears to be of greater importance in this tissue than in others, since most of carbon atom number 2 of glucose is oxidized by the latter pathway (*264*). Insulin has no effect on the total oxidation and it does not change the C-1:C-6 ratio of CO_2 (*261*).

The ocular lens is considered to be metabolically inert because it has a low rate of oxygen uptake. Nevertheless, if the metabolism of carbohydrate is interfered with, the lens becomes opaque. When isolated rabbit lenses are kept under conditions that simulate the *in situ* physiological state, glucose is converted mainly to lactate (*265*). As in the case of the cornea, the pentose phosphate cycle is responsible for the bulk of the CO_2 formed from the small amount of glucose oxidized by the lens, and the contribution of this pathway to glucose metabolism is estimated to be about 2% based on the C-1:C-6 ratio in lactate (*111*). A high galactose diet (*266*) or a high xylose diet (*267*) fed to rats causes the lenses to develop cataracts. In the former case, the pentose phosphate cycle activity diminishes progressively with time, whereas in the latter case, this activity initially declines, but later returns to the normal level. The conversion of G-6-P to 6-PG appears to be inhibited by galactose-1-phosphate, and therefore this may be the mechanism for the galactose effect.

The xylose effect is less clear, but the formation and utilization of D-xylulose is implicated. Certain pathological conditions also affect the activity of the pentose phosphate pathway. For example, in human subjects with primaquine-sensitive erythrocytes, there is a marked reduction of the lens G-6-P DH although the level of 6-PG DH is normal (*268*). Cataractous lens from these individuals also has a lower G-6-P DH content than normal while the 6-PG DH level is normal. On the other hand, cataractous lenses from humans with normal G-6-P DH in their erythrocytes have higher specific activities of both dehydrogenases, the more advanced the cataract, the higher the specific activities. Alloxan-induced diabetes decreases the formation of $C^{14}O_2$ from glucose-1-C^{14} by rat lens whereas that from glucose-6-C^{14} remains unaffected (*269*). Whereas insulin added *in vitro* to normal rat lens suspended in Krebs-Ringer bicarbonate buffer stimulates C-1 oxidation and inhibits C-6 oxidation to CO_2, insulin diminishes the former oxidation without affecting the latter in lens from the alloxan diabetic rat. [Insulin has no effect on either C-1 or C-6 oxidation when this tissue is suspended in Krebs-Ringer phosphate buffer. In contrast to these findings, von Holt *et al.* found that insulin had no effect on the total oxidation of glucose and did not alter the C-1:C-6 ratio of CO_2 (*261*).]

The utilization of glucose in cattle retina is almost exclusively via the EMP and TCA pathways (*270*). Under anaerobic conditions, however, the hexose monophosphate pathway is activated in intact retina in the presence of pyruvate. Rahman and Kerly, using the C-1:C-6 ratios of specific activity of lactate, concluded that in ox retina 1 of 4 moles of glucose is metabolized via the pentose phosphate cycle (*271*). G-6-P DH and 6-PH DH have been found in bovine, rabbit, and monkey (*Macaca rhesus*) retina (*272, 273*). Both dehydrogenases have the same specific activities in the cow's retina (*272*). Histochemical analyses showed that G-6-P DH is very rich throughout most of the first neuron of the retina of rabbit as well as monkey (*273*), the activity of this enzyme being about 10–30 times greater than that of the rest of the retina. The localization of DH activity of 6-PG parallels that of G-6-P DH, but at lower levels. Insulin added to retina significantly increases glucose oxidation but did not change the C-1:C-6 CO_2 (*261*).

9. *Intestines*

This highly specialized and functional organ consists of connective tissues, smooth muscles, and the mucosa, this last category making up one-fifth of the total mass of the intestines (*274*). In addition, the mucosa is an actively regenerating tissue, one-half of the cells turning over every 2 or 3 days. In this tissue there is a potentially active oxidative pentose phosphate cycle as evidenced by the presence of G-6-P DH and 6-PG DH in rabbit duodenal mucosa (*137*) and in the intestinal mucosa of cat, guinea pig, and rat (*275*). In the mucosa of these last three animals between 93 and 98% of the activities of the two dehydrogenases is located in the supernatant fraction, which is free of the nuclei, mitochondria, and microsomes. Furthermore, both dehydrogenases have about the same specific activities; however, their specific activities were lower by a factor of 4 than that of lactate dehydrogenase found in the mucosa. Landau and Wilson have measured the CO_2 C-1:C-6 ratios from labeled glucose and found that in hamster small intestinal tissue the ratios averaged 1.5 for the upper jejunum, the midgut, and the lower ileum (*276*). The C-1:C-6 lactate ratio from the metabolism of glucose-1-C^{14} and glucose-6-C^{14} in normal rat mucosa of the small intestines is approximately 0.8 (*277*). This ratio remained unchanged even after X-irradiation of the rat (600 roentgens), although the oxidation of the glucose to CO_2 and lactate increased. The TCA cycle seems to be entirely responsible for this increase while the EMP pathway seems to be unaffected by the irradiation. The contribution of the pentose phosphate cycle to the catabolism of glucose by mucosa of both normal and X-irradiated rats was estimated to be 6–8% assuming that no non-triose phosphate pathway occurs (*111*).

10. *Kidneys*

Aside from the usual renal function of maintaining homeostatic conditions, the kidney appears also to be an actively metabolizing entity. As it is with other mammalian organs, the kidney has the capacity to utilize glucose via the oxidative pentose phosphate cycle. This is clearly indicated by the occurrence of both G-6-P DH and 6-PG DH in the various tissues of this organ. A summary of the type of tissues, the mammalian sources, and the enzymes studied, as well as the investigators, is given in Fig. 4. The oxidation of glucose via these enzymes, however, is probably relatively small since the levels of the dehydrogenases in the cortex of kidney are less than 10% those found in the liver (*279*). These findings correlate well with the results of experiments using variously labeled glucose. The incorporation of C^{14} into CO_2 produced (*97, 281*) and into glycogen as well as fatty acids (*281*) all indicate that the contribution of the pentose phosphate cycle in the cortex and the medulla is insignificant.

Alterations in the physiological conditions of the animal may vary the levels of G-6-P DH and 6-PG DH in the kidney. For example, acute experimental ischemia caused by unilateral clamping of one renal artery increased the levels of these two enzymes in the macula densa of the ischemic kidney whereas those of the unclamped contralateral kidney decreased significantly (*280*). The change in renin content paralleled the enzymatic changes; thus a possible relationship between the enzymatic activity in the macula densa and renin formation was proposed. Massive doses of deoxycorticosterone plus high saline diet administered to rats or unilateral nephrectomy plus high saline diet decreased the G-6-P DH

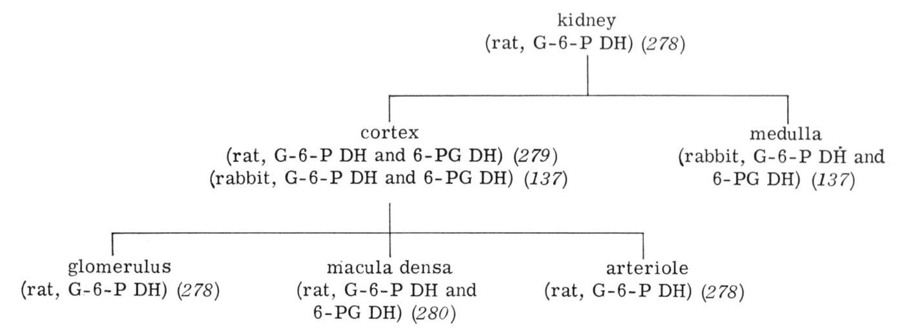

FIG. 4. Distribution of glucose-6-phosphate dehydrogenase and 6-phosphogluconate dehydrogenase in various tissues of the kidney.

activity in the macula densa cells accompanied by a concomitant decrease in the renin content of kidney homogenate (*282*). On the other hand, bilateral adrenalectomy plus a low-salt diet treatment of rats gave a rise in G-6-P DH activity. The role of the pentose phosphate cycle in the renin formation-enzyme activity relationship is unknown. Nephrosis, induced by administration of an aminonucleoside of puromycin to rats, also increased the activity of G-6-P DH in whole kidney homogenate, glomeruli, and renal arterioles (*278*).

11. *Liver*

The amount of literature dealing with carbohydrate metabolism by the pentose phosphate cycle in the liver is second only to that in erythrocytes. This fact is not too surprising in view of the easy availability of this organ and in view of the extensive characterization of this organ in terms of its physiology, anatomy, biochemistry, and pathology. There is no question that the liver is capable of catabolizing glucose via the shunt mechanism, various related enzymes being detected in liver homogenates of different mammalian sources. Some examples of these enzymes and their sources are itemized in Table III. It should be noted that G-6-P DH in mouse or rat liver cytoplasm is the least active when compared with enzymes involved in glycolysis, glycogenesis, glycogenolysis, and gluconeogenesis (*286*). In fact, if glucose were utilized under conditions where maximum rates exist, the oxidation of this sugar via G-6-P DH would be between one-fifth and one-tenth that of glycolysis, the rate of the latter pathway being controlled by the next least active enzyme, fructose-6-phosphate kinase. The conclusion would then be that, as an alternate pathway of glucose metabolism, the oxidative pentose phosphate cycle contributes between 10 and 20%. However, Katz

TABLE III
SOME PENTOSE PHOSPHATE CYCLE ENZYMES IN THE LIVER

Source	Pentose phosphate cycle enzymes	Reference
Guinea pig	G-6-P DH and 6-PG DH	(*283*)
Porcine	Transketolase and ribose-5-phosphate-3-epimerase	(*284*)
Rabbit	Nonoxidative enzymes plus nucleosidases	(*285*)
Mouse	G-6-P DH	(*286*)
Rat	G-6-P DH and 6-PG DH	(*287*)
	Nonoxidative enzymes	(*288*)
	6-Phosphogluconolactonase	(*289*)
Sheep	G-6-P DH and 6-PG DH[a]	(*290*)

[a] Existence suggested by homogenate which can oxidize glucose to CO_2 in the presence of ATP and TPN^+.

(*111*) states that in a multienzyme system there is little correlation between the actual *in vivo* rates obtained by measuring *in vitro* rates. Nevertheless, Weber (*279*) found that the enzymatic activities in kidney homogenates do correlate well with the conclusions drawn from experiments using isotopic techniques.

Experiments in which the C-1:C-6 ratios of CO_2 from the respectively labeled glucose were measured, gave results that may be described as markedly erratic. In this regard, numerous works have been cited by Katz (*111*) to illustrate the variability of these ratios; they range from 1.2 to 5.0. One is tempted to attribute these discrepancies to differences in strains of animals, dietary conditions, and other experimental factors, but Katz has pointed out that even under apparently identical conditions, one group of investigators found vastly different C-1:C-6 ratios.

The variability is also reflected in the relative contribution of the pentose phosphate cycle for glucose metabolism, even though parameters other than the C-1:C-6 ratios of CO_2 were used for the calculations. Thus Katz (*111*) has compiled data from numerous sources and obtained values between 4 and 20% as the fraction of the glucose metabolized via the pentose phosphate cycle in livers of normal fed rats. Whereas Muntz and Murphy estimated higher values for the relative contribution of the pentose phosphate cycle in the metabolism of glucose, 29 to 38% in the *in vivo* rat liver (*102*) and 55% in the perfused rat liver (*291*), these figures are no doubt overestimated since dilution of the radioactive compounds by a large unlabeled pool of compounds was not considered.

In spite of the difficulties encountered in the interpretation of the variable results, some conclusions can still be salvaged from the results of experiments with normal fed rats as compared with those of normal fasted rats. Listed in Table IV are the effects of fasting on the metabolism in normal rat liver. Actually the G-6-P DH level does change, but this depends on the number of days of starvation. After 24 hours of fasting, the liver G-6-P DH specific activity rises to 150% the normal level; however, after 48 and 72 hours the specific activity falls to 75 and 60% of the normal level, respectively (*295*). Six days of fasting causes the level to drop to only 5% of the normal fed animal (*296*). Because there is a depressed C-1:C-6 of CO_2 from labeled glucose in the fasted rat liver, and because a decreased lipogenesis means a lower rate of TPN^+ production, one might expect that the oxidative pentose phosphate cycle would also decrease. That the latter remains unchanged and, if anything, tends to be larger, suggests that the TCA cycle activity as reflected by the increased oxidation of acetyl coenzyme A is stimulated. Thus we have here a clear-cut example of a case where the C-1:C-6 ratio of CO_2 from labeled glucose decreases and yet the pentose phosphate cycle participation in the metabolism of glucose is relatively unaltered.

TABLE IV
EFFECT OF STARVATION ON THE METABOLISM OF RAT LIVER

Metabolic parameter	Effect of fasting as compared with normal fed rat liver	References
Lipogenesis	Decreased	(*111, 292, 293*)
C-1:C-6 of CO_2 from glucose	Decreased	(*111, 294*)
C-1:C-3 of CO_2 from lactate	Decreased	(*107, 111*)
G-6-P DH level	Unaltered	(*111*)
Oxidation of acetyl CoA	Increased	(*111*)
Relative contribution of pentose phosphate cycle	No change	(*111*)

The role of the oxidative pentose phosphate cycle in fatty acid metabolism appears to be quite clear by now. A large segment of the literature is devoted to this subject and the general consensus is that TPNH is the limiting factor in those cases where lipogenesis is reduced (*292, 297*). However, some investigators feel that this interpretation is somewhat oversimplified (*298*), because under conditions where there is enhanced lipid incorporation of C-1 and C-6 from glucose, the

C-1:C-6 ratio of incorporation decreases slightly whereas the C-1:C-6 of CO_2 increases markedly. Furthermore, Abraham *et al.* showed that both the oxidation of glucose-6-phosphate and citrate in alloxan-diabetic rat liver homogenate produced the same amount of TPNH (*299*). They concluded that TPNH production is not a controlling factor for fatty acid synthesis in these diabetic rat liver preparations. Finally, experiments with glucose-1-H^3 and lactate-2-H^3 using normal fed rat liver indicated that the contribution of the labeled glucose to lipogenesis is less than that of the labeled lactate (*300*). The conclusion is that the oxidative pentose phosphate cycle is not a major source of TPNH for this synthesis.

The effect of fasting on the oxidative pentose phosphate cycle activity in the liver of normal rats has already been mentioned. In Table V are summarized some effects of other types of dietary conditions on the liver pentose phosphate cycle activity. A few remarks are appropriate regarding some of these effects. With the choline (fat free) deficient diet, the rat liver shows signs of fatty degeneration. When the rat is fed this diet for a short time, no fatty degeneration is apparent in the liver. During this period, the G-6-P DH level rises above the normal level. After fatty degeneration has manifested itself in the liver, this dehydrogenase level drops below normal. Livers of rats fasted 48 hours and then refed a high-carbohydrate, low-fat diet give a large and progressive conversion of the C-1 of glucose to CO_2, whereas the conversion of C-6 remains constant. The effect of a high-fructose diet is strikingly greater than that of a high-glucose diet. In the ethionine experiment, this compound is not uniformly effective in blocking enzyme synthesis. Aside from a decrease in synthesis of 6-PG DH, ethionine interferes with the synthesis of glucose-6-phosphatase, phosphoglucomutase, fructose-1,6-diphosphatase, and phosphohexose isomerase. The experiments with the scorbutogenic diet also showed that there is no change in the oxidation rate of the C-1 of glucose to CO_2, but there is a decrease in that of C-6.

The intermediary metabolism of glucose has also been studied in the cold-acclimatized rat (*304, 305*). In one case, rats were maintained at 0–2°C. for longer than 120 days. When compared with control rats maintained at 25°C. for the same period of time, the cold acclimatized rats have depressed hepatic lipogenesis and carbohydrate metabolism (*304*). The C-1:C-6 ratios of CO_2 from glucose are not significantly different between the controls and the experimental animals, a result indicating that the reduced lipogenesis is not associated with the decreased glucose metabolism. Hannon and Vaughn, however, found that when rats are exposed to the cold (5 ± 1°C.) for only 3–4 weeks, the G-6-P DH and 6-PG DH levels are decreased markedly, the former to one-half and the latter to three-fourths those of the control animals maintained at 26 ± 1°C. (*305*). They attribute the discrepancy between the C-1:C-6 results and theirs to the much longer exposure of the animals to cold intervals, which perhaps may profoundly influence the tissue

TABLE V
EFFECT OF DIETARY CONDITIONS ON THE G-6-P DH AND/OR 6-PG DH ACTIVITIES IN THE RAT LIVER

Dietary conditions	Control diet	Effect on enzymatic activity	Reference
Choline-deficient (fat-free) diet	Normal diet; i.e., ad libitum	G-6-P DH: Initially above, then below control	(*295*)
Corn diet	15% casein diet	G-6-P DH and 6-PG DH: below control	(*301*)
Corn diet + lysine and/or tryptophan	15% casein diet	G-6-P DH and 6-PG DH: above corn diet, but still below control	(*301*)
Low-casein diet, minus threonine	15% casein diet	G-6-P DH and 6-PG DH: below control	(*301*)
Low-casein diet, plus threonine	15% casein diet	G-6-P DH and 6-PG DH: above control, former to greater extent than latter	(*301*)
Fasted 48 hr., refed high-carbohydrate, low-fat diet	Normal diet	G-6-P DH and 6-PG DH: markedly above control and increasing with refeeding time	(*298*)
High-glucose diet	Normal diet	G-6-P DH and 6-PG DH: above control	(*302*)
High-fructose diet	Normal diet	G-6-P DH and 6-PG DH: above control	(*302*)
Fasted 6 days, refed 1 day	Fasted 6 days	G-6-P DH and 6-PG DH: above control	(*303*)
Fasted 6 days, refed 1 day + ethionine	Fasted 6 days	G-6-P DH: above control 6-PG DH: same as control	(*303*)
Scorbutogenic diet[a]	Scorbutogenic diet plus ascorbate	G-6-P DH and 6-PG DH: above control	(*283*)

[a] Guinea pigs were used as experimental animals in this case.

metabolic rates. Since the cold-exposed rats have a depressed capacity for TPNH production, owing to the reduced activity of the dehydrogenases, then the decreased fatty acid synthesis observed may be ascribed to the decreased level of these enzymes. The reason for the reduced dehydrogenases activities is unknown, but the decrease is not due to hyperthyroidism in the cold, since this condition is known to lead to enhanced G-6-P DH and 6-PG DH activities.

The state of the endocrine and the administration of certain hormones also regulate the activities of the liver dehydrogenases. Thus, from Table VI, one can see that removal of the adrenals or the pituitary glands does not markedly affect the levels of G-6-P DH and 6-PG DH. Subsequent administration of hormones also has no striking effect. (The enhancement of activity of 6-PG DH to 159% of normal in the adrenalectomized

TABLE VI
EFFECT OF THE ENDOCRINE STATE AND DIET SCHEDULE ON THE ACTIVITIES OF G-6-P DH AND 6-PG DH IN THE RAT LIVER

Expt. no.	Endocrine state	Diet regime	% of control activity: G-6-P DH	% of control activity: 6-PG DH	Reference
1	Normal (C)[a]	Fed	100	100	*(287)*
	Adrenalectomized (A)	Fed	82	77	*(287)*
2	A + 0.9% NaCl (C)	Fed	100	100	*(287)*
	A + cortisone	Fed	89	127	*(287)*
	A (C)	Fed	100	100	*(303)*
3	A + cortisone	Fed	133	159	*(303)*
	A + cortisone + ethionine	Fed	126	86	*(303)*
	Normal (C)	Fed	100	100	*(296)*
4	Hypophysectomized (H)	Fasted 1 day	23	17	*(296)*
	H	Fasted 1 day, refed 1 day	28	28	*(296)*
5	H + 0.9% NaCl (C)	Fed	100	100	*(287)*
	H + cortisone	Fed	101	152	*(287)*

[a] (C) = control for the particular series of experiments.

rat treated with cortisone was not considered as significant whereas the increase of this same enzymatic activity in the case of the hypophysectomized rat plus cortisone was considered to be significant by these same workers.) In contrast to these results, Willmer (*306*) found that adrenalectomy of the rat decreases the activity of G-6-P DH, but does not alter that of 6-PG DH. *In vivo* administration of either cortisone or corticosterone to these rats restores the activity of G-6-P DH to normal.

On fasting the hypophysectomized animal, however, a complicated picture arises. First, such rats starved for 1 day decrease markedly both hepatic dehydrogenase activities. On refeeding them, no significant rise in either of the activities was observed. This is in sharp contrast to a 1-day fast of nonhypophysectomized rats which produces an increased level of G-6-P DH and which at the end of 2 days of fasting reduced the level to only 70% of normal. The most striking effect, however, is the response of the G-6-P DH levels to 1 day of refeeding. These levels soar well over twofold the activities found in the normal fed rat liver (*296*). Hypophysectomized rats treated further with growth hormone, growth hormone plus cortisone, or growth hormone plus hydrocortisone fail to exhibit any profound changes in the dehydrogenase activities. When these rats are fed and are administered simultaneously growth hormone, cortisone, and triiodothyronine, the combined G-6-P DH and 6-PG DH activities are elevated to over 220% the normal level (Table VII). This

TABLE VII

EFFECT OF STARVATION, REFEEDING, ENDOCRINE STATE, AND HORMONES ON THE COMBINED ACTIVITIES OF G-6-P DH AND 6-PG DH (*307*)

Endocrine state	Diet schedule	Dehydrogenase activity (% of control)
Normal (control)	Fed	100
Normal	Fasted 48 hr.	70
Normal	Fasted 48 hr., refed 48 hr.	230
Hypophysectomized	Fed	50
Hypophysectomized	Fasted 24 hr.	50
Hypophysectomized	Fasted 24 hr., refed 48 hr.	60
Hypophysectomized + growth hormone (GH)	Fed	70
Hypophysectomized + GH + cortisone (C)	Fed	60
Hypophysectomized + GH + hydrocortisone	Fed	90
Hypophysectomized + GH + C + triiodothyronine (T)	Fed	220
Hypophysectomized + GH + C + T	Fasted 48 hr., refed 48 hr.	420
Hypophysectomized	Fed via stomach tube	500

stimulation of activities is even more marked when the rats are fasted and then refed. Finally, the most remarkable effect occurred when the hypophysectomized rats were fed via stomach tubes; an extremely high activation of the dehydrogenases was obtained. No additional increase could be induced by treatment with the three hormones mentioned above. It appears, therefore, that liver cells of hypophysectomized rats can modify its enzyme profile selectively without calling upon the action of the pituitary hormones. It may be that the role of these hormones is to act on the food uptake and perhaps influence also the intestinal absorption rates.

One final word should be said about other factors that regulate the pentose phosphate cycle activity in rat liver. The case of alloxan-diabetic rats and insulinized diabetic rats has been adequately surveyed by Katz (*111*) and no further discussion will be given here. Since fatty acid synthesis is associated with the pentose phosphate cycle, it would seem reasonable to assume that other conditions that give rise to fatty liver might have an effect on the oxidation of glucose. Hence mice with a congenital obese-hyperglycemia syndrome have microscopically obvious fatty livers that oxidize glucose to CO_2 with a ratio of C-1:C-6 = 1.8 while lean normal littermates have livers that yield a C-1:C-6 ratio of 1.2 (*308*). However, the number of micrograms of glucose oxidized per 100 mg. of fat-free liver (dry weight) is, on the average, 17.7 from C-1 and 9.4 from C-6 in the obese mouse compared with normal values of 24.3 and 20.8, respectively. Therefore, the higher C-1:C-6 in obese mouse can be accounted for by a less active TCA cycle. As in the case of many other tissues, the addition of certain artificial electron carrier systems to rat liver slices preferentially oxidizes glucose-1-C^{14} to $C^{14}O_2$ while only mildly increasing the oxidation of G-6-C^{14} to $C^{14}O_2$. Examples of these compounds are methylene blue, phenazine methosulfate, and pyocyanine (*309*). On the other hand, dinitrophenol, an uncoupler of oxidative phosphorylation, increases both the oxidation of C-1 and C-6 of glucose although it decreases the conversion of glucose to glycogen and to fatty acids.

12. *Mammary Gland*

Among the more extensively studied tissues, the lactating mammary gland has the most active pentose phosphate cycle, this tissue being capable of metabolizing glucose via this pathway to the extent of 40% (*111*). The pioneering work on this tissue has been carried out by Glock and McLean, who showed that the specific activities of G-6-P DH and 6-PG DH (*310*), the levels of pyridine nucleotides (*311*), and the oxidation of glucose-1-C^{14} (*312*) in the mammary gland all increase as the rat progresses from pregnancy through the lactation and abruptly decrease on involution of the glands. These observations suggest that the pentose phosphate cycle has an active role in the lactating mammary gland. [For more detailed discussion of this subject, this reviewer recommends the reader to the widespread coverage by Glock and McLean (*313*) and by Hansen and Carlson (*314*).]

Research on carbohydrate metabolism in mammary glands has fallen mainly into two classes: *in vitro* experiments either with tissue slices or homogenates, usually from rats, but occasionally from mice, albino rabbits (*315*), and sheep (*312*); and *in vivo* experiments and perfusion experiments with lactating cows. In the case of lactating cows, Black *et al.*, measuring the incorporation of C^{14} from glucose-1-C^{14} and from glucose-6-C^{14} into fatty acids as well as the respired CO_2, concluded that the results were not in accords with the sole operation of the EMP pathway (*123*). Their estimate of glucose catabolized via the pentose phosphate cycle was rather high (greater than 50%), but more conservative values can be obtained from these data (*111*). Wood and his co-workers have centered their attention around the synthesis of lactose in the cow's udder (*122, 316*). The gist of their efforts is that when cows are injected with glycerol-1,3-C^{14} into the pudic artery or when the isolated udder is perfused with either glycerol-1,3-C^{14} or glycerol-1,3-C^{14} plus glucose-2-C^{14}, the glucose moiety of the milk lactose arises from the blood glucose, whereas the galactose moiety derived its carbons from glycerol via a transaldolase exchange reaction. Some evidence for compartmentalization and nonequilibration of hexose phosphate was also presented. In ketotic cows, data were obtained from measurements of the recovery of C^{14} in respiratory CO_2, casein, albumin, and citrate that indicate a decreased participation of the pentose phosphate cycle (*317*). This decrease correlates well with the defect in lipogenesis in the ketotic cow.

As would be expected, the addition of certain types of hormones, *in vitro,* affected the metabolic pathways in slices of the mammary glands. Insulin, for example, increased the yield of radioactive fatty acids derived from labeled glucose (*318*) and simultaneously gave a marked stimulation of $C^{14}O_2$ production from glucose-1-C^{14} (*318, 319*). Meanwhile the production of $C^{14}O_2$ from glucose-6-C^{14} is diminished and that from glucose-3,4-C^{14} remains unaltered (*318*). Since this hormone does not preferentially enhance the incorporation of radioactivity into fatty acids from glucose labeled at C-1 and C-6, the conclusion is that the alternate oxidative pathway is not stimulated.

Hormones of the anterior pituitary glands also have some similar effects to those with insulin. For example, growth hormone and ACTH elevate glucose oxidation of both C-1 and C-6 throughout lactation (*320*). Similarly, prolactin affects the oxidation of glucose-1-C^{14}, but it has a minimal effect on the oxidation of glucose-6-C^{14} in the late stage of lactation. In contrast to these results, McLean (*321*) found that prolactin had no consistent effect on the metabolism of specifically labeled glucose by mammary gland slices from lactating rats; although she observed an increase in the formation of $C^{14}O_2$ from both glucose-1-C^{14} and from glucose-6-C^{14}. Furthermore, there was an increased incorporation of both glucose carbons into the lipids by slices from pregnant rats, due to *in vitro* addition of prolactin. The discrepancy in the prolactin effect on the oxidation of variously labeled glucose between these two groups of investigators has yet to be resolved.

Other hormones of the anterior pituitary gland have also been tested in lactating rat mammary glands, such as interstitial cell-stimulating hormone, follicle-stimulating hormone, and thyroid-stimulating hormone; all these hormones fail to exhibit any effect on glucose oxidation (*320*).

Mammary glands of hypophysectomized rats in midpregnancy can be induced to undergo lactation by hormonal means (*322*). The hormones required for this lactation are either a mixture of prolactin, hydrocortisone, and growth hormone or a mixture of prolactin and hydrocortisone, all administered *in vivo;* any other combination is ineffective. As compared with normal lactating mammary glands, the metabolism of the induced-lactating mammary glands is similar on the basis of the incorporation of C^{14} into CO_2 and fatty acids from specifically labeled glucose and on the basis of the stimulatory effect of glucose on the conversion of acetate to fatty acid. In those cases where lactation was not established, the metabolic pattern resembles that of the mammary glands of the normal nonlactating rat. A major portion of the fatty acids formed from glucose is via the hexose monophosphate shunt in the mammary glands of the lactating hypophysectomized rat whereas in the nonlactating mammary glands, little glucose is utilized and the fatty acids are formed almost exclusively via the EMP pathway.

Oxytocin (*315, 323*) and vasopressin (*315*), both posterior pituitary hormones having milk-ejecting activity, increase the oxidation of glucose-1-C^{14} to $C^{14}O_2$ in lactating rat mammary glands. These hormones also stimulate the oxidation of glucose-6-C^{14} to $C^{14}O_2$, but to a lesser degree than that of the C-1 of glucose (*315*). However, the effect of these hormones on the activity of the oxidative pentose phosphate cycle is still obscure because the oxytocin effect on the C-1 oxidation of glucose is found in mammary slices from pregnant rats and rabbits as well as from lactating rabbits and mice. Acetylcholine, a substance involved in the transmittance of nerve stimuli, also influences similarly the glucose metabolism of lactating mammary glands (*315, 323*). Puromycin, a known inhibitor of protein synthesis, inhibits the stimulatory effect of both oxytocin and acetylcholine (*323*), but mammary tissues incubated with this inhibitor show no change in levels of both G-6-P DH and 6-PG DH relative to the uninhibited system.

Nonhormonal substances also have an influence on the glucose metabolism of lactating mammary glands. Thus bicarbonate gives a marked stimulation of the incorporation of glucose carbon into fatty acids along with a parallel enhancement of the oxidation of the glucose C-1 (*18*). In the presence of a suitable concentration of iodoacetate, fatty acid synthesis via the malonyl CoA pathway is inhibited while the oxidation of glucose via G-6-P DH and 6-PG DH is not. Under these conditions, iodoacetate reduces lipid synthesis and concomitantly decreases the oxidation of the glucose C-1. The data suggest that the rate-limiting factor in the oxidation of glucose via the pentose phosphate cycle is the reoxidation of TPNH. This notion is supported by a previous finding that phenazine methosulfate, an artificial electron acceptor, can increase the production of $C^{14}O_2$ from glucose-1-C^{14} (*319*). A point should be emphasized here—that the conversion of glucose-1-H^3 to fatty acids increases as lactation progresses whereas the conversion of lactate-2-H^3 to fatty acids decreases (*300*). These results indicate that the bulk of the TPNH arising from the pentose phosphate cycle is responsible for the synthesis of fatty acids, in contrast to the results from work on the liver.

The fact that the weight of the mammary gland is constant throughout lactation, after correcting for the milk content, and that the dehydrogenase activities increase during this time, suggests that the high dehydrogenase activities are associated with milk secretion rather than growth (*310*). In accord with this conclusion are the findings of experiments with hormonally induced lactating mammary glands from hypophysectomized rats (*322*), but with a further conjecture that the metabolic pattern is connected also with milk formation. Finally, Goodfriend and Topper suggested that the physiological effect of oxytocin on mammary glands may be related to the direct stimulation of metabolism in the secreting cells (*315*).

13. *Muscle*

Of all the mammalian tissues studied, there seems to be little doubt that muscle tissue metabolizes glucose almost exclusively by way of the EMP route. This fact has been established in rat diaphragm by isotopic techniques (*97, 111, 324*). The potential of this tissue to utilize glucose via the pentose phosphate cycle still exists, nevertheless, since the pentose phosphate cycle enzymes are present in this tissue (*111*). Although adrenalectomy enhances the incorporation of C^{14} from glucose-1-C^{14} and from glucose-6-C^{14} into protcins of isolated diaphragm, the proportion of the C-1 and C-6 incorporated into protein is unchanged (*324*). Under anaerobic conditions, however, pyruvate stimulates the production of CO_2 from the C-1 of glucose without affecting that from C-6 of glucose (*325*). The mechanism of this activation may be through a TPN-linked lactate dehydrogenase system. It is conceivable that under aerobic conditions, the activity of the EMP pathway far overshadows that of the pentose phosphate cycle. Skeletal muscle also has G-6-P DH and 6-PG DH in rats and mice (*137*), along with phosphopentose isomerase, D-ribulose-5-phosphate-3-epimerase in rabbits (*326*), transketolase in rabbits (*327*), and the necessary enzymes in rats to convert fructose-6-phosphate to heptose phosphate in the presence of fructose-1,6-diphosphate (*328*). The dehydrogenases as well as the isomerase activities seem to be least in this tissue as compared to all others examined. Apparently, few, if any, isotopic methods have been applied to the study of glucose metabolism in skeletal muscles.

14. *Skin and Bones*

The presence of G-6-P DH and 6-PG DH has been demonstrated in human skin by Hershey and his associates (*329–331*). In particular, in the three layers of the sole, the epidermal cells contain the highest level of 6-PG DH, the dermis the intermediate, and the keratin the lowest (*329*). This pattern is also followed by G-6-P DH, but in this study, the dermis was further subdivided into superficial and deep dermis regions, in which case the deep dermis has the lowest activity, even lower than that of the keratin G-6-P DH (*331*). A more thorough study of the enzymatic activity of G-6-P DH in the various strata and skin appendages revealed an interesting distribution pattern. The sebaceous glands have the highest activity, some 5.5-fold greater activity than that in the epidermis. The following skin layers and appendages have G-6-P DH in the order of decreasing activity: sebaceous glands, hair follicle, epidermis, sweat glands, superficial dermis, and deep dermis. Roughly the same distribution pattern of 6-PG DH activity was observed in the skin (*330*). That the sebaceous gland should have such a high level of dehydrogenases is not too surprising in view of the fact that lipid synthesis occurs in this tissue and thus TPNH is required. In fact, isocitrate dehydrogenase, another TPNH-generating system, gives the same picture of localization as those of G-6-P DH and 6-PG DH.

Measurements of the $C^{14}O_2$ production from glucose-1-C^{14} by young rat skin, indicated that there is a preferential oxidation of the glucose carbon atom 1 (*332*). The C-1:C-6 of the CO_2 formed, however, varied with time; at the end of 1 hour this ratio is ca. 4.7 whereas at greater than 3 hours it is ca. 2. The authors concluded that, qualitatively, the pentose phosphate cycle occurs in the young rat skin. Freinkel, while working with postmortem human skin slices from the scalp and abdomen, estimated that a major portion of the assimilated glucose which is oxidized to CO_2 and of the CO_2 formed is via the pentose phosphate cycle (*333*). Moreover, methylene blue can elevate the C-1:C-6 of CO_2 of either epidermal cells or dermis (with sebaceous glands) from a normal of about 2 to 8. With all the shortcomings of the isotopic techniques and the demonstration of the presence of enzymes in the skin, there is yet to be found a proof-positive method actually to demonstrate the operation of the pentose phosphate cycle in the skin. An attempt in this direction was carried out by Yardley and Godfrey (*334*). They incubated guinea pig skin slices from the ear with P_i^{32} in the presence of glucose and then examined the products chromatographically. Ribose-5-phosphate, sedoheptulose-7-phosphate and sedoheptulose-1,7-diphosphate are found among the products, indicating that the hexose monophosphate shunt is operative in this tissue.

Burns produced on the back by applying water for 5 minutes at 50° did not alter the epidermis G-6-P DH activity (*329*).

Bernstein *et al.* have characterized the literature on *in vitro* carbohydrate metabolism in cartilaginous tissues as scarce (*335*). This description may be applied as well to the operation of the pentose phosphate cycle in bone tissues. In the few cases examined, there are indications of the operation of the pentose phosphate cycle in both cartilaginous and osseous tissues. The cartilage was obtained from male weanling rats which develop tibial epiphyseal plates with a high density of chondrocytes induced by a high calcium rachitogenic diet. On feeding slices of these tibial epiphyses with glucose-1-C^{14} and glucose-6-C^{14}, the oxidation rate of the former substrate is greater than that of the latter by a factor of 1.9 (*335*). *In vitro* addition of insulin increases the formation of CO_2 from both C-1 and C-6 to a ratio of 2.5 whereas growth hormone has no effect. The recovery of the specifically labeled carbon into the tissue polysaccharides does not exhibit the selective loss of the C-1, and in fact more label from the C-1 was incorporated into the polysaccharides than that from C-6. Growth hormone, on the other hand, gave an increase in polysaccharide synthesis.

In the epiphyseal-metaphyseal bone slices of rabbits, lactate arises entirely from glucose aerobically. Most of this lactate is formed via the EMP pathway with only a small contribution, ca. 15%, via the pentose phosphate cycle (*336*). Parathyroid, which induces bone demineralization, administered *in vivo* to weanling rabbits, causes an elevated level of serum calcium. These treated animals yield epiphyseal-metaphyseal bone slices which give enhanced CO_2 formation from glucose with relatively more CO_2 from C-6 than from C-1 (*337*). The data suggest that the activity of the TCA cycle is activated, a suggestion which finds additional support in the ability of fluoroacetate to abolish completely the effect of the parathyroid extract on CO_2 production. During all these changes, the pentose phosphate cycle activity remains constant.

15. *Tumors*

Animal tumors are characterized by a high rate of lactate production both aerobically and anaerobically (*338*). This is in contrast with many normal adult tissues in which the anaerobic rate averages less than one-quarter that of the tumors, whereas the aerobic rate of the normal tissue is practically nonexistent. In this regard, the transfer of carbon from lactate to glutamate, aspartate, and alanine occurs rapidly in nontumorous tissues of rats whereas that in tumors is relatively less (*339*). Thus the difference in the lactate production by the tumors and the nontumors, *in vivo,* may be due not to a difference in the mechanism or the rate of glycolysis, but rather to the inability of the tumors to convert further the lactate under the conditions of the experiment.

Needless to say, the variety of tumors is enormous—for each type of host cell there is at least one kind of neoplastic tissue. Hence it is far beyond the scope of this review to encompass all aspects of glucose metabolism by the pentose phosphate cycle in these tissues; most of this material, anyway, is admirably covered by Aisenberg (*338*). Suffice it to say, the principal pathway of carbohydrate metabolism is via the EMP route and the TCA cycle in mammalian tumors. Katz (*111*) has estimated that, in the Novikoff hepatoma, between 6 and 8% of the glucose is metabolized by way of the pentose phosphate cycle, calculated on the basis of the data of Ashmore *et al.* (*340*) and assuming that the metabolism goes solely through the triose pathway with a negligible incorporation into glycogen. These values are apparently fairly typical of many other tumors. In fact, Table VIII records the relative contribution of the

TABLE VIII
PERCENTAGE OF GLUCOSE METABOLIZED VIA THE PENTOSE PHOSPHATE CYCLE IN VARIOUS MAMMALIAN TUMORS

Tumor	% of glucose converted to CO_2 via non-EMP pathway	
	Wenner and Weinhouse (*103*)	Recalculated by Katz[a] (*111*)
TA-3 ascites (mouse)	1 to 2	0
Rhabdomyosarcoma	0 to 2	7
Mammary adenocarcinoma, TA-3, solid (mouse)	4 to 16	2
Hepatoma (rat)	1 to 7	5

[a] Assuming that the non-triose pathway is negligible.

pentose phosphate cycle in glucose metabolism in several other types of tumors. The majority of rat and mouse neoplasms have active pentose phosphate cycles which scarcely exceed 10% of the glucose metabolized. The value of 16% obtained by Wenner and Weinhouse represents a maximum possible value and is probably a more optimistic number. Some even higher numbers were obtained for the percentages of CO_2 derived from non-EMP pathways: Gardner lymphosarcoma, 32%, and

Ehrlich ascites tumor, 23% (see Aisenberg, *338*). Abraham *et al.* obtained a range of 0.28–0.58 in mouse C_{954} hepatocarcinoma as the fraction of the fatty acids derived from glucose via the shunt mechanism (*341*). The liver of the tumor-bearing mouse (as well as of the normal mouse), on the other hand, converts glucose to fatty acids mainly through the EMP pathway; i.e., the relative contribution of the pentose phosphate cycle toward the formation of fatty acids from glucose is nearly zero.

Weber and his associates have studied the fate of glucose-6-phosphate in hepatoma in four different directions: glycolysis, the direct oxidative pathway, glycogenesis, and glucose release (*342*). Indicator enzymes for each of these four routes were phosphohexose isomerase, G-6-P DH, phosphoglucomutase, and glucose-6-phosphatase, respectively. Isotopic studies were also conducted in order to yield a quantitative estimate of the pathways taken by glucose during its metabolism in normal liver and hepatomas, the results of which are summarized in Table IX. Clearly

TABLE IX
PERCENTAGE OF GLUCOSE-6-PHOSPHATE METABOLIZED VIA VARIOUS PATHWAYS IN THE NORMAL RAT LIVER AND THE NEOPLASTIC LIVER (*342*)

Liver tissues	Glycolysis	Shunt	Glycogenesis	Glucose formation
Normal liver	25	2	18	55
Morris no. 5123 hepatoma	65	2	1	32
Novikoff hepatoma	88	10	2	0

then, glycolysis is markedly increased in the Morris No. 5123 hepatoma and in the Novikoff hepatoma whereas the pentose phosphate cycle activity is enhanced only in the Novikoff hepatoma. Both glycogenesis and glucose formation are decreased significantly in both hepatomas. These conclusions are supported, at least in two cases, by the changes in levels of enzymes concerned with the metabolism of glucose-6-phosphate; especially those of the hexose monophosphate shunt and of the glucose production (Table X). Inspection of other types of hepatomas of varying growth rates showed a definite trend as to the cellularity, the nitrogen content, and the glucose-6-phosphate dehydrogenase activity (*343*). Thus, the Morris No. 5123 hepatoma, with a slow growth rate (60–90 days), has a lower cellularity, a higher nitrogen content, and a lower G-6-P DH activity than the Reuber hepatomas, No. 5123 t.c., No. 3924A, No. 7288 B, and No. 3683, which have intermediate growth rates. The Novikoff tumor with a 7-day growth rate, has the highest cellularity, the lowest nitrogen content, and the highest G-6-P DH activity.

Another much-studied tumor is the Ehrlich ascites mouse tumor.

Wenner and Weinhouse estimated that the amount of glucose oxidized to CO_2 via a non-EMP pathway is between 1 and 3% (*103*), while 94% of the glucose is catabolized to lactate. Isotope studies showed that the limiting factor for the operation of the pentose phosphate cycle in this tumor is the availability of an electron acceptor (*72*). For example, *in vitro* addition of methylene blue, menadione, or phenazine methosulfate to both suspensions of the tumor or to homogenates of the tumor will stimulate the oxidation of glucose-1-C^{14}, but has only slight effect on the oxidation of glucose-6-C^{14}. Furthermore, under anaerobic conditions, the oxidation of the former substrate is enhanced by the presence

TABLE X
COMPARISON IN PERCENTAGE OF VARIOUS ENZYME ACTIVITIES IN HEPATOMAS WITH THE NORMAL[a] RAT LIVER (*342*)

Enzyme	Pathway represented	Morris hepatoma	Novikoff hepatoma
Glucose-6-phosphatase	Glucose production	56	0
Phosphoglucomutase	Glycogenesis	15	10
Glucose-6-phosphate dehydrogenase	Shunt	82	300
Phosphohexose isomerase	Glycolysis	66	80

[a] Normal liver equals 100%.

of pyruvate, matching the level obtained aerobically, but oxygen did not further stimulate the oxidation of the C-1 atom of glucose by the intact ascites tumors in the presence of a moderate concentration of pyruvate.

Much work has been devoted to the biosynthesis of nucleic acids, using tumors. Belousova (*344*) found that in one type of tumor, Ehrlich's and Yoshida's cancers, glucose elevated the *in vitro* incorporation of formate-C^{14} into nucleic acids whereas in another type, sarcomas no. 180, no. 37, and cancer of the rat testes, glucose depressed this incorporation. The reasons for these phenomena are believed to be due to a shift in the relative participation of the pentose phosphate cycle under the influence of a high concentration of glucose. The first group of tumors has a stimulated nucleic acid synthesis owing to a shift in favor of the shunt mechanism while the second group has a depressed nucleic acid synthesis because of a competition between the EMP pathway and the synthetic pathway of nucleic acids for the pyridine nucleotides.

Ascites tumors fed with labeled glucose gave results which suggested that acid-soluble nucleotide ribose (*345*) and nucleic acid deoxyribose (*346*) are not entirely derived from the oxidative decarboxylation of glucose. Some of the pentoses have been formed via the transketolase-transaldolase pathway. In fact, in the latter case, evidence is presented that glucose goes all the way to the level of triose phosphate before forming some of the deoxyribose since glucose-1-C^{14} yields deoxyribose labeled in the 5-position. Disturbing is the fact that, even now, the mechanism by which deoxyribose is synthesized remains obscure. Although Racker (*347*) found in *Escherichia coli* an enzyme system that will catalyze the condensation of acetaldehyde with glyceraldehyde-3-phosphate to form deoxyribose-5-phosphate, the reaction seems to be more in favor of the cleavage of deoxyribose phosphate than the formation. In studies with animal cells and bacteria there is a body of data to indicate that ribose is directly converted to deoxyribose while maintaining the glycosidic linkage intact in the nucleoside or nucleotide. A full account of this story is given by Beck (*348*).

The anaerobic utilization of ribose-5-phosphate by neoplastic tissues is relatively high when compared with normal tissues (*349*). Mouse ascites tumor cells do not degrade ribose after incubating for 4 hours, on the other hand (*350*). In the presence of radioactive bicarbonate, carboxyl-labeled lactate is formed, suggesting that an active phosphoribulosekinase and carboxydismutase are present in these tissues (*349*). We (N. G. Pon and K. K. Lonberg-Holm, unpublished results) have tested this hypothesis and found that, at least in cell-free homogenates of the Ehrlich ascites mouse tumor, no carboxydismutase is present. The labeling pattern can be explained by invoking the dicarboxylic acid shuttle. It might be surprising that ribose-5-phosphate is utilized at all owing generally to the nonpermeable nature of phosphorylated compounds, but Wu (*351*) demonstrated that certain enzymes preferentially leak from these tumor cells. Thus, he found that all glycolytic and pentose phosphate cycle enzymes (transketolase and transaldolase) were released into the suspending medium. Glyceraldehyde-3-phosphate dehydrogenase was rapidly inactivated, however, so that the metabolic pattern, after the addition of ribose-5-phosphate *in vitro* to the medium, was different from that of a total cell homogenate.

If cancer cells are to be considered as arising from host cells, then the problem of when a change in the metabolism of the developing tumor occurs should be faced. Experiments with tumors induced by 9,10-dimethyl-1,2-benzanthracene in hamsters' cheek pouches were conducted (*352*). During the development of the tumor, five different periods were recognized: I, no change, ca. 1st week; II, inflammation, 2nd and 3rd weeks; III, hyperplasia, after 3rd week; IV, preneoplastic hyperplasia and appearance of papillomas, ca. 7th week; and V, appearance of malignant tumor. Hexokinase, G-6-P DH, and 6-PG DH activities were assayed and were found to display different behaviors during the development of the neoplastic stage. Hexokinase activity is low in period

III and returns to normal, while G-6-P DH increases in periods IV and V. On the other hand, 6-PG DH is low at the hyperplasia stage to the preneoplastic hyperplasia stage. The workers concluded that the change in the 6-PG DH activity shows the greatest degree of correlation with the neoplastic stage as compared with the hyperplastic state.

16. *Miscellaneous Tissues*

Listed in Table XI are other animal tissues having the capacity for catabolizing glucose via the pentose cycle. In the uterus, the extracts of the mucous membrane lining (the endometrium) and the muscular

TABLE XI
MISCELLANEOUS TISSUES WITH THE POTENTIAL TO METABOLIZE GLUCOSE VIA THE PENTOSE PHOSPHATE CYCLE

Animal	Tissue	Measured parameters	Reference
Human	Uterus	G-6-P DH and 6-PG DH	(*353*)
Rat, ovariectomized	Uterus	G-6-P DH and 6-PG DH	(*354*)
Cow	Dental pulp	G-6-P DH and 6-PG DH	(*355*)
Rat	Spleen	Transketolase	(*356*)
Rat	Spleen	Nucleoside to sedoheptulose phosphate and ribose phosphate conversion	(*357*)
Mouse	Spleen	Phosphoketopentose epimerase	(*358*)
Calf	Spleen	Phosphoketopentose epimerase	(*359*)
Human	Stomach	G-6-P DH and 6-PG DH	(*353*)
Human	Lung	G-6-P DH and 6-PG DH	(*353*)
Rat	Lung	Transketolase	(*356*)
Rat	Lung	Nucleoside converted to sugar monophosphate	(*357*)

substance (myometrium) were examined (*354*). In the study of the dental pulp, both the peripheral and the central sections have dehydrogenase activity; however, the former has higher activity than the latter throughout all stages of development (from embryonic to young, to mature) (*355*). The spleen, in addition to having the enzymes to utilize pentose phosphates, synthesizes nucleotide ribose via the transketolase-transaldolase reactions (*360*) and can also transform ribosides to deoxyribosides without rupturing the glycosidic links (*361*). In thiamine-deficient rats, the transketolase content of spleen and lung extracts is decreased (*356*). Oxythiamine, administered intraperitoneally, also gives a decrease in the transketolase level in this tissue, whether in thiamine-deficient rats or not. The lack of thiamine in the diet of rats also causes a drop in the lung and spleen enzymes which utilize the ribose of nucleosides (*357*). Both the mucosa and the muscularis of the stomach were found to have the dehydrogenases of the pentose phosphate cycle (*353*).

A number of tissues (liver, brain, heart, lung, kidney, adrenal glands, and skeletal muscles) from the fetuses of human, rat, rabbit, and dog can oxidize glucose to CO_2, and, in many cases, with a preferential release of the C-1 of glucose (*362*). The lowest C-6:C-1 values were observed for the fetal adrenal glands, and they were even lower in the absence of oxygen. Th C-6:C-1 of CO_2, however, did not significantly change in any of these tissues over a fetal development period from 8 to 25 weeks gestational age. The G-6-P DH activity, on the other hand, is initially high in the guinea pig fetal liver but decreases with increasing time of gestation (*363*). The placenta's G-6-P DH and 6-PG DH, in rat, rabbit, guinea pig, and human, also decrease slightly toward parturition. When comparisons are made of rat liver G-6-P DH activity in the fetal stage, newborn, and adult stage, the following numbers were obtained (micromoles of TPN^+ reduced per minute per milligram of supernatant protein) (*364*): 19-day fetus, 5.9; newborn, 8.8; 3-day, 7.3; 7-day, 5.6; 12-day, 4.3; 14-day, 2.8; and adult, 7.9. On a per microgram DNA phosphorus basis, essentially the same pattern was obtained. The specific activity of the liver 6-PG DH also falls as the newborn rat ages (*365*). A conflicting observation was made by Stave (*366*), who found that in the liver and kidney of the fetal rabbit, just prior to birth, in newborns, and in animals between 2 and 4 weeks old, there was no marked alteration of G-6-P DH activity relative to adult values. Human blood cells of various types (leukocytes, thrombocytes, and erythrocytes) also give the same decreasing pattern of G-6-P DH activity with aging of the cells (*367*). The L-929 strain of mouse fibroblast cells, grown in tissue cultures, contain G-6-P DH, 6-PG DH, and pentose phosphate isomerase, but not transketolase or transaldolase (*368*). Surprisingly, however, ribose-5-phosphate is utilized by these cells although no sedoheptulose-7-phosphate, glyceraldehyde-3-phosphate, or fructose-6-phosphate is formed. Examination by cytochemical techniques showed that G-6-P DH is present in both the intra- and the extramitochondrial regions (*369*). Both G-6-P DH and 6-PG DH have been demonstrated in the tissue-cultured Earl's L cells (*370*). Noteworthy are some studies on human cell cultures in which skin biopsies were obtained from individuals with normal levels of G-6-P DH in the erythrocytes as compared with an individual with a deficiency of this enzyme (*371*). The cultured cells displayed the same pattern; i.e., those from normal individuals gave much higher G-6-P DH activity than that from the deficient individual.

B. Birds

Subdivision of this category on the basis of the various tissues or of different birds is not warranted, owing to the relative scarcity of published material on the pentose phosphate cycle activity in this class of animals. In general, most of the studies have been carried out on chickens, with an occasional mention of work done on pigeons and geese. In pigeons, the smooth stomach muscles contain enzymes which will convert G-6-P, 6-PG, and ribose-5-phosphate to lactate (*372*). Added TPN^+ is reduced to TPNH in the presence of G-6-P and 6-PG, while anaerobically triose phosphate and fructose-6-phosphate are formed from ribose-5-phosphate in the presence of iodoacetate. In the thiamine-deficient pigeons, the liver transketolase activity is diminished to about 30% of the normal value (*373*). This activity could not be restored by adding thiamine pyrophosphate or by adding thiamine pyrophosphate plus Mg^{++}.

When acetate-1-C^{14} was fed to chicks, the ribose of the purine nucleotides of nucleic acids from the internal organs contains the radioactivity mainly in the C-3 position, with lesser amounts in the C-1 and C-2 positions (*374*). A condensation of a two-carbon fragment with a three-carbon fragment was postulated as the mechanism of formation of ribose. Horecker and Mehler, however, imposed the action of transketolase and transaldolase to explain this distribution of label (*3*).

Bird tissues in which G-6-P DH and, in some cases, 6-PG DH have been demonstrated are itemized in Table XII. In the goose nucleated

TABLE XII
G-6-P DH and/or 6-PG DH in Various Tissues of Birds

Bird	Tissue	G-6-P DH	6-PG DH	References
Goose	Erythrocytes	Present	—	(*367*)
Chicken	Liver	Present	Present	(*375*)
Chick embryo	Chorioallantoic membrane	Present	Present	(*376, 377*)
Young chick	Wing web	Present	Present	(*377*)
Chick embryo	Whole homogenate	Present	—	(*378*)
Chick embryo	Skin and feather primordia	Present	—	(*379*)

erythrocytes, as with mammalian blood cells, aging causes a marked drop in the activity of this enzyme (*367*). The liver of the chicken also contains 6-PG DH; however, both hepatic G-6-P DH and 6-PG DH levels are lower than the corresponding hepatic dehydrogenases in rats (*375*). Otherwise the pattern of other enzymes is more or less the same in these two classes of animals. Certain nutritional factors induce alterations in the hepatic enzymatic levels which are essentially similar to those effects found in mammalian systems. Hence a chicken which has been starved for 7 days loses 100% of its hepatic G-6-P DH and about 50% of its 6-PG DH. On refeeding the chicken, one finds that both of its hepatic dehydrogenase levels markedly increase, G-6-P DH to 370% of the normal fed chicken and 6-PG DH only to 83% of normal. These results are in contrast to those of the rat liver system, where both dehydrogenases are enhanced above normal. Pathological conditions may often regulate the pentose phosphate activity in some manner. For instance, 48 hours after the inoculation of canary pox virus into a chick embryo, a rise in the rate of oxidation of the C-1 of glucose in the chorioallantoic membrane occurs (*376*). Viral infection apparently increases TPN-linked lactate dehydrogenase activity, thereby increasing the shunt activity, but neither the level of G-6-P DH nor the level of 6-PG DH is affected. Tumors grown in the chorioallantoic membrane by injection of Rous sarcoma virus into embryonated eggs of White Leghorn chicks have G-6-P DH and 6-PG DH activities 111% and 149%, respectively, of the value for the normal chorioallantoic membrane (*377*). Isotope studies showed that these tumors utilize glucose via the shunt mechanism to the extent of only 4% or less in wing web and in breast muscle (*380*) as well as in the chorioallantoic membrane (*381*). The G-6-P DH activity in the chick embryo fluctuates considerably as a function of incubation time so that any correlation is made difficult (*378*). The rate of utilization of ribose-5-phosphate by embryonic liver homogenates and slices seems to decrease steadily from 8 days of incubation until 20 days. The rate of metabolism of ribose phosphate by the embryonic liver slices on the 19th day of incubation is nearly identical to that by the adult chicken liver and amounts to approximately one-third the rate in the 12-day-old embryonic liver. The G-6-P DH activity in the skin plus feather primordia of the appendages varies from 1.9 units per milligram protein in the 12-day-old chicken embryo to 3.1 units per milligram protein on the 16th day of incubation, and thereafter decreases sharply to 0.9 units per milligram protein at hatching (*379*).

Deoxyribose synthesis occurs in the chicken embryo homogenate at the nucleotide level from the corresponding ribose compound (*382*). This seems also to be the case in the formation of deoxyribose in the embryonic chicken cartilage which has been cultivated *in vitro* on a chemically defined medium (*383*). The nucleotide ribose, on the other hand, arises via the action of the transketolase-transaldolase pathways plus the direct oxidative pathway on glucose.

C. Reptiles, Amphibians, and Fish

The only data, apparently, that exist concerning the occurrence of the pentose phosphate cycle for reptiles, are those studies on the cayman (or caiman) (*384*). From glucose-1-C^{14} and glucose-6-C^{14}, the radiochemical yield of respiratory CO_2 gave C-6:C-1 ratios of 0.08 and 0.40 for the tail muscle and the intercostal muscle, respectively, in Krebs-Ringer bicarbonate buffer. In Krebs-Ringer phosphate buffer, the tail muscle gave a higher C-6:C-1 ratio and the oxygen consumption was insignificantly low. Under the same conditions, rat diaphragm which has been shown repeatedly to catabolize glucose exclusively by the EMP scheme, has a C-6:C-1 ratio of about 1.2 either in Krebs-Ringer bicarbonate or in Krebs-Ringer phosphate medium. Possibly, the carboxylation of pyruvate to form malate with the concomitant production of TPN^+ may account for the enhanced activity of the oxidative portion of the pentose phosphate cycle in the presence of the bicarbonate buffer.

In the amphibian class, G-6-P DH and 6-PG DH activity were found in frog heart (*385*). The frog liver as well as the liver of the tadpole (*386*) were tested for G-6-P DH also. In this case, the adult frog liver has a lower activity of G-6-P DH than the tadpole liver. Metamorphosis, induced by thyroxine, caused a decrease in the dehydrogenase activity to 75–80% of the premetamorphic value. It is not known whether the fall in enzymatic activity is due to a change in the amount of enzyme, the removal or formation of inhibitor, or a change in the stability of the enzyme.

At least a half dozen different types of fishes have been examined with respect to glucose metabolism via the pentose phosphate cycle. By studying the incorporation of label from variously labeled glucose into CO_2 and fats under aerobic and anaerobic conditions, Hochachka concluded that the results can be explained by the sole operation of the EMP pathway (*387*) in the muscles of the trout *Salvelinus fontinalis*. In the goldfish, glucose is oxidized to CO_2 with a C-6:C-1 ratio of 0.9 under pure oxygen *in vivo;* however, there was evidence of preferential incorporation of carbon from glucose-6-C^{14} into liver and muscle glycogen as well as fat. Further studies of the effect of temperature acclimation on the pathways of glucose metabolism in the trout suggested that the predominant pathway of glucose metabolism in the 15° acclimated trout is the EMP route whereas in the 4° acclimated trout, there is an increased participation of the pentose phosphate cycle along with a higher rate of fatty acid synthesis (*388*). The latter findings confirmed that during anoxia, liver slices have an active pentose phosphate cycle (*387*). Belonging to the same family is the steelhead salmon, *Salmo gairdnerii,* and it is not too surprising to find the operation of the pentose phosphate cycle in this fish (*389*). However, intramuscular or intravenous injection of labeled 6-phosphogluconate showed that this ester is only slowly metabolized via the hexose monophosphate shunt. The comparative assessment of the relative participation of the two major pathways is yet to be made. Glucose-1-C^{14} or glucose-6-C^{14} administered to carps gave essentially the same recovery of respired CO_2 (*390*). These data along with other data on the equal incorporation of C^{14} from these two substrates into liver fat and protein-glutamic acid and alanine indicate that the oxidation of glucose in the carp is primarily via the EMP scheme and to a small extent by the shunt mechanism. In addition, the levels of both G-6-P DH and 6-PG DH in the carp liver are low. On the other hand, the carp tail muscle oxidizes glucose to yield a C-6:C-1 ratio of 0.07 in the presence of a bicarbonate buffer (*384*). Tarr has isolated, partially purified, and characterized phosphoribose isomerase and epimerase from the muscles of lingcod, *Ophiodon elongatus* (*391*). The intermediary metabolism by tissues of the electric fish *Electrophorus electricus,* is generally the same as that of the caiman or the carp tail muscle (*384*). Except for the brain of the electric fish, the ratios of radiochemical yields of CO_2 of the other tissues, such as the main organ, the Sachs organ, the intact electroplax, and the skin, average ca. 0.2.

VII. Arthropods

Carbohydrate metabolism in this phylum has been investigated mainly in three classes of animals: the crustacean, the insect, and the mite. Of the crustaceans, only those of the subclass belonging to the crab, lobster, and crayfish were studied. In the crabs *Cancer magister* (*392*) and *Hemigrapsus nudus* (*393*) there is no evidence that the pentose phosphate cycle is utilized to oxidize glucose to CO_2, although the former is quite capable of yielding labeled CO_2 from maltose-C^{14}, and the latter can utilize glucose as an oxidative substrate in all stages of the intermolt cycle. The stimulation of oxygen consumption in lobster (*Homarus americanus*) hepatopancreas homogenates by pentose phosphate cycle intermediates has already meen mentioned (cf. Section V, C) (*66*). In addition, when acetate-1-C^{14} was administered to tissue slices, in the presence and absence of fluoroacetate, the label was incorporated mostly into the carbon-3 and -4 positions of the glycogen glucose; however, there was some randomization of the label into the other four carbon atoms. From this fact, a 5–10% participation of the pentose phosphate cycle was estimated. The enzymes of both glycolysis and the shunt were found in the extramitochondrial fraction. Carbohydrate metabolism in the crayfish (*Orconectes virilis*) has been examined, a number of respiratory inhibitors (*394*) being used, and the respiration was compared between premolt tissues and intermolt tissues of this crustacean. The oxygen uptake was inhibited to a greater extent by fluoride and iodoacetate in the premolt tissue than in the intermolt tissue. On this basis, a hypothesis was forwarded that glycolysis may be the principal metabolic pathway during premolt whereas the hexose monophosphate shunt may be the main route during intermolt.

In a book on the biochemistry of insects, Gilmour has documented the names of many insects in which the reaction systems of the pentose phosphate cycle occur (*395*). Thus, the pea aphid, *Macrosiphum pisi;* the house fly, *Musca domestica;* the blow fly *Phormia regina;* and the honey bee all contain, in one form or another (i.e., acetone powder, homogenates, dialyzed extracts of eggs, larvae, and adult insects, etc.), some signs of the pentose phosphate cycle. More specifically, the house fly has both TPN-dependent G-6-P DH and 6-PG DH (*396*) as well as 6-phosphogluconolactonase, phosphopentose isomerase, phosphoketopentose epimerase, transketolase, and transaldolase (*397*). Both dehydrogenases are localized mainly in the cytoplasm of the flight muscle, but a significant amount of the G-6-P DH is in the sarcosomes. In general, both dehydrogenase activities are higher in the male than in the female, and the site of the highest activities for both of these enzymes is situated in the abdomen. The presence of TPN-specific dehydrogenase was also reported in the peach aphid, *Myzus persicae* (*396*). In a study of the bug *Triatoma infestans,* Agosin *et al.* demonstrated the existence of G-6-P DH in cell-free extracts of the thoraxes and legs of larvae, nymphs, and adults (*398*). Present also are 6-PG DH and phosphopentose isomerase. All these activities except phosphopentose isomerase are inhibited by previous exposure of the adult bug to DDT; however, only G-6-P DH is inhibited when the nymphs are subjected to the same treatment. From the fact that 6-PG DH is limiting, the pentose phosphate cycle in carbohydrate metabolism seems to play a minor role. The midgut of the 5th instar larvae of the silkworm, *Bombyx mori,* also has the potentials to transform glucose-6-phosphate to ribose plus sedoheptulose, 6-phosphogluconate to ribose, and ribose-5-phosphate to hexose plus sedoheptulose (*399*). The rate of oxidation of ribose-5-phosphate is lower than that of glucose-1-phosphate, glucose-6-phosphate, or fructose-6-phosphate. Silva *et al.* (*400*) applied the method of radiorespirometry (*104*) to the study of glucose metabolism in the cockroach *Periplaneta americana;* they found that in the intact male adult, between 4 and 9% of the glucose is degraded via the direct oxidative pathway.

As far as is known, the only arthropod of the order Acarina that has been analyzed for enzymes of the pentose phosphate cycle is the two-spotted spider mite, *Tetranychus telarius* L. (*86*). Homogenates of this mite contain active G-6-P DH, 6-PG DH, pentose phosphate isomerase, phosphoketopentose epimerase, transketolase, and transaldolase.

VIII. Segmented Worms

Cohen studied the ribose-forming pathway of the polychaete worm *Chaetopterus,* during its early embryonic stage (*401*). He found that there exist sufficient G-6-P DH and 6-PG DH in the unfertilized ovum to synthesize all the ribose in the ribonucleic acid in an interval of 10 hours at 25°. In fact, when the fertilized eggs divide and differentiate into a swimming ciliated form, both the ribonucleic acid content and the activities of the dehydrogenases in the embryonic annelid are constant during this interval of time. Other annelids possessing G-6-P DH and 6-PG DH activities are the earth worms *Lumbricus terrestris* and *Tubifex tubifex* (*402*).

IX. Mollusks

Examples of this phylum that have been studied with respect to pentose phosphate pathway activity are the cephalopod *Loligo pealei* and the gastropod *Lymnaea stagnalis.* In both cases, the presence of pentose phosphate cycle enzymes were demonstrated. Thus the sheath and the axoplasm of the giant axon of the squid contain both G-6-P DH and 6-PG DH (*403*). In the 7-day-old embryo of the snail *Lymnaea,* practically all the enzymes of the shunt were found (*404*); however, the 6-PG DH activity is very low. From this last fact, the author speculated that the contribution of the direct oxidative pathway to glucose metabolism must be minor, although the high G-6-P DH activity speaks for its role in TPNH-linked synthetic processes.*

X. Echinoderms

A representative of this phylum is the sea urchin. One of the early works already mentioned in Section V, A of this review (*60*) yielded the first suggestive evidence for the existence of the shunt mechanism of sea urchin eggs. More substantial proof for the occurrence of this route of metabolism was obtained by Lindberg (*405*) in the gametes of *Echinocardium cordatum,* by Krahl *et al.* (*406*) in the eggs of *Arbacia punctulata,* and by Bäckström (*407*) in the eggs of *Paracentrotus lividus* and *Psammechinus miliaris.* In all these examples, G-6-P DH was shown to be present, and in *Arbacia* the presence of 6-PG DH was also estab-

* Recently, another aquatic snail, *Physa halei* Lea, has been shown to contain TPN linked G-6-P DH and 6-PG DH (*404a*).

lished. The level of G-6-P DH did not change significantly during fertilization in the eggs of *Arbacia.* On the other hand, the activity of this enzyme increases rapidly immediately after fertilization of the eggs of *Paracentrotus* (slightly later in *Psammechinus*). Ultimately, two separate peaks of G-6-P DH activity are obtained, one at the late cleavage step and the other at hatching. Subsequently, a gradual decrease of the dehydrogenase activity takes place.

XI. Roundworms

In general, these worms are particularly rich in both G-6-P DH and 6-PG DH (*402*). Both enzymes are TPN specific, and in all the cases tested the activity of 6-PG DH was always less than that of G-6-P DH. The list of worms possessing one or both of these dehydrogenases is already fairly extensive. A partial list of such organisms is as follows: *Ascaris lumbricoides, Parascaris equorum, Toxacara canis, Ascaridia galli, Ascaridia columbae, Heterakis gallinae,* and *Strongylus edentatus* (*402*). Other researchers found G-6-P DH activity in homogenates of *Trichinella spiralis* larvae (*408*), and both G-6-P DH and 6-PG DH in extracts of *Ditylenchus triformis* and *D. dipsaci* (*409*). In addition, de Ley and Vercruysse (*402*) have shown that the extract of the female genital tract of *Ascaris lumbricoides*, in the presence of the proper substrates and TPN^+ regenerating system, forms sedoheptulose. Furthermore, ribose-5-phosphate isomerase, xylulose-5-phosphate isomerase (phosphoketopentose epimerase), transketolase (*410*), and transaldolase (*411*) were shown to be present in extracts of the muscles of this parasite. In spite of all these evidences, however, isotope studies indicate that the major pathway of glucose catabolism is via glycolysis (*411*).

XII. Flatworms

In this category, the activity of either G-6-P DH or 6-PG DH ranges from a very high value for the parasitic cestode *Anoplocephala perfoliata,* to intermediate values for the free-living planarian *Polycelis nigra* and the liver fluke *Fasciola hepatica,* to zero for the hydatid cyst of *Echinococcus granulosus* (*402*). Other platyhelminths containing these dehydrogenases, in varying degrees, are the planarian *Euplanaria torva;* the trematode *Dicrocoelium dendriticum;* and the cestodes *Moniezia benedeni, Taenia saginata, Taenia pisiformis,* and *Dipylidium caninum* (*402*). The findings that both G-6-P DH and 6-PG DH are lacking in the larval stage of *Echinococcus* of the horse liver is in contrast with the results that both these dehydrogenases do exist in the scolices of sheep liver hydatid cyst (*412*). In fact, almost all the enzymes of the pentose phosphate cycle except possibly phosphoketopentose epimerase have been found in this organism. One of the enzymes, phosphopentose isomerase, has been purified and characterized with respect to pH optimum, thermolability, sensitivity to inhibitors, equilibrium constant, etc., and was found to be clearly different from the corresponding alfalfa enzyme (*413*).

XIII. Protozoa

The organism *Entamoeba histolytica* is best known for its pathogenicity. This ameba is responsible for the disease amebic dysentery. When tested for G-6-P DH and for 6-PG DH, the former was found to be present, whereas the latter was found to be absent (*414*). The fact that ribose-5-phosphate is a growth requirement for this organism is indicative of the lack of the shunt mechanism. Actually, the end product of G-6-P metabolism is pyruvate and glyceraldehyde-3-phosphate (*415*). This result, along with findings on certain cofactor requirements, suggests that the Entner-Doudoroff pathway is in operation in *Entamoeba*. In contrast to these findings, the Laredo strain of this ameba from human host contains no G-6-P DH and no 6-PG DH activities even in the presence of added TPN^+ (*416*). Neither is ribose-5-phosphate metabolized by cell-free extracts of this organism, but 6-phosphogluconate is cleaved to pyruvate and triose phosphate. Experiments with specifically labeled glucose confirmed the notion that the pentose phosphate cycle is absent in this organism. Also all the EMP pathway enzymes have been demonstrated in the cell-free extracts. The fact that glucose-1-C^{14} yields acetate-2-C^{14} means that the predominant pathway is probably the EMP pathway. Associated with the growth of this ameba in a culture system is the organism *Bacteriodes symbiosus*. These bacteria also metabolize via the EMP pathway and produce 1 mole of hydrogen per mole of glucose utilized (as does the ameba). However, instead of using the Entner-Doudoroff pathway as an alternate route, these bacteria use the pentose phosphate cycle (*417*). Indeed, such bacteria, grown in cysteine (but not grown in thiomalate) were shown to possess relatively high levels of both G-6-P DH and 6-PG DH (*418*), although the cysteine-grown bacteria do not utilize ribose-5-phosphate, whereas the thiomalate-grown bacteria readily form ketohexose, ketoheptose, and triose from ribose-5-phosphate. Moreover, the latter bacteria catabolize 6-phosphogluconate to pentose and ketohexose. Thus it appears that the pentose phosphate pathway may be present in the thiomalate-grown *Bacteriodes symbiosus*. Efforts to demonstrate the existence of the Entner-Doudoroff cleavage enzyme, 2-keto-3-deoxy-6-phosphogluconate aldolase, in cell-free extracts of these bacteria failed. The data from experiments with variously labeled glucose are consistent with the predominant operation of the EMP pathway in this organism.

Other organisms of this phylum exhibiting G-6-P DH activity are the ameba *Chaos chaos* (*419*) and the parasitic flagellate *Trypanosoma rhodesiense* (*420*). The latter has been cultivated in an artificial medium and in the bloodstream; both forms have this dehydrogenase which is only TPN^+ specific. In the homogenate of the cultured form, the G-6-P DH activity in the particulate fraction is twice that of the soluble supernatant fraction. No 6-PG DH was found in homogenates of either form. A search was made for Entner-Doudoroff enzymes in either *Trypanosoma cruzi* or in *T. rhodesiense,* but with no success.

XIV. Bacteria and Fungi

Because the pathways of metabolism of glucose in these microorganisms have been elegantly reviewed by Cheldelin *et al.* (*421*), this reviewer has decided not to cover these two divisions of the plant kingdom. Their treatment of the subject is not only on a semiquantitative basis, but is extensive enough to have represented most of the important organisms of the microbial world. Admittedly, a given species of a particular genus does not necessarily utilize the same pathway for glucose metabolism as another species. For example, radiorespirometry showed that glucose metabolism in the genus *Arthrobacter* is of two types: type 1, which relies heavily on the operation of the EMP pathway with perhaps a minor contribution of the pentose phosphate cycle; and type 2, which involves mainly the Entner-Doudoroff scheme and the pentose phosphate cycle with glucose passing through gluconate (*422*). Bacteria possessing the first type of metabolism are *A. ureafaciens* and *A. globiformis,* and those having the second type are *A. simplex* and *A. atrocyaneus.* The other problem facing the reader is that any review article, no matter how new, cites references at least one or two years old, thus recent work would obviously be lacking. An example of a recent piece of work is that of Eagon and Wang (*423*), on the species *Pseudomonas natriegens,* which when grown in glucose aerobically, catabolizes glucose primarily via the EMP pathway and to a minor extent by way of the shunt.

One other important pathway that is barely mentioned in the review article by Cheldelin *et al.* is the reductive pentose phosphate cycle. This cycle, initially believed to be associated only with photosynthetic organisms, was later demonstrated to be found also in nonphotosynthetic organisms such as the bacteria. Fortunately, a review article dealing with this topic has become available recently (*424*). Table XIII lists some of the nonphotosynthetic microorganisms in which the reductive pentose phosphate cycle is operative. The assay was generally for carboxydismutase activity, usually by determining the CO_2 fixed in the presence of ribulose-1,5-diphosphate or in the presence of ribose-5-phosphate plus ATP. The products were examined chromatographically, in some cases. In this regard Quayle (*424*) has raised an objection to the interpretation of the data obtained in the experiment with *E. coli* grown on pentose on the grounds that the amount of radioactive 3-phosphoglycerate formed from $HC^{14}O_3^-$ and ribulose diphosphate is less than 10% of the total

TABLE XIII
OCCURRENCE OF THE REDUCTIVE PENTOSE PHOSPHATE CYCLE IN NONPHOTOSYNTHETIC MICROORGANISMS

Name	Evidence	References
Hydrogenomonas vinelandii grown as an autotroph	Enzyme assay	(*425*)
Hydrogenomonas ruhlandii	Enzyme assay?	(*426*)
Thiobacillus thioparus	Enzyme assay	(*427*)
Thiobacillus denitrificans	Labeling pattern, enzyme assay	(*69, 428*)
Thiobacillus thiooxidans	Enzyme assay	(*429, 430*)
Escherichia coli, grown on xylose and carbon dioxide	Enzyme assay	(*425*)
Micrococcus denitrificans grown as an autotroph	Enzyme assay plus labeling pattern	(*431*)
Pseudomonas oxalaticus (OX 1) grown in formate	Enzyme assay	(*432*)
Nitrobacter agilis	Labeling pattern	(*433*)
Hydrogenomonas facilis	Labeling pattern	(*434, 435*)
Nitrobacter winogradskyi	Labeling pattern	(*436*)

radioactive products and that there is no assurance that, in fact, this 3-PGA was not derived from other products. Conclusions reached by studies of the labeling pattern were obtained mainly by feeding the microorganisms $C^{14}O_2$. The formation of the products was examined kinetically. Although the data in Table XIII as such do not indicate the inducible nature of carboxydismutase in some microorganisms, other results clearly substantiate this viewpoint. Thus, if *Micrococcus denitrificans* is grown in acetate, no carboxydismutase is detectable in cell-free extracts of this bacterium (*431*). The same negative results were found in preparations from *Pseudomonas oxalaticus* grown in oxalate medium (*432*).

Carbon dioxide fixation by photosynthetic bacteria has been thoroughly reviewed by Elsden (*437*). Some aspects of this metabolism are summarized in Table XIV. When grown aerobically in the dark, *Rhodopseudomonas spheroides* has only trace amounts of carboxydismutase whereas the organism is rich in this enzyme when grown photoheterotrophically in malate-glutamate medium under anaerobic conditions (*438*). The same conditions also apply for *R. palustris* in order to obtain maximum carboxydismutase activity. Although the CO_2 fixation rate by *R. capsulatus* in the light is about ten times the rate of fixation in the dark, photoreduction still functions in the dark (*439*). Other enzymes besides carboxydismutase were found in cell-free extracts of *Chlorobium* and *Chromatium*. These include transketolase, transaldolase, phosphopentose isomerase, and phosphoketopentose epimerase (*87*). As

TABLE XIV
THE REDUCTIVE PENTOSE PHOSPHATE CYCLE IN PHOTOSYNTHETIC BACTERIA

Organism	Evidence	References
Rhodopseudomonas spheroides	Presence of carboxydismutase	(*438*)
Rhodopseudomonas capsulatus	CO_2 fixation pattern	(*439*)
Rhodopseudomonas palustris	Presence of carboxydismutase	(*438*)
Rhodospirillum rubrum	CO_2 fixation pattern, presence of carboxydismutase and TPN-linked glyceraldehyde-3-phosphate dehydrogenase	(*424, 425*)
Chlorobium thiosulfatophilum	Presence of carboxydismutase	(*87*)
Chromatium, strain D	Presence of carboxydismutase	(*11, 87*)

is typical with many other photosynthetic bacteria, these two bacteria also contain a DPN-linked triose phosphate dehydrogenase, but no TPN-linked enzyme. In general, the *Chlorobium* enzymes have lower activities than the corresponding *Chromatium* enzymes. In particular, carboxydismutase and phosphopentose isomerase are exceedingly low in activity in *Chlorobium*. Chromatium has been shown to possess, by indirect evidence, ribulose-5-phosphate kinase, another enzyme which is peculiar to the reductive pentose phosphate cycle (*11*). The carboxydismutase activity is markedly suppressed when *Chromatium* is grown heterotrophically.

A mutant of *R. spheroides* was discovered by Szymona and Doudoroff (*440*) which can grow well in glucose without accumulating acid in the medium. This mutant acquires 6-phosphogluconate dehydrase activity (see Fig. 3) whereas the parent wild-type strain has none. Since the parent strain possesses part of the necessary enzymes for the operation of the Entner-Doudoroff pathway, e.g., G-6-P DH and 2-keto-3-deoxy-6-phosphogluconate aldolase, it appears that the glucose-grown mutant utilizes glucose according to this route. Evidence was obtained for the occurrence of transaldolase, transketolase, ribose kinase, and phosphoketopentose epimerase from the fact that the parent wild-type strain accumulates gluconate and ketodeoxygluconate in the ribose medium. [An independent worker found that cell-free extracts of this type of bacteria can convert pentose phosphates to glucose phosphate and triose phosphate (*85*).] On the other hand, cell-free extracts of the glucose-strain form fructose-6-phosphate and glucose-6-phosphate in the presence of ribose-5-phosphate or ATP plus ribose-5-phosphate, but not ribose plus ATP. The parent strain, containing no 6-phosphogluconate dehydrase and no 6-PG DH (*85, 440*), seems not to be able to catabolize carbohydrates via the oxidative pentose phosphate cycle and the Entner-Doudoroff route.

XV. Algae

The occurrence of G-6-P DH and 6-PG DH in tissues and organisms has been used as an indicator for the potential operation of the oxidative pentose phosphate cycle. In Table XV are listed the various kinds of

TABLE XV
THE OXIDATIVE PENTOSE PHOSPHATE CYCLE IN ALGAE

Name	Type of algae	References
Anacystis nidulans	Blue-green	(*35, 70, 83*)
Anabaena variabilis	Blue-green	(*83*)
Tolypothrix lanata	Blue-green	(*441*)
Nostoc muscorum	Blue-green	(*83*)
Ceramium rubrum	Red	(*441*)
Chondrus crispus	Red	(*83*)
Chlorella pyrenoidosa	Green	(*70, 83, 85, 442, 443*)
Scenedesmus obliquus	Green	(*83*)
Ulva lactuca	Green	(*441, 444*)
Chlorella vulgaris	Green	(*443, 445*)
Ankistrodesmus	Green	(*443*)
Chaetomorpha linum	Green	(*446*)
Bryopsis plumosa	Green	(*446*)
Hydrodictyon reticulatum	Green	(*447*)
Cyanidium caldarium	Unclassified, has both green and blue-green characteristics	(*85*)
Euglena gracilis var. *bacillaris*	Colorless UV mutant of euglenoid	(*448*)
Prototheca zopfii	Colorless thiamine-deficient	(*449*)

algae in which one or both of these enzymes has been demonstrated. In addition, in many cases, other enzymes of the pentose phosphate pathway have been implicated by (*a*) direct measurement, (*b*) pentose phosphate utilization experiments, and/or (*c*) tracer techniques. The most prominent feature of this survey is that almost all of the blue-green algae have high levels of both G-6-P DH and 6-PG DH (*83*), suggesting that the major pathway for the dissimilation of hexose might be the oxidative pentose phosphate cycle. It is noteworthy also that these same dehydrogenases occur in a red alga *Chondrus* with very low activities. It is interesting to note further that the two colorless mutants exhibit oxidative pentose phosphate activity while a naturally occurring one, *Astasia longa*, strain J, metabolizes glucose solely via glycolysis (*450*).

In Table XVI are itemized a large number of algae in which the reductive pentose phosphate cycle occurs. This list was compiled on

TABLE XVI
ALGAE CONTAINING THE REDUCTIVE PENTOSE PHOSPHATE CYCLE ACTIVITY

Name	Type of algae	References
Nostoc muscorum	Blue-green	(*451*)
Nostoc. sp.	Blue-green	(*451*)
Phormidium	Blue-green	(*451*)
Synechococcus cedrorum	Blue-green	(*451*)
Romeria	Blue-green	(*452*)
Iridophycus flaccidum	Red	(*453*)
Porphyridium	Red	(*451*)
Nitella	Yellow-green	(*451*)
Vaucheria	Yellow-green	(*451*)
Chlorella pyrenoidosa	Green	(*10, 70, 88, 451*)
Scenedesmus obliquus	Green	(*10, 424, 451*)
Chlorella variegata, autotroph	Green	(*425*)
Chlamydomonas reinhardi, wild type	Green	(*454*)
Chlamydomonas reinhardi, mutant strain (ac-21)	Green	(*454*)
Haematococcus	Green	(*451*)
Spirogyra	Green	(*451*)
Chlorococcum	Green	(*451*)
Ulva lactuca	Green	(*444*)

the premise that the presence of carboxydismutase and/or TPN-specific glyceraldehyde-3-phosphate dehydrogenase is considered to be good suggestive evidence for the operation of the cycle. In some instances, the CO_2 fixation pattern was the measured parameter. These criteria are obviously inadequate, as will be seen when the case of the blue-green algae is discussed.

Carbon dioxide fixation by *Euglena* is the center of some very interesting studies by itself. Because it occupies a unique position in the phylogenetic tree, its biochemistry might be also unique. Indeed, when CO_2 is fixed by *Euglena* in the dark, the pattern of compounds into which carbon dioxide is fixed strongly resembles that of photosynthetic carbon dioxide fixation (*455*). Two of the key enzymes, carboxydismutase and TPN-linked triose phosphate dehydrogenase, have been demonstrated in cell-free extracts of the green *Euglena* (*425*). When the *Euglena* is grown in the dark, however, or when it is bleached with streptomyocin, the extracts no longer contain these enzymes. On the other hand, the naturally colorless euglenoid *Astasia* possesses carboxydismutase activity, but no TPN-specific triose phosphate dehydrogenase activity.

With regard to the blue-green algae, at least in two types, *Anacystis* and *Nostoc*, the TPN-dependent glyceraldehyde-3-phosphate dehydrogenase was found in cell-free extracts (*83*). Furthermore, carboxydismutase was detected in cell-free extracts of *Anacystis nidulans* (*70*). These indications, considered along with the typical photosynthetic CO_2 fixation pattern of compounds obtained in *Nostoc muscorum* (*451*), would lead one to believe that the carbon reduction cycle as shown in Fig. 2 is operative in the blue-green algae. Fewson *et al.*, however, have shown without any doubt that fructose-1,6-diphosphate aldolase is absent in four such algae: *Anacystis, Anabaena, Nostoc,* and *Tolypothrix* (*83*). Thus, a controversial point is raised concerning the validity of the reductive pentose phosphate cycle or the carbon reduction cycle. Peterkofsky and Racker pointed out that certain enzymes of this cycle are deficient even in green algae and leaves so that the cycle cannot support the rate of photosynthesis by the intact cell (*88*). These and other evidences, such as the asymmetric labeling of glucose from $C^{14}O_2$ fixation in the light and the sensitivity toward iodoacetate inhibition (*456*), are not compatible with the operation of the reductive pentose phosphate cycle as such. Hence, an alternate pathway was proposed that did not involve the hydrolytic cleavage of the presumed six-carbon intermediate of the carboxydismutase reaction, and did not involve the recondensation of two molecules of triose phosphates (*456*). This whole question has been discussed in great detail by Wassink in his review article on photosynthesis (*457*). Before leaving this problem altogether, it seems to this reviewer that another possibility exists for the condensation of three-carbon compounds to form hexoses via the reversal of the Entner-Doudoroff pathway since it has been recently shown that the 2-keto-3-deoxy-6-phosphogluconate aldolase is reversible (*458*). So far, however, no such enzyme has been detected in algae.

Just as in the case of the autotrophic bacteria, carboxydismutase in algae is apparently an inducible enzyme. In Table XVI, *Chlorella variegata* as an autotroph is listed as containing reductive pentose phosphate cycle activity. The heterotrophically grown *C. variegata,* on the other hand, possessing no chlorophyll, also has no carboxydismutase activity

(*425*). Perhaps there is a parallel relationship between the formation of the chlorophyll and the enzyme in a manner similar to the suggestions made by Lascelles (*438*).

XVI. Higher Plants

A. The Oxidative Pentose Phosphate Cycle

The catabolism of glucose by higher plants much resembles that of the mammals. Tissues of higher plants have served as source material for studies in this regard for innumerable experiments. Generally, these tissues have the capacity to degrade carbohydrates via the oxidative pathway no matter what the source: the fruit, the leaves, the stems or stalks, the roots or tubers, or the seeds or seedlings. Some examples of each of these categories should illustrate the point.

One of the enzymes of the nonoxidative portion of the pentose phosphate pathway, phosphoribose isomerase, has been detected in the flavedo of the orange and in the avocado fruit (*459*). The Kadota fig fruit contains D-*altro*-heptulose (*460*). In studying the pathway of synthesis of L-ascorbate in the fruit of the strawberry, *Fragaria*, Loewus concluded that L-ascorbate is formed via two pathways, one involving the inversion of a six-carbon sugar and the other not inverting this sugar (*461*). The latter, he postulated as going through the direct oxidative pathway via 6-phosphogluconate and eventually to L-ascorbate. Wang and his co-workers have examined the role of the hexose monophosphate pathway in the catabolism of glucose in a number of fruits. Using the radiorespirometric method, they estimated that over 25% of the glucose is degraded via this alternate pathway in the tomato (*462*) and between 30 and 35% in the fruit of four varieties of the pepper *Capsicum frutescens* Longum (*463*). Other fruits yielding relatively large C-1:C-6 ratios of respiratory CO_2 from the respectively labeled glucose are the cucumber, the lime, and the orange (*464*). In the pre-ripe banana, the pentose phosphate cycle seems to be quite active as suggested by the lack of inhibition by fluoride of respiration, by the ability of the fruit to utilize both glucose-6-phosphate and ribose-5-phosphate, and by the inability of the fruit to metabolize fructose-1,6-diphosphate (*465*). As the climacteric is approached, however, the whole metabolic pattern shifts toward the EMP scheme, which manifests itself by the appearance of an active aldolase, carboxylase, the metabolism of hexose diphosphate, and an increased sensitivity toward fluoride inhibition of the respiration in the pulp.

The pentose phosphate cycle is evident in the leaves by (*a*) the presence of the cycle enzymes, (*b*) the presence of some intermediates of the cycle, or (*c*) by the utilization and conversion of pentose phosphate cycle intermediates to other intermediates.

Examples of the first type (*a*) are as follows: Spinach leaves contain phosphoribose isomerase (*459*), transketolase (*466*), and phosphoketopentose epimerase (*467*). Pea leaves contain phosphoribose isomerase (*459*) along with 6-PG DH and transketolase (*468*). Phosphoribose isomerase derived from alfalfa is one of the best-characterized enzymes with respect to its biochemical and physical chemical properties (*459*). Both G-6-P DH and 6-PG DH have been detected in leaves of tobacco, *Nicotiana tabacum,* by use of triphenyl tetrazolium (*469*). The activity of the former enzyme has also been observed in extracts of corn leaves (*470*).

(*b*) The presence of intermediates might also be an indication that the pentose pathway is in operation. Three such examples come to mind: Fig leaves (*460*) and *Sedum spectabile,* one of the Crassulaceae (succulent plant) (*471*), both possess sedoheptulose. Alfalfa, when grown in nutrient cultures and fed D-ribose, yields a very marked increase in sedoheptulose (*472*).

(*c*) The utilization and conversion of pentose phosphate cycle intermediates are of two types: to phosphorylated intermediates or to CO_2. Both types of reactions have been investigated in the tobacco leaf. Ribose-5-phosphate was transformed to ribulose-5-phosphate, sedoheptulose-7-phosphate, fructose-6-phosphate, and glucose-6-phosphate by extracts of tobacco leaves (*473*). Leaf disks of tobacco administered variously labeled glucose yielded radioactive carbon dioxide, starch, sugars, and organic acids (*474*). These researchers estimated that the amount of added glucose metabolized via the EMP route and via the pentose phosphate cycle is in the ratio of 3:2. Gibbs and Horecker, in a classic experiment, reported the presence of an active transketolase system in pea (*Pisum sativum*) leaves which can partly account for the correct intramolecular distribution of label in the hexose molecule when the leaves are fed specifically labeled ribose-5-phosphate (*475*). The example of Tolbert and Zill has already been mentioned in Section V, D; however, examples were not given. Radioactive sedoheptulose was rapidly converted to C^{14}-labeled sugar phosphate, under illumination and in the presence of nitrogen, by sugar beet leaves, Wintex barley leaves, and tobacco leaves (*67*). Finally, Ross *et al.* have shown that the leaves of two herbaceous plants, *Chenopodium murale* L. and *Polygonum orientale* L., are able to oxidize glucose-1-C^{14} to $C^{14}O_2$ preferentially over that of glucose-6-C^{14} (*476*).

As compared to the data on pentose phosphate cycle metabolism by leaves, those of stems and stalks are relatively sparse. In the stalks of *Sedum spectabile* are present sedoheptulose (*471*). Bean (*Phaseolus vulgaris* var. Black Valentine) stem tissues contain enzymes that will yield a C-6:C-1 ratio of the respiratory CO_2 equal to approximately 0.5 from the respectively labeled glucose (*477*). Indirect evidence from phosphorylated substrate utilization and conversion in the mitochondrial preparation from the apical parts of etiolated young pea plants strongly implicate the presence of G-6-P DH, 6-PG DH, phosphohexose isomerase, pentose phosphate isomerase, phosphoketopentose epimerase, and transketolase (*478*). This is a surprising result in view of the fact that most pentose phosphate cycle enzymes are localized in the soluble (probably cytoplasmic) fraction of mammalian tissue cells.

A freshly cut carrot has the potential to oxidize glucose via the shunt mechanism, especially when stimulated by the addition of methylene blue (*479*). In fact, if the carrots are not freshly cut, the respiration rises and the oxidation of carbon atom 1 of glucose is accelerated more than that of carbon atom 6 (*480*). Washing of the slices induces a fully developed respiration rate and the respiratory CO_2 ratio of C-1:C-6 reaches 4 to 5. The same observations were made with potato slices (*480, 481*). Mitochondria isolated from potato tissues have been shown to contain enzymes that will oxidize fructose-6-phosphate in the presence of TPN^+ and will transform ribose-5-phosphate to ribulose-5-phosphate and sedoheptulose-7-phosphate (*478*).

The root tips of corn seedlings, although having a shunt mechanism in operation, is severely limited by the supply of TPN^+ (*482*). The shunt activity can be stimulated by adding nitrite. Enzymes such as G-6-P DH, 6-PG DH, enzymes that utilize ribose-5-phosphate, and transforming enzymes can be found in these root tips (*483*). Extracts of pea seedling root tips will metabolize variously labeled ribose-5-phosphate to form radioactive hexose monophosphate with a distribution of label which is accountable only by invoking the combined actions of transketolase and transaldolase (*475*). In fact, this extract exhibits G-6-P DH and 6-PG DH activities along with many EMP scheme enzymes (*484*). Humphreys and Dugger, showed that root tips from a number of seedlings (pea, *Pisum sativum* L.; corn, *Zea mays* L.; and oat, *Avena sativum* L.) gave C-6:C-1 ratios of respiratory CO_2 generally less than unity (*485*).

Other seedlings with indications of the occurrence of the hexose monophosphate pathway are those of pine (*486*), etiolated *Sorghum vulgare* (*487*), and mung bean, *Phaseolus radiatus* (*488*). Wheat germ extracts can catalyze the oxidative degradation of glucose-6-phosphate to CO_2 which is TPN-dependent (*489*).

The effect of aging on the activity of the pentose phosphate cycle seems to be generally one of an increase. Thus during the pollen germination of pine seeds, the anaerobic pathway is partly supplemented by the aerobic hexose monophosphate pathway (*486*). The activity of the TPN^+-reducing system, linked with pentose phosphate cycle substrates, is also highest in extracts of seedlings and young leaves (*473*). (At midstalk or below, in the mature plant, no such activity is present.) In the growing pea leaves, the 6-PG DH activity increases sharply from germination to a peak value and then decreases to a low value (*468, 490*). Since the system utilizing ribose-5-phosphate also rises with increasing time of germination, the conclusion was reached that the EMP pathway plays a major role in glucose metabolism in the embryonic tissue, but the pentose phosphate cycle increases its contribution with increasing age (*490*). More or less the same findings were obtained from the aging of mung-bean seedlings (*488*); i.e., the amounts and specific activities of both G-6-P DH and 6-PG DH rise with increasing germination time up to 48 hours. Seventy-two hours afterward, both activities decrease until, after 96 hours, the extract of the mung-bean seedlings is completely devoid of the dehydrogenases. This last result is in contradiction with the conclusions reached by other investigators (*477, 490*).

Dichlorophenoxyacetic acid (2,4-D) affects the metabolism of glucose differently in different species. For example, in the bean stem tissues, treatment by 2,4-D results in an increased participation of the EMP pathway (*477*). On the other hand, in root tips of pea, corn, and oat seedlings, the effect of 2,4-D is to increase the amount of glucose catabolized via the pentose phosphate cycle (*483, 485*). Sorghum seedlings also give the same response to 2,4-D treatment (*487*).

Studies with fluoride-sensitive species of *Chenopodium* and *Polygonum* showed that the fluoride-damaged leaves had markedly lower C-6:C-1 ratio of the respiratory CO_2 derived from glucose-6- and -1-C^{14} than that of the control (undamaged) leaves (*476*). The authors attributed the decreased C-6:C-1 to the inhibition of enolase by fluoride ion; however, in some cases, the rates of oxygen uptake and of the oxidation of glucose-6-C^{14} actually increased in HF fumigated *Chenopodium* and in fluoride treated *Polygonum.* Fluoride added to potatoes susceptible to *Phytophthora infestans* inactivates a major portion of the total respiration (*491*). Nevetheless, a high level of oxidation still occurs by way of the shunt mechanism. It appears that the respiration of hexose monophosphates participates in the protective reaction against infection. In this last regard, Daly *et al.* found that higher plants infected by obligate plant parasites have a characteristically high rate of respiration and a low C-6:C-1 ratio (*492*). They concluded that nearly all the increased respiration is accommodated by the hexose monophosphate pathway.

Later, it was shown that rust-affected safflower and bean tissues yield only trace amounts of radioactive ribose (formed from radioactive glucose) in the neutral compounds fraction (*493*).

Moisture conditions also govern the oxidation of glucose (*494*). Thus the C-6:C-1 ratio is about 0.5 when the root tips of corn seedlings are grown under limiting moisture conditions. When the growth conditions are quite wet, this CO_2 ratio approaches unity (*485*).

Even the medium in which respirometry was measured can affect the outcome of the results. Thus when etiolated seedlings of *Sorghum* are grown in distilled water and then the respiratory CO_2 is measured in phosphate medium, the glucose catabolized via the shunt is markedly reduced whereas when the measurements were performed in an inorganic nutrient medium, a much greater proportion of the glucose was metabolized via this pathway (*487*).

B. The Reductive Pentose Phosphate Cycle

Respecting carbohydrate metabolism, the photosynthetic fixation of carbon dioxide is one that belongs uniquely to plants and a few bacteria. This process gives rise to a typical pattern (referred to as the labeling or carbon dioxide fixation pattern, cf. Section XIV) of incorporation of C^{14} from $C^{14}O_2$ into intermediates of the cycle. The pattern is characterized by the presence of radioactivity in phosphorylated intermediates, particularly, phosphoglycerate, sugar monophosphates and diphosphates, after brief photosynthesis. In some cases, however, owing to the presence of some highly active phosphatases, only the corresponding dephosphorylated compounds are found in the pattern. Another distinctive feature is the C^{14} distribution in the hexose molecule. The radioactivity is concentrated predominantly in the C-3 and the C-4 positions (*10*), the C^{14} being slightly less in the former position than in the latter (*110*). Furthermore, the radioactivity in positions 1 and 2 is generally greater than that in positions 5 and 6 (*110*).

Practically all varieties of higher plant leaves exhibit the so-called CO_2 fixation pattern of photosynthesis when they are exposed to radioactive carbon dioxide in the light. Examples of these higher plants are barley seedlings, mature sugar beet, alfalfa, soybean, *Vicia faba*, *Kalanchoe blossfeldiana*, and *Crassula arborescens* (*495*). The yew, juniper, squash, tomato, and ivy plants along with avocado seedlings also display more or less the same fixation pattern (*451*). In the dark, the CO_2 fixation pattern in *Bryophyllum* suggested the presence of carboxydismutase (*496*).

Arnon and his associates, in a series of classic experiments, have shown that the chloroplasts are capable of performing all the light and dark reactions of photosynthesis (*497*). The rate of CO_2 fixation, however, is low and amounts to a maximum of 1–2.5% that in the intact leaf (*498*), which may be due to a loss of photosynthetic pyridine nucleotide reductase (*499*). Recently, Heber and Tyszkiewicz obtained an extrapolated rate equal to 15% the maximum rate of the intact leaf by conducting the experiment with a concentrated suspension of aqueous prepared chloroplasts supplemented with proteins from nonaqueous prepared chloroplasts (*500*).

Trebst *et al.* first showed that the light and dark reactions of photosynthesis can be physically separated by centrifuging osmotically swollen spinach chloroplasts (*501*). The resulting pale-colored supernatant solution is able to carry out the CO_2 fixation whereas the green precipitate can carry out the light reactions, generating ATP and reducing power along with the production of oxygen. Later, Park and Pon confirmed these findings and showed further that even very small green fragments, obtained by sonically rupturing chloroplasts, are able to carry out the light reaction at full capacity (*502*).

When isolated chloroplasts from various species are exposed to $C^{14}O_2$, the fixation patterns for the different species are nearly identical (*503*). Most of the label is located in the sugar monophosphates, and lesser amounts are found in the diphosphates, dihydroxyacetone, and phosphoglycerate. The species studied were spinach, sugar beet, pokeweed, sunflower, and New Zealand spinach (*Tetragonia expansa*). The rates of CO_2 fixation, under illumination, ranged from 1.4 to 3.5 μmoles carbon fixed per hour per milligram chlorophyll. Maximum rates for the intact spinach leaves are about 200 μmoles per hour per milligram chlorophyll.

Evidence for the presence of carboxydismutase in spinach chloroplasts was obtained by Fuller and Gibbs (*425*) and by Lyttleton and Ts'o (*504*). The former workers found that the chloroplasts contain the bulk of the carboxylase activity when compared with the whole cell. By using nonaqueous techniques for the isolation of the chloroplasts, Smillie and Fuller showed an excellent correlation between the carboxydismutase activity and the chlorophyll content of different fractions (*94*), indicating that the enzyme is associated with the chloroplasts. Finally, Heber *et al.* obtained quantitative data that clearly show the complete localization of carboxydismutase in the chloroplasts of tobacco, spinach, and New Zealand spinach (*95*).

The occurrence of carboxydismutase in higher plants is widespread. Some examples of higher plants containing this carboxylase activity are itemized in Table XVII. In these higher plant tissues, the enzymatic activity was assayed directly in the presence of bicarbonate and ribulose diphosphate, but in some cases ribose-5-phosphate plus ATP were substituted for ribulose-1,5-diphosphate (*506*). This latter substitution assumes, then, that two other enzymes are active in the extracts of the tissue, namely, phosphoribose isomerase and phosphoribulokinase. In comparing the two citrus fruits, in all cases the enzymatic activity is higher in the trifoliate orange tissues than in the corresponding rough lemon tissues (*506*).

TABLE XVII
THE OCCURRENCE OF CARBOXYDISMUTASE IN HIGHER PLANTS

Plant material	Investigators	References
Nicotiana tabacum L. chloroplasts	Heber *et al.*	(*95*)
Tetragonia expansa Murr. chloroplasts	Heber *et al.*	(*95*)
Spinacia oleracea L. chloroplasts	Heber *et al.*	(*95*)
Ryegrass	Weissbach *et al.*	(*505*)
Cabbage leaves	Racker	(*9*)
Pea chloroplasts	Smillie and Fuller	(*94*)
Barley seedlings, normal green	Fuller and Gibbs	(*425*)
Trifoliate orange leaves	Huffaker and Wallace	(*506*)
Rough lemon leaves	Huffaker and Wallace	(*506*)
Trifoliate orange flavedo	Huffaker and Wallace	(*506*)
Rough lemon flavedo	Huffaker and Wallace	(*506*)
Phaseolus vulgaris var. Black Valentine leaves	Margulies	(*507*)

Although normal green barley seedling contains carboxydismutase activity, the X-ray albino mutant did not (*425*). Studies with etiolated barley seedling leaves indicated initially the presence of carboxydismutase activity (*508*). Upon illumination of these leaves for progressively longer times, the carboxylase activity rises until, after 20 hours of illumination, a peak is reached. Thereafter the activity of the enzyme gradually decreases. An experiment of a similar nature was conducted by Margulies (*507*). Etiolated leaves of *Phaseolus* were made green by illumination, in the presence and absence of chloramphenicol, an inhibitor of protein synthesis. The carboxydismutase level in the greened leaves in the presence of this inhibitor is lower than that in the absence of this inhibitor. The Hill reaction activity in the particles from the former is similarly lower than that in the latter.

In germinating pea leaves the carboxydismutase activity starts at a low level after 5 days of germination, rises to a maximum after 9 days of germination, and then falls gradually to about 50% of the peak value after 15 days of germination (*468*).

The TPN-dependent glyceraldehyde-3-phosphate dehydrogenase is another key enzyme of the reductive pentose phosphate cycle. Its distribution in higher plants is also widespread, as evident from the list in

Table XVIII. This enzyme is absent in etiolated corn leaves and low in albino corn plants (*470*). In the pea roots, only the DPN-linked dehydrogenase was found (*77*). The X-ray induced albino mutant of the barley seedlings has only about one-fifth the level of TPN-linked enzyme in the

TABLE XVIII
THE PRESENCE OF TPN-LINKED GLYCERALDEHYDE-3-PHOSPHATE DEHYDROGENASE IN HIGHER PLANTS

Plant material	Investigators	References
Mature corn leaves	Hageman and Waygood	(*470*)
Mature barley leaves	Hageman and Waygood	(*470*)
Wheat leaves	Hageman and Waygood	(*470*)
Oat leaves	Hageman and Waygood	(*470*)
Sugar beet leaves	Arnon *et al.*	(*82*)
Mature sunflower leaves	Arnon	(*78*)
Mature tobacco leaves	Arnon	(*78*)
Pea stems and leaves	Gibbs	(*77*)
Trifolium repens L. chloroplasts	Heber *et al.*	(*95*)
Secale cereale L. chloroplasts	Heber *et al.*	(*95*)
Vicia faba L., spp. minor chloroplasts	Heber *et al.*	(*95*)
Spinacia oleracea L. chloroplasts	Heber *et al.*	(*95*)

normal green seedlings (*425*). The TPN-specific triose phosphate dehydrogenase is nearly completely localized in the chloroplasts of clovers (*T. repens*), beans (*V. faba*), rye (*Secale cereale*), and spinach (*Spinacia oleracea*) (*95*). On the other hand, the DPN-dependent enzyme is distributed partly in the chloroplast and partly in the cytoplasm.

A third enzyme, phosphoribulokinase, is also an integral part of the carbon reduction cycle. This enzyme has been found in spinach extracts (*88, 509*), *Euglena gracilis,* and high and low temperature *Chlorella pyrenoidosa* (*88*). Aside from these direct enzymological studies, there are indirect indications of this enzyme; for example, the carboxydismutase activity in oranges was assayed by using ribose-5-phosphate plus ATP as a substitute for the actual carboxydismutase substrate, ribulose-1,5-diphosphate (*506*). This method, therefore, assumes that both phosphopentose isomerase and phosphoribulokinase are present in the extracts of the orange tissue. A negative result might mean the absence of any one of the three enzymes; however, this is not very likely to occur in a crude extract.

XVII. Closing Remarks

The widespread occurrence of the pentose phosphate cycle in life under an atmosphere of oxygen makes one wonder what it might have been like in primitive times. Was the oxidative pentose phosphate cycle operative then? The answer to this question hinges on the composition of the primordial atmosphere of the earth. The general consensus is that the early atmosphere was a highly reducing one. From this premise Horecker (*510*) proposed that the oxidative portion of the pentose cycle could only come into prominence when the atmosphere turned "oxidizing." From this point of view, at least, the enzymes such as the dehydrogenases evolved rather recently whereas such enzymes as transketolase and transaldolase may be considered as more primitive. The existence of these last two enzymes along with enzymes of the EMP pathway in the primitive organism can thus permit it to carry out metabolism whether it be photosynthesis or chemosynthesis.

References

1. E Bueding and E. Farber, *in* "Comparative Biochemistry" (M. Florkin and H. S. Mason, eds.), Vol. I, p. 411. Academic Press, New York, 1960.
2. S. Weinhouse, *J. Am. Chem. Soc.* **83**, 2597 (1961).
3. B. L. Horecker and A. H. Mehler, *Ann. Rev. Biochem.* **24**, 207 (1955).
4. E. Racker, *Advances in Enzymol.* **15**, 141 (1954).
5. B. Axelrod and H. Beevers, *Ann. Rev. Plant Physiol.* **7**, 267 (1956).
6. M. Gibbs, *Ann. Rev. Plant Physiol.* **10**, 329 (1959).
7. L. O. Krampitz, *in* "The Bacteria" (I. C. Gunsalus and R. Y. Stanier, eds.), Vol. II, p. 209. Academic Press, New York, 1961.
8. S. Abraham, P. Cady, and I. L. Chaikoff, *Endocrinology* **66**, 280 (1960).
9. E. Racker, *Arch. Biochem. Biophys.* **69**, 300 (1957).
10. J. A. Bassham and M. Calvin, "The Path of Carbon in Photosynthesis." Prentice-Hall, Englewood Cliffs, New Jersey, 1957.
11. R. C. Fuller, R. M. Smillie, E. C. Sisler, and H. L. Kornberg, *J. Biol. Chem.* **236**, 2140 (1961).
12. H. A. Krebs and H. L. Kornberg, *Ergeb. Physiol. biol. Chem. u. exptl. Pharmakol.* **49**, 212 (1957).
13. S. S. Cohen, *Cold Spring Harbor Symposia, Quant. Biol.* **12**, 35 (1947).
14. A. C. Neish, *Ann. Rev. Plant Physiol.* **11**, 55 (1960).
15. J. J. Burns, *in* "Metabolic Pathways" (D. M. Greenberg, ed.), Vol. I, p. 341. Academic Press, New York, 1960.
16. R. Bressler and S. J. Wakil, *J. Biol. Chem.* **236**, 1643 (1961).
17. R. G. Langdon, *J. Am. Chem. Soc.* **77**, 5190 (1955).
18. P. McLean, *Biochim. et Biophys. Acta* **57**, 620 (1962).
19. N. O. Kaplan, M. N. Swartz, M. E. Frech, and M. M. Ciotti, *Proc. Natl. Acad. Sci. U. S.* **42**, 481 (1956).
20. I. C. Gunsalus and C. W. Shuster, *in* "The Bacteria" (I. C. Gunsalus and R. Y. Stanier, eds.), Vol. II, p. 1. Academic Press, New York, 1961.
21. O. Warburg and W. Christian, *Biochem. Z.* **238**, 131 (1931).
22. R. O. Loebel, *Biochem. Z.* **161**, 219 (1925).
23. E. S. G. Barron and G. A. Harrop, Jr., *J. Biol. Chem.* **79**, 65 (1928).
24. P. A. Levene and F. B. LaForge, *J. Biol. Chem.* **18**, 319 (1914).
25. E. B. Fred, W. H. Peterson, and J. A. Anderson, *J. Biol. Chem.* **48**, 385 (1921).
26. O. Warburg, W. Christian, and A. Griese, *Biochem. Z.* **282**, 157 (1935).

27. F. Dickens, *Nature* **138**, 1057 (1936).
28. F. Lipmann, *Nature* **138**, 588 (1936).
29. O. Warburg and W. Christian, *Biochem. Z.* **287**, 440 (1936).
30. O. Warburg and W. Christian, *Biochem. Z.* **292**, 287 (1937).
31. F. Dickens, *Biochem. J.* **32**, 1626 (1938).
32. F. Dickens, *Biochem. J.* **32**, 1645 (1938).
33. Z. Dische, *Naturwissenschaften* **26**, 252 (1938).
34. F. Schlenk and M. J. Waldvogel, *Arch. Biochem.* **9**, 455 (1946).
35. F. Schlenk and M. J. Waldvogel, *Arch. Biochem.* **12**, 181 (1947).
36. M. J. Waldvogel and F. Schlenk, *Arch. Biochem. Biophys.* **14**, 484 (1947).
37. E. Racker, *Federation Proc.* **7**, 180 (1948).
38. S. S. Cohen, *Bacteriol. Revs.* **15**, 131 (1951).
39. B. L. Horecker and P. Z. Smyrniotis, *Arch. Biochem. Biophys.* **29**, 232 (1950).
40. B. L. Horecker, *in* "Phosphorus Metabolism" (W. D. McElroy and B. Glass, eds.), Vol. I, p. 117. Johns Hopkins Press, Baltimore, Maryland, 1951.
41. B. L. Horecker and P. Z. Smyrniotis, *Federation Proc.* **10**, 199 (1951).
42. B. L. Horecker and P. Z. Smyrniotis, *J. Biol. Chem.* **193**, 371 (1951).
43. B. L. Horecker, P. Z. Smyrniotis, and J. E. Seegmiller, *J. Biol. Chem.* **193**, 383 (1951).
44. S. S. Cohen, *in* "Phosphorus Metabolism" (W. D. McElroy and B. Glass, eds.), Vol. I, p. 148. Johns Hopkins Press, Baltimore, Maryland, 1951.
45. B. L. Horecker, P. Z. Smyrniotis, and H. Klenow, *J. Biol. Chem.* **205**, 661 (1953).
46. E. Racker, G. de la Haba, and I. G. Leder, *J. Am. Chem. Soc.* **75**, 1010 (1953).
47. B. L. Horecker and P. Z. Smyrniotis, *J. Am. Chem. Soc.* **75**, 2021 (1953).
48. P. A. Srere, J. R. Cooper, V. Klybas, and E. Racker, *Arch. Biochem. Biophys.* **59**, 535 (1955).
49. J. Hurwitz and B. L. Horecker, *J. Biol. Chem.* **223**, 993 (1956).
50. M. Gibbs and R. D. DeMoss, *Federation Proc.* **10**, 189 (1951).
51. M. Calvin and A. A. Benson, *Science* **107**, 476 (1948).
52. H. Gaffron, E. W. Fager, and J. L. Rosenberg, *Symposia Soc. Exptl. Biol.* **5**, 262 (1951).
53. M. Calvin, J. A. Bassham, A. A. Benson, V. H. Lynch, C. Ouellet, L. Schou, W. Stepka, and N. E. Tolbert, *Symposia Soc. Exptl. Biol.* **5**, 284 (1951).
54. M. Calvin and P. Massini, *Experientia* **8**, 445 (1952).
55. A. T. Wilson and M. Calvin, *J. Am. Chem. Soc.* **77**, 5948 (1955).
56. J. R. Quayle, R. C. Fuller, A. A. Benson, and M. Calvin, *J. Am. Chem. Soc.* **76**, 3610 (1954).
57. A. Weissbach, P. Z. Smyrniotis, and B. L. Horecker, *J. Am. Chem. Soc.* **76**, 3611 (1954).
58. E. Racker, *Nature* **175**, 249 (1955).
59. E. Lundsgaard, *Biochem. Z.* **250**, 61 (1932).
60. J. Runnström, *Biochem. Z.* **258**, 257 (1933).
61. S. B. Barker, E. Shorr, and M. Malam, *J. Biol. Chem.* **129**, 33 (1939).
62. N. Entner and M. Doudoroff, *J. Biol. Chem.* **196**, 853 (1952).
63. J. MacGee and M. Doudoroff, *J. Biol. Chem.* **210**, 617 (1954).
64. F. N. Brenneman, W. Vishniac, and W. A. Volk, *J. Biol. Chem.* **235**, 3357 (1960).
65. S. Pontremoli, A. Bonsignore, E. Grazi, and B. L. Horecker, *J. Biol. Chem.* **235**, 1881 (1960).

66. P. W. Hochachka, J. M. Teal, and M. Telford, *Can. J. Biochem. and Physiol.* **40,** 1043 (1962).
67. N. E. Tolbert and L. P. Zill, *Arch. Biochem. Biophys.* **50,** 392 (1954).
68. V. Moses, *J. Gen. Microbiol.* **20,** 184 (1959).
69. J.-P. Aubert, G. Milhaud, and J. Millet, *Compt. rend. acad. sci.* **242,** 2059 (1956).
70. G. Richter, *Naturwissenschaften* **46,** 604 (1959).
71. J. M. Earl and M. Gibbs, *Plant Physiol.* **30,** iv (1955).
72. C. E. Wenner, J. H. Hackney, and F. Moliterno, *Cancer Research* **18,** 1105 (1958).
73. D. E. Koshland, Jr., and F. H. Westheimer, *J. Am. Chem. Soc.* **72,** 3383 (1950).
74. O. Warburg and W. Christian, *Biochem. Z.* **254,** 438 (1932).
75. B. Axelrod, *in* "Metabolic Pathways" (D. M. Greenberg, ed.), Vol. I, p. 98. Academic Press, New York, 1960.
76. S. Tewfik and P. K. Stumpf, *J. Biol. Chem.* **192,** 519 (1951).
77. M. Gibbs, *Nature* **170,** 164 (1952).
78. D. I. Arnon, *Science* **116,** 635 (1952).
79. R. H. Hageman and D. I. Arnon, *Arch. Biochem. Biophys.* **57,** 421 (1955).
80. M. Gibbs, *in* "Methods in Enzymology" (S. P. Colowick and N. O. Kaplan, eds.), Vol. I, p. 411. Academic Press, New York, 1955.
81. B. Axelrod, R. S. Bandurski, C. M. Greiner, and R. Jang, *J. Biol. Chem.* **202,** 619 (1953).
82. D. I. Arnon, L. L. Rosenberg, and F. R. Whatley, *Nature* **173,** 1132 (1954).
83. C. A. Fewson, M. Al-Hafidh, and M. Gibbs, *Plant Physiol.* **37,** 402 (1962).
84. P. A. Marks, A. Szeinberg, and J. Banks, *J. Biol. Chem.* **236,** 10 (1961).
85. G. Richter, *Biochim. et Biophys. Acta* **48,** 606 (1961).
86. K. N. Mehrotra, *Comp. Biochem. Physiol.* **3,** 184 (1961).
87. R. M. Smillie, N. Rigopoulos, and H. Kelley, *Biochim. et Biophys. Acta* **56,** 612 (1962).
88. A. Peterkofsky and E. Racker, *Plant Physiol.* **36,** 409 (1961).
89. K. Yamada and N. Shimazono, *Biochim. et Biophys. Acta* **54,** 205 (1961).
90. K. Paigen and C. E. Wenner, *Arch. Biochem. Biophys.* **97,** 213 (1962).
91. M. B. Allen, D. I. Arnon, J. B. Capindale, F. R. Whatley, and L. J. Durham. *J. Am. Chem. Soc.* **77,** 4149 (1955).
92. U. Heber, *Z. Naturforsch.* **15b,** 95 (1960).
93. C. R. Stocking, *Plant Physiol.* **34,** 56 (1959).
94. R. M. Smillie and R. C. Fuller, *Plant Physiol.* **34,** 651 (1959).
95. U. Heber, N. G. Pon, and M. Heber, *Plant Physiol.* **38,** 355 (1963).
96. B. Bloom, M. R. Stetten, and D. Stetten, Jr., *J. Biol. Chem.* **204,** 681 (1953).
97. B. Bloom and D. Stetten, Jr., *J. Am. Chem. Soc.* **75,** 5446 (1953).
98. S. Abraham, P. F. Hirsch, and I. L. Chaikoff, *J. Biol. Chem.* **211,** 31 (1954).
99. E. C. Heath and H. Koffler, *J. Bacteriol.* **71,** 174 (1956).
100. K. F. Lewis, H. J. Blumenthal, R. S. Weinrach, and S. Weinhouse, *J. Biol. Chem.* **216,** 273 (1955).
101. E. A. Dawes and W. H. Holms, *Biochim. et Biophys. Acta* **29,** 82 (1958).
102. J. A. Muntz and J. R. Murphy, *J. Biol. Chem.* **224,** 971 (1957).
103. C. E. Wenner and S. Weinhouse, *J. Biol. Chem.* **222,** 399 (1956).
104. C. H. Wang and J. K. Krackov, *J. Biol. Chem.* **237,** 3614 (1962).
105. S. Korkes, *Ann. Rev. Biochem.* **25,** 685 (1956).
106. H. G. Wood, *Physiol. Revs.* **35,** 841 (1955).

107. J. Katz and H. G. Wood, *J. Biol. Chem.* **235**, 2165 (1960).
108. I. A. Bernstein, K. Lentz, M. Malm, P. Schambye, and H. G. Wood, *J. Biol. Chem.* **215**, 137 (1955).
109. P. A. Marks and B. L. Horecker, *J. Biol. Chem.* **218**, 327 (1956).
110. M. Gibbs and O. Kandler, *Proc. Natl. Acad. Sci. U. S.* **43**, 446 (1957).
111. J. Katz, *in* "Radioactive Isotopes" (H. Schwiegk and F. Turba, eds.), Vol. I, p. 705. Springer, Berlin, 1961.
112. J. Tepperman, "Metabolic and Endocrine Physiology," p. 22. Year Book Publishers, Chicago, Illinois, 1962.
113. W. W. Shreeve, *J. Clin. Invest.* **37**, 999 (1958).
114. H. H. Hiatt, *J. Clin. Invest.* **37**, 1461 (1958).
115. S. Segal, M. Berman, and A. Blair, *J. Clin. Invest.* **40**, 1263 (1961).
116. H. H. Hiatt, *J. Clin. Invest.* **37**, 1453 (1958).
117. H. H. Hiatt and J. Lareau, *J. Biol. Chem.* **233**, 1023 (1958).
118. C. H. Wang, L. P. Snipper, O. Bilen, and B. Hawthorne, *Proc. Soc. Exptl. Biol. Med.* **111**, 93 (1962).
119. J. J. Burns, P. G. Dayton, and F. Eisenberg, Jr., *Biochim. et Biophys. Acta* **25**, 647 (1957).
120. H. H. Hiatt, *J. Biol. Chem.* **224**, 851 (1957).
121. H. R. V. Arnstein and D. Keglevic, *Biochem. J.* **62**, 199 (1956).
122. H. G. Wood, R. Gillespie, S. Joffe, R. G. Hansen, and H. Hardenbrook, *J. Biol. Chem.* **233**, 1271 (1958).
123. A. L. Black, M. Kleiber, E. M. Butterworth, G. B. Brubacher, and J. J. Kaneko, *J. Biol. Chem.* **227**, 537 (1957).
124. J. Katz and H. G. Wood, *J. Biol. Chem.* **238**, 517 (1963).
125. G. F. Cahill, Jr., B. Leboeuf, and R. B. Flinn, *J. Biol. Chem.* **235**, 1246 (1960).
126. G. Weber, G. Banerjee, and J. Ashmore, *Biochem. Biophys. Research Communs.* **3**, 182 (1960).
127. A. I. Winegrad, W. N. Shaw, F. D. W. Lukens, and W. C. Stadie, *J. Biol. Chem.* **234**, 3111 (1959).
128. B. Leboeuf and G. F. Cahill, Jr., *J. Biol. Chem.* **236**, 41 (1961).
129. A. I. Winegrad, W. N. Shaw, F. D. W. Lukens, W. C. Stadie, and A. E. Renold, *J. Biol. Chem.* **234**, 1922 (1959).
130. H. Wörner and K. F. Weinges, *Klin. Wochschr.* **39**, 243 (1961).
131. B. Jeanrenaud and A. E. Renold, *J. Biol. Chem.* **234**, 3082 (1959).
132. A. E. Renold, G. R. Zahnd, B. Jeanrenaud, and B. R. Boshell, *Ann. N. Y. Acad. Sci.* **74**, 490 (1959).
133. G. Hollifield, J. A. Owen, Jr., and W. Parson, *J. Lab. Clin. Med.* **58**, 826 (1961).
134. J. Christophe, B. Jeanrenaud, J. Mayer, and A. E. Renold, *J. Biol. Chem.* **236**, 642 (1961).
135. J. Christophe, B. Jeanrenaud, and A. E. Renold, *Proc. Soc. Exptl. Biol. Med.* **106**, 405 (1961).
136. A. Beloff-Chain, R. Catanzaro, E. B. Chain, and F. Pocchiari, *Selected Sci. Papers Ist. Super. Sanita* **2**, 132 (1959).
137. G. E. Glock and P. McLean, *Biochem. J.* **56**, 171 (1954).
138. T. L. Kelley, E. D. Nielson, R. B. Johnson, and C. S. Vestling, *J. Biol. Chem.* **212**, 545 (1955).
139. L. J. Greenberg and D. Glick, *J. Biol. Chem.* **235**, 3028 (1960).

140. R. B. Cohen and J. D. Crawford, *Endocrinology* **70**, 288 (1962).
141. R. B. Cohen and J. D. Crawford, *Endocrinology* **71**, 847 (1962).
142. E. A. Tsutsui, P. A. Marks, and P. Reich, *J. Biol. Chem.* **237**, 3009 (1962).
143. D. B. Villee, L. L. Engel, and C. A. Villee, *Endocrinology* **65**, 465 (1959).
144. J. D. Marks, N. Roesky, and M. J. Carver, *Arch. Biochem. Biophys.* **95**, 192 (1961).
145. R. Hilf, F. F. Burnett, and A. Borman, *Biochem. Biophys. Research Communs.* **8**, 191 (1962).
146. R. Hilf, C. Breuer, and A. Borman, *Nature* **194**, 867 (1962).
147. J. B. Field, I. Pastan, B. Herring, and P. Johnson, *Endocrinology* **67**, 801 (1960).
148. A. Colajacomo, V. Vallerino, and E. Chisale, *Ital. J. Biochem.* **10**, 205 (1961).
149. E. S. Higgins, *Experientia* **18**, 461 (1962).
150. B. Bloom, *Proc. Soc. Exptl. Biol. Med.* **88**, 317 (1955).
151. D. DiPietro and S. Weinhouse, *Arch. Biochem. Biophys.* **80**, 268 (1959).
152. P. M. Dreyfus and R. Moniz, *Biochim. et Biophys. Acta* **65**, 181 (1962).
153. E. Robins, D. E. Smith, and M. K. Jen, *Progr. in Neurobiol.* **2**, 205 (1957).
154. M. V. Buell, O. H. Lowry, N. R. Roberts, M.-L. W. Chang, and J. I. Kapphahn, *J. Biol. Chem.* **232**, 979 (1958).
155. D. B. McDougal, Jr., D. W. Schulz, J. V. Passonneau, J. R. Clark, M. A. Reynolds, and O. H. Lowry, *J. Gen. Physiol.* **44**, 487 (1961).
156. O. Onoda, *Chem. Abstr.* **54**, 9049e (1960).
157. S. S. Hotta, *J. Neurochem.* **9**, 43 (1962).
158. F. C. G. Hoskins, *Biochim. et Biophys. Acta* **40**, 309 (1960).
159. D. A. Rappoport and R. R. Fritz, *Comp. Biochem. Physiol.* **4**, 33 (1961).
160. A. Geiger, Y. Kawakita, and S. S. Barkulis, *J. Neurochem.* **5**, 323 (1960).
161. G. W. Kittinger, B. C. Wexler, and B. F. Miller, *Proc. Soc. Exptl. Biol. Med.* **104**, 616 (1960).
162. N. Haugaard, G. Inesi, and R. R. Blanken, *Arch. Biochem. Biophys.* **90**, 31 (1960).
163. P. Beaconsfield, *Experientia* **18**, 276 (1962).
164. A. J. Sbarra, R. F. Gilfillan, and W. A. Bardawil, *Biochem. Biophys. Research Communs.* **3**, 311 (1960).
165. P. Mandel and E. Kempf, *Compt. rend. acad. sci. Paris* **255**, 2315 (1962).
166. J. E. Kirk, I. Wang, and N. Brandstrup, *J. Gerontol.* **14**, 25 (1959).
167. R. L. Jolley, V. H. Cheldelin, and R. W. Newburgh, *Biochim. et Biophys. Acta* **33**, 64 (1959).
168. L. I. Rice and D. A. Berman, *J. Pharmacol. Exptl. Therap.* **127**, 11 (1959).
169. D. T. Armstrong and R. O. Greep, *Endocrinology* **70**, 701 (1962).
170. L. Fridhandler, *Exptl. Cell Research* **22**, 303 (1961).
171. S. S. Lazarus and M. Bradshaw, *Proc. Soc. Exptl. Biol. Med.* **102**, 463 (1959).
172. C. H. Smith and P. E. Lacy, *Federation Proc.* **20**, 81 (1961).
173. J. B. Field, P. Johnson, B. Herring, and A. N. Weinberg, *Nature* **185**, 468 (1960).
174. J. E. Dumont, *Biochim. et Biophys. Acta* **42**, 157 (1960).
175. C. J. Goodner and N. Freinkel, *J. Clin. Invest.* **40**, 261 (1961).
176. J. E. Dumont, *Biochim. et Biophys. Acta* **50**, 506 (1961).
177. B. R. Landau, W. Merlevede, and G. Weaver, *J. Clin. Invest.* **41**, 1375 (1962).
178. M. Lee, J. R. Debro, and S. P. Lucia, *Arch. Biochem. Biophys.* **98**, 49 (1962).

179. P. F. Mulvey, Jr., J. J. Kelleher, and D. W. Slingerland, *Endocrinology* **70**, 481 (1962).
180. I. Pastan, B. Herring, P. Johnson, and J. B. Field, *J. Biol. Chem.* **236**, 340 (1961).
181. I. Pastan, B. Herring, P. Johnson, and J. B. Field, *J. Biol. Chem.* **237**, 287 (1962).
182. I. Pastan and J. B. Field, *Endocrinology* **70**, 656 (1962).
183. J. B. Field, I. Pastan, B. Herring, and P. Johnson, *Biochim. et Biophys. Acta* **50**, 513 (1961).
184. G. Tremblay and A. G. E. Pearse, *Brit. J. Exptl. Pathol.* **40**, 66 (1959).
185. M. Niemi and M. Ikonen, *Endocrinology* **70**, 167 (1962).
186. T. W. Scott, I. G. White, and E. F. Annison, *Biochem. J.* **83**, 398 (1962).
187. S. H. Wu, F. F. McKenzie, S. C. Fang, and J. S. Butts, *J. Dairy Sci.* **42**, 110 (1959).
188. C. Schneider and H. H. Wagner, *Intern. Rev. Cytol.* **13**, 135 (1962).
189. M. Brin and R. H. Yonemoto, *J. Biol. Chem.* **230**, 307 (1958).
190. J. R. Murphy, *J. Lab. Clin. Med.* **55**, 286 (1960).
191. T. W. Redding and P. C. Johnson, *Proc. Soc. Exptl. Biol. Med.* **109**, 153 (1962).
192. J. H. Strömme and L. Eldjarn, *Biochem. J.* **84**, 406 (1962).
193. P. A. Marks and J. Banks, *Proc. Natl. Acad. Sci. U. S.* **46**, 447 (1960).
194. L.-I. L. Eng, *Nature* **195**, 1110 (1962).
195. Y. S. Brownstone and O. F. Denstedt, *Can. J. Biochem. and Physiol.* **39**, 527 (1961).
196. Y. S. Brownstone and O. F. Denstedt, *Can. J. Biochem. and Physiol.* **39**, 533 (1961).
197. Y. S. Brownstone and O. F. Denstedt, *Can. J. Biochem. and Physiol.* **39**, 545 (1961).
198. G. Bucolo and G. R. Bartlett, *Biochem. Biophys. Research Communs.* **3**, 620 (1960).
199. Z. Dische and D. Igals, *Arch. Biochem. Biophys.* **93**, 201 (1961).
200. F. J. Lionetti, W. L. McLellan, N. L. Fortier, and J. M. Foster, *Arch. Biochem. Biophys.* **94**, 7 (1961).
201. I. D. Golovatsky, *Ukrain. Biochem. J.* **34**, 435 (1962).
202. A. W. Shafer and G. R. Bartlett, *J. Clin. Invest.* **41**, 690 (1962).
203. D. Rubinstein, P. Ottolenghi, and O. F. Denstedt, *Can. J. Biochem. and Physiol.* **34**, 222 (1956).
204. M. Brin, S. S. Shohet, and C. S. Davidson, *J. Biol. Chem.* **230**, 319 (1958).
205. P. A. Marks, A. B. Johnson, E. Hirschberg, and J. Banks, *Ann. N. Y. Acad. Sci.* **75**, 95 (1958).
206. F. H. Bruns, E. Noltmann, and E. Vahlhaus, *Biochem. Z.* **330**, 483 (1958).
207. C. E. Shields, *Am. J. Clin. Nutrition* **10**, 257 (1962).
208. N. N. Prochoroff, R. Kattermann, and H. Holzer, *Biochem. Biophys. Research Communs.* **9**, 477 (1962).
209. F. H. Bruns, E. Dünwald, and E. Noltmann, *Biochem. Z.* **330**, 497 (1958).
210. Z. Dische, H. T. Shigeura, and E. Landsberg, *Arch. Biochem. Biophys.* **89**, 123 (1960).
211. H. A. Pearson and R. Druyan, *J. Lab. Clin. Med.* **57**, 343 (1961).
212. G. E. Glock and P. McLean, *Biochem. J.* **61**, 390 (1955).
213. F. H. Bruns and P. H. Werners, *Advances in Clin. Chem.* **5**, 237 (1962).

214. R. H. Herman, J. Berkowitz, L. E. Clayton, and J. L. Sherman, Jr., *Nature* **195**, 500 (1962).
215. E. A. Tsutsui and P. A. Marks, *Biochem. Biophys. Research Communs.* **8**, 338 (1962).
216. H. N. Kirkman and E. M. Hendrickson, *J. Biol. Chem.* **237**, 2371 (1962).
217. A. Szeinberg and P. A. Marks, *J. Clin. Invest.* **40**, 914 (1961).
218. K. Tada and Y. Watanabe, *Tôhoku J. Exptl. Med.* **76**, 307 (1962).
219. E. Beutler, *Blood* **14**, 103 (1959).
220. R. T. Gross and P. A. Marks, *Ann. N. Y. Acad. Sci.* **75**, 106 (1958).
221. C. Fornaini, C. Leoncini, L. Luzzatto, and C. Segni, *J. Clin. Invest.* **41**, 1446 (1962).
222. E. Beutler, M. Robson, and E. Buttenwieser, *J. Clin. Invest.* **36**, 617 (1957).
223. S. Schrier, R. Kellermeyer, P. Carson, and A. S. Alving, *J. Lab. Clin. Med.* **50**, 951 (1957).
224. E. Beutler, R. J. Dern, and A. S. Alving, *J. Lab. Clin. Med.* **44**, 439 (1954).
225. A. R. Tarlov, G. J. Brewer, P. E. Carson, and A. S. Alving, *A.M.A. Arch. Internal Med.* **109**, 209 (1962).
226. G. Cohen and P. Hochstein, *Science* **134**, 1756 (1961).
227. H. N. Kirkman, *in* "Molecular Genetics and Human Disease" (L. I. Gardner, ed.), pp. 106–133. Charles C Thomas, Springfield, Illinois, 1961.
228. P. E. Carson, S. L. Schrier, and R. W. Kellermeyer, *Nature* **184**, 1292 (1959).
229. B. Ramot, I. Ashkenazi, A. Rimon, A. Adam, and C. Sheba, *J. Clin. Invest.* **40**, 611 (1961).
230. C. Kidson and J. G. Gorman, *Biochem. Biophys. Research Communs.* **7**, 268 (1962).
231. A. Szeinberg and C. Sheba, *Biol. Abstr.* **33**, 44927 (1959).
232. M. Siniscalco, L. Bernini, B. Latte, and A. G. Motulsky, *Nature* **190**, 1179 (1961).
233. W. H. Zinkham, R. E. Lenhard, Jr., and B. Childs, *Bull. Johns Hopkins Hosp.* **102**, 169 (1958).
234. A. C. Allison, *Nature* **186**, 531 (1960).
235. J. Sonnet and J. L. Michaux, *Nature* **188**, 504 (1960).
236. H. M. Gilles, J. Watson-Williams, and B. C. Taylor, *Nature* **185**, 257 (1960).
237. B. Ramot, C. Sheba, A. Adam, and I. Ashkenazi, *Nature* **185**, 931 (1960).
238. F. Vella, *Experientia* **17**, 181 (1961).
239. B. P. K. Ryan and I. C. Parsons, *Nature* **192**, 477 (1961).
240. C. Kidson, *Nature* **190**, 1120 (1961).
241. P. A. Marks and R. T. Gross, *J. Clin. Invest.* **38**, 2253 (1959).
241a. B. Childs, W. Zinkham, E. A. Browne, E. L. Kimbro, and J. V. Torbert, *Bull. Johns Hopkins Hosp.* **102**, 21 (1958).
242. A. Adam, *Nature* **189**, 686 (1961).
243. I. H. Porter, J. Schulze, and V. A. McKusick, *Nature* **193**, 506 (1962).
244. F. Vella, *Experientia* **16**, 284 (1960).
245. C. Kidson and J. G. Gorman, *Nature* **196**, 49 (1962).
246. P. E. Carson, C. L. Flanagan, C. E. Ickes, and A. S. Alving, *Science* **124**, 484 (1956).
247. A. Bonsignore, G. Fornaini, G. Segni, and A. Seitun, *Biochem. Biophys. Research Communs.* **4**, 147 (1961).
248. R. V. Coxon and R. J. Robinson, *Proc. Roy. Soc.* **B145**, 232 (1956).
249. W. S. Beck, *J. Biol. Chem.* **232**, 271 (1958).

250. W. S. Beck, *Ann. N. Y. Acad. Sci.* **75**, 4 (1958).
251. F. Belfiore, *Chem. Abstr.* **57**, 13085e (1962).
252. R. L. Stjernholm and E. P. Noble, *J. Biol. Chem.* **236**, 614 (1961).
253. R. L. Stjernholm and E. P. Noble, *J. Biol. Chem.* **236**, 3093 (1961).
254. E. P. Noble, R. L. Stjernholm, and L. Ljungdahl, *Biochim. et Biophys. Acta* **49**, 593 (1961).
255. M. Zatti and F. Rossi, *Ital. J. Biochem.* **10**, 19 (1961).
256. M. L. Karnovsky, *Physiol. Revs.* **42**, 143 (1962).
257. W. H. Evans and M. L. Karnovsky, *Biochemistry* **1**, 159 (1962).
258. W. H. Evans and M. L. Karnovsky, *J. Biol. Chem.* **236**, PC30 (1961).
259. S. Kit, J. Klein, and O. L. Graham, *J. Biol. Chem.* **229**, 853 (1957).
260. J. H. Kinoshita and T. Masurat, *Arch. Biochem. Biophys.* **53**, 9 (1954).
261. C. von Holt, H. Lüth, I. Hallmann, L. von Holt, and I. Voelker, *Biochem. Z.* **331**, 239 (1959).
262. J. H. Kinoshita, T. Masurat, and M. Helfant, *Science* **122**, 72 (1955).
263. J. H. Kinoshita, *J. Biol. Chem.* **228**, 247 (1957).
264. J. H. Kinoshita and T. Masurat, *Chem. Abstr.* **54**, 25131g (1960).
265. J. H. Kinoshita and C. Wachtl, *J. Biol. Chem.* **233**, 5 (1958).
266. S. Lerman and F. M. Heggeness, *Biochem. J.* **79**, 224 (1961).
267. S. Lerman, *Nature* **184**, 1406 (1959).
268. W. H. Zinkham, *Bull. Johns Hopkins Hosp.* **109**, 206 (1961).
269. R. Levari, E. Wertheimer, E. R. Berman, and W. Kornblueth, *Nature* **192**, 1075 (1961).
270. S. Futterman and J. H. Kinoshita, *J. Biol. Chem.* **234**, 723 (1959).
271. M. A. Rahman and M. Kerly, *Biochem. J.* **78**, 536 (1961).
272. E. de Berardinis, *Chem. Abstr.* **54**, 15574e (1960).
273. O. H. Lowry, N. R. Roberts, D. W. Schulz, J. E. Clow, and J. R. Clark, *J. Biol. Chem.* **236**, 2813 (1961).
274. R. P. Spencer and W. E. Knox, *Federation Proc.* **19**, 886 (1960).
275. G. Hübscher and H. S. A. Sherratt, *Biochem. J.* **84**, 24P (1962).
276. B. R. Landau and T. H. Wilson, *J. Biol. Chem.* **234**, 749 (1959).
277. R. E. Kay and C. Entenman, *J. Biol. Chem.* **234**, 1634 (1959).
278. U. C. Dubach and L. Recant, *J. Clin. Invest.* **39**, 1364 (1960).
279. G. Weber, *Proc. Soc. Exptl. Biol. Med.* **108**, 631 (1961).
280. R. Hess and A. G. E. Pearse, *Brit J. Exptl. Pathol.* **40**, 243 (1959).
281. J. B. Lee, V. K. Vance, and G. F. Cahill, Jr., *Am. J. Physiol.* **203**, 27 (1962).
282. R. Hess and F. Gross, *Am. J. Physiol.* **197**, 869 (1959).
283. N. C. Ganguli and A. B. Banerjee, *J. Biol. Chem.* **236**, 979 (1961).
284. F. J. Simpsom, *Can. J. Biochem. and Physiol.* **38**, 115 (1960).
285. M. J. Waldvogel and F. Schlenk, *Arch. Biochem.* **22**, 185 (1949).
286. R. von Fellenberg, H. Eppenberger, R. Rictherich, and H. Aebi, *Biochem. Z.* **336**, 334 (1962).
287. G. Weber, G. Banerjee, and S. B. Bronstein, *J. Biol. Chem.* **236**, 3106 (1961).
288. A. Bonsignore, S. Pontremoli, A. de Flora, and B. L. Horecker, *Ital. J. Biochem.* **10**, 106 (1961).
289. M. Kawada, Y. Kagawa, H. Takiguchi, and N. Shimazono, *Biochim. et Biophys. Acta* **57**, 404 (1962).
290. C. H. Gallagher and S. H. Buttery, *Biochem. J.* **72**, 575 (1959).
291. J. R. Murphy and J. A. Muntz, *J. Biol. Chem.* **224**, 971, 987 (1957).
292. J. Tepperman and H. M. Tepperman, *Am. J. Physiol.* **193**, 55 (1958).

293. E. J. Masoro, I. L. Chaikoff, S. S. Chernick, and J. M. Felts, *J. Biol. Chem.* **185**, 845 (1950).
294. J. G. Coniglio, D. L. Cate, B. Benson, and G. W. Hudson, *Am. J. Physiol.* **197**, 674 (1959).
295. I. Knoche and F. Hartmann, *Biochem. Z.* **334**, 269 (1961).
296. G. Weber and H. MacDonald, *Exptl. Cell. Research* **22**, 292 (1961).
297. M. D. Siperstein and V. M. Fagan, *J. Clin. Invest.* **37**, 1196 (1958).
298. J. Tepperman and H. M. Tepperman, *Am. J. Physiol.* **200**, 1069 (1961).
299. S. Abraham, K. J. Matthes, and I. L. Chaikoff, *Biochim. et Biophys. Acta* **36**, 556 (1959).
300. J. M. Lowenstein, *J. Biol. Chem.* **236**, 1213 (1961).
301. S. A. Singal and P. Matthews, *Federation Proc.* **21**, 88 (1962). Abstract.
302. W. M. Fitch, R. Hill, and I. L. Chaikoff, *J. Biol. Chem.* **234**, 1048 (1959).
303. G. Weber, G. Banerjee, and S. B. Bronstein, *Biochem. Biophys. Research Communs.* **4**, 332 (1961).
304. E. J. Masoro, J. M. Felts, and S. S. Panagos, *Am. J. Physiol.* **189**, 479 (1957).
305. J. P. Hannon and D. A. Vaughan, *Am. J. Physiol.* **198**, 375 (1960).
306. J. S. Willmer, *Can. J. Biochem. and Physiol.* **38**, 1449 (1960).
307. H. M. Tepperman and J. Tepperman, *Am. J. Physiol.* **202**, 401 (1962).
308. B. Hellman, S. Larsson, and S. Westman, *Acta Endocrinol.* **39**, 457 (1962).
309. G. F. Cahill, Jr., A. B. Hastings, J. Ashmore, and S. Zottu, *J. Biol. Chem.* **230**, 125 (1958).
310. G. E. Glock and P. McLean, *Biochim. et Biophys. Acta* **12**, 590 (1953).
311. P. McLean, *Biochim. et Biophys. Acta* **30**, 316 (1958).
312. P. McLean, *Biochim. et Biophys. Acta* **30**, 303 (1958).
313. G. E. Glock and P. McLean, *Proc. Roy. Soc.* **B149**, 354 (1958).
314. R. G. Hansen and D. M. Carlson, *in* "Milk: The Mammary Gland and Its Secretion" (S. K. Kon and A. T. Cowie, eds.), Vol. I, p. 371. Academic Press, New York, 1961.
315. T. L. Goodfriend and Y. J. Topper, *J. Biol. Chem.* **236**, 1241 (1961).
316. R. G. Hansen, H. G. Wood, G. J. Peeters, B. Jacobson, and J. Wilken, *J. Biol. Chem.* **237**, 1034 (1962).
317. E. G. Tombropoulos and M. Kleiber, *Biochem. J.* **80**, 414 (1961).
318. S. Abraham, P. Cady, and I. L. Chaikoff, *J. Biol. Chem.* **224**, 955 (1957).
319. P. McLean, *Nature* **183**, 182 (1959).
320. A. N. Weinberg, I. Pastan, H. E. Williams, and J. B. Field, *J. Biol. Chem.* **236**, 1002 (1961).
321. P. McLean, *Biochim. et Biophys. Acta* **42**, 166 (1960).
322. S. Abraham, P. Cady, and I. L. Chaikoff, *Endocrinology* **66**, 280 (1960).
323. J. Cohen, A. R. Brenneman, and Y. J. Topper, *Biochim. et Biophys. Acta* **63**, 554 (1962).
324. I. G. Wool and E. I. Weinshelbaum, *Am. J. Physiol.* **198**, 360 (1960).
325. A. Beloff-Chain, R. Catanzaro, E. B. Chain, L. Longinotti, I. Masi, and F. Pocchiari, *Biochim. et Biophys. Acta* **56**, 153 (1962).
326. F. Dickens and D. H. Williamson, *Biochem. J.* **64**, 567 (1956).
327. E. Racker, *in* "The Enzymes" (P. D. Boyer, H. Lardy, and K. Myrbäck, eds.), Vol. 5, p. 397. Academic Press, New York, 1961.
328. V. Moret and S. Sperti, *Experientia* **15**, 59 (1959).
329. C. Carruthers, "Biochemistry of Skin in Health and Diseases." Charles C Thomas, Springfield, Illinois, 1962.

330. F. B. Hershey, *J. Invest. Dermatol.* **32,** 1 (1959).
331. F. B. Hershey, C. Lewis, Jr., J. Murphy, and T. Schiff, *J. Histochem. and Cytochem.* **8,** 41 (1960).
332. S. H. Pomerantz and M. T. Asbornsen, *Arch. Biochem. Biophys.* **93,** 147 (1961).
333. R. K. Freinkel, *J. Invest. Dermatol.* **34,** 37 (1960).
334. H. J. Yardley and G. Godfrey, *Biochem. J.* **86,** 101 (1963).
335. D. S. Bernstein, B. Leboeuf, and G. F. Cahill, Jr., *Proc. Soc. Exptl. Biol. Med.* **107,** 458 (1961).
336. D. V. Cohn and B. K. Forscher, *J. Biol. Chem.* **237,** 615 (1962).
337. D. V. Cohn and B. K. Forscher, *Biochim. et Biophys. Acta* **65,** 20 (1962).
338. A. C. Aisenberg, "The Glycolysis and Respiration of Tumors." Academic Press, New York, 1961.
339. H. Busch, E. Fujiwara, and L. M. Keer, *Cancer Research* **20,** 50 (1960).
340. J. Ashmore, G. Weber, and B. R. Landau, *Cancer Research* **18,** 974 (1958).
341. S. Abraham, I. L. Chaikoff, and P. Cady, *Cancer Research* **21,** 938 (1961).
342. G. Weber, *Advances in Cancer Research* **6,** 403 (1961).
343. G. Weber and H. P. Morris, *Proc. Am. Assoc. Cancer Research* **3,** 370 (1962).
344. A. K. Belousova, *Biochemistry* (*U. S. S. R.*) (*Engl. Transl.*) **25,** 698 (1961).
345. D. B. Ellis and P. G. Scholefield, *Can. J. Biochem. and Physiol.* **40,** 343 (1962).
346. B. L. Horecker, G. Domagk, and H. H. Hiatt, *Arch. Biochem. Biophys.* **78,** 510 (1958).
347. E. Racker, *J. Biol. Chem.* **196,** 347 (1952).
348. W. S. Beck, *in* "Cell Physiology of Neoplasia," p. 374. Univ. of Texas Press, Austin, Texas, 1960.
349. E. S. G. Barron, M. Villavicencio, and D. W. King, Jr., *Arch. Biochem. Biophys.* **58,** 500 (1955).
350. W. Nagel, N. Sanpitak, and F. Willig, *Z. physiol. Chem. Hoppe-Seyler's* **326,** 1 (1961).
351. R. Wu, *Cancer Research* **19,** 1217 (1959).
352. D. B. M. Scott, A. L. Morris, A. B. Reiskin, and A. M. Pakoskey, *Cancer Research* **22,** 857 (1962).
353. E. Schmidt and F. W. Schmidt, *Klin. Wochschr.* **38,** 957 (1960).
354. D. B. M. Scott, *Chem. Abstr.* **54,** 25153h (1960).
355. D. O. de Shazer, *J. Dental Research* **41,** 986 (1962).
356. M. Brin, *J. Nutrition* **78,** 179 (1962).
357. H.-G. Sie, V. N. Nigam, and W. H. Fishman, *Biochim. et Biophys. Acta* **50,** 277 (1961).
358. G. Ashwell and J. Hickman, *J. Am. Chem. Soc.* **77,** 1062 (1955).
359. G. Ashwell and J. Hickman, *J. Biol. Chem.* **226,** 65 (1957).
360. H. H. Hiatt and J. Lareau, *J. Biol. Chem.* **235,** 1241 (1960).
361. P. M. Roll, H. Weinfeld, E. Carroll, and G. B. Brown, *J. Biol. Chem.* **220,** 439 (1956).
362. C. A. Villee and J. M. Loring, *Biochem. J.* **81,** 488 (1961).
363. M. A. Lea and D. G. Walker, *Biochem. J.* **85,** 30P (1962).
364. L. Stevens, *Comp. Biochem. Physiol.* **6,** 129 (1962).
365. H. B. Burch, E. G. Diamant, A. M. Kuhlman, and J. Skerjance, *Federation Proc.* **20,** 80 (1961).
366. U. Stave, *Biol. Neonatorum* **2,** 18 (1960).

367. G. W. Löhr and H. D. Waller, *Klin. Wochschr.* **37,** 833 (1959).
368. M. K. Johnson and E. J. Johnson, *Proc. Soc. Exptl. Biol. Med.* **111,** 149 (1962).
369. J. L. Conklin, M. M. Dewey, and R. H. Kahn, *Am. J. Anat.* **110,** 19 (1962).
370. V. B. Slotnick, *Nature* **193,** 876 (1962).
371. S. M. Gartler, E. Gandini, and R. Ceppellini, *Nature* **193,** 602 (1962).
372. N. Bargoni, *Z. physiol. Chem. Hoppe-Seyler's* **312,** 154 (1958).
373. A. Colajacomo, I. Bologna, and R. Bardellini, *Chem. Abstr.* **55,** 24959c (1961).
374. I. A. Bernstein, *J. Biol. Chem.* **205,** 317 (1953).
375. G. Weber, G. Banerjee, D. Bixler, and J. Ashmore, *J. Nutrition* **74,** 157 (1961).
376. E. Kun, J. E. Ayling, and B. V. Siegel, *Proc. Natl. Acad. Sci. U. S.* **46,** 622 (1960).
377. G. Weber, G. Banerjee, A. S. Levine, and J. Ashmore, *J. Natl. Cancer Inst.* **27,** 869 (1961).
378. A. Cazorla and E. S. G. Barron, *Exptl. Cell Research* **14,** 68 (1958).
379. W. C. Mahaffey, *Federation Proc.* **20,** 83 (1961).
380. J. Ashmore, G. Weber, G. Banerjee, and W. C. Love, *J. Natl. Cancer Inst.* **27,** 863 (1961).
381. A. S. Levine, R. Uhl, and J. Ashmore, *J. Natl. Cancer Inst.* **27,** 597 (1961).
382. P. Reichard, *Biochim. et Biophys. Acta* **27,** 434 (1958).
383. J. A. Lucy, M. Webb, and J. D. Biggers, *Biochim. et Biophys. Acta* **54,** 259 (1961).
384. F. C. G. Hoskin, *Arch. Biochem. Biophys.* **85,** 141 (1959).
385. S. S. Cohen, *Biol. Bull.* **99,** 369 (1950).
386. N. de Groot and P. P. Cohen, *Biochim. et Biophys. Acta* **59,** 588 (1962).
387. P. W. Hochachka, *Can. J. Biochem. and Physiol.* **39,** 1937 (1961).
388. P. W. Hochachka and F. R. Hayes, *Can. J. Zool.* **40,** 261 (1962).
389. H. L. A. Tarr, *Can. J. Biochem. and Physiol.* **41,** 313 (1963).
390. W. D. Brown, *J. Cellular Comp. Physiol.* **55,** 81 (1960).
391. H. L. A. Tarr, *Can. J. Biochem. and Physiol.* **37,** 961 (1959).
392. V. R. Meenakshi and B. T. Scheer, *Comp. Biochem. Physiol.* **3,** 30 (1961).
393. P. W. Bergreen, V. R. Meenakshi, and B. T. Scheer, *Comp. Biochem. Physiol.* **2,** 218 (1961).
394. M. A. McWhinnie and R. J. Kirchenberg, *Comp. Biochem. Physiol.* **6,** 117 (1962).
395. D. Gilmour, "The Biochemistry of Insects," p. 82. Academic Press, New York, 1961.
396. W. Chefurka, *Enzymologia* **18,** 209 (1957).
397. W. Chefurka, *Can. J. Biochem. and Physiol.* **36,** 83 (1958).
398. M. Agosin, N. Scaramelli, and A. Neghme, *Comp. Biochem. Physiol.* **2,** 143 (1961).
399. T. Ito and Y. Horie, *Arch. Biochem. Biophys.* **80,** 174 (1959).
400. G. M. Silva, W. P. Doyle, and C. H. Wang, *Nature* **182,** 102 (1958).
401. S. S. Cohen, *Biol. Bull.* **101,** 237 (1951).
402. J. de Ley and R. Vercruysse, *Biochim. et Biophys. Acta* **16,** 615 (1955).
403. N. R. Roberts, R. R. Coelho, O. H. Lowry, and E. J. Crawford, *J. Neurochem.* **3,** 109 (1958).
404. H. J. Horstmann, *Z. physiol. Chem. Hoppe-Seyler's* **319,** 120 (1960).
404a. C. G. Beames, Jr., *Comp. Biochem. and Physiol.* **8,** 109 (1963).

405. O. Lindberg, *Arkiv Kemi Mineral. Geol.* **16A**, No. 15 (1943).
406. M. E. Krahl, A. K. Keltch, C. P. Walters, and G. H. A. Clowes, *J. Gen. Physiol.* **38**, 431 (1955).
407. S. Bäckström, *Exptl. Cell Research* **18**, 347 (1959).
408. M. Agosin and L. C. Aravena, *Exptl. Parasitol.* **8**, 10 (1959).
409. L. R. Krusberg, *Phytopathology* **50**, 9 (1960).
410. N. Entner, *Arch. Biochem. Biophys.* **71**, 52 (1957).
411. N. Entner and C. Gonzalez, *Exptl. Parasitol.* **8**, 471 (1959).
412. M. Agosin and L. Aravena, *Exptl. Parasitol.* **10**, 28 (1960).
413. M. Agosin and L. Aravena, *Enzymologia* **22**, 281 (1960).
414. D. M. Hilker and A. G. C. White, *Exptl. Parasitol.* **8**, 539 (1959).
415. D. M. Hilker, *Dissertation Abstr.* **19**, 3112 (1959).
416. P. D. Bragg and R. E. Reeves, *Exptl. Parasitol.* **12**, 393 (1962).
417. R. E. Reeves, P. D. Bragg, and N. G. Latour, *Federation Proc.* **21**, 83 (1962).
418. P. D. Bragg and R. E. Reeves, *J. Bacteriol.* **83**, 76 (1962).
419. K. Borner and H. Mattenheimer, *Biochim. et Biophys. Acta* **34**, 592 (1959).
420. J. F. Ryley, *Biochem. J.* **85**, 211 (1962).
421. V. H. Cheldelin, C. H. Wang, and T. E. King, *in* "Comparative Biochemistry" (M. Florkin and H. S. Mason, eds.), Vol. III, p. 427. Academic Press, New York, 1962.
422. A. C. Zagallo and C. H. Wang, *J. Gen. Microbiol.* **29**, 389 (1962).
423. R. G. Eagon and C. H. Wang, *Bacteriol. Proc.* (*Soc. Am. Bacteriologists*) **62**, 113 (1962).
424. J. R. Quayle, *Ann. Rev. Microbiol.* **15**, 119 (1961).
425. R. C. Fuller and M. Gibbs, *Plant Physiol.* **34**, 324 (1959).
426. W. Vishniac, B. L. Horecker, and S. Ochoa, *Advances in Enzymol.* **19**, 1 (1957).
427. M. Santer and W. Vishniac, *Biochim. et Biophys. Acta* **18**, 157 (1955).
428. P. A. Trudinger, *Biochem. J.* **64**, 274 (1956).
429. I. Suzuki and C. H. Werkman, *Arch. Biochem. Biophys.* **77**, 112 (1958).
430. H. Iwatsuka, M. Kuno, and M. Maruyama, *Plant and Cell Physiol.* **3**, 157 (1962).
431. H. L. Kornberg, J. F. Collins, and D. Bigley, *Biochim. et Biophys. Acta* **39**, 9 (1960).
432. J. R. Quayle and D. B. Keech, *Biochim. et Biophys. Acta* **31**, 587 (1959).
433. E. Malavota, C. C. Delwiche, and W. D. Burge, *Biochem. Biophys. Research Communs.* **2**, 445 (1960).
434. B. A. McFadden, *J. Bacteriol.* **77**, 339 (1959).
435. F. H. Bergmann, J. C. Towne, and R. H. Burris, *J. Biol. Chem.* **230**, 13 (1958).
436. V. A. Khoudokormoff, *Ann. inst. Pasteur* **100**, 257 (1961).
437. S. R. Elsden, *in* "The Bacteria" (I. C. Gunsalus and R. Y. Stanier, eds.), Vol. III, p. 1. Academic Press, New York, 1962.
438. J. Lascelles, *J. Gen. Microbiol.* **23**, 499 (1960).
439. A. O. M. Stoppani, R. C. Fuller, and M. Calvin, *J. Bacteriol.* **69**, 491 (1955).
440. M. Szymona and M. Doudoroff, *J. Gen. Microbiol.* **22**, 167 (1960).
441. J. de Ley, *Proc. Intern. Congr. Biochem. 3rd Congr., Brussels, 1955,* p. 182 (1956).
442. E. Racker, *in* "The Enzymes" (P. D. Boyer, H. Lardy, and K. Myrbäck, eds.), Vol. V, p. 407. Academic Press, New York, 1961.

443. P. J. Casselton and P. J. Syrett, *Ann. Botany* [N.S.] **26,** 71 (1962).
444. G. Jacobi, *Planta* **49,** 1 (1957).
445. P. J. Casselton and P. J. Syrett, *Ann. Botany* [N.S.] **26,** 83 (1962).
446. G. Jacobi, *in* "Physiology and Biochemistry of Algae" (R. A. Lewin, ed.), p. 130. Academic Press, New York, 1962.
447. G. Richter, *Z. Naturforsch.* **12b,** 662 (1957).
448. R. E. Hurlbert and S. C. Rittenberg, *J. Protozool.* **9,** 170 (1962).
449. O. Ciferri, *Enzymologia* **24,** 283 (1962).
450. S.-N. C. Barry, *J. Protozool.* **9,** 395 (1962).
451. L. Norris, R. E. Norris, and M. Calvin, *J. Exptl. Botany* **6,** 64 (1955).
452. R. C. Fuller and M. Gibbs, *Plant Physiol.* **31,** xxxi (1956).
453. R. C. Bean and W. Z. Hassid, *J. Biol. Chem.* **212,** 411 (1955).
454. R. P. Levine, *Proc. Natl. Acad. Sci. U. S.* **46,** 972 (1960).
455. V. H. Lynch and M. Calvin, *Ann. N. Y. Acad. Sci.* **56,** 890 (1953).
456. O. Kandler, I. Lissenkötter, and B. A. Oaks, *Z. Naturforsch.* **16b,** 50 (1961).
457. E. C. Wassink, *in* "Comparative Biochemistry" (M. Florkin and H. S. Mason, eds.), Vol. V, p. 347. Academic Press, New York, 1963.
458. H. P. Meloche and W. A. Wood, *Bacteriol. Proc.* (*Soc. Am. Bacteriologists*) **62,** 111 (1962).
459. B. Axelrod and R. Jang, *J. Biol. Chem.* **209,** 847 (1954).
460. A. Bevenue, L. M. White, G. E. Secor, and K. T. Williams, *J. Assoc. Offic. Agr. Chemists* **44,** 265 (1961).
461. F. A. Loewus, *Ann. N. Y. Acad. Sci.* **92,** 57 (1961).
462. C. H. Wang, W. P. Doyle, and J. C. Ramsey, *Plant Physiol.* **37,** 1 (1962).
463. W. P. Doyle and C. H. Wang, *Can. J. Botany* **36,** 483 (1958).
464. R. D. Barbour, D. R. Buhler, and C. H. Wang, *Plant Physiol.* **33,** 396 (1958).
465. J. M. Tager, *Chem. Abstr.* **51,** 16749f (1957).
466. B. L. Horecker and P. Z. Smyrniotis, *in* "Methods in Enzymology" (S. P. Colowick and N. O. Kaplan, eds.), Vol. I, p. 371. Academic Press, New York, 1955.
467. J. Hurwitz and B. L. Horecker, *J. Biol. Chem.* **223,** 993 (1956).
468. R. M. Smillie, *Plant Physiol.* **37,** 716 (1962).
469. F. Solymosy and G. L. Farkas, *Nature* **195,** 835 (1962).
470. R. H. Hageman and E. R. Waygood, *Plant Physiol.* **34,** 396 (1959).
471. F. B. LaForge and C. S. Hudson, *J. Biol. Chem.* **30,** 61 (1917).
472. V. V. Rendig and E. A. McComb, *Arch. Biochem. Biophys.* **89,** 323 (1960).
473. R. A. Clayton, *Arch. Biochem. Biophys.* **79,** 111 (1959).
474. G. Maclachlan and H. K. Porter, *Biochim. et Biophys. Acta* **46,** 244 (1961).
475. M. Gibbs and B. L. Horecker, *J. Biol. Chem.* **208,** 813 (1954).
476. C. W. Ross, H. H. Wiebe, and G. W. Miller, *Plant Physiol.* **37,** 305 (1962).
477. S. C. Fang, F. Teeny, and J. S. Butts, *Plant Physiol.* **35,** 405 (1960).
478. O. Servettaz, *Chem. Abstr.* **50,** 13187g (1956).
479. T. A. Rees and H. Beevers, *Plant Physiol.* **35,** 830 (1960).
480. T. A. Rees and H. Beevers, *Plant Physiol.* **35,** 839 (1960).
481. J. A. Romberger and G. Norton, *Plant Physiol.* **34,** xii (1959).
482. V. S. Butt and H. Beevers, *Biochem. J.* **80,** 21 (1961).
483. C. C. Black, Jr., and T. E. Humphreys, *Plant Physiol.* **37,** 66 (1962).
484. M. Gibbs, J. M. Earl, and J. L. Ritchie, *Plant Physiol.* **30,** 463 (1955).
485. T. E. Humphreys and W. M. Dugger, Jr., *Plant Physiol.* **32,** 136 (1957).
486. N. T. Mirov and R. G. Stanley, *Ann. Rev. Plant Physiol.* **10,** 223 (1959).

487. D. J. Reed, *Plant Physiol.* **36,** xxxii (1961).
488. M. Chakravorty and D. P. Burma, *Biochem. J.* **73,** 48 (1959).
489. E. E. Conn and B. Vennesland, *J. Biol. Chem.* **192,** 17 (1951).
490. M. Gibbs and J. M. Earl, *Plant Physiol.* **34,** 529 (1959).
491. B. A. Rubin and O. L. Ozeretskovskaya, *Doklady Akad. Nauk S.S.S.R.* **133,** 976 (1960).
492. J. M. Daly, R. M. Sayre, and J. H. Pazur, *Plant Physiol.* **32,** 44 (1957).
493. J. M. Daly, R. E. Inman, and A. Livne, *Plant Physiol.* **37,** 531 (1962).
494. H. Beevers and M. Gibbs, *Plant Physiol.* **29,** 322 (1954).
495. A. A. Benson, J. A. Bassham, M. Calvin, A. G. Hall, H. E. Hirsch, S. Kawaguchi, V. Lynch, and N. E. Tolbert, *J. Biol. Chem.* **196,** 703 (1952).
496. S. L. Ranson and M. Thomas, *Ann. Rev. Plant Physiol.* **11,** 81 (1960).
497. F. R. Whatley, M. B. Allen, L. L. Rosenberg, J. B. Capindale, and D. I. Arnon, *Biochim. et Biophys. Acta* **20,** 462 (1956).
498. O. Holm-Hansen, N. G. Pon, K. Nishida, V. Moses, and M. Calvin, *Physiol. Plantarum* **12,** 475 (1959).
499. M. Gibbs, C. C. Black, and B. Kok, *Biochim. et Biophys. Acta* **52,** 474 (1961).
500. U. Heber and E. Tyszkiewicz, *J. Exptl. Botany* **13,** 185 (1962).
501. A. V. Trebst, H. Y. Tsujimoto, and D. I. Arnon, *Nature* **182,** 351 (1958).
502. R. B. Park and N. G. Pon, *J. Mol. Biol.* **3,** 1 (1961).
503. F. R. Whatley, M. B. Allen, A. V. Trebst, and D. I. Arnon, *Plant Physiol.* **35,** 188 (1960).
504. J. W. Lyttleton and P. O. P. Ts'o, *Arch. Biochem. Biophys.* **73,** 120 (1958).
505. A. Weissbach, B. L. Horecker, and J. Hurwitz, *J. Biol. Chem.* **218,** 795 (1956).
506. R. C. Huffaker and A. Wallace, *Proc. Am. Soc. Hort. Sci.* **74,** 348 (1959).
507. M. M. Margulies, *Plant Physiol.* **36,** L (1961).
508. D. O. Hall, R. C. Huffaker, L. M. Shannon, and A. Wallace, *Biochim. et Biophys. Acta* **35,** 540 (1959).
509. B. L. Horecker, J. Hurwitz, and A. Weissbach, *J. Biol. Chem.* **218,** 785 (1956).
510. B. L. Horecker, *Comp. Biochem. Physiol.* **4,** 363 (1962).

CHAPTER 2

Chitin and Mucosubstances

P. W. Kent

Department of Biochemistry, University of Oxford, Oxford, England

I. Introduction

In 1799, Hachett (*1*) decalcified shells of crabs, lobsters, prawns, and crayfish with mineral acids, observing that they "produced a moderate effervescence and in a short time were found to be soft and plastic of a yellowish color and like a cartilage, which retained the original figure." Although this is the first mention of calcified chitin in invertebrates, its recognition is usually ascribed to Odier (*2*) in 1823, who obtained a hornlike material after treatment of cockchafer elytra with potassium hydroxide and proposed the name *chitin*. The nitrogenous nature of chitin was revealed by the experiments of Children (*3*) in 1825. Until quite recently these methods for isolating "pure" chitin by decalcification with acids and deproteinization with alkalis have continued virtually unchanged. It is now evident that chitin, considered exclusively as a polysaccharide, is not normally found, and *in situ* it is associated with other substances, notably proteins, by hydrogen bonds and covalent linkages. A convenient method of distinction proposed by Hackman (*4*) reserves the name *chitin* for the chemically purified material and *native chitin* for the complex in which it is involved in tissues.

The chemical structure of chitin is generally agreed to be that of an unbranched polysaccharide in which *N*-acetyl-D-glucosamine (2-acetamido-2-deoxy-D-glucopyranose) residues are linked in the β-($1 \rightarrow 4$) positions (Fig. 1).

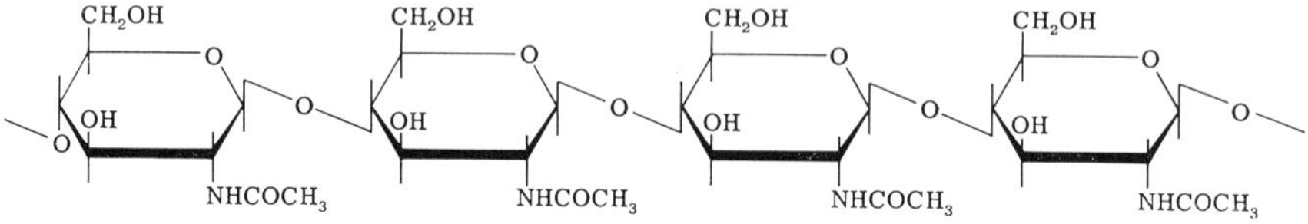

Fig. 1. Structure of chitin.

The use of X-ray diffraction analysis in the study of chitin represents one of the earliest applications of this technique to a problem of macromolecular structure, and the results have been of great value not only in confirming the type of glycosidic attachments, but also in elucidating the molecular interactions that contribute to the high tensile strength of chitin fibers. Furthermore, X-ray diffraction techniques serve to show the close similarities in the macromolecular dispositions of chitin and the identically linked cellulose.

There is a copious literature on the occurrence of chitin in a great diversity of different species. Much of this is based on older techniques of histochemistry, and in the majority of cases there is need for reinvestigation with modern techniques to which study of specific enzymes and degradative procedures have contributed. Here again X-ray diffraction techniques provide valuable information, particularly when used in conjunction with other methods of investigation.

This comparative survey of the structure and functions of chitin is compiled as a study in molecular biology, of which it is now almost a classical example.

Chitin is outstanding in its stability and is of considerable interest in that it survives in fossils (*5 7*), particularly in mollusks, in which it has been detected in the shell.

A number of general reviews of chitin are available: chemical aspects are dealt with by Meyer (*8*), Whistler and Smart (*9*), Kent and Whitehouse (*10*), and Foster and Webber (*11*), and biological aspects by Richards (*12, 13*), Wigglesworth (*14*), Picken (*15*), and Rudall (*12a*).

II. Distribution of Chitin

A. In Microorganisms

Although there is extensive evidence of the presence of D-glucosamine in many types of microorganisms and of their ability to synthesize this sugar and to incorporate it into polysaccharides and other carbohydrate-containing polymers, there is little information concerning the presence of chitin. Its presence in Saccharomycetes is still controversial. Greater diversity exists among microorganisms in the number and variety of amino sugars synthesized (*16*) in contrast to higher living forms. Not only are D-glucosamine and D-galactosamine found, but also such sugars as D-fucosamine (2-amino-2-deoxy-D-fucose), D-galactosaminouronic acid, and neuraminic acids (*17–19*).

These occur with other sugars generally as constituents of bacterial polysaccharides (*20, 21*) which, though associated with the bacterial cell wall, are not generally considered to be part of it. An amino sugar polymer, colominic acid, synthesized by *Escherichia coli* K253, is comprised of *N*-acetylneuraminic acid residues glycosidically linked (*22*). There is evidence of the presence of this material also in other species, e.g., *Citrobacter freundii*. There is no morphological basis for comparison of colominic acid with chitin, nor reason to associate it with the structure of bacterial cell walls.

With the development of new methods of isolation of cell wall components (*23*), evidence suggests that gram-positive organisms, as in Actinomycetales, possess a basal cell-wall membrane in which amino sugars including muramic acid participate. This membrane may indeed play a structural role analogous to that of chitin, but decisive evidence on this is not yet available.

Elsewhere, there is increasing evidence (*24*) of the importance of complex phosphorylated molecules, teichoic acids, in bacterial cell walls. These substances, accounting for 40–60% of the cell wall of *Lactobacillus arabinosus*, *Bacillus subtilis*, *Staphylococcus aureus*, and *Staphylococcus albus*, are comprised of a main chain of polyglycerol or polyribitol phosphates to which amino sugars and amino acids are attached as side groups. Thus, the teichoic acid from *S. albus* H is a ribitol phosphate polymer with *N*-acetylglucosamine residues located at position 4 of each ribitol unit. D-Alanine residues are attached at position 2 or 3 of ribitol (Fig. 2).

In *S. lactis* N.T.C.C. 7944, the teichoic acid consists of a chain of

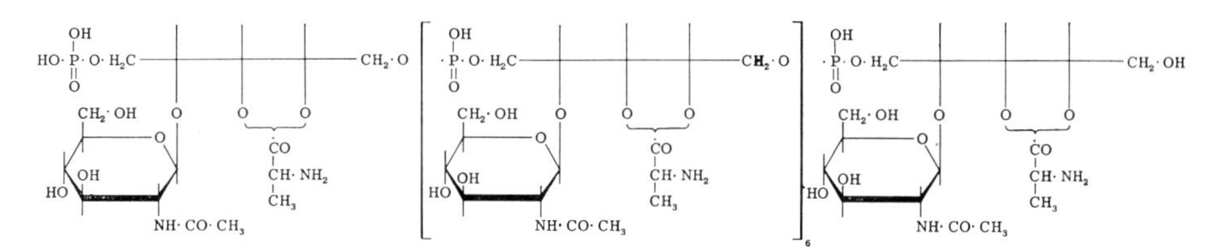

FIG. 2. Teichoic acid from cell wall of *Staphylococcus aureus*.

polyglycerol phosphate carrying D-alanine and *N*-acetyl-D-galactosamine as side groups attached at position 2 of the glycerol residues (*25*). Although residues occur in pairs and an amino-sugar residue on every third glycerol residue, titration, phosphatase action, and periodate oxidation indicate that these chains are composed of about 18 units (Fig. 3).

```
        CH3                                              CH3
        |                                                |
        CH·NH2                                           CH·NH2
        |                                                |
        CO                                               CO
        |                                                |
  OH    O            OH          OR          OH          O
  |     |            |           |           |           |
-----P·O·H2C—+—CH2·O·P·O·H2C—+—CH2·O·P·O·H2C—+—CH2·O-----
  ||                 ||                      ||
  O                  O                       O
```

FIG. 3. Teichoic acids from *Lactobacillus arabinosus* (intracellular, R = α-D-glucosyl) and *Staphylococcus albus* (wall, R = α-D-*N*-acetylgalactosaminyl).

These cell wall constituents [reviewed by Baddiley (*26*)] occur intracellularly also and do not seem to be associated with mucopeptide. The complex structures of the teichoic acids contrast sharply with the relatively simple structure of chitin and points to the distinctive elaboration of microbial biosynthetic functions.

Mention must also be made of muramic acid (3-*O*-α-carbethoxy-D-glucosamine) an amino sugar detectable in hydrolyzates of the cell walls of many strains of bacteria (*27, 28*) [*Corynebacterium, Lactobacillus, Streptococcus, Staphylococcus,* and other gram-positive organisms (*29,*

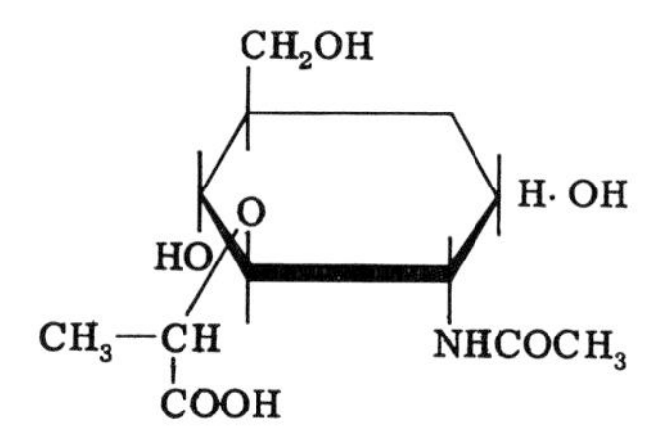

FIG. 4. Muramic acid.

30)]. It has been found also in the cell walls of *Micrococcus lysodeikticus* as well as in the spore peptides of *Bacillus megatherium* (*31*). Its presence is not confined to the gram-positive group; it has been detected in gram-negative *E. coli.* Muramic acid (Fig. 4) is not known to function as a structural unit in polysaccharides, nevertheless it is clearly intimately connected with the cell walls of many, if not all, bacteria.

B. IN PLANTS

Fungal chitin, first recognized (*32*) in 1811 as an alkali-resistant substance under the name "fungine," appears to be confined to fungi and green algae (Chlorophyceae). Elsewhere, in plants, cellulose provides the principal mechanical support. All fungi, with the exception of Oomycetaceae, Monoblepharideae, and Laboulbeniales contain chitin. By X-ray diffraction methods, chitin from the sporangiophores of *Phycomyces blakesleeanus* displayed a structure closely similar to that of the crustacean *Palinurus vulgaris*. In general, fungal chitin appears to be identical with that isolated from crustacea; like cuticular chitin, it has been found in highly oriented molecular forms. In view of the close molecular similarity of chitin and cellulose at the macromolecular level, it is tempting to consider them as biological alternatives, as for instance for the phylogenetic classification of related groups, particularly of fungi (*33*). *Actinomyces nocardia*, and species of *Streptomyces* and *Micromonosperma* are all devoid of both chitin and cellulose and may be thus considered to be more closely related to bacteria than to fungi.

Chitin in small amounts has been reported in the cell wall of many species of yeast (*34, 35*) and in *Nadsonia fulvescens*, *Rhodotorula glutinis*, and *Sporobolomyces roseus*, where it comprises about 10% of the walls (*36*).

The amount of chitin in fungal walls varies between traces and 50–60% of the dry weight. In the mushroom a yield of 35% chitin was obtained, and its identity was confirmed by X-ray diffraction. As in cuticle, fungal chitin is associated with other substances, mainly carbohydrate, in the cell walls.

General reviews of fungal chitin have been compiled by Tracey (*37*) and by Foster and Stacey (*38*).

C. In Animals

Chitin is commonly found in the supporting tissues of invertebrate animals; it is rarely found in chordates. It can occur both as "soft" chitin (as in wing hinges of locusts) or, as in arthropod cuticle, hardened by mineralization or sclerotization. In either form it is found mostly in invertebrate exoskeletons, and in tendons, gut lining, and egg shells.

Chitin is absent from all Protozoa and, in general, from Porifera, though it is reported in the gemmules of the freshwater sponge *Spongilla*. Among Coelenterata, it is reported from the perisarc of hydromedusae (even from the fossil *Graptozoa*). Genera without a perisarc, on the other hand, do not give reactions of chitinous material. It has not yet been detected in Ctenophora, nor is it known from the body covering of flatworms (Platyhelminthes), roundworms (Nematoda), nor Acanthocephala, but it occurs in their egg shells. There are no reports of chitin from the body walls of annelid worms, but it does occur in jaws, gut lining, and setae. In the Mollusca, chitin occurs in the internal skeleton of cephalopods and in the radulae of Gastropods. It is also found in the exoskeletons of most Ectoprocta and in Pogonophora.

Extensive reviews of the distribution of chitin over wide ranges of animals are available, notably by the following authors: Biedermann (*39*), Kunike (*40*), Campbell (*41*), Koch (*42*), Wigglesworth (*14*), Richards (*12*) and Rudall (*12a*). Many surveys employed classical methods of detection and, with the advent of more precise procedures, confirmation seems to be very desirable in the majority of cases.

In the Arthropoda, chitin is not uniformly distributed throughout the cuticle but is localized in the inner layer, the procuticle. The outer layer (epicuticle) is invariably free from chitin. All arthropod cuticles exhibit zonal structure, though there is some difference in the nomenclature applied to the strata. The general scheme (I) of classification of the cuticular subdivision was proposed by Richards (*12*):

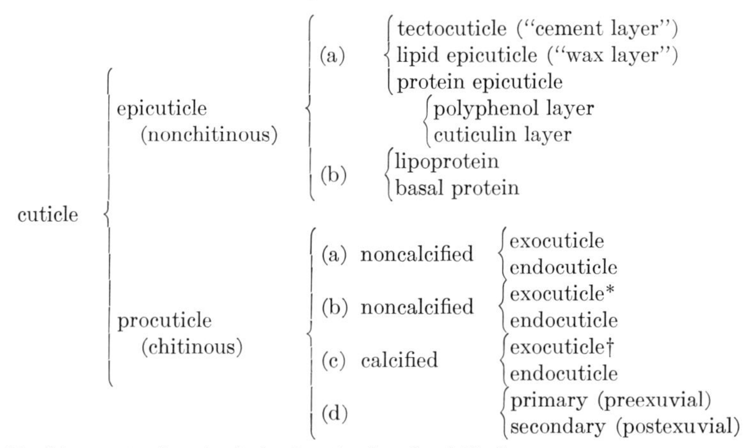

* Hard but not sclerotized; † sclerotized and calcified.

SCHEME I
(Courtesy University of Minnesota Press.)

The major subdivision is thus into epicuticle and procuticle (*14*), both of which derive from an epidermal cellular layer. There may be also associated with this, unicellular glands (tegumental and dermal glands) concerned with cuticle production and connected to the exterior by minute ducts. A semidiagrammatic representation of the cuticular structure of *Rhodnius prolixus* is given in Fig. 5.

Hardening takes place in the procuticular region, the outer portion of which may become hard and dark due to sclerotization leaving lower layers transparent and soft. It is uncertain where the enzymes for this process arise, but it is not improbable that they are secreted into the procuticle by the epidermis and that the more ready access of necessary atmospheric oxygen (*43*) to its outer boundary results in the topographical sclerotization observed. In calcified chitin, as in Crustacea, the exocuticle and outer part of the endocuticle are sites of mineralization.

Chitin is present in the procuticle, and it is with this layer (its substrata) and the epidermis from which it is derived, that the present review is concerned. The procuticle, when more than a few microns thick, shows internal laminations visible microscopically in cross sections, particularly so in polarized light. The thickness of these layers varies not

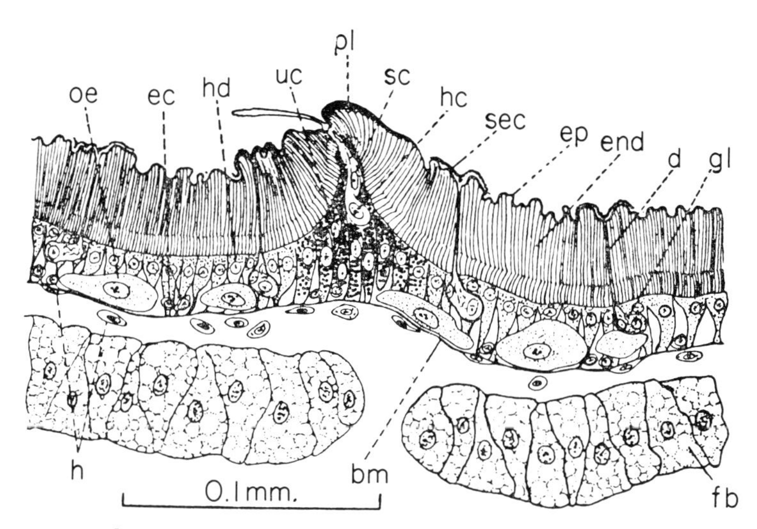

FIG. 5. Semidiagrammatic longitudinal section of the tergites of a fourth instar nymph of *Rhodnius prolixus*. *bm*, Basement membrane; *d*, duct of dermal gland; *ec*, "embryonic cells"; *end*, endocuticle; *ep*, epicuticle; *fb*, fat body (adipose tissue); *gl*, dermal gland; *h*, hematocytes or blood cells; *hc*, trichogen (hair-forming cell); *hd*, epidermal cells; *oe*, oenocytes; *pl*, plaque bearing a bristle; *sc*, tormogen (socket-forming) cell; *sec*, secretion of dermal gland; *uc*, urate cells. After Wigglesworth (*14*). (Courtesy Oxford University Press.)

only from one species to another (e.g., 0.01 μ in *Peripatus* to several millimeters in moist cuticle of *Limulus*), but during growth. The larval cuticle of *Bombyx* increases from 10 μ to 40 μ, and that of *Sarcophaga*, from 10 μ to 240 μ during the instar (*44*). The procuticle can be considered as a secretory product of the epidermis, although instances are known in which polymerization continues when the layer is not in contact with the secretory cells (*44, 45*). The lamellae in procuticle are true layers (0.2–10 μ) since they can be stripped one from another in swollen cuticle and comprise alternating layers of optically dense and less dense materials. Lamination, Picken maintains, is not due to periodic deposition of different chemical entities in alternation, and it is suggested that the lamination arises from mechanical forces influencing the orientation of chitin crystallites during deposition.

A résumé of the chitin-bearing species among the Arthropoda has been made by Richards (*12*).

III. Molecular Structure and Function of Chitin

A. Physical Structure and Properties

Investigations of the precise macromolecular relationships of chitin are beset by problems due to insolubility of the material and to difficulties of bringing it into solution without degradation. The chemical evidence favors a linear polysaccharide in which 2-acetamido-2-deoxy-β-D-glucosyl residues are linked through the 4-positions. In general principle, chitobiose comprises the structural repeating unit though there is as yet no firm evidence about the chain length of chitin nor whether all chains are identically constituted. The macrostructure thus appears to have features in common with the fiber structure of cellulose, supplemented with enhanced possibilities of intercalary hydrogen bonding of adjacent *N*-acetyl groups. The tensile strength of purified chitin is reported to vary with the source and with moisture content, in the dry state having values (*46, 47*) up to 35–38 kg./mm. and when moist (*48*), 1.8 kg./mm.; in these respects it is a fibrous material stronger than hair or silk fibroin. As with cellulose (*49*) and silk fibroin (*50*), the density of chitin (*51*) (1.41–1.42) also varies with source and moisture content. Further mechanical properties of chitin, in particular elasticity, hardness, swelling, and optical properties, have been reviewed by Richards (*12, 13*).

The optical rotation of chitin has not been extensively studied, although it is known (*52*) that "solutions" of the material in concentrated hydrochloric acid exhibit values of $[\alpha]_D^{20}$—14°; degradation must be presumed to have commenced under these conditions, however.

Birefringence [earlier work being reviewed by Frey-Wyssling (*53*)] has been much used in examining the lamellar distribution of chitin. Since the first observation (*54*) of the birefringent properties of chitinous tendons, the property has provided extensive data regarding the direction and degree of orientation of anisotropic chitin molecules. It is of particular importance that observations are concerned with chitin *in situ*, that is, not merely with poly-(*N*-acetylglucosamine), but with the protein-polysaccharide or other complex structures in which it is combined (see page 119). Whatever may the nature be of such complexes, it is clear that these form a variety of higher states of aggregation (*55–59*), ranging from micelles to microfibers (70–200 Å.) and in cuticle, to microscopically visible fibers ("*Balken*"). This view receives substantial support from direct electron and ultraviolet microscopic examinations.

It is believed that, the optical axis being aligned with the micellar axis, the micelles are in many cases of cuticular chitin, arranged in part, parallel to the surface. Higher degrees of orientation are reported in setae (*60, 61*) and in muscle tendons (*62*).

1. *Orientation of Chitin Fibers*

The visible laminated structure of anthropod cuticle appears to arise from alternating layers of greater and less density rather than from different chemical constituents (*63*), the layers varying (*64*) in thickness between 0.2 μ and 10 μ. In *Schistocerca gregaria* Forskål, the rubberlike ligaments of the prealar arm has a lamellar structure in which chitin is reported to be interconnected with resilin. Similar regions were reported (*65*) in the main hinge of the forewings. The chitin deposition in this rubberlike cuticle, in which pore canals are absent, is quantal in nature, each postimaginal lamella arising from the secretion of a constant amount of chitin. In these locust tissues, the frequency of lamella formation declines with age. In *Sarcophaga,* the outer zone of the procuticle increases in thickness and laminates after separation from epithelium (epidermis) by new endocuticle. The formation of lamellae does not appear to be dependent on immediate contact with cells, or alternatively their formation involves diffusion and deposition processes. The extracellular formation of laminated structures has been found also by Picken *et al.* (*45*).

Most work, however, has been carried out on micelles and microfibers, using thin membranes. These have been found particularly suitable for direct electron microscopic examination. The value of 100 Å. for microfibers, it has been suggested (*66*), represents an average size of crystallite that can fit across the main longitudinal axis of microfibers.

In thin lamellae from *Donacia,* chitin chains appear to be oriented in the plane of the lamella, in a mosaic-like arrangement of differing extents of crystallinity. The common forms of orientation in this cocoon were at 90 degrees and at 45 degrees to its long axis.

The role of proteins and other agents forming complexes with poly-*N*-acetylglucosamine is of considerable importance in relation to the formation of lamellae. In *Hypoderma,* microfibers are reported (*55*) to decrease in diameter on being treated under such conditions as to remove protein, and there is growing evidence for the existence of such interaction products.

Consideration must be given to the view that orientation of chitin crystallites may be influenced by the molding forces operating in the deposition of cuticle (*15*). In *Palinurus* (*67*), in segments of blow fly puparium (*68*), and in the tarantula leg, crystallites are oriented with respect to a morphological axis, in the latter case being parallel to the direction of maximum strength.

In the peritrophic membrane of insects, the lamellae are constructed (*69*) of triplet fibrils inclined at 60 degrees to each other. Picken (*15*) has pointed out that this favors the idea that biosynthesis of chitin chains and their precipitation is an extracellular process, perhaps from a protein-polysaccharide complex (*70*).

Elsewhere it appears possible that isotropic chitin is a statistical effect either at the molecular level or through variations in successive lamellae (*71–73*).

In addition, other processes are known for the cross-linking of proteinaceous structures, particularly in *hard* chitin, involving condensation of reactive groups on adjacent macromolecules by "tanning agents" such as *o*-quinones. These processes of sclerotization have been reviewed elsewhere (*13, 43*).

To this must be related a second biological process of importance in the formation of hard chitin by calcification. Practically all cuticles contain inorganic constituents ranging between trace quantities and 99%, chiefly in the form of calcium salts though magnesium, iron, aluminum, and silicon have also been detected (*74*). The commonest crystalline deposits (*75–79*) are forms of calcium carbonate, particularly *aragonite.* This occurs in mollusk shells whereas arthropods seldom if ever contain this modification. *Calcite* is commonly reported and occurs in arthropods as extremely thin plates or granular aggregates, frequently with different orientations in adjacent areas. The resulting effect is to produce a mosaic-like structure. The variation in orientations of crystal plates has been ascribed to the initiation of crystal lattices at different faces, crystallization continuing until impeded by adjacent plate boundaries.

In principle, the calcification of cuticle resembles that of bone in higher animals; i.e., it is a discreet biochemical process in which the mineral deposits do not reflect the composition of the ionic substances of blood nor, in this case, that of a possible external aqueous environment. Furthermore, as in bone, calcification involves mineral deposition in a preformed organic matrix. In cuticle, the laminar structure is, however, characteristic. A general trend in which the extent of calcification is inversely related to the amount of protein present in cuticle is discerned from the work of Lafon (*80*). Hence during the course of calcification, the proportion of protein to chitin decreases markedly (*81*). In some species, e.g., *Gammarus,* the calcification occurs rapidly (*82*) and is complete within 24 hours. The mineralization may proceed by crystal growth from generally distributed foci or by growth from some outer layer or boundary. Kleinholtz (*83, 84*) points out that molting appears to be under hormonal control whereas calcification does not. The recycling of calcium deposits in cuticle during molting and the resorption of Ca^{2+} has been intensively studied (*85*), and it is apparent that at least in part these cations are conserved for the formation of new cuticle. The means of calcium transport in the blood of arthropods is not certain, but it seems likely that some type of protein complexes may be involved.

Using the technique of tilting infra spectra (*86–88*), it has been found that crab chitin crystallites and blow fly cuticle chitin show different uniplanar orientations.

In cell walls, unicellular bristles (*Drosophila*), and scales (*Ephestia sericarium*), there is evidence of parallel alignment of protein and chitin (poly-*N*-acetylglucosamine) in the direction of growth. From initial development both bristles and scales inhibit strong birefringence (*89*). This molecular arrangement conforms to the protein and poly-*N*-acetylglucosamine parallel interactions proposed by Rudall (*12a, 90*).

2. *Macromolecular Structure of Chitin*

Investigations of the relative intermolecular arrangements of chitin chains represents one of the earliest applications of X-ray analysis to a problem of biological interest. It must be emphasized, however, that the degree of crystallinity necessary for such work is influenced by the source and extent of "purification" of the chitin specimen, and that alkali-treated "pure" chitin may exhibit considerably higher degrees of hydrogen bonding and hence of intermolecular orientation than is normally present *in vivo*.

Following early reports by Herzog (*91*) and Gonell (*92*), on the existence of chitin crystallites the general similarity of fibers of this material and cellulose became apparent. Meyer and Mark (*93*), in 1928, suggested that the acetylglucosamine residues in chitin were linked and bonded in the same fashion as the D-glucose residues in cellulose, assuming in each case β-D-$(1 \rightarrow 4)$ glycosidic bonds. As a result of a more detailed examination of crustacean chitin, Meyer and Pankow (*67*) confirmed earlier work (*94*) and reported a rhombic unit cell in which eight 2-acetamido-2-deoxy-D-glucose residues were located, having the dimensions (*51, 62*) $a = 9.40$ Å., $b = 10.46$ Å., and $c = 19.25$ Å. Of these b represents the fiber axis of the α-chitin chain. The acetamido groups were shown to alternate from one side of the main chain to the other in adjacent amino sugar residues (due to the β-linkage); as in cellulose, equal numbers of molecular chains are arranged in opposite directions, but in this case, each chain was paired with one running in the opposite sense (Fig. 6).

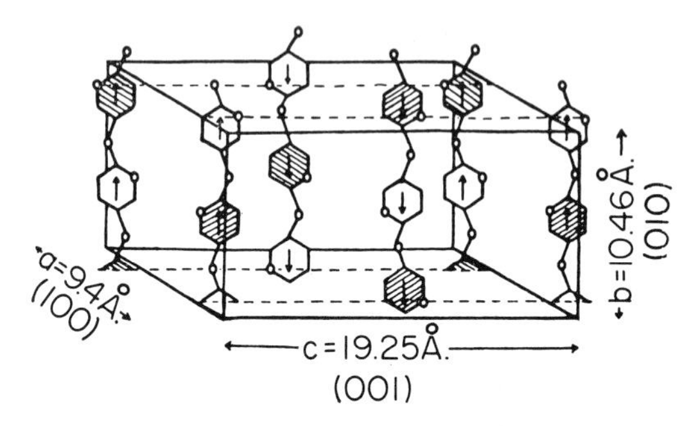

FIG. 6. The chitin space lattice as determined by Meyer and Pankow (67). Arrows indicate the alternation in direction of chains. (Courtesy Helvetica Chimica Acta.)

A reexamination of α-chitin (alkali treated) from *Homarus americanus* by Carlstrom (95), confirming the general molecular dispositions discovered by Meyer and Pankow, resulted in a new model (Fig. 7) taking account of the bonding of side groups. The macrostructure of

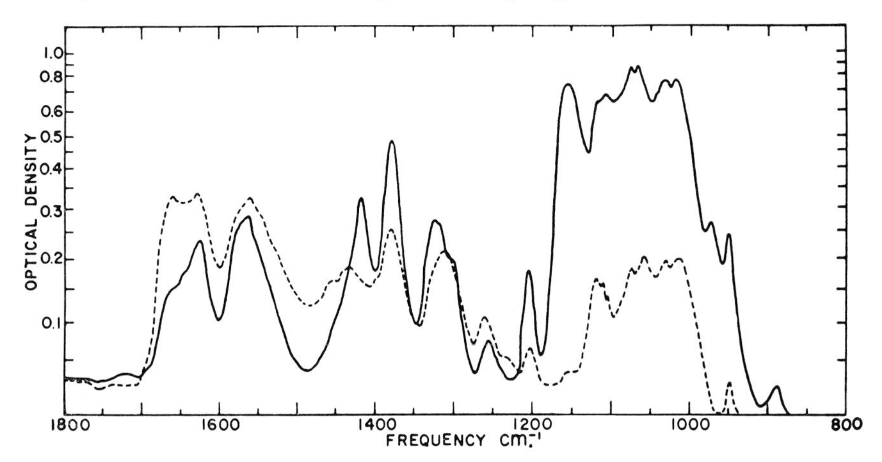

FIG. 8. Infrared absorption spectra of well-oriented α-chitin; electric vibration direction parallel (full line) and perpendicular (dotted line) to the fiber axis. After Carlstrom (95). (Courtesy Rockefeller Institute Press.)

chitin in many respects is said (*96, 97*) to resemble that of cellulose III but involves both amidic and hydroxyl types of hydrogen bonds. The infrared spectrum (Fig. 8) of chitin investigated by Carlstrom (95) agrees with the new model.

The extent to which chitin is capable of exhibiting interchain hydro-

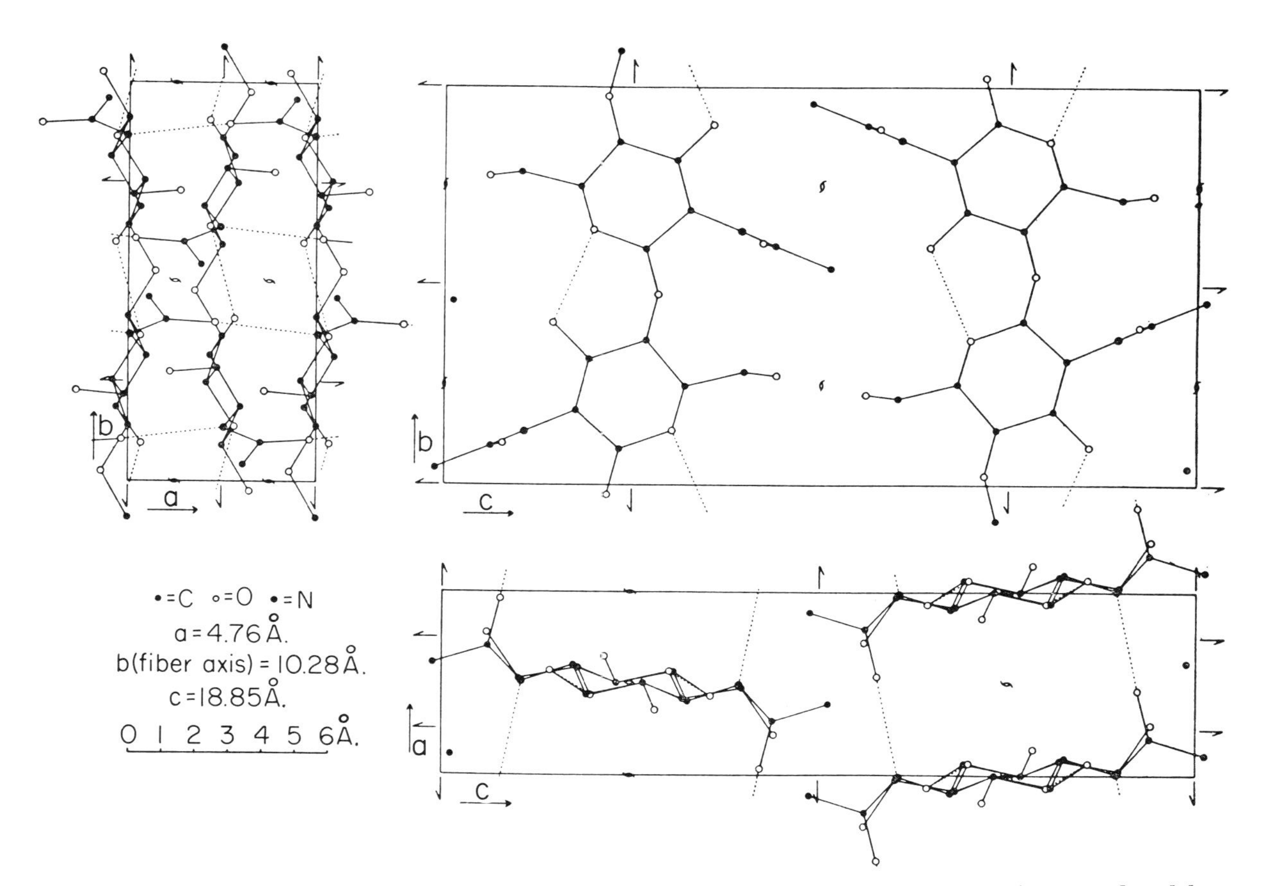

FIG. 7. Structure of α-chitin. Three main projections of the unit cell. Hydrogen bonds are shown as dotted lines. After Carlstrom (95). (Courtesy Rockefeller Institute Press.)

gen bonding has been widely investigated. By X-rays and polarized infrared spectroscopy, it was shown (*97*) that the C=O and NH groups of *N*-acetyl residues make significant contributions. Further, Clark and Smith (*62*) in earlier findings gave *a* as 9.25, and Lotmar and Picken (*51*) in 1950 reported *b* as 10.27 Å. Comparable figures for fungal chitin are *a* = 9.70, *b* = 10.4, and *c* = 4.6 Å. In general, similar values are obtained for anthropod and fungal chitins, and this type of structure has been designated α-chitin. Similar X-ray patterns are also reported for plant (*98, 99*), insect (*51, 100*), and *Sarcophaga* chitins (*100*).

A second form of the polymer, β-chitin, was first reported by Lotmar and Picken (*51*) on the basis of X-ray diffraction patterns, in the "pen" of the common squid *Loligo* and in the chetae of *Aphrodite*. This form, characterized by its cell dimensions, *a* = 9.32, *b* = 10.17, and *c* = 22.15 Å., is not derived merely by hydration of the α-form. In cephalopods, α-chitin occurs in beak, radula, and lining of the gut in contrast to the β-form in the "pen." It has been pointed out (*96, 101*) that α-chitin can occur alone or in association with such proteins as arthropodin or, possibly, resilin. After solution of β-chitin in formic acid or in 45% nitric acid, the reisolated material exhibits the α-chitin pattern. Acidic hydrolysis (*102*) of β-chitin, like α-chitin, yields only D-glucosamine hydrochloride. The α- and β-forms thus appear to differ at the macromolecular level.

Dweltz (*103*) has performed an X-ray crystallographic examination of β-chitin (a specimen from *Loligo*, deproteinized by 10% potassium hydroxide at 40° for 4 hours) and reported it to be monoclinic (space group P_{21}) with *a* = 4.7, *b* = 10.5, and *c* (fiber repeat) = 10.3 Å. The monoclinic angle was about 90 degrees, hence the unit cell had an approximately rectangular cross section through which one polysaccharide chain passed. The unit cell was calculated to contain two *N*-acetylglucosamine residues. As in α-chitin, the NH and CO groups of acetamido side chains are hydrogen bonded along the *a* axis, while in the *b* axis, a hydroxyl group of one chain is bonded by one molecule of water to a $—CH_2OH$ of an adjacent chain (Figs. 9a and 9b). Dweltz (*103*) states that β-chitin in the dry state can be regarded as a monohydrate ($C_8H_{13}O_5N \cdot H_2O$). Thus in the β-form, chains are all parallel and, separated by the water molecule, readily take up more water in humid conditions. In the α-form half the chains are parallel and half antiparallel and the side chains are believed to be directly linked. The X-ray data for α-chitin has been reconsidered (*104*) in the light of Dweltz and Carlstrom's findings, and it is concluded that the findings of the latter author give a somewhat better fit.

Most of these views relate to "purified" chitin, and it must be

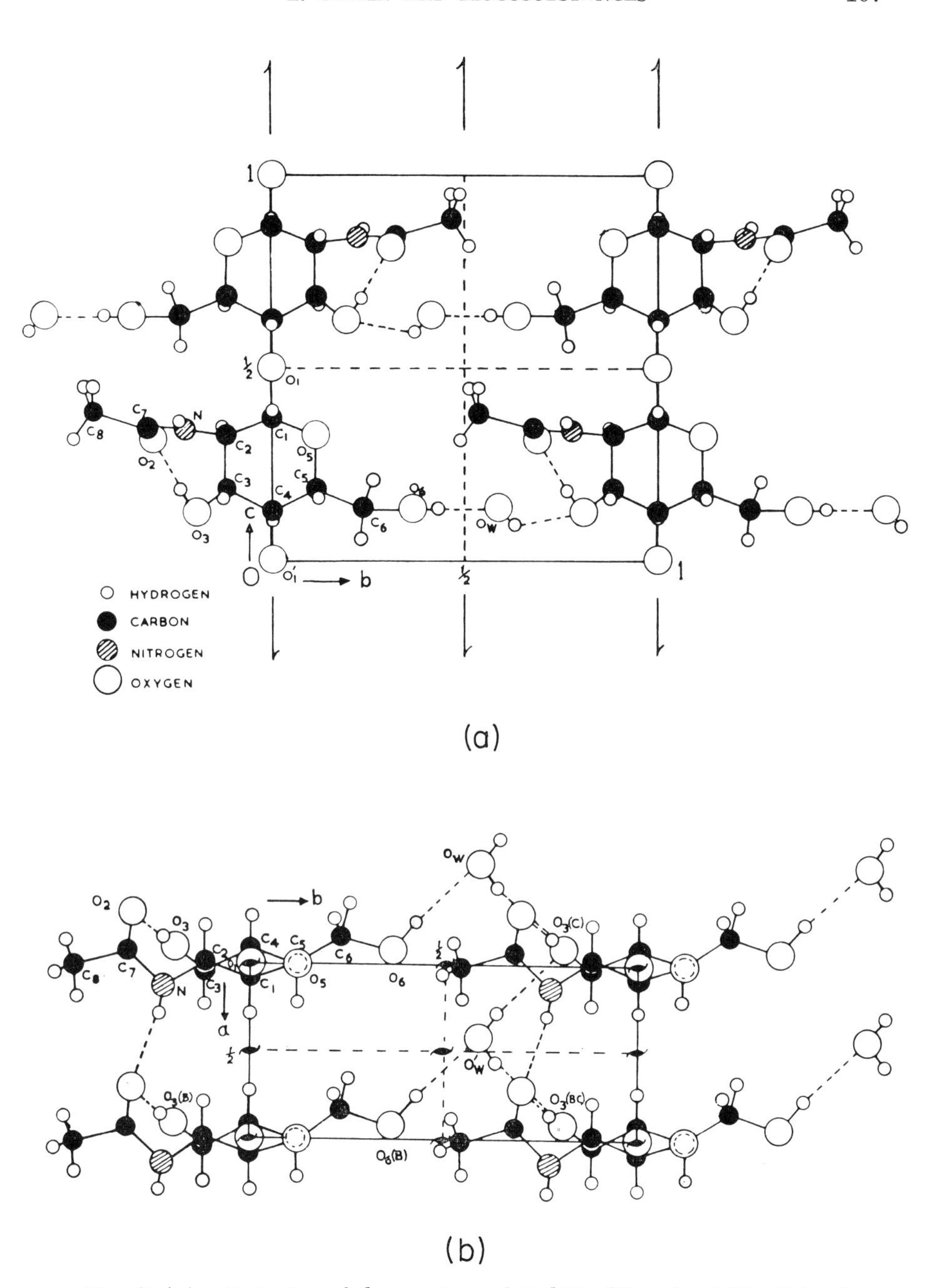

FIG. 9. (a) *a*-Projection of the structure of *β*-chitin (Deweltz, *102*); (b) *c*-Projection (fiber axis) of one half of the unit cell. (Courtesy Elsevier Publishing Co.)

envisaged that *in situ* the hydrogen bonding takes places between polysaccharide chains and proteins, in the first instance (*68*).

Comparison of chitins of diverse biological origins by X-ray methods indicates a wide degree of similarity (*98, 99, 103a*), e.g., *Phycomyces blakesleeanus,* sinews of *Palinurus vulgaris* and *Periplaneta.* In another study (*104a*), chitins from crayfish, *Aspergillus niger, Psalliota campestris,* and *Armillaria mellea* proved to be essentially similar.

B. Chemical Structure of Chitin

Detailed chemical investigation of the structure of chitin has been beset throughout by the insoluble and inert nature of the substance. It is an amorphous solid, insoluble in water, dilute acids, or alkalis. In hot concentrated alkali, chitin undergoes partial deacetylation and degradation, giving a mixture of substances collectively known as chitosan [recently reviewed by Foster and Webber (*11*)]. As stated earlier, sources of chitin frequently include variable amounts of inorganic salts ($CaCO_3$ and calcium phosphate) and proteins. The former have been most commonly removed by dilute acids or more recently by milder procedures using ethylenediaminetetraacetic acid (*105*). In some cases protein may be largely removable from soft cuticle by aqueous extraction. With hard cuticle, quantitative deproteinization is seldom if ever achieved even when the chitin sample is taken into solution with lithium thiocyanate. Chitin can however be dissolved also in concentrated hydrochloric and sulfuric acids, in formic acid, and in phosphoric acid, with some degree of degradation. The material is reported not to dissolve in Schweitzer's solution, and only with difficulty in liquid ammonia. It is, however, known to dissolve in aqueous solutions of some neutral salts in particular lithium and calcium thiocyanates. It is uncertain whether in the presence of oxygen and in alkaline conditions the reducing end of a poly-*N*-acetylglucosamine chain undergoes oxidative changes similar to those reported for cellulose, but such a possibility cannot be discounted.

At least two observations (*62, 103*) indicate that chitin fibers regenerated from solutions have recognizable X-ray diffraction patterns of α-chitin. Examination of solutions of purifed crab and fungal chitins in nitric acid have given values (*106*) of 143 and 141 for the viscosity constant ($k \times 10^3$).

Difficulties in the isolation of pure chitin are reflected also in the diversity of nitrogen contents reported for different chitin specimens. The theoretical nitrogen content (6.89%) is seldom obtained, commonly found values lying in the range 6.45–6.7% for what would be considered good specimens. The nature of the impurities is not known, but it must be remembered that chitin, particularly after alkaline treatment, is a powerful absorbent of organic substances as well as inorganic ones. Use of this property of chitin has been made for chromatographic analytical purposes (*107*).

1. *Chemical Hydrolysis of Chitin*

The course of degradation of chitin by mineral acids gives a variety of products, depending on the concentration of acid employed and the time and temperature of the hydrolysis. Under vigorous conditions (e.g., 6 *N*-hydrochloric acid at 100° for 12 hours), extensive hydrolysis to D-glucosamine (2-amino-2-deoxy-D-glucose) occurs, with some decomposition of the amino sugar. It was by such degradation that this sugar was first shown (*108*) to be present in the polymer, though its exact structure was not established until 1939, when it was synthesized by an unequivocal route by Haworth *et al.* (*109*). The amino sugar had already been synthesized earlier (*110*), though not in such a manner as to leave its configuration beyond doubt. In the hydrolysis, cleavage of *N*-acyl groups occurs (*111*); it was shown by Brach (*112*) that acetic acid and amino sugar were formed in equimolar quantities. It is not entirely clear, however, that acetyl groups are the sole amino substituents, and investigation by more accurate, modern methods seems desirable.

In an extensive study, Hackman (*113*) showed that at 20° chitin from *Jasus verreauxi* H. M. Edw. (prepared by washing in dilute acid and alkali) underwent extensive degradation in 10 *N* hydrochloric acid, 21 *N*-sulfuric acid, or 85% phosphoric acid, most of the degradation occurring in the first few minutes and leading to partly deacetylated oligosaccharides and to *N*-acetyl glucosamine. The free sugar was present only in traces. In 2 *N* hydrochloric acid little hydrolysis occurs at 25°, but at 100° in 24 hours considerable amounts of glucosamine and oligosaccharides are formed (see Fig. 13).

Under milder conditions of acidic hydrolysis (*114*) (e.g., 1 *N* hydrochloric acid at 100° for 1 hour) glycosidic bonds are cleaved preferentially (*62*), and the principal product is thus *N*-acetyl-D-glucosamine. Hackman (*115*) has reported that in 2 *N* hydrochloric acid at 100°, 6.6% conversion of chitin to the amino sugar hydrochloride takes place in 7 hours.

By means of carefully controlled conditions (*116*), oligosaccharides have been obtained from chitin which have been of considerable importance in the study of its molecular structure. Acetolysis represents one of the early methods used in such an approach, and gave small yields of a fully acetylated derivative of the disaccharide chitobiose (di-*N*-

acetylhexa-*O*-acetylchitobiose, Fig. 10a) together with the corresponding trimer (Fig. 10b).

Chitobiose in the form of the free sugar is known as the crystalline bishydrochloride. It has reducing properties toward alkaline cupric and silver reagents. In the Morgan and Elson test, di-*N*-acetylchitobiose gives less than 6% of the color given by an equimolar quantity of *N*-acetylglucosamine (*117*), and thus behaves like other derivatives of this sugar, substituted at position 4.

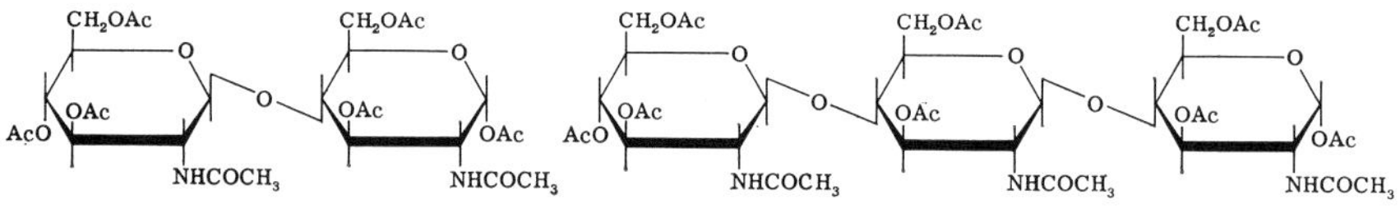

FIG. 10. (a) Acetylated derivative of di-*N*-acetylchitokiose. (b) Acetylated derivative of tri-*N*-acetyl chitotriose.

The disaccharide, together with glucosamine and the chitotriose results (*118, 119*) when chitin is treated with hydrochloric acid for 15 days at 20°. Latterly, di-*N*-acetylchitobiose (*120*) was obtained as a crystalline reducing sugar (m.p. 245–247°; $[\alpha]_D^{25} + 39.5 \rightarrow + 18.5$) by chromatographic analysis of the products of acetolysis, after alkaline deacetylation. The complexity of such products, however, substantially limits the usefulness of acetolysis.

Somewhat more promising results were obtained by taking advantage of the alkaline degradation of chitin. Under vigorous conditions acetyl groups are cleaved from chitin, thus exposing free NH_2 groups. The resulting deacetylated product, known as chitosan, is a mixture of substances, since it cannot be assumed that deacetylation is the only reaction involved. Considerable shortening of the chain length (to 20–30 units) is believed to occur (*121*) when chitin is heated in 50% sodium hydroxide at 100° for 30–40 minutes. The fate of the reducing end group under these conditions is uncertain.

Chitosan, being soluble in aqueous media, overcomes the need for powerful reagents to dissolve chitin itself. Partial hydrolysis of chitosan (*122*) followed by ion-exchange chromatography has given a series from di- to pentasaccharides. The first seven members of the series have been obtained (*117, 123*) by fractionation of chitosan hydrolyzates (after *N*-acetylation) on charcoal-Celite, or by ion exchange.

The chemistry of chitosan, as well as chitin derivatives (acetates, nitrates, sulfate esters, methyl ethers, etc.) are reviewed by Foster and Webber (*11*).

2. *Glycosidic Bonds of Chitin*

The currently accepted view of chitin as an unbranched polymer of 2-acetamido-2-deoxy-D-glucopyranose linked in the β-(1→4) positions is based on three principal sources of evidence: (*a*) analysis and degradation of chitobiose; (*b*) characterization of oligosaccharides from chitin; (*c*) X-ray diffraction analyses of chitin crystallites and the similarity of the patterns with those of cellulose.

Chitobiose, obtained by partial degradation of chitin as its "octa-acetate" was shown to contain six oxygen-linked ester groups and two *N*-acetyl groups. The disaccharide lost its reducing properties when oxidized by sodium hypoiodite to the corresponding chitobionic acid. Treatment of the acid with acetic anhydride and sodium acetate led to an unsaturated glycoside in which a double bond was located between C-2 and C-3 of the lactone ring (*116*). The formation of this derivative, probably by β-elimination, provides evidence for the glycosidic linkage of chitobionic acid at C-4. Glucosaminic acid, under similar conditions leads to a conjugated lactone (α-pyrone) and has double bonds dispersed between C-2 and C-3 and between C-4 and C-5 (Fig. 11).

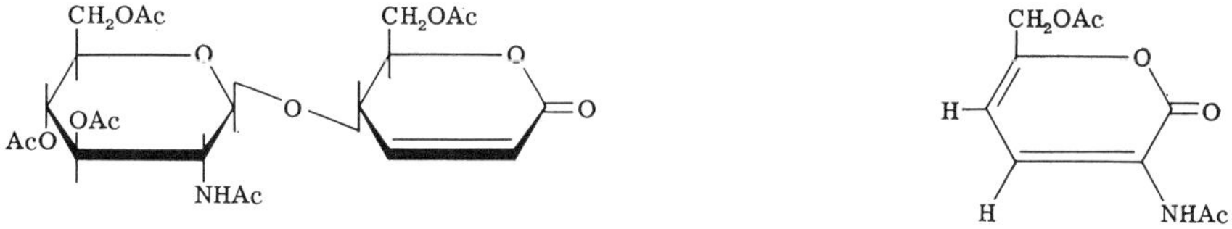

FIG. 11. Products of acetolysis of chitobiose.

The β-linkage in chitobiose has been assigned on the basis of the similarity found between chitin and cellulose in X-ray diffraction studies, the change in optical rotation ($[\alpha]_D^{20}$ $-14° \rightarrow +56°$) during hydrolysis of chitobiose by enzyme preparations from emulsin, which catalyze rapid hydrolysis of methyl-2-acetamido-2-deoxy-β-D-glucoside (*118, 119*).

The reducing group of di-*N*-acetylchitobiose has been successfully reduced by $NaBH_4$ giving di-*N*-acetylchitobiitol (*117*). Both the latter (and tri-*N*-acetylchitotriitol) are rapidly oxidized by sodium metaperiodate, consuming 1 mole of the oxidant in 24 hours and liberating 1 mole of formaldehyde. In the subsequent 24 hours, a further mole of the periodate is consumed, consistent with the presence of the β-(1→4) linkage (Fig. 12). A few nonacetylated amino groups may account for the weak periodic acid-Schiff reaction which chitin exhibits (assuming that the reaction arises in the polysaccharide, not from proteins or lipids). Though the presence of such linkages has been estab-

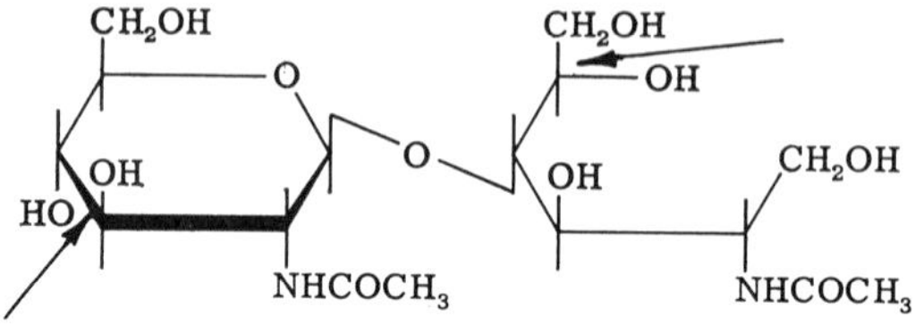

$$\text{[Structure: di-}N\text{-acetylchitobiitol; labels: CH}_2\text{OH, O, OH, HO, NHCOCH}_3\text{]}$$

Fig. 12. Sites of periodate oxidation of di-N-acetylchitobiitol.

lished in chitin, it is not yet clear that these are the only types present. The structures of the derived oligosaccharides in which no other type of bond has been reported, makes it likely, however, that this is the case.

IV. Biochemistry of Chitin

The cuticle with its chitinous constituents comprises not only the exoskeletal structure of arthropods but it is also a part of the metabolic pool (*124*). Evidence indicates (*125*) that no part of the cuticle can be regarded as permanent or static. The greatest period of biochemical activity is exhibited during molt, when 80–90% of the old cuticle may be reabsorbed through the intervention of enzymes contained in the epidermal molting fluid. Comparable observations have been made on the resorption of Ca^{2+} from hard cuticle during molt (*13, 79, 125*). Introduction of C^{14}-amino acids into the molting fluid of *Hyalophora cecropia* resulted in labeling of tissue proteins with 24 hours. These authors also showed the presence of tyrosinase in exuvial fluid initially (*134*). Later, a proteinase and chitinase were detectable in the molting fluid.

It is thus necessary to account for the biochemical progress of degradation of chitin and for its synthesis in epidermal layers.

A. Enzymatic Degradation

Enzyme systems which promote the hydrolytic degradation of chitin are widely distributed in bacteria, fungi, and arthropods. *In toto*, these act by cleavage of the β-glycosidic bonds yielding N-acetylglucosamine and, in some cases, traces of glucosamine itself.

After earlier reports (*126, 127*) of the breakdown of chitin and cellulose in the digestive systems of snails, Zechmeister and co-workers (*128–130*) separated two enzymes, supposedly from the digestive juice of *Helix pomatia* by chromatography on bauxite. The first was a polysaccharidase, chitinase, which catalyzed the degradation of chitin into chitodextrins; and the second was chitobiase, which hydrolyzed chitodextrins but was inactive toward chitin. The principal product of the system is N-acetylglucosamine. The biological status of chitolytic enzymes has been explored by the extensive and important researches of

Jeuniaux (*131, 132*), who showed that in *Helix pomatia* these enzymes arise predominantly from bacterial flora of the gut, rather than as secretions of the hepatopancreas.

Chitinases are also found in the molting fluids of insects (*132*), particularly in the larval nymph stages, those of *Carabus* and *Tenebrio* being notably active. The chitinases from these sources resemble the bacterial enzymes in pH optima (4.9–5.5) and in temperature optima (ca. 37°). The kinetics of hydrolysis are uncertain owing to the insoluble nature of the substrate, although some success has been obtained by the use of "colloidal chitin" (*123, 133*) (Fig. 13). This is

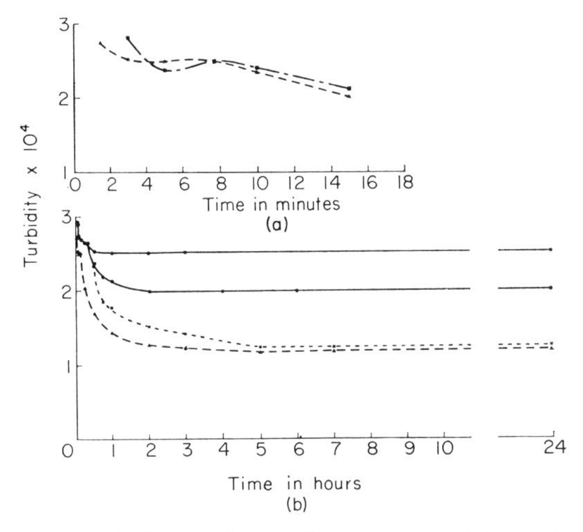

FIG. 13. Change in turbidity with time for solutions of chitin (5 mg.) in concentrated mineral acids (10 ml.). (Courtesy Commonwealth Scientific and Industrial Research Organization, Australia.) KEY:

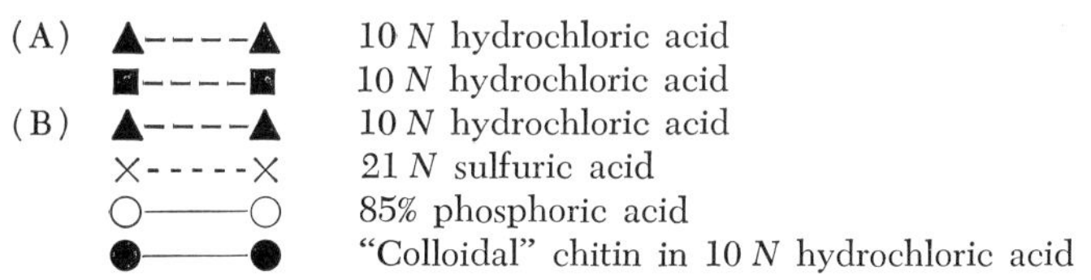

obtained from finely powdered "pure" chitin, by solution and reprecipitation from concentrated mineral acids. Chitinase activity does not appear to be present throughout the molt, and, in *Hyalophora* (*Platysamia*) *cecropia,* is found (*134*) only during the latter third of the development. Renaud (*135*) reported a similar phasic enzyme occurrence in *Maia squinado.* Amino sugar was released by enzyme extracts (in glycerol) obtained at premolt in contrast to those of the intermolt period.

Renaud (*135*) also followed the variation in glycogen content of the

TABLE I-A
CHITINOLYTIC ENZYMES IN DIGESTIVE JUICES OF SOME VERTEBRATES[a]

Species	Digestive juices or contents	Activity of chitinolytic system: acetylglucosamine liberated (μg./hr./ml.)
Carassius auratus L.	Anterior intestine	113
C. auratus	Posterior intestine	814
Gasterosteus aculeateus L.	Whole digestive contents	872
Lacerta viridis Laur.	Gastric juice	1200
Testudo hermanni J. F. Gmelin	Gastric juice	0
T. hermanni	Intestinal contents	0
Passer domesticus L.	Gastric juice	180
Turdus merula L.	Gastric juice	1550
Oryctolagus cuniculus L.	Gastric contents	0
O. cuniculus	Intestinal contents	2.5[b]
O. cuniculus	Cecal contents	0

[a] From Jeuniaux (*144*). (Courtesy MacMillan and Co., New York and London.)
[b] Nonsignificant result.

hepatopancreas and hypodermis of the edible crab *Cancer pagurus* during the molting cycle. An approximately sixfold increase in this carbohydrate reserve occurs in both tissues before molt. Similar changes have been found (*136*) for the spring lobster *Panulurus argus*. The hexosamine content of the body cavity liquid of *C. pagurus* rose sharply during the premolt phase while that of the hypodermis was fairly constant at 1–2 gm. per 100 gm. dry weight of tissue, falling only during anecdysis. In blood of *Hemigrapsus nudus*, the glucose (in contrast to the total reducing substances) does not rise during premolt, maximal values being found early in the intermolt period. The presence of chitinase has been detected in the hypodermis of *Carcinus maenas*, together with *N*-acetyl-β-glucosaminidase (*137*). Using colloidal chitin as substrate, the latter enzyme action (optimum pH 5) was found to continue after the chitinase had terminated.

In insects too, there is evidence of the extensive utilization of glycogen of the fat body during molting. Glycogen is reported to accumulate in the epidermal cells of *Bombyx mori* and to diminish in quantity when new cuticle is laid down (*138, 139*).

The biochemical aspect of these dynamic changes in integument is thus one of carbohydrate mobilization prior to molting involving a general demand on the carbohydrate synthetic mechanisms coupled with the possible reutilization of integumental carbohydrates, to which

TABLE I-B
DISTRIBUTION AND LOCALIZATION OF CHITINASE AND CHITOBIASE IN DIGESTIVE GLANDS AND TISSUES OF SOME VERTEBRATES[a]

Species	Organs	Activity: acetylglucosamine liberated (μg./hr./gm. fresh tissues)		
		Chitinolytic system[b]	Chitinase[c]	Chitobiase[d]
Carassius auratus L.	Mucosa anterior intestine	43–88	490	440
C. auratus	Mucosa posterior intestine	288	—	72
C. auratus	Pancreas (+ liver)	—	67	62
Lacerta viridis Laur.	Gastric mucosa	1437–1570	8064	250–740
L. viridis	Intestine	0–3.3[e]	—	45
L. viridis	Pancreas	810–1350	13,120	0–160
Testudo hermanni	Gastric mucosa	0	0	45
J. M. Gmelin	Intestinal mucosa	0	0	57
T. hermanni				
Turdus merula L.	Mucosa of glandular stomach	340	3114	89
T. merula	Intestine (first third)	26	144	56
T. merula	Pancreas	13[e]	13[e]	0
Rhinolophus ferrum-equinum Schreb.	Gastric mucosa	347	5280	71
R. ferrumequinum	Intestine	0	12[e]	23
R. ferrumequinum	Pancreas	0	0	29
Oryctolagus cuniculus L.	Intestine	0	0	70
O. cuniculus	Pancreas	0	7.8[e]	72

[a] From Jeuniaux (*144*). (Courtesy MacMillan and Co., New York and London.)
[b] Liberation of acetylglucosamine from chitin, by the enzymatic extract.
[c] Liberation of acetylglucosamine from chitin, by the enzymatic extract after addition of an excess of chitobiase.
[d] Liberation of acetylglucosamine from "depolymerized chitin," a preparation containing chitobiose and other small polymers of acetylglucosamine.
[e] Nonsignificant results.

chitinolytic enzymes may contribute. Further aspects of this are considered in relation to chitin biosynthesis (page 116).

Microbial chitinolytic enzymes from *Streptomyces griseus* have been examined in detail by Reynolds *et al.* (*123, 140*). The system on zone electrophoresis could be resolved into two chitinases and a chitobiase. The former acted on chitin, liberating di-*N*-acetylchitobiose and *N*-acetylglucosamine. Though chitodextrins were not detected, when added they were nevertheless degraded by the chitinases to the corresponding tri- and tetrasaccharides and finally to the *N*-acetylated di- and monosaccharides. Chitobiase promoted the hydrolysis of synthetic substrates (e.g., phenyl *N*-acetyl-β-D-glucosaminide) as well as di-*N*-acetylchitobiose and the trisaccharide, in a similar fashion to chitobiase in emulsin. Further fractionation of a *Streptomyces* chitinase into three fractions has been reported by Jeuniaux (*141–143*). Chitinolytic enzymes have been found (*144*) in the digestive juices, washed glands, and mucosae of a number of species (Tables I-A and I-B) of insectivorous or chitin-consuming animals. Weak chitinolysis is very widespread even in herbivores. The pancreas of *Lacerta,* gastric mucosae of *Turdus* and *Rhinolophus* are comparatively rich in chitinase while containing little chitobiase.

B. Biosynthetic Pathways

Comparatively little is known of the metabolic transformations occurring in cuticle, in particular in the epidermis, leading to the formation of chitin. It is however considered unlikely that reversal of chitinase has any significance (*145*) in the synthesis of di- or oligosaccharides, notwithstanding the demonstration *in vitro* of its ability to synthesize a β-glycoside from *N*-acetylglucosamine (*146*).

In a survey of the nucleotides of the hypodermal tissues (*147*) of *Carcinus maenas, Homarus vulgaris,* and *Maia squinado,* ion-exchange chromatography of hot water extracts revealed the presence of 5′-phosphates of adenosine, cytosine, uridine, and guanosine, together with adenosine triphosphate. Uridine diphosphate *N*-acetylglucosamine (UDPAG) was present in the hepatopancreas of the lobster (0.15–0.75 μmole per gram tissue, wet weight) and of *C. maenas* (0.22 μmole per gram tissue, wet weight); it is possible therefore that this nucleotide, here too, may be a precursor of chitin. Evidence for the biosynthesis of chitin by the desert locust has been presented by Kilby and Candy (*148*).

Glaser and Brown (*149, 150*) succeeded in obtaining an enzyme system from *Neurospora crassa* which catalyzed the incorporation of C^{14} uridine diphosphate *N*-acetyl-D-glucosamine (UDPAG) into chitin *in vitro.* The amino sugar moiety, fully [C^{14}] labeled, was enzymatically transferred to an added chitodextrin primer without which no significant incorporation occurred. The [C^{14}] product retained its labeling throughout extensive purification procedures and was recovered as [C^{14}] 2-amino-2-deoxy-D-glucose when the product was hydrolyzed by acid. Evidence for the chitin structure of the labeled product was obtained from its degradation by emulsin chitinase to [C^{14}] *N*-acetyl-D-glucosamine. Curiously, *N*-acetyl-D-glucosamine stimulated the incorporation of label into product although neither this sugar nor its 6- or 1-phosphate could replace UDPAG. The biosynthesis is apparently irreversible since incubation of radioactive chitin with UDPAG resulted in no exchange of label. Roseman (*151*) has pointed out the anomalous nature of the apparent reversal of the chitin synthetase of Glaser and Brown (*149*).

A considerable body of evidence is available on the biochemical steps in the transformation of D-glucose into D-glucosamine in microorganisms [reviewed by Roseman (*151*), Kent (*152, 153*), Pigman *et al.* (*154*)]. The overall scheme for the enzyme stages possibly involved in the synthesis and turnover of chitin can be represented as in Fig. 14.

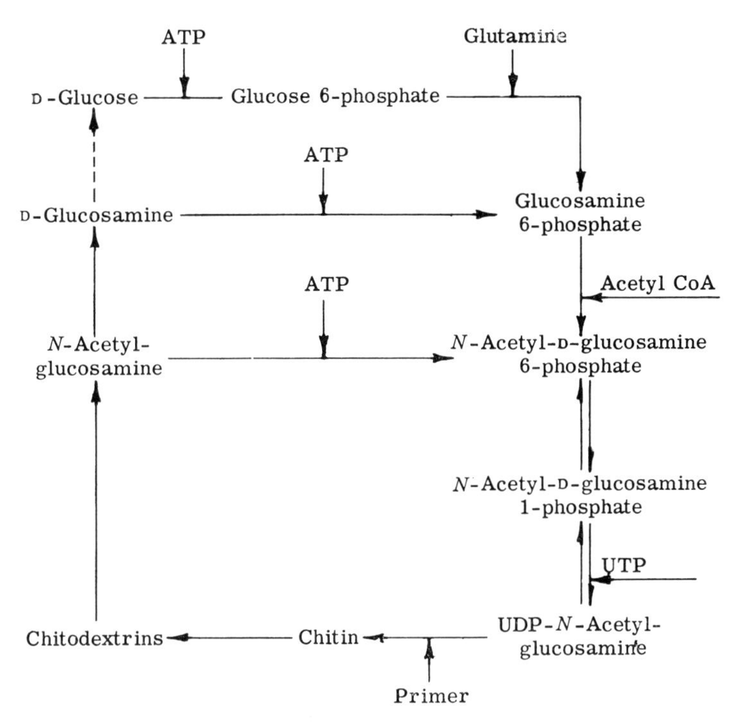

FIG. 14. Enzymatic steps in the synthesis and degradation of chitin.

The metabolic fate of *N*-acetyl-D-glucosamine by enzymatic deacetylation for reentry at the glucose or glucosamine stage is uncertain though a specific deacetylase has been reported in *E. coli* (*155*). In general, however, direct enzymatic regeneration of glucosamine appears to be uncommon or elusive of demonstration.

A chitinase system, in the blood, digestive juices, cuticle, and saliva of cockroaches, acts on native chitin (95% chitin–5% peptide) yielding principally *N*-acetylglucosamine and traces of glucosamine (*156*). A similar system was also demonstrated in the termite *Coptotermes lacteus*. No evidence could be found for the presence of a deacetylase, however, and the traces of glucosamine detected in the products of chitinase digestion were attributed to free NH_2 groups in the chitin substrate.

Deacetylation of *N*-acetyl-D-glucosamine reported in bacteria may be significant in terms of glucosamine turnover.

V. Chitin in Relation to Mucosubstances

A. Interaction Complexes

1. *Lipid Constituents*

The composition of the chitinous exoskeletons of a now wide variety of biological species indicates that although chitin is widely distributed, it seldom accounts for more than 70% of the total organic constituents, and frequently values in the range 25–50% are encountered (*80*). A further type of exoskeletal structure can be distinguished in arthropods of nonchitinous nature, in which the organic components consist principally of sclerotized proteins (*157*), as in the oothecae of *Periplaneta americana, Blatella germanica,* and *Orthodera ministralis.* In these oothecae, mechanical rigidity is achieved by "tanning," a complex series of rapid reactions in which proteins are believed to become cross-linked by a quinone (*43*). These oothecae have been found (*157–159*) to contain calcium oxalate (0.2–8%), and it has been suggested (*158, 159*) that calcium ions may associate with protein, stabilizing it prior to tanning. Considerable amounts of calcium as yet unaccounted for are, however, present in some other form. The existence of protein–calcium complexes may account for this situation, as in the marine snail *Busycon caniculatum,* where protein is considered (*160*) to be linked to carbohydrate through calcium ions.

In chitinous exoskeletons, lipids and proteins are found in addition to chitin. Paraffin chains and thermostable bound lipids have been detected by X-rays and electron diffraction in epicuticle of a number of insects: *Periplaneta americana* (*161*), *Tenebrio molitor* (*162*), and *Calliphora erythrocephala* (*163*). In *Tenebrio,* the lipid molecules are oriented to the cuticular surface. The existence of a lipid surface layer appears to play a significant biological role in maintaining the water balance of these animals. The lipid deposition is a late stage in the formation of epicuticle, and lipid is reported (*164, 165*) to be transported by means of some solubilizing agent (*161*) from the epidermal cells, forming a discontinuous layer on a tanned protein matrix. There is, however, little information (*166, 167*) on the chemical nature of the lipids concerned; some evidence points to the presence of an eight-carbon compound. Histochemical evidence suggests the possible involvement of a sterol in endocuticle.

Epicuticle does not give a positive chitosan test and in most groups is characterized by the absence of chitin. The available evidence thus indicates that lipid constituents of the cuticle are primarily associated with modified protein structures rather than with chitin.

2. *Protein Constituents*

Accumulating evidence indicates that *in situ* native chitin is associated with proteins in a precise fashion. Much of the protein (arthropodin) in soft cuticle of arthropods is extractable by hot water (*168*) and has been studied by Fraenkel and Rudall (*68*). These authors proposed that the protein was present as extended polypeptide chains, oriented parallel to extended chitin chains. A further protein fraction (sclerotin) is extractable by the action of dilute acids and alkalis, and in hard cuticle this fraction is substantially greater than the water-soluble material. Picken and Lotmar (*169*) subsequently showed that distinctive features of X-ray diffraction patterns additional to that of chitin itself exhibited by nonpurified chitins from *Limulus, Palinurus, Aeschna, Sirex, Aphrodite,* and other species, were not present in alkali-extracted materials. These features, it was suggested (*15*), were attributable to the possible presence of tanned oriented proteins. Picken points out that the vigorous conditions required to deproteinize scleratized cuticles are not necessarily indicative of tenacious chitin-protein interactions but may be due to the high stability of a tanned protein constituent.

Chemical investigation of the protein extract obtained by aqueous extraction at 0° of blow-fly puparia cuticles revealed that, whereas it was soluble in hot water, it is precipitated by 10% trichloroacetic acid, by ethanol (>50%) ammonium sulfate, and by saturated solutions of sodium chloride.

Arthropodin appears to be chemically distinct from silk gelatin (sericin) and from egg shell proteins. It is poor in glycine but rich in tyrosine (*70, 170*). It occurs in the unusual extended β-configuration and is not precipitated on heating. In such configurations, arthropodin could readily participate in interactions with chitin. In relation to the chitin structure, *N*-acetylglucosamine combines *in vitro* with arthropodin, peptides, and amino acids and notably with tyrosine, giving complexes dissociable at acidic pH values but stable at higher values (*171*). Chitin readily absorbs up to 8% of its weight of protein, giving temperature-stable complexes, sensitive, however, to the presence of electrolytes and partly dissociable with varying pH (*172*). At pH 9, the dissociation is complete. This indicates at least the possibility of weak chitin arthropodin complexes in which steric interactions and hydrogen bonds may contribute. Though such complexes may be of biological significance (*172*), there is evidence of chemical bonds linking the two macromolecules. Cuticle from puparia (*Sarcophaga falculata*) and from decalcified *Cancer pagurus* can be dissolved in solutions of lithium thiocyanate and reprecipitated, retaining a chitin-protein complex (*105*). The existence of a chemically combined chitin-protein complex in the form of a glycoprotein is indicated in the larval cuticle of *Agrianome spinicollis* and elsewhere. Using relatively mild reagents (ethylenediaminetetraacetic acid) to decalcify cuticle of *Cancer pagurus*, such a glycoprotein was isolated, containing 5% of peptide constituents (*105, 173*).

The protein moiety was not removed by the action of such reagents as *N,N*-dimethylformamide or phenol-water, nor by solution and reprecipitation from aqueous lithium thiocyanate. It was presumed therefore to represent a firm chemical linkage.

Using mild methods of isolation (i.e., avoidance of hot alkaline solutions) Hackman (*4*) has obtained a series of glycoproteins of varying peptide content (Table II). It is of interest that papain removed

TABLE II
PROTEIN CONTENT OF GLYCOPROTEINS CONTAINING CHITIN[a]

Source of glycoprotein	Percentage protein (calc. from nitrogen content)
Agrianome spinicollis larval cuticle[b]	50
Agrianome spinicollis larval cuticle (papain)	5
Scylla serrata cuticle (EDTA)	15.6
Cancer pagurus cuticle (EDTA)[c]	7.5
Cuttlefish shell (EDTA)	51.2
Loligo sp. skeletal pen (lithium thiocyanate)	13.2

[a] From Hackman (*4*). (Courtesy Commonwealth Scientific and Industrial Research Organization, Australia.)
[b] Hackman and Goldberg (*173*).
[c] Foster and Hackman (*105*).

protein from larval cuticles of *Agrianome spinicollis* more efficiently than did either pepsin or trypsin.

In the six specimens investigated, it can be tentatively concluded that there is evidence for a covalent chemical bond between chitin and protein on the following grounds: (a) the methods of isolation minimize the survival of labile linkages; (b) the protein content can be reduced, but amino acids still persist in the products even after treatment with hot alkaline solutions; (c) preparations reisolated after solution in lithium thiocyanate by fractional precipitation contain both chitin and peptides. In no case was protein-free chitin obtained.

The amino acids retained even after alkali treatment of chitin (*Lucilia cuprina*) could be isolated after acidic hydrolysis. These were identified provisionally as aspartic acid and histidine, and it is suggested that these may be involved in the chitin-protein bonds. Glycoproteins are found with both α- and β-chitin. Results of analyses of the amino acid contents of the glycoproteins are shown in Table III.

TABLE III
AMINO ACID COMPOSITION OF PROTEIN COMPONENTS OF GLYCOPROTEINS[a,b]

	Source of glycoprotein			
Amino acid	Larval cuticle of *Agrianome spinicollis* (papain)	Cuticle of *Scylla serrata* (EDTA)	Cuttlefish shell (EDTA)	*Loligo* skeletal pen (lithium thiocyanate)
Alanine	84	90	95	121
Arginine	82	190	47	24
Aspartic acid	125	109	142	55
Cystine and/or cysteine	Absent	Absent	43	20
Glutamic acid	139	97	52	42
Glycine	Trace	Trace	80	102
Histidine	37	51	55	43
Hydroxyproline	Absent	Absent	Absent	Absent
Leucine and/or isoleucine	103	72	47	89
Lysine	Trace	Trace	39	20
Methionine	Absent	Absent	Absent	Absent
Phenylalanine	78	109	35	28
Proline	55	38	41	58
Serine	Trace	Trace	38	29
Threonine	113	78	26	33
Tyrosine	171	120	129	62
Valine	138	129	63	56

[a] From Hackman (*4*). (Courtesy Commonwealth Scientific and Industrial Research Organization, Australia.)

[b] Amino acid composition is expressed as milligrams amino acid obtained from 1 gm. protein.

The absence of hydroxyproline in the squid and cuttlefish protein components indicate that neither is of the collagen type. In the glycoprotein of *Agrianome,* two histidyl residues and one aspartyl residue were found per 400 residues of glucosamine.

Collagen has been detected principally by X-ray methods in a variety of invertebrate tissues, e.g., stalks of octocorals (*174*), body wall of *Alcyonium* (*175*), byssus threads of *Mytilus edulis* (*176*). In the lobster

TABLE IV

AMINO ACID COMPOSITION OF RESILIN FROM WING HINGE (RUNS 1 AND 3) AND PREALAR ARM (RUN 2) OF THE LOCUST *Schistocerca gregaria*[a]

Amino acid	Resilin: Weight anhydro amino acid per 100 gm. protein			Resilin: Residues/10^5 g protein			Comparisons: residues per 10^5 gm. of:		
	Run 1	Run 2	Run 3	Run 1	Run 2	Run 3	Collagen (*181*) (oxhide)	Elastin (*182*) (ox ligamentum nuchae)	Silk fibroin (*183*) (*Bombyx mori*)
Asp	12.5	14.1	13.3	109	122	116	52	4.5	16
Thr	3.7	3.4	3.4	37	34	33.5	19	8	12
Ser	8.0	8.0	7.95	92	91	89	41	8	160
Glu	6.2	7.0	7.3	48	54	57	76	14	14
Pro	8.2	8.7	8.8	84	89	90	125	156	5
Gly	26.9	23.7	24.3	471	414	425	354	398	590
Ala	9.45	8.5	8.9	133	120	125	116	212	389
Val	3.1	2.8	2.9	31	36	29	21	148	30
Met	Nil	Nil	Nil	Nil	Nil	Nil	6.5	(1)	Nil
Ileu	1.9	2.1	2.55	16.5	19	23	14	31	9
Leu	2.6	3.1	3.25	23	27	29	28	66	7
Tyr	4.0	5.8	5.35	24.5	35	33	5	9	69
Phe	4.4	3.95	4.6	30	27	31	14	30	8
Amide N				(126)	—	(78)	(46)	(3)	—
Lys	0.85	Total 9.0	0.7	6.6	Total 60	5.5	27	3	4
His	1.7	(calculated	1.0	12.2	(calculated	7.4	4.5	0.5	2
Arg	6.5	from Run 1)	6.0	41.5	from Run 1)	38	47	5	6
Total	100	100	100	1159	1128	1131	1063 (incl. 106 hydroxyproline + 7 hydroxylysine)	1093	1321
Calculated N content (%)				19.5		19.5			
Average residue weight				88.5 (Runs 1 and 3)			94.0	91.5	75.7

[a] From Bailey and Weis-Fogh (*180*). (Courtesy Elsevier Publishing Co.)

Homarus, collagen occurs (*175*) in subcuticular tissue, and in the barnacle *Lepas* in the peduncle. In general however, collagen where present is associated with fibrous structures and there is little evidence for α-chitin-collagen interactions. In the brachiopod *Lingula*, β-chitin is thought to occur in association with collagen. In arthropods, it is the cuticular protein interacting with chitin that does not appear to be collagenous, and this finding is supported by the absence of the characteristic amino acid, hydroxyproline, in chitinous glycoproteins (*4*). These should, however, be regarded as tentative conclusions until more detailed results are available on the precise structure of these cuticular proteins. Collagen-chitin distribution has been reviewed by Rudall (*101*).

TABLE V
NUMBER OF RESIDUES OR GROUPS PER 100 RESIDUES IN SOME STRUCTURAL PROTEINS RESEMBLING RESILIN IN CHEMICAL COMPOSITION[a]

Residue or group	Resilin, Runs 2 + 3 (insect)	Collagen (mammal)	Silk fibrin (insect)	Elastin (mammal)
Nonpolar[b]	66	63	78.5	95
Glycine	31	33	45	36
Basic	4.5	8.0[c]	0.9	0.9
Total acid[d]	15.5	12.0	2.3	1.7
Free acid[e]	4.0	0.3	—	0.6
Total hydroxyl	14.0	16.7[c]	18.6	2.3
Hydroxyproline + hydroxylysine	Nil	10.6	Nil	Trace
Tyrosine	3.0	0.5	5.2	0.8
Methionine	Nil	0.6	Nil	Trace
Cysteine	Nil	Nil	Nil	Trace

[a] From Bailey and Weis-Fogh (*180*). (Courtesy Elsevier Publishing Co.)
[b] Pro, Gly, Ala, Val, Met, Ileu, Leu, Phe.
[c] Including hydroxylysine.
[d] Dicarboxylic acids + amides.
[e] Total acid (bases + amide).

A further protein system of importance in the molecular structure of soft ("rubberlike") cuticle (*177*) in locusts has been identified by Weis-Fogh (*178*) and termed resilin (*resilire* = to spring back). Resilin may be present as pure masses of protein, but more commonly it is found as continuous layers, 2.5 μ thick, separating thin (0.2 μ) chitinous lamellae (*179, 180*). When fully grown, the prealar arm contains 76% of resilin and 24% of chitin whereas the wing hinge contains 86% and 14%, respectively. The elastic region of the tendons of dragonfly is reported to contain 99% of resilin. In these cases, analytical data are largely based on estimations of resilin as a readily acid hydrolyzable (0.1 *N* HCl) protein and chitin as a resistant substance. Analyses of the amino acids (*180*) in resilin and other proteins is shown in Tables IV and V. The material remaining after removal of resilin consists of chitin with about 2% of protein. Resilin is a structural elastic protein with a three-dimensional network of peptide chains, in which a new type of cross-linkage participates (*178, 180*). The mechanical properties of the tissue appear to be dependent on this type of molecular structure (*184, 185*). Anderson (*186*) has evidence that two new fluorescent amino acids are involved in the cross linkage; "compound II" brings about the junction of two peptide chains and "compound I" (the less abundant) links three chains. Since these amino acids absorb at λ_{max} 320 mμ in alkaline conditions and resilin is distinguishable from tyrosine-containing proteins (absorbing at maximally about λ300 mμ), it has been possible to show the lineal increase in the concentration of compounds I and II with the amount of resilin. In the maturation of the adult locust rubberlike cuticle (e.g., wing hinge ligament), the total weight increase in chitin and resilin plus fibrous protein is constant at 5 days after emergence. Only resilin continues to be formed after 1 week in the course of reaching full cuticular maturity. Though resilin is found in close proximity to chitin, it is not clear whether the two associate as complementary molecular chains.

B. Skeletal and Associated Mucosubstances

In chitinous structures in different species, a number of proteins are associated with chitins, and it is of importance to consider to what extent chitin may be replaced by other types of carbohydrate-containing polymers.

1. *Cellulose*

Cellulose was one of the first polysaccharides to be recognized in invertebrate skeletal tissues (*187*), under the name of *tunicin.* This was detected in *Cynthia papillata,* on account of its unusual stability. Subsequently it was found in ascidians and in the larvae of *Phallusia mammilaris,* where it constitutes the mantle. There is strong evidence that in the latter, cellulose is synthesized by epidermal, as opposed to mesodermal, cells. In *Pyrosoma,* the polysaccharide appears to arise from a cytoplasmic process of ectodermal cells penetrating through the integument. Reports (*188*) of the presence of cellulose in the tubes of Pogonophora are not substantiated. In *Siboglinum atlanticum, S. inermis,* and *S. caulyeri* Brunet and Carlisle (*189*) showed that although the tubes were notably stable to alkali and to Schweitzer's solution, acidic or enzymatic degradation led to glucosamine or to its *N*-acetyl derivative. Thus the presence of chitin in these species must be extremely probable. Comment is required on the unusual stability of tunicin, which in crystalline structure resembles bacterial and *Valonia* celluloses (*190*). Mann and Marrinan (*191*) have found it to be highly crystalline and in its unit cell structure to resemble the cellulose of higher plants. The enhanced stability is attributed to the higher degree of macromolecular orientation rather than to the presence of different types of bonds.

The species where cellulose is present appear to be largely confined to the tunicates; elsewhere, however, there is much greater diversification. In the fungi, cellulose and chitin appear to be generally alternative though a few cases are reported where both chitin and cellulose occur together (*192, 193*). In fungi and cellulose-synthesizing bacteria, the cellulose is frequently obtained in a pure form, i.e., unassociated with protein, and is synthesized in a primarily oriented form in contrast to invertebrate chitin where a secondary orienting process follows biosynthesis. Whereas invertebrate chitin is formed in a protein matrix, development of plant cellulose fibers takes place in association with hemicelluloses.

2. *Other Carbohydrate Complexes*

Chitin represents a distinctive integumental constituent of invertebrates, structurally identical or closely similar to that found in fungi, produced by both ectodermal and endodermal cells. Where cellulose is present, it occurs both outside the epidermis as well as interior to it. In biochemical terms, however, the wide incidence of chitin in so many invertebrate species can be regarded as indicating a dominant position of amino sugar metabolism, for structural as well as for reserve purposes. In this context, chitin is only one of many related mucopolysaccharides in which amino sugars participate. Mucopolysaccharides in invertebrates are found as epithelial mucins performing biological functions of lubrication and protection similar to those in the vertebrates.

In vertebrates, development of calcified bone is preceded by the synthesis of a mucopolysaccharide matrix in conjunction with which collagen microfibers are formed. Calcification then takes the form of crystal deposition of apatite-type minerals, initiated in the molecular spacings of the collagen macrostructure. As in the crustacean integument, mammalian bone is a metabolic reserve as well as a structural element and is equipped with enzymatic apparatus for resorption of both its organic and mineral constituents. In connective tissue similarly, collagen formation increases with age and, by adding to the ground substance, results in a corresponding decrease in the cellularity of this tissue. The principal mucosubstances characterized in connective tissues and bone include two forms of chondroitin sulfate (A and C), derman sulfate

(*194–197*) keratosulfate, hyaluronic acid (*198*), heparin and heparitin sulfates (*195*).

In all these cases, D-glucosamine or D-galactosamine occurs, the acidic properties arising partly from ester-sulfate groups and partly from uronic acids. Chondroitin sulfate A, found predominantly in costal and tracheal cartilage, nasal septa, aorta, and bone, consists of a repeating disaccharide in which D-glucuronic acid is linked through the β-($1 \rightarrow 3$) positions to *N*-acetyl D-galactosamine. The ester sulfate is believed to be located at C-4 of each amino sugar residue (Fig. 15).

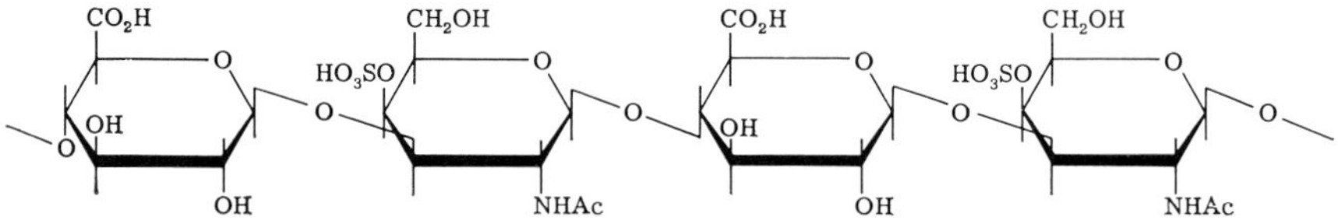

FIG. 15. Chondroitin sulfate A.

Chondroitin sulfate C, found in skin, heart valves, bone, and tendon, like A is an unbranched structure. In this case (Fig. 16), the sulfate ester groups are located at C-6 of the amino sugar residues. Both A and C are

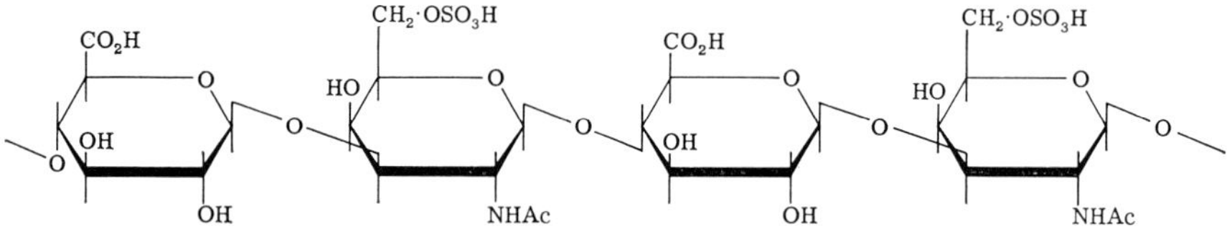

FIG. 16. Chondroitin sulfate C.

hydrolyzed by testicular hyaluronidase and in two respects differ from derman sulfate (formerly chondroitin sulfate B), found particularly in skin and aorta. This sulfated substance is comprised of *N*-acetyl-D-galactosamine linked to L-iduronic acid, with sulfate esters located at C-4 of the amino sugar residues (Fig. 17).

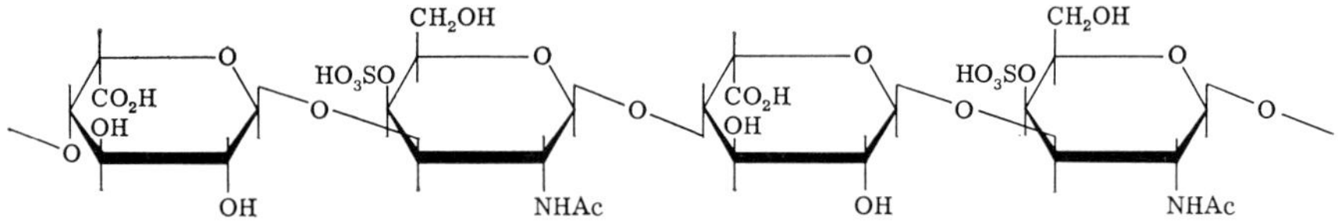

FIG. 17. Derman sulfate (chondroitin sulfate B).

Keratosulfate of skin and cornea, on the other hand, is uronic acid free and is comprised of D-galactose and *N*-acetyl-D-glucosamine, these being linked alternately in β-($1 \rightarrow 4$) and β-($1 \rightarrow 3$) positions (Fig. 18)

(*195*). Despite the difference in monosaccharide constituents, these sulfated substances have the same glycosidic linkages and are unbranched structures. There is now evidence, however, that *in situ* they are present to a large extent chemically combined to protein possibly through seryl linkages.

Although these sulfated substances can all be found simultaneously in mammalian connective tissues, their proportions vary with age. Thus in early fetal stages, bovine skin has a low collagen content (somewhat higher in tendon and sclera). Embryonic pig skin contains 5–10% chondroitin sulfate C and derman sulfate and relatively large amounts of hyaluronic acid (*199*). Adult pig skin, on the other hand, is predominantly collagenous, but 64% of its carbohydrate constituents have been found to be derman sulfate, and 30% hyaluronic acid (Fig. 19).

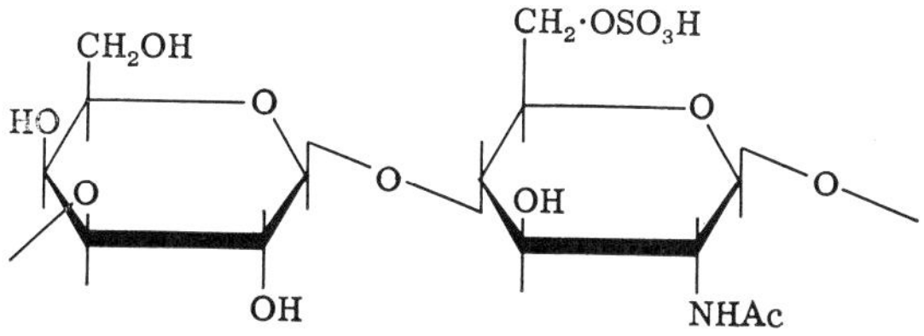

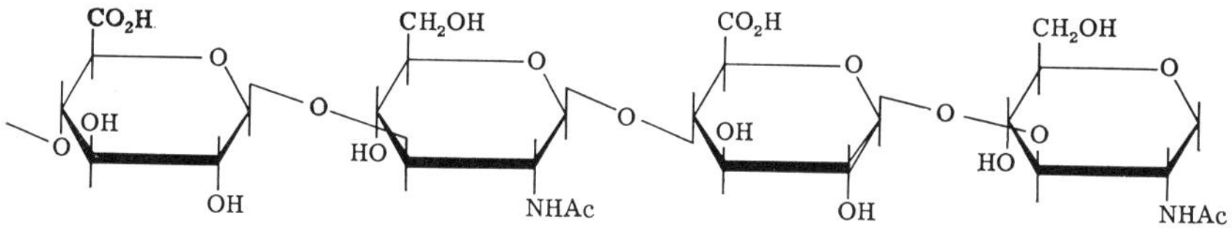

CH_2OH $CH_2 \cdot OSO_3H$ HO O O O O OH OH NHAc

FIG. 18. Repeating pattern of keratosulfate.

CO_2H CH_2OH CO_2H CH_2OH O O O O O O O O OH HO OH HO O OH NHAc OH NHAc

FIG. 19. Hyaluronic acid.

Chondroitin sulfate C has been found in cartilage of elasmobranchs: sting ray (*200*), shark (*201, 202*).

Some authors attribute these sulfated structures to connective tissues, distinguished from acidic mucoproteins held to be characteristic of epithelial and glandular secretions (*17, 18, 203*). In cases where detailed results are available, e.g., bovine submaxillary mucin, urinary mucoprotein, α_1-seroglycoprotein, the acidic properties are found to arise principally from the presence of sialic acids (=acylneuraminic acids = nonulosaminic acids). Though sulfate esters may be present in small amounts, these mucoproteins (sometimes referred to as sialoproteins) are highly branched, globular structures in which polypeptides (30–60%) are chemically linked to oligosaccharides. It is, however, incorrect now to consider the sialoproteins as distinctive only of epithelial secretions, and there is evidence of their participation in connective tissues and in bone (*204, 205*).

The composition and role of these vertebrate mucosubstances find parallel counterparts in invertebrate species.

In *Helix pomatia,* whereas chitin-protein complexes are the basis of the structural elements of the exoskeleton, a polysaccharide, $[\alpha]_D^{20} -16.1$ containing D- and L-galactose acts as a mucin in facilitating the movement of the body within the shell (*206*). Hydrolysis of the methylated galactan yielded 2,3,4,6-tetra-*O*-methyl-D-galactose, and the 2,4-di-*O*-methyl-D-sugar. It consisted of a highly branched structure in which both 1,6 and 1,3 glycosidic bonds feature. L-Galactose was considered to be linked to this structure as side groups (*206*). A protective function for mucins appears in the echinoderms, where the ova are protected by molecular complexes containing some 20–25% of protein and 75–80% of polysaccharide (some amino sugar free) esterified by sulfate groups. Ova of *Echinus esculentus* (*207–209*) secrete metachromatic extracellular mucopolysaccharide comprising only of L-galactose units bearing 31% of sulfate esters (Fig. 20). Similarly, *Echinocardium cordatum* (*207*) synthesizes a polyfucose sulfate whereas in the mucopolysaccharides of *Strongylocentrotus droebachiensis* and *Paracentrotus lividus,* fucose and galactose have been found (*210*).

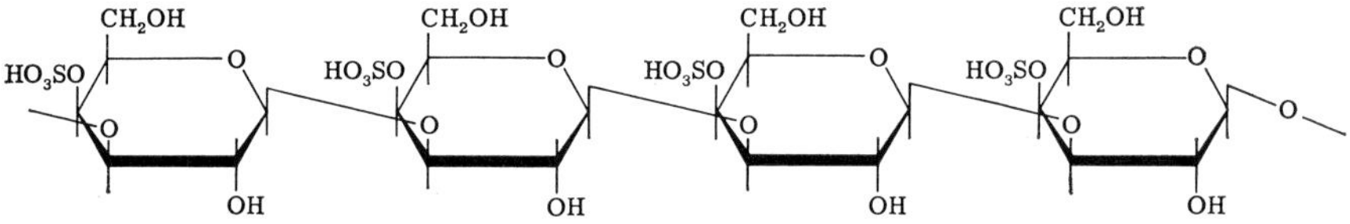

Fig. 20. Suggested structure of polygalactan sulfate from *Echinus esculentus.*

Other sulfated carbohydrate-containing polymers, mactans resembling the heparins of vertebrates, have been isolated from clam tissues (*211*), and a polysaccharide having features resembling keratosulfate occurs in the hypobranchial gland of *Busycon caniculatum* (*212–214*).

A sulfated polysaccharide, limacoitin sulfate, containing ester sulfate L-fucose, galactose, mannose, galacturonic acid, and glucosamine, has been reported in the mucin of a Japanese snail (*215*). Mucin of the marine snail *Charonia lampas* (*216, 217*) contains polyglucose sulfate, and enzyme systems capable of transferring sulfate from phenolic sulfates to carbohydrate acceptors have been obtained from this source. Lash and Whitehouse (*218*) showed that polyglucose sulfate is present also in invertebrate connective tissue, the odontophore of *Busycon caniculatum,* where it is thought to play a part similar to that of keratosulfate and chondroitin sulfates in cartilage of higher animals. The chondroid odontophore has a typical hyaline metachromatic matrix. In addition to this material, the hypobranchial gland of this welk also synthesizes a mucopolysaccharide containing D-glucosamine, D-galactosamine, and ester sulfate (*214*). The brittle star *Ophiocomina nigra* similarly produces a metachromatic sulfated mucin (*219*) in connection with a detritus feeding mechanism. A similar mucin is produced by *Amphipholis squamata.*

Mucins are secreted by many types of worm, but as yet comparatively little is known of their structure or composition. In certain annelids, mucins form a more or less permanent envelope in which the animal exists, and Defretin (*220*) has shown that these mucins contain considerable amounts of carbohydrate (Table VI). The mucins of *Hyalinoecia*

TABLE VI
COMPOSITION OF ANNELID MUCINS[a]

Species	Glucosamine	Galactose	Glucose	Arabinose	Ribose	Fucose
Myxicola infundibulum	+	+	+	+	+	+
Sabella pavonina	−	−	+	+	−	−
Lanice conchilega	−	+	+	+	−	−
Pectinaria koreni	−	+	+	+	+	+

[a] From Defretin (*220*).

tubicola, Leiochone clypeata, Petaloproctus terricola, Lanice and *Spirographis* spp. are hydrolyzed by testicular hyaluronidase and presumably therefore have some structural resemblance to hyaluronic acid of bacteria and mammals.

In the plant kingdom, chitin, in comparison to plant polysaccharides, is of relatively minor importance, quantitatively in its limited distribution and functionally in its rather simple structure. A wide variety of plant polysaccharides is now known in some detail (*221–223*). In general these are soluble viscous materials in which several types of monosaccharide are usually combined. In terrestrial plants, acidic properties, where present, generally arise from the presence of D-glucuronidic or D-galacturonidic residues. Acidic polysaccharides bearing a considerable number of sulfate esters, occur in aquatic forms particularly marine algae, as for example in the galactan polysulfates, carageenin and agar-agar from red seaweeds, and the fucan polysulfates from brown seaweeds. *Dilsea edulis* has an acidic polysaccharide comprised of D-galactose, D-glucuronic acid, xylose, 3,6-anhydrogalactose, and ester sulfate. These algal sulfated polysaccharides bear a structural resemblance to those synthesized by marine invertebrates, particularly the echinoderms.

In biochemical perspective, it is probable that invertebrate integument, no less than connective and osseous tissues of vertebrates, cannot be considered to be a static structure. The composition of macromolecular constituents varies not only from one species to another, but also in terms of the age of the animal. Arguments concerning the possibility of collagen being characteristic of one form of skeletal structure and chitin of another are at least premature since they consider final compositions and overlook the antecedent developmental steps and the spectrum of enzymatic changes involved, some perhaps inducible, and the biosynthetic control mechanism at subcellular levels.

In evolutionary terms (*10*) the biosynthesis of amino sugars and their incorporation appears to be common to bacteria and animals, although outside the fungi it is rarely encountered in plants. The quantitative climax of this biochemical feature is reached in the invertebrates in relation to chitin and exoskeletal structures. In higher animals, though still important in development of connective tissue and bone, it is a minor pathway of carbohydrate metabolism.

References

1. C. Hachett, *Phil. Trans. Roy. Soc. London* pp. 315–334 (1799).
2. A. Odier, *Mém. soc. hist. nat. Paris* **1**, 29–42 (1823).
3. J. G. Children, *Zool. J.* **1**, 101–115 (1825).
4. R. H. Hackman, *Australian J. Biol. Sci.* **13**, 568–577 (1960).
5. P. Kraft, *Zentr. Mineral.* pp. 285–288 (1923).
6. E. Abderhalden and K. Heynes, *Biochem. Z.* **259**, 320–321 (1933).
7. D. R. Rome, *Bull. musée roy. hist. nat. Belg. (Brussels)* **12**(31), 1–7 (1936).
8. K. H. Meyer, "Natural and Synthetic High Polymers." Wiley (Interscience), New York, 1942.
9. R. L. Whistler and C. E. Smart, "Polysaccharide Chemistry." Academic Press, New York, 1953.
10. P. W. Kent and M. W. Whitehouse, "Biochemistry of the Amino-Sugars." Butterworths, London, 1955.
11. A. B. Foster and J. M. Webber, *Advances in Carbohydrate Chem.* **15**, 371–393 (1960).
12. A. G. Richards, "The Integument of Arthropods." Univ. of Minnesota Press, Minneapolis, Minnesota, 1951.
12a. K. M. Rudall, *Advances in Insect Physiol.* **1**, 257–313 (1963).
13. A. G. Richards, *Ergeb. Biol.* **20**, 1–26 (1958).
14. V. B. Wigglesworth, *Quart. Microscop. Sci.* **76**, 269–318 (1933).
15. L. E. R. Picken, "The Organization of Cells." Oxford Univ. Press, London and New York, 1960.
16. D. A. L. Davies, *Advances in Carbohydrate Chem.* **15**, 271–340 (1960).
17. G. Blix, *Proc. 4th Intern. Congr. Biochem., Vienna* Vol. 1, pp. 94–105 (1958).
18. A. Gottschalk, "The Chemistry and Biology of Sialic Acids and Related Substances." Cambridge Univ. Press, London and New York, 1960.
19. F. Zilliken and M. W. Whitehouse, *Advances in Carbohydrate Chem.* **13**, 237–263 (1958).

20. M. Burger, "Bacterial Polysaccharides." Charles C Thomas, Springfield, Illinois, 1950.
21. S. A. Barker and M. Stacey, "Polysaccharides of Microorganisms." Oxford Univ. Press, London and New York, 1960.
22. T. Barry, *J. Exptl. Med.* **107,** 507–521 (1958); G. T. Barry and W. F. Goebel, *Nature* **179,** 206 (1957).
23. M. R. J. Salton, *Symposium Soc. Gen. Microbiol.* **6,** 81–110 (1956); "Microbial Cell Walls." Wiley, New York, 1961.
24. J. J. Armstrong, J. Baddiley, J. G. Buchanan, and B. Carss, *Nature* **181,** 1692–1693 (1958).
25. D. E. Ellwood, M. V. Kelemen, and J. Baddiley, *Biochem. J.* **86,** 213–225 (1963).
26. J. Baddiley, *J. Roy. Inst. Chem.* pp. 366–371 (1962).
27. L. H. Kent, *Biochem. J.* **67,** 5P (1957).
28. R. E. Strange and L. H. Kent, *Biochem. J.* **71,** 333–339 (1959).
29. C. S. Cumming and H. Harris, *J. Gen. Microbiol.* **14,** 583–600 (1956).
30. R. E. Strange and J. F. Powell, *Biochem. J.* **58,** 80–85 (1954).
31. R. E. Strange and F. A. Dark, *Nature* **177,** 186–188 (1956).
32. H. Bracconot, *Ann. chim.* (*Paris*) **79,** 265–304 (1811).
33. R. J. Avery and F. Blank, *Can. J. Microbiol.* **1,** 140–143 (1954).
34. P. A. Roelofsen and I. Hoette, *Antonie van Leeuwenhoek J. Microbiol. Serol.* **17,** 27 (1951).
35. P. A. Roelofsen, *Biochim. et Biophys. Acta* **10,** 477–478 (1953).
36. D. R. Kreger, *Biochim. et Biophys. Acta* **13,** 1–9 (1954).
37. M. V. Tracey, *in* "Modern Methods of Plant Analysis" (K. Paech and M. V. Tracey, eds.), Vol. 2, p. 264. Springer, Berlin, 1955.
38. A. B. Foster and M. Stacey, *in* "Encyclopaedia of Plant Physiology" (W. Ruhland, ed.), Part VI, p. 518. Springer, Berlin, 1958.
39. W. Biedermann, *in* "Handbuch der vergleichenden Physiologie" (H. Winterstein, ed.), Vol. III, Part 1, pp. 319–1188. Fischer, Jena, 1914.
40. G. Kunike, *Z. vergleich. Physiol.* **2,** 233–253 (1925).
41. F. L. Campbell, *Ann. Entomol. Soc. Am.* **22,** 401–426 (1929).
42. C. Koch, *Z. Morphol. Ökol. Tiere* **25,** 730–756 (1932).
43. H. S. Mason, *Advances in Enzymol.* **16,** 105–184 (1955).
44. R. Dennell, *Proc. Roy. Soc.* **B133,** 348–373 (1946).
45. L. E. R. Picken, M. G. M. Pryor, and M. M. Swann, *Nature* **159,** 434 (1947).
46. R. O. Herzog, *Angew. Chem.* **39,** 297–302 (1926).
47. G. Kunike, *Chem. Zentr.* **97,** 2129 (1926).
48. C. J. B. Thor and W. F. Henderson, *Am. Dyestuff Reptr.* (*Proc. Am. Assoc. Textile Chemists Colorists*) **29,** 461–464 (1940).
49. P. H. Hermans, "Contributions to the Physics of Cellulose Fibres." Elsevier, Amsterdam, 1946.
50. A. C. Goodings and L. H. Turl, *J. Textile Inst.* **31,** T69–80 (1940).
51. W. Lotmar and L. E. R. Picken, *Experientia* **6,** 58 (1950).
52. J. C. Irvine, *J. Chem. Soc.* **95,** 564–570 (1909).
53. A. Frey-Wyssling, "Sub-microscopic Morphology of Protoplasm." Elsevier, Amsterdam, 1953.
54. W. Biedermann, *Anat. Anz.* **21,** 485–490 (1902).
55. K. Enigk and W. Pfaff, *Z. Morphol. Ökol. Tiere* **43,** 124–153 (1954).
56. G. Kümmel, *Z. Morphol. Ökol. Tiere* **45,** 309–342 (1956).

57. W. Pfaff, *Höfchen-Briefe* **5**, 93–160 (1952).
58. A. G. Richards, *Biol. Bull.* **103**, 201–225 (1952).
59. M. G. M. Pryor, *Proc. Roy. Soc.* **B128**, 378–407 (1940).
60. A. D. Lees and L. E. R. Picken, *Proc. Roy. Soc.* **B131**, 87–110 (1945).
61. L. E. R. Picken, *Phil. Trans. Roy. Soc.* **B234**, 1–28 (1949).
62. G. L. Clark and A. F. Smith, *J. Phys. Chem.* **40**, 863–879 (1936).
63. A. G. Richards and T. F. Anderson, *J. Morphol.* **71**, 135–183 (1942).
64. M. Lafon, *Bull. inst. océanog.* **No. 850**, 1–11 (1943).
65. A. C. Neville, *J. Insect Physiol.* **9**, 177–186 (1963).
66. E. Ribi, *Nature* **168**, 1082–1083 (1951).
67. K. H. Meyer and G. W. Pankow, *Helv. Chim. Acta* **18**, 589–598 (1935).
68. G. Fraenkel and K. M. Rudall, *Proc. Roy. Soc.* **B129**, 1–35 (1940).
69. E. H. Mercer and M. F. Day, *Biol. Bull.* **103**, 384–394 (1952).
70. A. R. H. Trim, *Biochem. J.* **35**, 1088–1098 (1941).
71. A. G. Richards and F. H. Korda, *Entomol. News* **58**, 141–145 (1947).
72. T. H. Waterman, *Science* **111**, 252–254 (1950).
73. P. Schulze, *Z. Morphol. Ökol. Tiere* **25**, 508–533 (1932).
74. F. W. Clarke and W. C. Wheeler, *U. S. Geol. Survey Profess. Papers* **No. 124** (1922).
75. W. J. Schmidt, "Die Bausteine des Tierkörpers im polarisierten Lichte." Cohen, Bonn, Germany, 1924.
76. E. Dudich, *Zoologica (Stuttgart)* **30**, 1–154 (1931).
77. P. Drach, *Compt. rend. acad. sci.* **205**, 249–251 (1937).
78. P. Drach, *Compt. rend. acad. sci.* **205**, 1173–1176 (1937).
79. P. Drach, *Ann. inst. océanog.* **19**, 103–392 (1939).
80. M. Lafon, *Ann. sci. nat. zool. et biol. animale* **5**, 113–146 (1943).
81. P. Drach and M. Lafon, *Arch. zool. exptl. et gén.* **82**, 100–118 (1942).
82. D. M. Reid, *Nature* **151**, 504–505 (1943).
83. L. H. Kleinholz, *J. Cellular Comp. Physiol.* **18**, 107–117 (1941).
84. L. H. Kleinholz, *Biol. Revs. Cambridge Phil. Soc.* **17**, 91–119 (1942).
85. J. D. Robertson, *Biol. Revs. Cambridge Phil. Soc.* **16**, 106–133 (1941).
86. C. Y. Liang and R. H. Marchessault, *J. Polymer Sci.* **43**, 85–100 (1960).
87. F. G. Pearson, R. H. Marchessault, and C. Y. Liang, *J. Polymer Sci.* **43**, 101–116 (1960).
88. R. H. Marchessault, F. G. Pearson, and C. Y. Liang, *Biochim. et Biophys. Acta* **45**, 499–507 (1960).
89. L. E. R. Picken, *Phil. Trans. Roy. Soc. London* **B234**, 1–28 (1949).
90. K. M. Rudall, *Progr. in Biophys. and Biophys. Chem.* **1**, 39–72 (1950).
91. R. O. Herzog, *Naturwissenschaften* **12**, 955–960 (1924).
92. H. W. Gonell, *Z. physiol. Chem. Hoppe-Seyler's* **152**, 18–30 (1926).
93. K. H. Meyer and H. Mark, *Ber.* **61**, 1932–1936 (1928).
94. J. R. Katz and H. Mark, *Physik. Z.* **25**, 431–445 (1924).
95. D. Carlstrom, *J. Biophys. Biochem. Cytol.* **3**, 669–683 (1957).
96. A. Frey-Wyssling, *Biochim. et Biophys. Acta* **18**, 166–168 (1955).
97. S. E. Darmon and K. M. Rudall, *Discussions Faraday Soc.* **No. 9**, 251–260 (1950).
98. A. N. J. Heyn, *Proc. Acad. Sci. Amsterdam* **39**, 132–135 (1936).
99. A. N. J. Heyn, *Protoplasma* **25**, 372–396 (1936).
100. G. Fraenkel and K. M. Rudall, *Proc. Roy. Soc.* **B134**, 111–143 (1947).
101. K. M. Rudall, *Symposia Soc. Exptl. Biol.* **No. 9**, 49–71 (1955).

102. N. E. Dweltz and N. Anand, *Biochim. et Biophys. Acta* **50,** 357 (1961).
103. N. E. Dweltz, *Biochim. et Biophys. Acta* **51,** 283–294 (1961).
103a. G. van Iterson, Jr., K. H. Meyer, and W. Lotmar, *Rec. trav. chim.* **55,** 61–63 (1936).
104. G. N. Ramachandran and C. R. Ramakrishnan, *Biochim. et Biophys. Acta* **63,** 307–309 (1962).
104a. Y. Khouvine, *Compt. rend. acad. sci.* **195,** 396–397 (1932).
105. A. B. Foster and R. H. Hackman, *Nature* **180,** 40–41 (1957).
106. H. Fikentscher, *Cellulosechemie* **13,** 58–64 (1932).
107. P. M. Townsley, *Nature* **191,** 626 (1961).
108. G. Ledderhose, *Ber.* **9,** 1200–1201 (1876).
109. W. N. Haworth, W. H. G. Lake, and S. Peat, *J. Chem. Soc.* pp. 271–274 (1939).
110. E. Fischer and H. Leuchs, *Ber.* **36,** 24–29 (1903).
111. G. Ledderhose, *Z. physiol. Chem.* (*Hoppe-Seyler's*) **2,** 213–217 (1878–1879).
112. H. Brach, *Biochem. Z.* **38,** 468–491 (1912).
113. R. H. Hackman, *Australian J. Biol. Sci.* **15,** 526–537 (1962).
114. S. Fränkel and A. Kelly, *Monatsh. Chem.* **23,** 123–132 (1902).
115. R. H. Hackman, *Australian J. Biol. Sci.* **7,** 168–178 (1954).
116. M. Bergmann, L. Zervas, and E. Silberkweit, *Ber.* **64,** 2436–2440 (1931).
117. S. A. Barker, A. B. Foster, M. Stacey, and J. M. Webber, *J. Chem. Soc.* pp. 2218–2227 (1958).
118. L. Zechmeister and G. Tóth, *Ber.* **64,** 2028–2032 (1931).
119. L. Zechmeister and G. Tóth, *Ber.* **65,** 161–162 (1932).
120. F. Zilliken, G. A. Braun, C. S. Rose, and P. György, *J. Am. Chem. Soc.* **77,** 1296–1297 (1955).
121. K. H. Meyer and H. Wehrle, *Helv. Chim. Acta* **20,** 353–362 (1937).
122. S. T. Horowitz, S. Roseman, and H. J. Blumenthal, *J. Am. Chem. Soc.* **79,** 5046–5049 (1957).
123. L. R. Berger and D. M. Reynolds, *Biochim. et Biophys. Acta* **29,** 522–534 (1958).
124. M. le Goffe, *Bull. soc. sci. Bretagne* **16,** 35–50 (1939); *Chem. Abstr.* **40,** 2899 (1946).
125. V. B. Wigglesworth, *Discussions Faraday Soc.* **No. 3,** 172–177 (1948).
126. P. Karrer, *Kolloid-Z.* **52,** 304–319 (1930).
127. P. Karrer and A. Hoffmann, *Helv. Chim. Acta* **12,** 616–637 (1929).
128. W. Grassman, L. Zechmeister, R. Bender, and G. Tóth, *Ber.* **67B,** 1–5 (1934).
129. L. Zechmeister and G. Tóth, *Naturwissenschaften* **27,** 367 (1939).
130. L. Zechmeister, G. Tóth, and E. Vajda, *Enzymologia* **7,** 170–175 (1939).
131. C. Jeuniaux, *Mém. acad. roy. Belg.* **28,** No. 7 (1954).
132. C. Jeuniaux, *Mém. soc. entomol. Belg.* **27,** 312–319 (1955).
133. C. Jeuniaux, *Arch. intern. physiol. et biochem.* **66,** 408–427 (1958).
134. J. V. Passonneau and C. M. Williams, *J. Exptl. Biol.* **30,** 545–560 (1953).
135. L. Renaud, *Ann. inst. océanog.* **24,** 259–262 (1949).
136. M. A. McWhinnie and B. T. Scheer, *Science* **128,** 90 (1958).
137. M. R. Lunt and P. W. Kent, *Biochim. et Biophys. Acta* **44,** 371–373 (1960).
138. A. Paillot, *Compt. rend. soc. biol.* **127,** 1502–1504 (1938).
139. L. Billard, *Bull. inst. océanog.* **No. 866,** 4 pp (1944); *Chem. Abstr.* **41,** 2499 (1947).

140. D. M. Reynolds, *J. Gen. Microbiol.* **11,** 150–159 (1954).
141. C. Jeuniaux, *Arch. intern. physiol. et biochem.* **54,** 522–524 (1956); *Acta soc. linnéenne Bordeaux* **97,** 1–8 (1957).
142. C. Jeuniaux, *Arch. intern. physiol. et biochem.* **65,** 135–138 (1957); **67,** 597–617 (1959).
143. C. Jeuniaux, *Biochem. J.* **66,** 27P (1957).
144. C. Jeuniaux, *Nature* **192,** 135–136 (1961).
145. J. L. Strominger, *Physiol. Revs.* **40,** 55–111 (1960).
146. R. Kuhn and H. Tiedman, *Chem. Ber.* **87,** 1141–1147 (1954).
147. M. R. Lunt and P. W. Kent, *Biochem. J.* **78,** 128–134 (1961).
148. B. A. Kilby and D. J. Candy, *J. Exptl. Biol.* **39,** 129–140 (1962).
149. L. Glaser and D. H. Brown, *Biochim. et Biophys. Acta* **23,** 449–450 (1957).
150. L. Glaser and D. H. Brown, *J. Biol. Chem.* **228,** 729–742 (1957).
151. S. Roseman, *Ann. Rev. Biochem.* **28,** 545–578 (1959).
152. P. W. Kent, *Scand. J. Clin. Lab. Invest.* **10,** suppl. 31, 166–190 (1957).
153. P. W. Kent, *Biochem. Soc. Symposia (Cambridge, Engl.)* **20,** 90–108 (1960).
154. W. Pigman, K. Nisizawa, and S. Tsuiki, *Ann. Rev. Biochem.* **28,** 15–38 (1959).
155. H. Veldkamp, *Nature* **169,** 500 (1952); *Mededeel. Landbouwhoogeschool Wageningen* **55,** 127–174 (1957).
156. D. F. Waterhouse, R. H. Hackman, and J. W. McKellar, *J. Insect Physiol.* **6,** 96–112 (1961).
157. P. C. J. Brunet, *Quart. J. Microscop. Sci.* **93,** 47–69 (1952).
158. B. Stay, A. King, and L. M. Roth, *Ann. Entomol. Soc. Am.* **53,** 79–86 (1960).
159. R. H. Hackman, *J. Insect Physiol.* **5,** 73–78 (1960).
160. V. E. Shashoua and H. Kwart, *J. Am. Chem. Soc.* **81,** 2899–2905 (1959).
161. R. Dennell and S. R. A. Malek, *Proc. Roy. Soc.* **B143,** 239–257 (1955).
162. M. W. Holgate and M. Seal, *J. Exptl. Biol.* **33,** 82–106 (1956).
163. H. Hurst, *J. Exptl. Biol.* **27,** 238–251 (1950).
164. J. W. L. Beament, *Nature* **167,** 652–653 (1951).
165. V. B. Wigglesworth, *Biol. Revs. Cambridge Phil. Soc.* **23,** 408–451 (1948).
166. J. W. L. Beament, *J. Exptl. Biol.* **32,** 514–538 (1955).
167. K. Kaidsumi, *J. Insect Physiol.* **1,** 40–51 (1957).
168. R. H. Hackman, *Biochem. J.* **54,** 362–370 (1953).
169. L. E. R. Picken and W. Lotmar, *Nature* **165,** 599–600 (1950).
170. Gh. Duchâteau and M. Florkin, *Physiol. Comparata et Oecol.* **3,** 365 (1954).
171. R. H. Hackman, *Australian J. Biol. Sci.* **8,** 83–96 (1955).
172. R. H. Hackman, *Australian J. Biol. Sci.* **8,** 530–536 (1955).
173. R. H. Hackman and M. Goldberg, *J. Insect Physiol.* **2,** 221–231 (1958).
174. M. H. Marks, R. S. Bear, and C. H. Blake, *J. Exptl. Zool.* **111,** 55–78 (1949).
175. K. M. Rudall, *Symposia Soc. Exptl. Biol.* **No. 9,** 49–71 (1955).
176. G. Champetier and E. Fauré-Frémiet, *Compt. rend. acad. sci.* **207,** 1133–1135 (1938).
177. M. Jensen and T. Weis-Fogh, *Phil. Trans. Roy. Soc.* **B245,** 137–169 (1962).
178. T. Weis-Fogh, *J. Exptl. Biol.* **37,** 889–907 (1960).
179. A. C. Neville, *J. Insect Physiol.* **9,** 265–278 (1963).
180. K. Bailey and T. Weis-Fogh, *Biochim. et Biophys. Acta* **48,** 452–459 (1961).
181. J. H. Bowes, R. G. Elliott, and J. A. Moss, *Biochem. J.* **61,** 143–150 (1955).
182. R. E. Neuman, *Arch. Biochem.* **24,** 289–298 (1949).

183. F. Lucas, J. T. B. Shaw, and S. G. Smith, *Advances in Protein Chem.* **13**, 107–242 (1958).
184. T. Weis-Fogh, *J. Mol. Biol.* **3**, 520–531 (1961).
185. T. Weis-Fogh, *J. Mol. Biol.* **3**, 648–667 (1961).
186. S. O. Anderson, *Biochim. et Biophys. Acta* **69**, 249–262 (1963).
187. M. P. E. Berthelot, *Compt. rend. acad. sci.* **47**, 227–230 (1858).
188. L. H. Hyman, *Biol. Bull.* **114**, 106–112 (1958).
189. P. C. J. Brunet and D. B. Carlisle, *Nature* **182**, 1689 (1958).
190. H. J. Marrinan and J. Mann, cited in ref. 15.
191. J. Mann and H. J. Marrinan, *J. Polymer Sci.* **32**, 357–370 (1958).
192. M. Locquin, *Bull. mens. soc. linnéenne, Lyon* **12**, 110–112, 122–128 (1943); *Chem. Abstr.* **40**, 623 (1944).
193. R. C. Thomas, *Ohio J. Sci.* **40**, 60–62 (1942).
194. See, for instance, G. E. Wolstenholme and M. O'Connor, eds., "Chemistry and Biology of Mucopolysaccharides." Churchill, London, 1958.
195. P. Hoffman and K. Meyer, *Federation Proc.* **21**, 1064–1069 (1962).
196. M. Stacey and S. A. Barker, "Carbohydrates of Living Tissue." Van Nostrand, Princeton, New Jersey, 1962.
197. K. Meyer, P. Hoffman, and A. Linker, *in* "Connective Tissue, Thrombosis and Atherosclerosis" (I. H. Page, ed.), p. 181. Academic Press, New York, 1959.
198. R. W. Jeanloz and P. J. Stoffyn, *Federation Proc.* **21**, 81 (1962).
199. G. Loewi and K. Meyer, *Biochim. et Biophys. Acta* **27**, 453–454 (1958).
200. O. Fürth and T. Bruno, *Biochem. Z.* **294**, 153–173 (1957).
201. N. Naganashi, N. Takahashi, and F. Egami, *Bull. Chem. Soc. Japan* **29**, 434–438 (1956).
202. M. B. Mathews, *Nature* **181**, 421–422 (1958).
203. P. W. Kent, *Gastroenterology* **43**, 292–303 (1962).
204. A. A. Castellani, G. Ferri, L. Bolognani, and V. Graziano, *Nature* **185**, 37 (1960).
205. P. W. Kent and G. M. Herring, *Biochem. J.* **82**, 17P (1962); **89**, 405–414 (1963).
206. E. Baldwin and D. J. Bell, *J. Chem. Soc.* 1461–1465 (1938); *ibid.* 125–132 (1941).
207. J. Runnström, A. Tiselius, and E. Vasseur, *Arkiv Kemi Mineral. Geol.* **15A**, No. 16 (1942).
208. E. Vasseur, *Acta Chem. Scand.* **2**, 900–913 (1948); **4**, 1144–1145 (1950).
209. E. Vasseur and J. Immers, *Arkiv Kemi* **1**, 39–41, 253–256 (1949).
210. J. Runnström, *Symposia Soc. Exptl. Biol.* **No. 6**, 39–88 (1952).
211. S. L. Burson, Jr., M. J. Fahrenbach, L. H. Frommhagen, R. A. Riccardi, R. A. Brown, J. A. Brockman, H. V. Lewry, and E. L. R. Stokstad, *J. Am. Chem. Soc.* **78**, 5874–5878 (1956).
212. M. Bacila and R. R. Ronkin, *Biol. Bull.* **103**, 296 (1952).
213. H. Kwart and V. E. Shashoua, *Trans. N. Y. Acad. Sci. Ser. 2*, **19**, 595 (1957).
214. V. E. Shashoua and H. Kwart, *J. Am. Chem. Soc.* **81**, 2899–2905 (1959).
215. H. Masamune and Z. Yosizawa, *Tôhoku J. Exptl. Med.* **65**, 57–62 (1956).
216. T. Soda and H. Tereyama, *J. Chem. Soc. Japan* **69**, 65–69 (1948).
217. F. Egami, T. Asaki, N. Takahashi, S. Suzuki, S. Shidata, and K. Nisizawa, *Bull. Chem. Soc. Japan* **28**, 685–692 (1955).
218. J. W. Lash and M. W. Whitehouse, *Biochem. J.* **74**, 351–355 (1960); *Arch. Biochem. Biophys.* **90**, 159 (1960).

219. A. R. Fontaine, *Nature* **176**, 606 (1955).
220. R. Defretin, *Compt. rend. soc. biol.* **145**, 115–119 (1951); *Compt. rend. acad. sci.* **232**, 888–890 (1951).
221. T. Mori, *Advances in Carbohydrate Chem.* **8**, 315–350 (1953).
222. W. D. Richardson and E. T. Dewar, *Nature* **182**, 1779–1781 (1958).
223. E. L. Hirst, *Proc. Chem. Soc.* pp. 177–187 (1958).

CHAPTER 3

Cellular Aspects of Active Transport

Ernest Schoffeniels

Institut Léon Fredericq, University of Liège, Liège, Belgium

I. Introduction

The ultimate purpose of the studies on living membrane permeability is not only to obtain information concerning the organization and the chemistry of such membranes, but also to integrate the various functions which can be ascribed to the membrane within the more general framework of cell metabolism. Despite the important progress made during the last decade, we are far from having a coherent picture of what is happening at the cell boundary. Most of the work done in the permeability field is still, for obvious reasons, at the purely descriptive "morphological" phase, and thus essentially concerned with the determination of the permeability characteristics of a living membrane. In some tissues we already have a little information concerning the functional structure of a living membrane, i.e., the way some of the functions so far identified are organized and distributed in the membrane. But we still lack some of the most fundamental knowledge enabling us to present a coherent picture of the membrane integrated in the cell functioning as an independent unit. However, in a limited number of cases, we are beginning to have enough knowledge to enable us to discuss the possible relationships existing between the various permeability characteristics of a membrane and the general metabolism of the cell.

We shall thus formulate some general concepts emerging from the comparative study of membrane permeability and shall attempt to correlate them with some aspects of the metabolism of the cell taken as a living unit.

II. The Permeability Characteristics of a Living Membrane

A. Origin of the Concentration Difference Existing between Two Liquid Phases Separated by a Living Membrane

1. *Inorganic Ions*

The difference in composition between two liquid phases separated by a living membrane may generally be explained by any combination of diffusion force, electric field, solvent drag, or active transport. By active transport one generally defines a transfer that cannot be accounted for by physical forces only. In order to characterize the behavior of an ion, one has therefore to relate the fluxes of the species under study to the various physical forces mentioned. Thus, for an ion moving across a membrane under the influence of physical forces only, one may write (*1*)

$$\ln M_{\text{in}}/M_{\text{out}} = \ln c_o/c_i + zFE/RT + Dw/D \int_0^{x_0} 1/A dx \qquad (1)$$

where M_{in} is the influx, M_{out} the outflux, c_o the concentration of the ion in the outside solution, c_i the concentration in the inside solution, E the potential difference between the solutions i and o, z the valence of the ion, F the number of Faraday, R the gas constant, T the absolute temperature, Dw the volume rate of the solvent flow through unit area of the membrane, D the free diffusion coefficient of the ion in water, A the fraction of the area available to flow, x the distance from the outside boundary of the membrane, x_o the total thickness of the membrane.

If the existence of pores through which there is a net flow of solvent can be ruled out or disregarded, simple passive diffusion through any membrane is characterized by Eq. 2 which is identical to Eq. 1 except

$$\ln M_{\text{in}}/M_{\text{out}} = \ln c_o/c_i + zFE/RT \tag{2}$$

for the term expressing the solvent drag effect.

The application of Eq. 2 can be illustrated by the analysis of the behavior of sodium ions in the isolated frog skin. Using Na^{22} and Na^{24} as tracers, it is possible to determine influx and outflux simultaneously (*2*). Table I shows some results obtained when the isolated skin is bathed

TABLE I
THE INFLUENCE OF 2,4-DINITROPHENOL (DNP) ON INFLUX AND OUTFLUX OF SODIUM THROUGH THE FROG SKIN[a]

Sample	M_{in}	M_{out}	E (mv)	$M_{\text{in}}/M_{\text{out}}$, found	$M_{\text{in}}/M_{\text{out}}$, calc.
Control	0.34	0.093	62	3.66	0.011
DNP	0.25	1.57	−11	0.16	0.15
Control	0.445	0.145	82	3.07	0.025
DNP	0.049	0.56	−6	0.087	0.126
Control	0.228	0.008	72	28.5	0.017
DNP	0.032	0.216	−7	0.148	0.132

[a] Skin is bathed with Ringer on the inside and Ringer diluted 1:10 on the outside (*3*).

with Ringer on the inside and Ringer diluted ten times on the outside (*3*). In the periods marked control, the electrical potential difference is rather high, the inside solution being positive with respect to the outside. Nevertheless the influx of sodium is always greater than the outflux, indicating a net movement of Na against the electrochemical gradient. The values of the flux ratios found are very different from those calculated according to Eq. 2. Thus the results indicate clearly that physical forces cannot be responsible for the net flux of Na. Sodium ions are therefore actively transported across the frog skin; that is, metabolic energy has to be supplied to bring about the net flux observed. In the presence of dinitrophenol (DNP), which is thought to dissociate oxidation from adenosine triphosphate (ATP) synthesis, the behavior of Na is that predicted from Eq. 2, indicating that under these conditions sodium ions move according to the physical forces available.

During the last few years, evidence has been accumulated indicating that in many instances where an unequal distribution of ions is observed between two liquid phases separated by a living membrane or between a cell and its surroundings, this is due to an active transport of one or more of the ionic species involved. The literature on the subject has been extensively reviewed and the reader is referred to Volume II of this treatise (Chapters 8 and 10) for a more complete analysis of the subject.

2. *Organic Ions*

a. Amino Acids. Since Van Slyke and Meyer (*4*) showed half a century ago, that amino acids enter tissues against apparent concentration gradients, our knowledge of the intimate nature of the process has not progressed much. Most of the work devoted to the matter was little more than a refinement of the original observation. Considering the results accumulated during the last decade, it seems that cells can be classified into three categories with respect to amino acids: (*a*) cells where an accumulation of amino acids from the extracellular medium can be demonstrated (monocellular organism, cells of the central nervous system, muscle fibers, etc.); (*b*) cells exhibiting a transcellular transport of amino acids—intestinal and renal epithelium, Ehrlich cells in certain experimental conditions (*5*); and (*c*) cells showing a regulation of the intracellular amino acid pool mainly through a balance between synthesis and catabolism of amino acids—nerve and muscle fibers in invertebrates, for instance.

If we consider the first two categories defined above (*a* and *b*), it is only in a very limited number of cases, surprisingly enough, that a direct demonstration of the nature of the process responsible for the flux of amino acids observed has been given. This is mainly owing to the technical difficulties encountered in the determination of the various parameters required to ascertain the nature of the forces involved. In the case of accumulation of amino acids by cells, dependence of the process on other metabolic events has been demonstrated with few exceptions (*6*). Glycolysis as well as respiration can provide the necessary energy (*6–9*).

Experiments with animal cells and tissues have shown that amino acids with rather different structures compete with one another in the uptake process (*10–16*). D-Amino acids seem also to be accumulated in certain specific cases (*17, 18*), but generally they inhibit the accumulation of the L form. In the cell nuclei, the D form is never accumulated and does not interfere with the accumulation process of the L form (*19*).

Each of the above arguments is, however, of little value in establishing the nature of the force involved (see Section II, A, 1), and one has to rely on various lines of evidence to consider that the uptake is indeed active. On the other hand, when we are dealing with transcellular accumulation, the nature of the forces responsible can be more readily defined. Various techniques have been proposed, the most generally used being those of the everted isolated segments of small intestine (*20*), the

TABLE II
AMINO ACIDS ABSORBED FROM THE LUMEN OF THE INTESTINE OF VARIOUS ANIMAL SPECIES

Amino acids	Concentration (M)	Methods	Species	Reference
L-Histidine	10^{-3}	*In vitro*	Rat	(*22*)
		In vivo	Rat	(*22*)
L-Methionine	10^{-3}	*In vivo*	Rat	(*22*)
L-Valine	10^{-3}	*In vivo*	Rat	(*22*)
L-Leucine	10^{-3}	*In vivo*	Rat	(*22*)
L-Histidine	2×10^{-2}	*In vivo*	Rat	(*23*)
L-Methionine	2×10^{-2}	*In vivo*	Rat	(*23*)
L-Tryptophan[a]	5×10^{-3}	*In vitro*	Hamster	(*24*)
L-Phenylalanine	5×10^{-3}	*In vitro*	Hamster	(*24*)
L-Tyrosine	5×10^{-3}	*In vitro*	Hamster	(*24*)
L-Tyrosine	3×10^{-3}	*In vitro*	Chick	(*25*)
L-Tyrosine	3×10^{-3}	*In vitro*	Rabbit	(*25*)
L-Tyrosine	3×10^{-3}	*In vitro*	Hamster	(*25*)
L-Tyrosine	3×10^{-3}	*In vitro*	Rat	(*25*)
L-Methionine	7×10^{-4}	*In vivo*	Chick	(*26*)
L-Histidine	7×10^{-4}	*In vivo*	Chick	(*26*)
L-Alanine	10^{-2}	*In vitro*	Green frog[b]	(*27*)
Glycine	10^{-2}	*In vitro*	Green frog	(*27*)
L-Histidine	10^{-2}	*In vitro*	Green frog	(*27*)
L-Alanine	—	*In vivo*	Cat	(*28*)
L-Histidine	—	*In vivo*	Dog	(*21*)
L-Alanine	—	*In vivo*	Dog	(*21*)

[a] Not concentrated at 2×10^{-2} M.
[b] *Rana clamitans.*

vascularized intestinal loop *in vivo* or the Thiry-Vella fistulas (*21*).

It has thus been possible to show that some amino acids are concentrated in the serosal fluid whereas others are not. Table II lists the amino acids absorbed from the lumen of the intestine of various species.

As far as the D enantiomorph of those amino acids is concerned, all the data available so far indicate that in certain specific cases they also seem to be accumulated, but to a lesser extent. Generally speaking also, if both forms are present, the D form inhibits the accumulation of the L form (Table III).

In the dog, L-histidine and L-alanine are accumulated to a greater extent than the D form. In the cat *in vivo* experiments show that the concentration of D-alanine found in the blood irrigating an isolated intestinal loop is less than the concentration of the L form in the same conditions (*28*).

These results are generally interpreted as indicating a fixation of the D form on a hypothetical carrier, thus preventing the L form from reaching it. The D form seems, however, unable to activate further the mechanism of transport. As shown in Table III, there also seems to be competition between the various amino acids concentrated in the serosal fluid.

TABLE III
INTERFERENCE BETWEEN AMINO ACIDS DURING INTESTINAL ABSORPTION

Amino acids		Inhibition			
Absorbed	Competitor	(%)	Method	Species	Reference
L-Histidine	L-Methionine	29.4	*In vitro*	Rat	(*22*)
L-Methionine	L-Histidine	0	*In vivo*		
L-Valine	L-Leucine	60.0			
L-Leucine	L-Valine	50.1			
L-Valine	L-Leucine L-Isoleucine	72.1–78.5			
L-Histidine	L-Methionine	71.8	*In vivo*	Rat	(*23*)
L-Methionine	L-Histidine	24.6			
L-Histidine	D-Methionine	20.0			
L-Methionine	D-Histidine	ca. 0			
L-Tyrosine	L-Phenylalanine		*In vitro*	Rat	(*25*)
3 m*M*	5 m*M*	15			
	15 m*M*	81			
	30 m*M*	88			
	D-Phenylalanine				
	5 m*M*	6			
	15 m*M*	18			
	30 m*M*	16			
	L-Methionine				
	15 m*M*	92			

It has also been shown that tryptophan and phenylalanine can successfully compete with the accumulation of L-histidine (*29*), and tryptophan with the accumulation of phenylalanine (*30*). Intestinal absorption of methionine and histidine was studied in adult chickens having permanent Thiry-Vella fistulas. The L isomers of both amino acids were absorbed from the fistulas more rapidly than the D isomers. At a concentration of 10^{-3} *M*, 2,4-DNP retarded absorption of L-methionine, but not of the D form. The absorption of L-histidine was impaired in the presence of equimolar concentrations of either L- or D-methionine. Racemization of D-methionine during absorption could not be demonstrated. The L isomers of both methionine and histidine appear to be absorbed from the chicken intestine by a common specific transport mechanism, D-methionine being able to participate in at least one stage of this mechanism (*26*).

Jervis and Smyth (*23*) have studied the relationships between the rate of absorption and concentration of D and L enantiomorphs of different amino acids. The values obtained for the Michaelis constants are of interest, particularly the low values for L-methionine; they suggest a relatively high affinity of L-methionine for the transport mechanism (Table IV).

Wiseman (*31*) found that L-methionine could compete successfully with L-histidine *in vitro* for the transport mechanism. Agar *et al.* (*29*) have demonstrated the same effect *in vivo* and Jervis and Smyth (*23*)

TABLE IV
ABSORPTION OF AMINO ACIDS IN THE RAT INTESTINE[a]

L-Methionine	D-Methionine	L-Histidine	D-Histidine
9.55	33.1	40.3	19.1

[a] Estimated values of the Michaelis-Menten constant (m*M*) (*23*).

found that L-methionine could compete successfully *in vivo* with L-histidine and D-histidine for intestinal absorption. All these results are consistent with the low Michaelis constant for L-methionine obtained in the experiments of Jervis and Smyth (*23*). The values of the constant for L- and D-histidine and D-methionine do not differ significantly from each other, and no conclusions can be drawn about their relative affinities for the transport mechanism.

The fact that there is preference for absorption of L-amino acids certainly suggests that an enzymatic process is concerned at least in the absorption of L isomer of amino acids. It seems likely that there is also a stage common to both L and D forms which shows kinetics approximating to the Michaelis-Menten scheme, and probably it is at this stage that competition between D and L forms takes place.

The renal tubule possesses an active transport system for the reabsorption of the basic amino acids L-lysine, L-ornithine, and L-arginine (*32–35*).

L-Cystine appears to share the same absorption mechanism, as suggested by studies of the human genetic defect cystinuria. Individuals with this condition excrete in their urine abnormally large amounts of L-cystine plus the three basic amino acids, the absorption of the other amino acid being unaffected (*36, 37*). Previous *in vitro* studies of the intestine indicated that while L-cystine was actively transported against a concentration gradient (*38*), L-lysine and L-ornithine were not thus transported (*31*). On the other hand, L-lysine was absorbed more rapidly than its D enantiomorph under *in vivo* conditions (*39*). It was also shown that intravenous injection of pyridoxine stimulated L-lysine absorption in vitamin B_6-deficient rats (*15*). These latter results suggest that the absorption of at least one of the basic amino acids might be mediated by a special carrier. Recently an important observation was made by Milne *et al.* (*40*), who reported that patients with cystinuria showed a defect in the intestinal absorption of L-lysine and L-ornithine. From this observation it would appear that the epithelial cells of the intestine may possess the same carrier system for the basic amino acid which is present in the proximal tubules of the kidney, and that the same mutation affects both systems. In view of these findings Hagihira *et al.* (*41*) have reinvestigated the problem, using the technique of the everted sacs of hamster intestine in order to see if an absorption of basic amino acids could be demonstrated in the intestinal epithelium.

Everted sacs of hamster intestine were incubated in Krebs Henseleit bicarbonate saline containing a C^{14}-labeled amino acid on both sides of the intestinal wall. Table V shows the active transport of the three basic

TABLE V
ACTIVE TRANSPORT OF BASIC AMINO ACIDS BY THE HAMSTER INTESTINE (*41*)

Amino acids	Initial concentration (m*M*)	Number of experiments	Final concentration, serosal/mucosal	Net transport (μM/100 mg. tissue/H)
L-Lysine C^{14}	1.0	3	5.1	0.77
L-Arginine[a]	1.0	5	1.5	0.21
DL-Ornithine-C^{14}	1.0	3	2.7	0.51
DL-Ornithine-C^{14}	2.0	5	2.0	0.62

[a] Rat instead of hamster was used because rat intestine contained less arginase.

amino acids against concentration gradients. It should be noted that in all cases the transport was against an electrical gradient, as the serosal side of the *in vitro* intestine is positive with respect to the mucosal side (*16, 42, 43*). The maximal rates of transport for these amino acids are one-tenth to one-twentieth of the rates for the transport of some neutral amino acids., e.g., glycine, L-alanine, L-proline (*31*). The small capacity for the transport of the basic amino acids explains the difficulty in obtaining significant net transport with high initial concentration.

Table VI shows that L-cystine and L-arginine inhibit the transport of L-lysine much more than that of glycine. Conversely L-methionine is a more effective inhibitor of glycine than of L-lysine. Previous studies have shown that the three basic amino acids have little or no inhibitory

TABLE VI
SEPARATE TRANSPORT FOR NEUTRAL AND BASIC AMINO ACIDS IN THE HAMSTER INTESTINE (*41*)

Inhibitor	Concentration (m*M*)	Per cent inhibition of tissue accumulation of: Glycine, 1 m*M*	L-Lysine, 1 m*M*
L-Arginine	2.0	16	89
L-Cystine	0.8	0	45
L-Lysine	1.0	14	—
Glycine	1.0	—	0
L-Methionine	1.0	73	32

effect on the transport of the neutral amino acids L-histidine and mono-iodo-L-tyrosine (*29, 31, 44*). In addition L-lysine does not inhibit the transport of L-isoleucine or L-methionine (*45*). It may be concluded that the intestinal epithelium cells possess a basic amino acid transport system similar to that found in the proximal tubules of the kidney.

Another interesting case of transcellular concentration of amino acids is given by the experiments carried out with a layer of Ehrlich ascites carcinoma cells 4 to 5 cells thick deposited on a filter separating two chambers (*5*).

The distribution of radioactive glycine, α-aminoisobutyric acid, and glutamate was examined in the presence or absence of pyridoxal in one of the solutions. It is indeed well known that pyridoxal stimulates the uptake of amino acids by carcinoma cells (*46*). When Krebs Ringer bicarbonate medium containing 10 m*M* glycine was placed on each side of the membrane, no detectable asymmetry of glycine developed. If 18 m*M* pyridoxal was added in one phase after a lag of 15 minutes, glycine began to concentrate in the other phase. The same result was obtained with pyridoxal phosphate. The membrane concentrated also amino acids from buffered solutions toward the side to which an excess of potassium or alanine was added. Similarly potassium was concentrated toward the side where glycine was added. Since the amino acids were also concentrated in the cells, the authors concluded that the transcellular concentration arose from intracellular concentration. This can be easily explained if there is an asymmetry in amino acid influx, i.e., pyridoxal would stimulate the influx across the cellular membranes facing the solution containing this compound.

A technique introduced more recently (*16*) meets all the requirements necessary to ascertain unequivocally the nature of the forces responsible for the movement of an ion or molecule across the intestinal epithelium. It is patterned on the method used with the single isolated electroplax of *Electrophorus electricus* L. (*47, 48, 49*). A segment of intestine is opened flat and the epithelium is gently stripped off the muscle layers. This operation can be done with many species without harm to the epithelium, but it is more easily performed with the guinea pig and various species of turtle. Histological sections of the epithelium have shown that this procedure does not alter visibly the microscopic morphology of the tissue. This observation is furthermore substantiated by permeability studies showing that the functional integrity of the epithelium is well preserved. The epithelium is then inserted between two Plexiglas

TABLE VII

INFLUX AND OUTFLUX OF GLYCINE ACROSS THE ISOLATED SMALL INTESTINE OF THE TURTLE *Testudo hermanni* G. F. GMELIN[a]

Expt.	E.P.	Influx	Expt.	E.P.	Outflux
1	4	0.10	7	2	0.019
2	1	0.088	8	2	0.0094
2	1	0.131			
3	4	0.071			
4	0.5	0.105			
4	0.5	0.106			
4	0.5	0.103			
5	0.5	0.16			
5	0.5	0.17			
6	0.5	0.062			
6	0.5	0.060			

[a] The duration of the experimental periods (E.P.) is given in hours; flux values in micromoles per square centimeter per hour. The potential difference is short-circuited; 5 μM/ml. of glycine in both solutions (*16*).

frames separating two pools of fluid. The saline is circulated and oxygenated by means of an air lift. Thus a separation of the two sides of the epithelium has been achieved, since the solution contained in one pool is in contact with the serosal side, while the other solution bathes the mucosal side of the epithelium. Any transfer of material from one chamber to the other is made through the epithelium. The potential difference arising between the two solutions is measured through agar bridges connected to calomel electrodes. Two other agar bridges are inserted at the end of the chambers and connected to a battery and a variable resistor. It is thus possible to pass an electric current through the preparation in such a way that the potential difference existing across the epithelium is abolished. This is the short circuit current. The intensity of the current is read on a microammeter.

TABLE VIII
INFLUX AND OUTFLUX OF GLYCINE ACROSS THE ISOLATED COLON OF THE TURTLE *Testudo hermanni* G. F. GMELIN[a]

Expt.	E.P.	Influx	Expt.	E.P.	Outflux
9	0.5	0.0031	13	2	0.0067
9	0.5	0.0026	13	2.5	0.0056
9	0.5	0.0037			
9	0.5	0.0037	14	1	0.0056
9	1.0	0.0037	14	2	0.0053
10	4	0.0041			
11	0.5	0.0057			
11	0.5	0.0066			
12	0.5	0.028			
12	0.5	0.024			
12	0.5	0.024			

[a] Conditions as in Table VII (*16*).

Tables VII–IX give the results of some experiments using glycine-C^{14} and glutamate-C^{14} with the isolated intestinal epithelium of the turtle *Testudo hermanni* G. F. Gmelin (*16*). Some of these experiments were carried out by measuring at regular time intervals the appearance of

TABLE IX
INFLUX AND OUTFLUX OF L-GLUTAMATE ACROSS THE ISOLATED INTESTINAL EPITHELIUM OF THE TURTLE *Testudo hermanni* G. F. GMELIN[a]

Expt. no.	Small intestine		Colon	
	Influx	Outflux	Influx	Outflux
1	0.018	0.015	0.0088	0.0089
2	—	—	0.0092	0.0096

[a] The potential difference is short-circuited. Influx and outflux were determined after an experimental period of 3 hours and are expressed in micromoles per square centimeter per hour; 5 μM/ml. of L-glutamate on both sides (*16*).

radioactivity in the solution bathing one or the other face of the epithelium. In other experiments the activity was measured at the end of the experiment. The three following findings were noted in the case of glycine: (*a*) A steady state for the influx is reached generally after 30 minutes across both the colon and small intestine. However, in the latter, this time is variable, since in some experiments it was found that influx reaches a constant value after 75 minutes. (*b*) With the small intestine the influx values are of an order of magnitude higher than those of the outflux. (*c*) In the colon, the flux values are very similar and always smaller than the values found with the small intestine. Thus the results demonstrate unambiguously that glycine is actively transported across the epithelium of the small intestine whereas it moves passively across the colon.

Table IX shows the results obtained with glutamate. It can be seen that in the colon, as well as in the small intestine, the flux ratio is very close to 1, thus demonstrating the passive behavior of this amino acid. It is also interesting to note that the permeability of the colon to glutamate is lower than the permeability of the small intestine for the same compound. Using this technique it has also been demonstrated that L-glutamate and L-arginine are without effect on the influx of glycine across the small intestine and the colon. On the contrary, L-alanine reduces the influx of glycine across the small intestine. This result is interpreted as showing that a common step is involved in the active transport of L-alanine and glycine. Other experiments are, however, necessary to decide whether or not we are dealing with a true competitive phenomenon obeying Michaelis-Menten kinetics.

It may thus be concluded that a number of L-amino acids are transported by the intestine against a concentration gradient, whereas the D-isomers tested are not.

Among several amino acids transported, certain ones inhibit the transport of others. L-Methionine was found to be the most potent inhibitor in this respect. Although the intestinal transport system has an unambiguous requirement for the stereo configuration at the α carbon of the amino acid, its specificity for the side chain is difficult to define. Thus the transport of both L-tyrosine and glycine were inhibited by L-methionine, suggesting a common carrier for these compounds, although they have very different side chains. However, in the studies on L-tyrosine analog (DL-*m*-tyrosine, DL-*o*-tyrosine, 3,5-diiodotyrosine), slight alterations in the ring of the side chain greatly affects the rate of transport (25).

The different results on the specificity of the amino acid transport system in these two kinds of experiments might be explained if both entrance and exit permeations are selective and have different structural requirements.

It has been shown repeatedly that the cells of the Ehrlich mouse ascites tumor transfer amino acids into their interior as do most cells of pluricellular organisms. There is, however, a difficulty when one has to define the exact nature of the forces involved in this concentration process. The main obstacle arises from the fact that we have little, if any, control on the intracellular phase. The various parameters defined in Section II are not experimentally accessible, and some hypothesis must be made as to the intracellular physicochemical state of the compound under study. It has been shown that glycine could be 20 times as concentrated in the interior of the isolated cells as in the surrounding medium (*12*). If glycine is free in the cell, its concentration must be the result of an active transport. At the physiological pH, glycine is indeed mostly a molecule without net electric charge, a small part of it being anionic; the only important parameter is then the concentration, or more precisely, the activity. If, however, glycine is bound, it could enter the cell passively, bind some cytoplasmic constituent, and thus simulate an active transport. A distinction between these two modes of entry is not possible from steady state distribution or from the simple observation that the transfer is dependent upon metabolic process. The binding could indeed be endergonic.

It has been assumed on the basis of various observations that most of the intracellular amino acids are free. Fragments of cancer cells obtained by sudden pressure release (*50*), or by grinding after freeze-drying (*51*), are unable to accumulate amino acids. Accumulation of amino acids at high concentration was found to disturb the osmotic equilibrium between intra- and extracellular fluid (*11*). As will be discussed in more detail in a following section, amino acids are an important constituent of the osmoregulatory mechanisms in invertebrates, suggesting that they are osmotically active and thus really free. The loss of radioactivity from cells previously incubated with labeled glycine is not enhanced on addition of large amounts of unlabeled glycine to the medium (*51*). These observations, if they do not prove, at least strongly suggest, that amino acids are free in the cell interior. More direct and conclusive evidence has been published by Heinz (*52*) and Oxender and Christensen (*5*). The experiments of Oxender and Christensen have already been discussed above. Heinz has produced more direct information as to the nature of the forces involved in the transfer process of glycine in the Ehrlich mouse ascites cells by studying the kinetics of the fluxes with and without inhibition. He was able to show that cells in the steady state with respect to the distribution of glycine exchange more than 90% of their glycine in about 5 minutes. The kinetics of this exchange seems to indicate that intracellular glycine behaves as though most of it is freely dissolved in a single compartment. It can therefore be concluded that the accumulation within the cell is the effect of a metabolically linked active transport mechanism.

b. Fatty Acids. As far as fatty acids are concerned, not many data are available in the literature to clarify the nature of the forces responsible for the absorption of these organic ions from the lumen of the intestine. It is known that in some parts of the digestive tract of different herbivorous or phytophagous mammals, the enzymatic degradation of cellulose by bacterial cellulase is followed by the fermentation of hydrolytic products into carbonic anhydride and volatile fatty acids like acetic, propionic, and butyric acids (*53–56*). This degradation takes place not only in the rumen when this structure is present, but also in the cecum and colon. Fatty acids are then absorbed: venous blood irrigating these organs is more concentrated in fatty acids than venous blood irrigating the small intestine. These observations have been made not only at the level of the rumen and cecum of different ruminants, but also in the colon of the horse and the pig and in the cecum of the beaver, the rat, and the rabbit (*54, 56a,b, 57, 57a*).

More recently, experiments have been described in which transfer of short-chain fatty acid by an *in vitro* intestinal preparation of rat has been demonstrated (*58*). It is however, difficult, on the basis of these experiments, to decide whether or not there is an active transport of fatty acids, since the flux values were not correlated with the spontaneous potential difference existing across the intestinal wall. It should indeed be remembered that conditions known to modify the potential difference as well as the active transport of glucose and sodium, affect also the transfer of fatty acids.

Long-chain fatty acids are continuously absorbed from the solution bathing the mucosal side of the golden hamster intestine and appear in the serosal solution as triglycerides with small amounts of diglycerides and free fatty acids (*59*). The distribution of glyceride activity in the intestinal wall is similar to that in the serosal solution. These results suggest the greatest caution in interpreting results on the transfer of long-chain fatty acids since they demonstrate that the fatty acid transported appears mainly as another chemical species in the serosal fluid. This fact has thus to be taken into consideration, before applying to this phenomenon the well-defined and strictly restricted concept of active transport.

3. *Organic Molecules: Sugars*

There are a number of *in vitro* observations, using the everted intestine sac technique (*20*), showing that sugars may be divided into two groups: (*a*) those that are transported against an apparent concentration gradient and (*b*) those that are not.

The experiment begins with sugar at the same concentration on both sides of the intestine. It is relevant at this point to mention that the membrane potential will not be expected to exert a strong influence on the movement of sugar, as we are dealing with an uncharged species.

At the end of a period of incubation the contents of the sac are recovered and analyzed for sugar. If the concentration has remained unchanged, no net flux occurred and active transport may be ruled out. If the concentration increased in one of the solutions, it may be ascertained that sugar has been moved by an active process, providing that the sugar remains the same free unchanged chemical species on both sides of the membrane, and that this change in concentration cannot be accounted for by a change in volume. Using this technique, it has been shown that D-glucose is actively transported across the intestinal wall of the following species: rat (*59a–61*), golden hamster (*62*), guinea pig (*61*), catfish (*Ameiurus nebulosus*) (*63*), toad (*Bufo bufo*) (*64*), and turtle (*Chrysemis picta*) (*65*).

Studies of specificity with nonmetabolizable analogs of glucose and other sugars have also been performed on the golden hamster intestine (*62*). The results are shown in Table X.

Sugar transport systems have also been demonstrated in monocellular preparations as well as across muscle cell membrane. As already pointed out for inorganic ions and amino acids, when we are dealing with intracellular transport, it is very arduous to define the nature of the forces responsible for the movements observed, since we have little control, if any, on the intracellular phase. Direct evidence for the entry of free monosaccharides into yeast cell was lacking until recently (*66, 67*). Previously, yeast cell membrane was found impermeable to these sugars (*68, 69*), as well as to fermentable sugars (*69–71*). Centrifuged yeast is 80% water in volume and 30–33% of the volume is extracellular space (*68*). On the basis of this observation it is evident that only a distribution of a substance into a volume greater than 33% of the packed yeast volume represents entry into the cell. Table XI shows the results obtained with various nonfermentable sugars (*72*).

It is evident from these data that the first three sugars listed showed maximum distribution into the total aqueous space without accumulation, while the presence of the other sugars was limited to the extracellular space. Among the pairs of molecules of equal size listed in Table XI, xylose entered while arabinose did not; sorbose entered while galactose did not; α-methyl-D-glucoside entered while α-methyl-D-mannoside did not. Entry was therefore stereospecific and indicated that the process is more complicated than a simple diffusion.

A carrier-mediated distribution between extra- and intracellular space could explain the results obtained. This type of transport first proposed

TABLE X
SPECIFICITY OF INTESTINAL SUGAR TRANSPORT: RESULTS OBTAINED WITH GLUCOSE, NONMETABOLIZABLE ANALOGS OF GLUCOSE AND OTHER SUGARS (*62*)

Compounds actively transported	
D-Glucose	4-*O*-Methyl-D-galactose
1,5-Anhydro-D-glucitol	D-Allose
2-C-Hydroxymethyl-D-glucose	6-Deoxy-D-glucose
D-Glucoheptulose	6-Deoxy-D-galactose
3-*O*-Methyl-D-glucose	6-Deoxy-6-fluoro-D-glucose
D-Galactose	7-Deoxy-D-glucoheptose
3-Deoxy-D-glucose	α-Methyl-D-glucoside
Compounds not actively transported	
D-Mannoheptulose	3-*O*-Propyl-D-glucose
D-Mannose	3-*O*-Butyl-D-glucose
D-Talose	3-*O*-Hydroxyethyl-D-glucose
1,5-Anhydro-D-mannitol	1,4-Anhydro-D-glucitol
2-Deoxy-D-glucose	Gold-thioglucose
2-Deoxy-D-galactose	D-Gulose
2-*O*-Methyl-D-glucose	6-Deoxy-6-iodo-D-galactose
D-Glucosamine	6-*O*-Methyl-D-glucose
N-Acetyl-D-glucosamine	L-Galactose
2,4-Di-*O*-methyl-D-galactose	L-Glucose
D-Fructose	L-Sorbose
3-*O*-Methyl-D-fructose	6-Deoxy-L-galactose
3-*O*-Ethyl-D-glucose	6-Deoxy-L-mannose
d-Xylose	Mannitol
L-Xylose	Sorbitol
D-Ribose	Glycerol
L-Arabinose	
D-Arabinose	

by Ussing (*73*) differs from simple diffusion, in that it is carrier dependent, produces no net flux, and is specific. Sugar uptake has most of these characteristics. It occurs without accumulation, is stereospecific, and is inhibited by glucose, presumably owing to competition for entry sites (*72*). The observation that glucose inhibits transport of nonfermentable sugars suggests a competition for some membrane transport sites.

In human or rabbit red cells, sugar transport seems also to involve a carrier molecule, but without uphill transport. Thus this does not appear to be an active transport mechanism. Glucose inhibits the exchange of galactose and maltose inhibits the transfer of glucose or galactose in erythrocytes (*74*).

Specificity, competition between different sugars for the transport, saturation kinetics, indicate that binding with graded affinities to a limited number of binding sites is involved (*75*).

The L-cell strain fibroblasts of mouse connective tissue origin, has been used to study sugar accumulation. They take up galactose and glucose against a concentration gradient. Glucose uptake is inhibited by galactose, 2-deoxyglucose, phloridzin, and phloretin (*76*).

TABLE XI
FREE SPACE OF CENTRIFUGED BAKERS' YEAST TO NONFERMENTABLE SUGARS (*72*)

Sugar	Free space (%)
L-Sorbose	80
D-Xylose	80
α-Methyl-D-glucoside	80
D-Galactose	33
L-Arabinose	35
α-Methyl-D-mannoside	35
Lactose	33

As far as muscle fibers are concerned (cardiac muscle or diaphragm in rat), the view generally accepted is that glucose enters the cell through a carrier-mediated mechanism in the membrane and is freed in the intracellular space, but failure to show accumulation arises from the fact that it is metabolized as rapidly as it enters the cell; transport is normally the rate-limiting step (*77, 78*).

Any factor that inhibits oxidative phosphorylation accelerates transport of monosaccharide in muscle. Insulin and certain ions (Na, Li, K) also stimulate the transport of sugar (*78–84*), whereas calcium is inhibitory (*84*).

4. *Significance of the Concentration Differences*

When dealing with sugars, amino acids, fatty acids, the reason why a cell or an organism should possess a mechanism enabling it to concentrate the molecules in one phase is pretty obvious, since we are dealing with molecules constituting the building stones or the chemical energy sources needed to carry on the process of life. In the case of inorganic ions, the reasons are more subtle and require a more thorough analysis. It is generally assumed that life originated in a liquid phase, the concentration of which, in inorganic salts, was very close to that of actual sea water, that is a medium where the concentration of sodium is high in respect to that of potassium. Most cells maintain intracellularly high potassium and low sodium concentrations by virtue of a mechanism of active sodium transport outward, coupled more or less tightly to an active transport of potassium directed inward.

One thus wonders why the cell would possess a specialized mechanism to control the cation content of its interior. It has been proposed that the enzymatic activity of the cell is possible only in a special ionic environment. While this is certainly the case, the possibility still remains that this is a secondary adaptation to a situation created by a more urgent necessity.

Another remarkable property of living cells is indeed their ability to maintain a constant volume throughout life. As the cell interior contains molecules that cannot go through the membrane, inflow of extracellular solution tends to produce swelling of the cell. Swelling can be avoided if the cell possesses a rigid membrane or a membrane impermeable to a large fraction of the solutes in the extracellular medium. In the first solution, adopted by some bacterial and plant cells (*85*), an intracellular hydrostatic pressure is developed to balance the osmotic inflow of solution. The second solution, i.e., impermeability of the cell membrane, has never been shown to occur. The only remaining possibility for solving the problem of swelling is therefore for the membrane to possess a mechanism regulating its ionic content.

B. Origin of the Potential Difference Existing across Most Living Membranes

While there is still some controversy with regard to the exact nature of the potential difference existing across a living membrane, it is well demonstrated that the potential difference is a consequence of the metabolic activity of the cell.

1. *Zeta Potential*

Some authors consider that the potential difference is of an electrokinetic nature (ζ-potential). On this view, the potential difference should result from the presence of fixed charges in the membrane. Charges of opposite signs are spatially separated within the membrane owing to the metabolic activity of the cell. This gives rise to the formation of counterion layers and subsequently a potential difference (*86–88*).

2. *Oxidoreduction Potential*

Another theory about the nature of the transmembrane potential has been proposed recently (*89*). It is a reinterpretation of the Lund theory (*90*) that transmembrane potentials are primarily oxidoreduction potentials. It is assumed that two oxidation-reduction enzyme systems are located at the two faces of the cell membrane. They are connected by transmembrane lipoid substances with conjugated bonds. Electrons are transmitted by resonance under electronic pressure from the reactions of the enzyme systems. If this is the primary source of electromotive force in the membrane, it is then possible to explain the transport of ions, assuming the existence of pores selective for different ions [see also (*91*)].

3. *Electrochemical Potential*

Most workers, however, consider the potential difference as being electrochemical in nature; the picture we arrive at is that, owing to unequal distribution of ions and selective permeability characteristics of the living membrane, a potential difference takes place according to the relation shown in Eq. 3.

$$E_1 - E_2 = RT/zF \ln \left(\frac{P_{K}[K_1] + P_{Na}[Na_1] + P_{Cl}[Cl_2]}{P_{K}[K_2] + P_{Na}[Na_2] + P_{Cl}[Cl_1]} \right) \tag{3}$$

where $E_1 - E_2$ is the electrical potential difference existing between solutions 1 and 2, the *P*'s are the coefficients of relative permeability. The subindexes 1 and 2 refer to solutions 1 and 2, respectively; *R*, *T*, *z*, and *F* have their usual meaning (*92*). This relation is derived from the constant field membrane of Goldman (*93*), i.e., the electric field developed across the membrane by the difference in ionic mobilities is continuous. This thus implies that the architecture responsible for the permeability characteristics is homogeneous throughout. Equations have also been derived considering that the electric field of the membrane is distributed discontinuously across its thickness (*94*). Another limitation of Eq. 3 is that the *P*'s are supposed to remain constant over a wide range of concentration for the various ions considered. This is certainly not the case, as will be shown below [Section VII; see also (*92, 95*)].

4. *Significance of the Potential Difference*

In the most generally accepted theory about the origin of bioelectric potential, it is assumed that an electrical potential difference exists owing to the selective permeability of the membrane and the unequal distribution of ions. The following model of a cell may thus be proposed (*96*) (Fig. 1). The intracellular concentration of Na, Na_i^+, is kept low while that of K, K_i^+ is high, because of the active transport mechanism. There is a leakage of Na and K through the structure responsible for the passive permeability characteristics of the membrane, and the potential difference is given by Eq. 4.

$$E_i - E_o = E = \frac{RT}{zF} \ln \left(\frac{P_K K_i + P_{Na} Na_i}{P_K K_o + P_{Na} Na_o} \right) \tag{4}$$

The equilibrium potential for Cl is given by Eq. 5.

$$E = -\frac{RT}{zF}\ln\frac{\mathrm{Cl}_o}{\mathrm{Cl}_i} \tag{5}$$

Equations 4 and 5 express the equality between the diffusion potential due to K and Na leaks and the equilibrium potential for Cl, and thus explain the mechanism by which the intracellular concentration in Cl is kept low. The portion of the outflux of an ion which depends on the

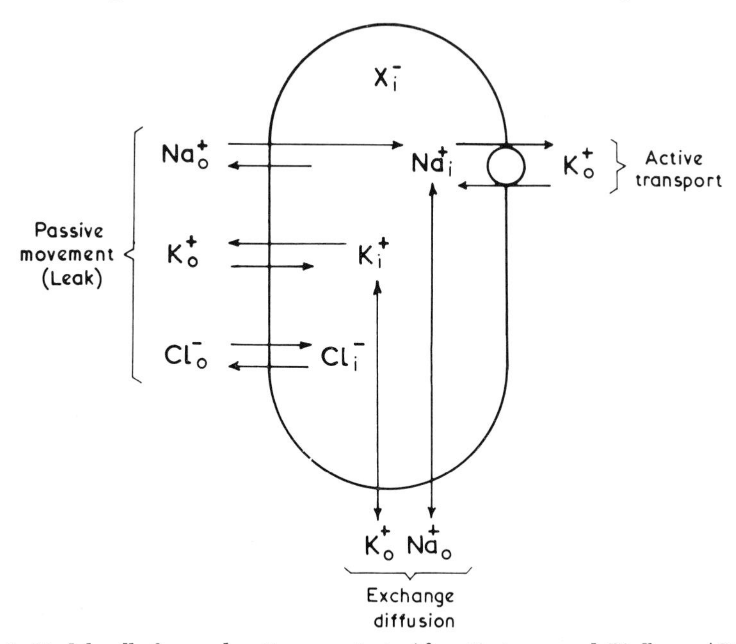

FIG. 1. Model cell; for explanation, see text. After Tosteson and Hoffman (*96*).

presence of the ion in the external solution is generally taken to be a measure of the exchange diffusion component (*73*) of the total flux. In this process there is no net exchange of ions between the cell and its surroundings and thus no contribution to the potential difference measure. X_i^- is the intracellular concentration of nondiffusible solute.

From the above model, it is clear that it is rather difficult to dissociate potential difference and unequal distribution of ions. It is apparent that the distribution of Cl is determined by the magnitude of E, the potential difference. E itself is directly related to the relative values of Na and K leaks as given by the values of P_{Na} and P_{K}. Since a living membrane is permeable to free ions, a potential difference will develop as long as there is a difference in the permeability of the membranes to the various ions and as long as the unequal distribution is maintained by the active transport of some ionic species. The potential difference can thus be considered as a direct consequence of the mechanism enabling the cell to keep its volume constant.

Interesting adaptations are offered by the different categories of conducting cells (neurons, nerve fibers, electric organs of fishes, etc.) since they make use of the free energy accumulated as concentration gradients and electrical potential to produce an electric current. This aspect of the problem has been considered more extensively in a preceding chapter (Volume II, Chapter 10) (*92*).

III. Cellular Differentiation and Permeability Characteristics

As shown above, one may thus explain very satisfactorily the origin of the concentration differences, as well as the potential difference existing across a living membrane, by the permeability characteristics of this membrane.

Our purpose now is to show that cellular differentiation at the level of the ionic regulation (permeability characteristics of the membrane) seems to be the result of physiological radiations of a biochemical system rather than of a true biochemical differentiation of membrane components* (*42, 97, 98*). In other words, the diversity in the field by permeability would generally be achieved through a spatial rearrangement of permeability characteristics. This, however, does not exclude discrete biochemical modification of the membrane in the course of adaptation to different environmental conditions.

A. Amphibian Skin

To illustrate this proposition let us analyze in more detail some observations demonstrated using the isolated amphibian skin as experimental material.

As we have already mentioned, the skin of the frog is the site of an active transport of Na from the outside solution toward the internal medium. There is thus an asymmetry as far as the movement of sodium is concerned, and one may expect the cellular membrane facing outside to have characteristics different from those of the membranes facing inward. This is indeed the case: (*a*) the effect of various compounds on Na flux or potential difference is dependent on the site of application (*99–102*); (*b*) pH variations, using a PO_4 buffer, affect the skin differently according to the site of application, optimum values being above 6 in the solution bathing the outside of the skin, while they are above 8 in the solution bathing the inside of the skin (*103*); (*c*) cellular mem-

* It is, however, evident that physiological radiation is dependent on genic control and thus implies a biochemical differentiation at this level.

branes facing outside are permeable to Na and impervious to K, while the contrary holds true for the membrane facing inside (*104*); (*d*) if a microelectrode is introduced through the skin the potential difference recorded between the solutions bathing the skin is established through successive steps (one or two) (*105*); (*e*) lack of K in the inside solution inhibits the active transport of Na, but a potassium-free outside medium is without any effect (*104*).

The accompanying schematic representation (Fig. 2C) describes satisfactorily how the frog skin behaves under a wide variety of conditions.

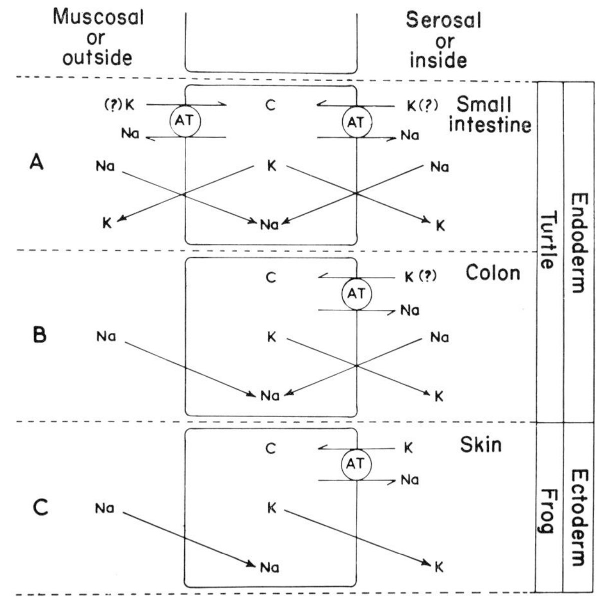

FIG. 2. Schematic representation of epithelial cells: (A) from the turtle small intestine; (B) from the turtle colon; (C) from the frog skin (*42*).

Let us first consider the case when the skin is bathed by Ringer solution on both sides. Figure 2C represents an epithelial cell of the skin in contact with Ringer on the outside and the inside. The outer membrane is permeable to Na, to Cl, and to water; the inner membrane is permeable to K, Cl, water, and the active transport of Na is also located at this level.

Since the active transport of Na is inhibited in the absence of K in the inside solution, this observation is best explained if one considers that the active transport of Na is coupled more or less closely with a movement of K inward.

Sodium diffuses into the cell through the outside border and gives rise to a diffusion potential which makes the cell positive in relation to the outside. Potassium diffuses out in the opposite direction. The magnitude of the potential difference across the outer border, designated 1, is given by Eq. 6

$$E_o - E_c = \frac{RT}{zF} \ln \frac{P_{Na}{}^1(\mathrm{Na})_o + P_{Cl}{}^1(\mathrm{Cl})_c}{P_{Na}{}^1(\mathrm{Na})_c + P_{Cl}{}^1(\mathrm{Cl})_o} \tag{6}$$

where $E_o - E_c$ *is* the potential difference between the outside solution *o* and the intracellular fluid *c*, *P*'s the coefficients of relative permeability for Na and Cl of the outer membrane 1. The other symbols have their usual meaning. The potential difference across the inner border is accordingly given by

$$E_c - E_i = \frac{RT}{zF} \ln \frac{P_K{}^2(\mathrm{K})_c + P_{Cl}{}^2(\mathrm{Cl})_i}{P_K{}^2(\mathrm{K})_i + P_{Cl}{}^2(\mathrm{Cl})_c} \tag{7}$$

where $E_c - E_i$ is the potential difference across the inner border, *P*'s the coefficients of relative permeability for K and Cl of the inside membrane, 2.

The total potential difference between the solutions *o* and *i* is

$$E_o - E_i = (E_o - E_c) + (E_c - E_i) \tag{8}$$

Thus in the case just considered the asymmetry in potential difference is achieved (*a*) by virtue of a concentration gradient for Na and K resulting from the existence of an active transport mechanism; (*b*) the spatial arrangement of some permeability characteristics.

So far little has been said about the spatial arrangement of the permeability characteristics of either inner and outer membrane. Consider, for instance, the outer membrane. In the system depicted it is permeable to Na, Cl, and water. Does that mean that the three species move through the same channel, or are we dealing with two or more channels spatially individualized?

In order to elucidate this problem let us analyze in some detail the effect of various compounds known to affect the permeability characteristics of living membrane. Some years ago Kirschner (*99*) showed that the addition of curare to the solution bathing the outside of the isolated frog skin produces a reversible increase in the active transport of Na. These results have been confirmed by others, who observed a similar effect with a variety of neurotropic compounds such as local anesthetics (*100*), pilocarpine, atropine, pyridine-2-aldoxime methiodide (2-PAM), and so on (*101, 102, 106–108*).

On the other hand, the capricious response of the skin of *Rana temporaria* L. to curare, already noted by Kirschner, was also confirmed and shown to result, at least partly, from hormonal variations (*102*). In order to explain the enhancement of the active transport of Na, it has been proposed that curare acts by increasing the passive permeability to Na of the membrane of the epithelial cells of the skin which face the outside (*100, 106*). This results in an increase in potential difference and in intracellular Na concentration which in turn stimulates the active transport mechanism for Na.

It is also well demonstrated that the increase in potential difference is due to an increase in Na permeability, by the fact that, in the presence of a nonpenetrating anion (SO_4) as substitute for Cl, no increase in potential difference is observed, as might be expected from the examination of Eq. 6. The results, however, do not exclude the possibility of a modification of the Cl permeability.

On the basis of studies carried out with 2-PAM and local anesthetics, it may be concluded that the increase in permeability to Na is brought about under the following conditions: (*a*) the compound must be applied to the solution bathing the outside of the skin; (*b*) the nitrogen must be cationic; (*c*) the molecule bearing the cationic nitrogen must have a particular structure.

If a quaternary nitrogen derivative is made lipid soluble by the addition of a long-chain alkyl group, there is initially an increase in potential difference and active transport of Na, followed by a decrease in potential difference and an inhibition of active transport (*101, 102*). The same effect is observed with local anesthetics if the pH of the outside solution is such that the compound is mainly in the form of an undissociated base (*100*). It may thus be concluded from these experiments that quaternary nitrogen derivatives enhance the passive permeability to Na of the membrane of the skin facing outside. If they are able to reach the site of the active transport mechanism, they also inhibit this mechanism, as shown by our results with 2-PAD (*107*). As for the local anesthetics, it is still possible that, since the undissociated base is in equilibrium with the cationic form at the site of the active transport, the active transport mechanism may be inhibited by the cationic form.

Lipid-soluble quaternary nitrogen derivatives are ionic detergents. The effects observed could therefore be due to the fact that the molecules dissolve in some lipid phase of the membrane and thus modify the structure of the membrane. However, a nonionic detergent, like polyethylene glycol, has no effect on the potential difference or the ion flux across the frog skin. On the other hand, a cationic detergent (benzalkonium chloride) or an anionic detergent (sodium lauryl sulfate) when applied on either side of the skin produces first an increase in potential difference followed by a decrease (*109*). This is the same type of response obtained with noracetylcholine 12 (noracetylcholine dodeciodide) or pyridine-2-aldoxime dodeciodide (2-PAD). These effects are independent of Ca concentrations.

These results suggest that to be effective in changing the permeability of the skin a detergent must bear an electric charge, its action being then rather unspecific and perhaps localized essentially to that part of the membrane responsible for its condenser-like properties (*109a*).

We have also measured the net flux of water across the skin of *Rana temporaria temporaria* L. before and after application of curare and other compounds known to affect the potential difference and the active transport of Na. The results are shown in Table XII (*108, 110*).

TABLE XII
EFFECT OF CURARE ON THE POTENTIAL DIFFERENCE AND NET FLUX OF WATER ACROSS THE ISOLATED SKIN OF *Rana temporaria temporaria* L.[a]

	Control		Curare		
Expt. No.	Time (hours)	Net flux of water (μl. cm.$^{-2}$ hr.$^{-1}$)	Time (hours)	Net flux of water (μl. cm.$^{-2}$ hr.$^{-1}$)	Δ Potential difference (mv.)
1	4	5	4	8	—
2	4	3	3.5	7	4
3	4	3	4	4	11
4	4	3	3	16	6.5
5	4	3	3.5	15	7
6	3.5	3	3.5	9	4
7	3	5	1.5	12	−9.5
8	3	4	2.5	11	−1.5

[a] Ringer's solution inside; Ringer at 1:10 outside. The time in hours indicates the duration of the control or experimental periods. Δ potential difference is the maximum variation of the potential difference observed after application of 170 μg./ml. of *d*-tubocurarine chloride in the outside solution. The minus sign indicates a decrease in potential difference (*110*).

It can be seen that, at the concentrations used, curare consistently enhances the net flux of water. In some instances, the flux rate is five times that of the control although in most experiments the rate is enhanced two- to threefold. In the case of atropine sulfate or pilocarpine chlorohydrate, we observe an increase in both net flux of water and electrical potential difference (*106–108*).

These results are consistent with the hypothesis that curare acts on the frog skin by increasing the diameter of membrane pores. However, it is important to note that, despite the increase in membrane permeability to water under the influence of curare, the membrane potential is not consistently enhanced. This again is a confirmation of previous results concerning the capricious way in which *R. temporaria* responds to curare and other neurotropic compounds. Although alternative explanations are possible, these results may suggest that the increase in water and Na permeabilities are two independent processes: thus, water and Na move through different channels in the frog skin. This explanation seems to be very likely if one considers the following.

While 2-PAM increases the potential difference, it is without effect on the net flux of water. We have thus taken advantage of the fact that curare or ADH consistently increase the net flux of water across the amphibian skin and the toad bladder (*111, 112*). Application of 2-PAM gives rise to an increase in potential difference. Then, if curare or ADH is added, there is an additional increase in potential difference, but no effect on water flux (Fig. 3) (*108*). If the reverse experiment is carried

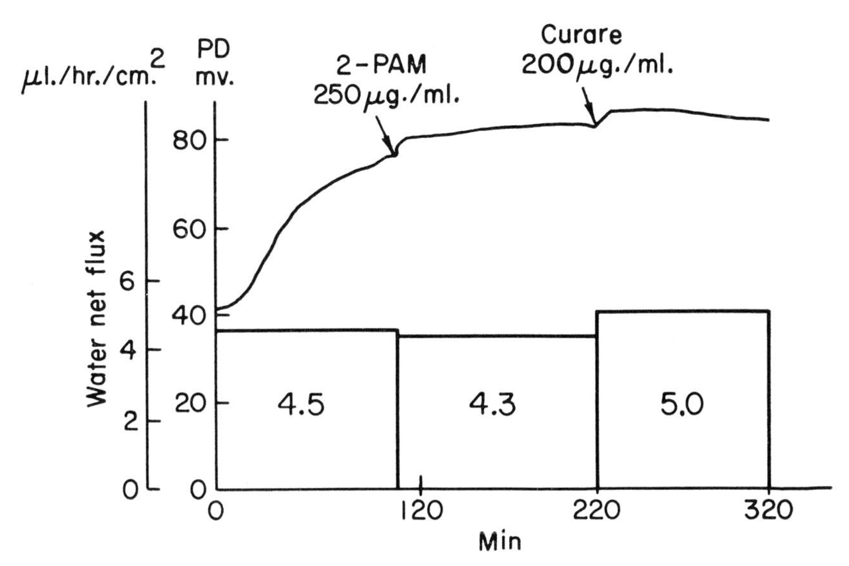

Fig. 3. Action of 2-PAM (250 μg./ml.) and curare (200 μg./ml.) on the potential difference and the net flux of water. Curare and 2-PAM are added outside (*108*).

out, the following result is observed. An application of ADH gives rise to an increase in both potential difference and net flux of water. Subsequent applications of 2-PAM are followed by an increase in potential difference while the net flux of water goes back almost to the control value (Fig. 4) (*108*). It is thus possible to dissociate net flux of water and increase in Na permeability. This result is consistent with the hypothesis that Na and water move through channels spatially separated at the outer border of the epithelial cells of the frog skin. It is also worth noting that 2-PAM seems to be able to occupy the site responsible for the increase in water permeability without being able to activate them, as shown by the fact that the increase in net water flux following application of ADH is inhibited by application of 2-PAM. More experiments, however, are necessary before we can decide whether we are dealing with an inhibition of a true competitive type.

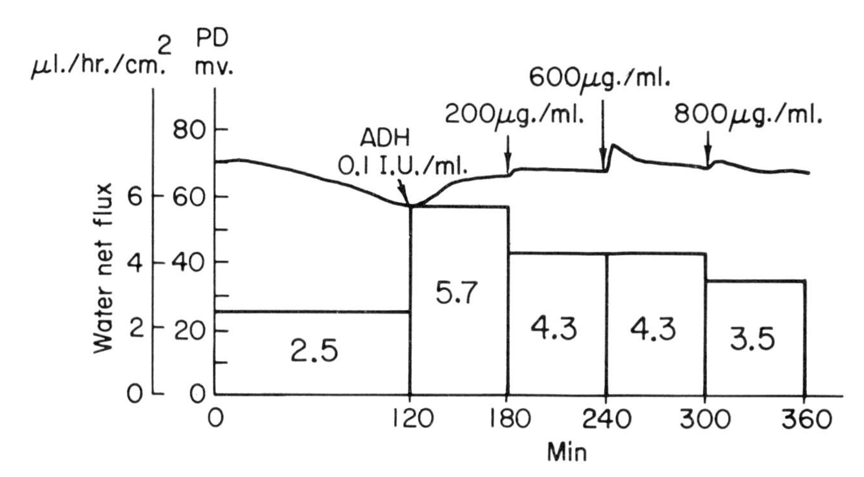

FIG. 4. Action of ADH (0.1 I.U./ml.) and 2 PAM (200 800 µg./ml.) on the potential difference and the net flux of water. ADH is added inside, 2-PAM outside (*108*).

With respect to Cl permeability we have no information to indicate whether or not Cl movement goes through a specific channel.

The results presented above thus suggest that the permeability characteristics of the frog skin are spatially separated and thus may correspond to well-defined structural arrangements in the membrane, differently affected by a large number of pharmacodynamically active agents. 2-PAM, while able to occupy the sites responsible for the passive movement of Na and water, is however unable to activate these sites equally. Other compounds (i.e., atropine, curare, pilocarpine, ADH) are good activators of both sites. 2-PAM seems to compete for the same sites with the other class of compounds since 2-PAM, a poor activator of the site responsible for water movement, is, however, able to prevent the action of ADH, a good activator of this site (*108*).

B. Intestinal Epithelium of the Turtle

Since we have examined at length the case of the amphibian skin in order to demonstrate the methodological approach used in our studies, a brief summary of the results obtained with the intestinal epithelium of the turtle (*Testudo hermanni* G. F. Gmelin) will be sufficient to illustrate our point.

The permeability characteristics of the intestinal epithelium of the turtle may be represented schematically as follows (Fig. 2, A and B) (*42, 113*).

In the small intestine the membranes in contact with the mucosal side are permeable to Na and K and seem to be the site of an active transport mechanism for Na. The same situation is found for the serosal membranes in the small intestine and in the colon. On the contrary, the mucosal membranes of the colon are permeable only to Na, a situation thus resembling that found in the frog skin. It is interesting to note that the intestinal epithelium is of endodermic origin whereas that of the frog skin comes from the ectoderm. This schematic representation (Fig. 2) emerges from studies of electrical potential difference recorded under various conditions of ionic composition. As pointed out above (Section II, B) it is based on the assumption that the ionic composition is without appreciable effect on the coefficient of relative permeability of the membrane for the ions involved. As discussed elsewhere, this is certainly not the case (*95*). If this invites one to be cautious concerning quantitative treatment of the results, it still remains well established, that, under the same experimental conditions, the epithelium of the small intestine and the colon behave differently, thus suggesting that the permeability characteristics are also different. In the present state of our knowledge, they are best represented by the scheme of Fig. 2.

IV. Relations between Inorganic Ions, Sugar, Amino Acids, Fatty Acids, and Bioelectric Potentials

The electrical potential difference recorded at the level of the small intestine of many species is always very small, around 0.5–4 mv., the lumen being negative with respect to the serosal side (*113*).

If glucose, certain amino acids, or fatty acids were added in physiological saline, an increase in potential difference was observed (*114*). This is well demonstrated by the following experiment (*115*): L-Alanine was added at the concentration of 5 μmoles/ml. in the solution bathing the mucosal side of an isolated piece of turtle small intestine. The potential difference goes from 0.5 to 5.25 mv. If the concentration of L-alanine is further increased to 10 μmoles/ml. it reaches the value of 9 mv. (Fig. 5). The same result is observed with other amino acids known to be actively transported: glycine and L-serine, for instance. On the contrary, amino acids moving passively across the epithelium, e.g., L-glutamic acid, L-arginine, L-lysine, are without effect.

The short-circuit current is also affected by these amino acids actively

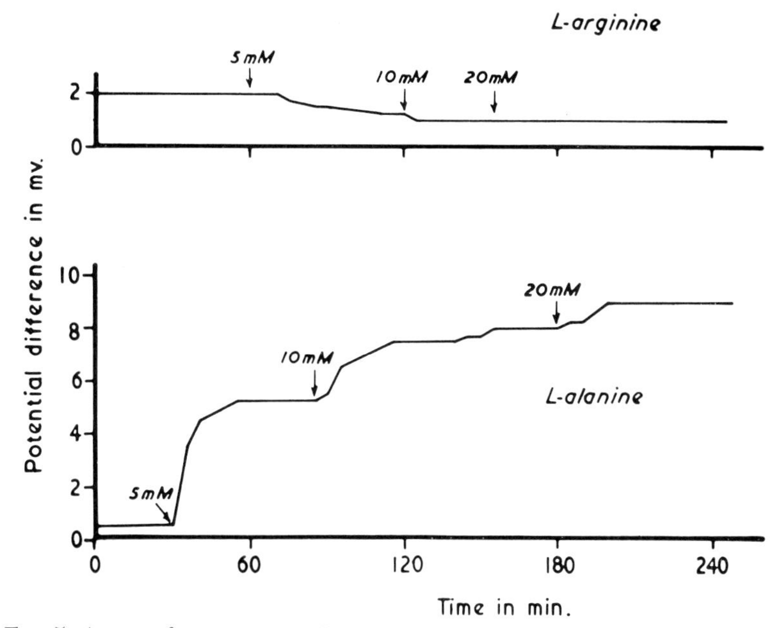

FIG. 5. Action of L-arginine and L-alanine on the potential difference across the isolated small intestine of the turtle *Testudo hermanni* Gmelin. Ordinate: potential difference in millivolts; abscissa: time in minutes. After Baillien and Schoffeniels (*115*).

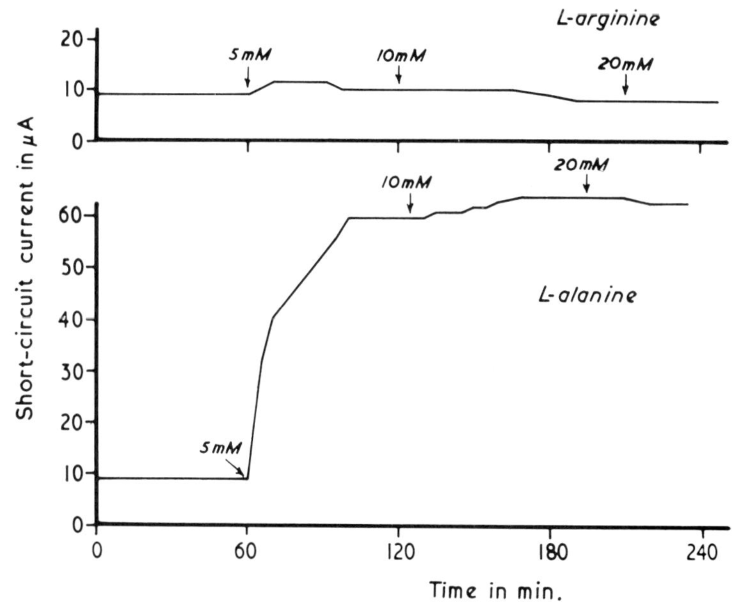

FIG. 6. Action of L-arginine and L-alanine on the potential difference across the isolated small intestine of the turtle *Testudo hermanni* Gmelin. Ordinate: short-circuit current; abscissa: time in minutes. After Baillien and Schoffeniels (*115*).

transported, whereas it remains unchanged with the others (Fig. 6). However, in the case of L-glutamic acid, although the potential is never affected, the short-circuit current always increases.

Glucose also increases the potential difference across the small intestine, as shown by Fig. 7 (*114*).

The most interesting observation, however, is that inorganic ions are essential for the active transport of organic ions or molecules. In the absence of Na, glucose transport is abolished in the toad and guinea pig

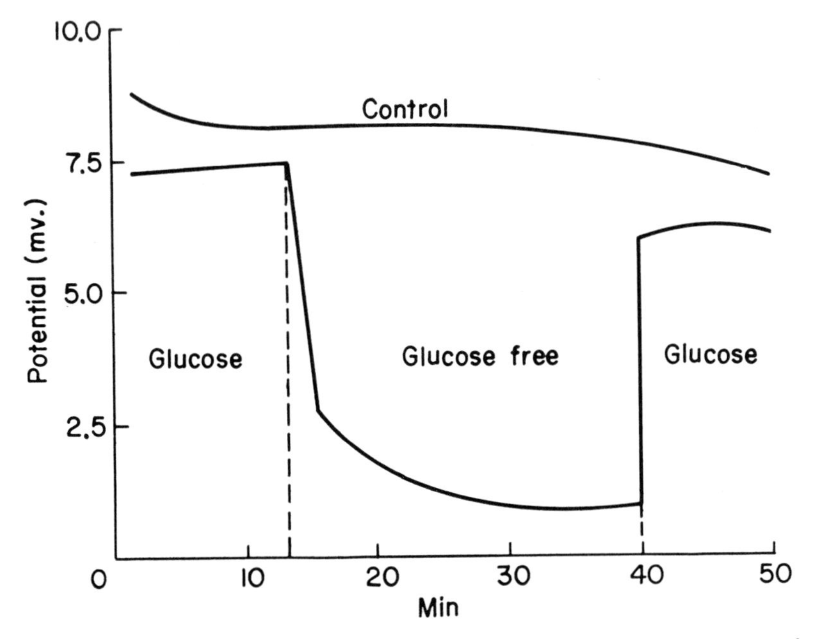

FIG. 7. Effect of glucose on the electrical potential across isolated segments of rat small intestine. After Clarkson *et al.* (*114*).

intestine. In the presence of Na, a suitable concentration of K is necessary for the transport to be maximum (Fig. 8) (*61*). There is also a complex association between K distribution and amino acid transport in the Ehrlich mouse ascites carcinoma cells (*46*). The results point to a potentiation of amino acid transport by the presence of an adequate cellular level of K.

The active transport of Na across the intestine is responsible for at least part of the short-circuit current measured, and together with the other permeability characteristics it explains satisfactorily the unequal distribution of ions between the cell and its surroundings, as well as the potential difference observed (*113*). In the absence of Na in the mucosal solution, the active transport of Na is inhibited; in the presence of glucose or of an actively transported amino acid, it is stimulated. There is thus a reciprocal relation in the active transport of inorganic and organic ions or molecules.

Many hypothesis may be formulated to explain this reciprocity. Let us first consider the effect of amino acids on the potential difference and the short circuit current of the intestinal epithelium. The fact that only those amino acids which are actively transported are able to modify the bioelectric potential could suggest that the activation of the transport

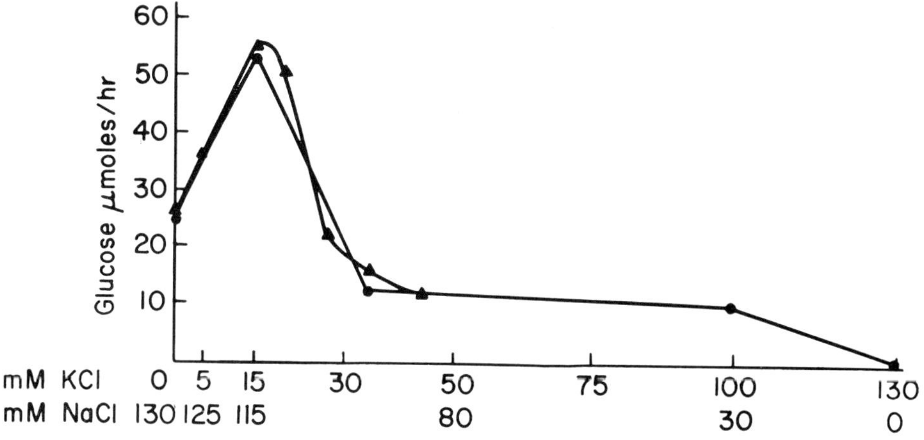

FIG. 8. Isolated surviving guinea pig intestine. Rate of transport of glucose in relation to content of K^+ and Na^+ ions of perfusing physiological saline. Ordinate: glucose transported into serosal solutions (μM/hour). Abscissa: concentration of K^+ and Na^+ in perfusing solution (mM). KEY: ▲ = K^+ variable, Na^+ constant (122 meq./liter). ● = K^+ and Na^+ variable, but $Na^+ + K^+ = 128$ meq./liter. After Riklis and Quastel (*61*).

mechanism for amino acids is directly responsible for the increase in potential difference. In other words, active transport of amino acids would be electrogenic. But glycine, in the experimental conditions of pH is mainly an electrically neutral molecule, only a small fraction being anionic (*16*). If this glycine could be transported as an anion, this would then result in a decrease in electrical potential gradient. We have indeed shown that abolition of the potential difference with an outside electromotive force has no effect on the flux values of this amino acid (*16*).

It could also be suggested that the activation of the transport mechanism results in the production of an intermediary substance which is then responsible for the effect observed on the potential difference. Such a mechanism has been proposed (*116*) to explain the action of the antidiuretic hormone on the net flux of Na and water across the isolated toad bladder. The authors postulate an indirect action by formation of an intermediary cyclic adenylic acid (3′,5′-AMP). In this hypothesis, 3′,5′-AMP, would act on the passive permeability to Na and to water.

Another possibility would be that, besides being actively transported, the amino acid acts directly and independently on the passive permeability characteristics of the membrane in the manner of certain quaternary ammonium derivatives (see Section III).

Finally it may be proposed that the amino acid being catabolized in the cell, it increases the amount of ATP available for the active transport of the inorganic ions directly involved in the generation of the potential difference.

If we now turn to the effect of cations on the active transport of glucose, amino acids, or fatty acids, it has been proposed that they would have a direct action on the movement of the carrier for the organic molecules (*46*). In this hypothesis, amino acid uptake, for instance, could be wholly driven by the energy inherent in the asymmetry of cellular alkali metal distribution (*117*).

Another possibility, however, is that the cationic content of the cell sets the rate of the transport of organic ions and molecules by direct action on the enzyme systems involved in the process. We favor this view because, as we will show later (Section V), there is experimental evidence in favor of the idea that the rate of synthesis as well as the breakdown of amino acids is directly dependent on the intracellular content in Na and K. We also know that an enzyme system, a microsomal adenosine triphosphatase, requires very well-defined amounts of Na and K for optimal activity (*118*).

We may summarize the results by saying that in epithelia without enough endogenous substrate, e.g., the small intestine epithelium, the active transport of cations needs an external source of substrate for optimal activity. Increase in the potential difference is a consequence of the activation of the cation "pump." On the other hand, active transport of glucose, amino acids, or fatty acids is possible only in the presence of a saline having a well-defined ionic composition, as the enzyme systems involved in the transport mechanisms have well-defined requirements in cations.

V. Some Aspects of the Regulation of the Intracellular Pool of Free Amino Acids

Besides their well-known roles and functions in the general metabolism of an organism (development, neurosecretion, amino donors, transpeptidation, and so on) (*119, 120*) free amino acids are believed to play an active part in the osmotic regulation of aquatic invertebrates.

To illustrate this proposition, it may be appropriate to consider the following observations.

The osmolar concentration in inorganic ions of the muscle of marine invertebrates is very low with respect to the concentration prevailing in the extracellular fluid. The muscles are nevertheless in equilibrium with the milieu intérieur, in which ionic concentrations are nearly the same as in sea water. It has thus been postulated that small organic molecules should be found in the intracellular fluid in order to explain the osmotic pressure observed (*121*). Glycine and taurine have indeed been found in tissues of various marine invertebrates, and more recently a systematic study of the intracellular pool of free amino acids has been undertaken in this laboratory in relation to the problem of animal adaptation to the aquatic life (*122–129*).

If we consider Table XIII, giving the nonprotein free amino acids found in some invertebrate muscle and blood, it can be seen that: (*a*) the concentration of 15 amino acids in blood serum is generally

TABLE XIII

FREE AMINO ACID CONTENT[a] OF SERUM AND MUSCLE IN VARIOUS SPECIES (*122, 123*)

	Homarus vulgaris		*Mytilus edulis*	*Ostrea edulis*	*Anodonta cygnea*	*Sipunculus nudus*	*Hirudo medicinalis*
Amino acid	Serum	Muscle		←	Muscle	→	
Alanine	8.7	205	340	646.0	8.8	116.0	8.5
Arginine	1.6	1110	415.5	66.6	36.5	467.0	2.0
Aspartic acid	7.0	26.6	200.4	26.1	4.4	30.4	9.2
Glutamic acid	3.5	500	317.0	264.0	29.4	44.8	81.6
Glycine	24.0	1510	399.0	248.0	13.2	1300.0	11.7
Histidine	3.5	15.5	12.1	22.9	2.5	3.5	2.1
Isoleucine	—	—	24.8	19.2	6.3	8.1	2.6
Leucine	4.2	78.7	15.4	12.9	3.6	3.0	5.4
Lysine	2.1	43.8	39.4	22.0	8.2	12.9	5.0
Methionine	0.0	14.9	9.8	8.4	0.4	2.7	0.4
Phenylalanine	0.2	16.5	9.6	8.5	1.6	1.2	1.6
Proline	6.0	1200	29.0	166.0	1.0	18.8	5.2
Threonine	0.0	11.9	30.5	9.7	3.6	8.0	7.6
Tyrosine	3.3	0.0	12.7	10.3	2.2	2.7	2.0
Valine	0.0	35	14.4	10.8	3.3	2.5	7.9

[a] Values are given as milligrams per 100 gm. fresh weight.

lower than that in the intracellular fluid; (*b*) the total concentration of the 15 amino acids studied is higher in the marine species than in the freshwater species. This observation suggests that free amino acids play an important role in the osmoregulation of the intracellular fluid and could explain the osmotic deficit already noticed by Léon Fredericq in 1901 (*121*). Evidence more direct can be found if one studies the variation of the intracellular pool of free amino acids in a euryhaline species *Eriocheir sinensis* Milne Edwards, for instance, living in media of various concentrations. Table XIV gives the results of analysis per-

TABLE XIV
COMPOSITION OF AMINO ACIDS OF THE MUSCLE FIBERS ISOLATED FROM CRABS (*Eriocheir sinensis* MILNE EDWARDS) ADAPTED TO FRESH WATER AND TO SEA WATER (*128*)

Amino acid	Fresh water[a]	Sea water[a]
Alanine	124	300
Arginine	520	720
Aspartic acid	58	120
Glutamic acid	180	400
Glycine	280	400
Isoleucine	14	44
Leucine	23	59
Phenylalanine	0	Traces
Proline	170	320
Serine	44	59
Taurine	144	125
Threonine	43	138
Tyrosine	0	Traces
Valine	0	70

[a] Concentration in milligrams per 100 grams fresh weight.

formed on the muscle of crabs living in sea water or adapted to fresh water (*125, 128*). The concentration of most of the amino acids studied is modified when the crab is transferred from one medium to another.

Figure 9 gives the results obtained with nerves isolated from the meropodites of the claws and walking legs (unpublished results). It can be seen that the total concentration of 9 amino acids is much higher in sea water than in fresh water. The general shape of the histogram is the same, indicating that the increase in concentration involves all the amino acids except arginine. If one now considers the case of another euryhaline crab, *Carcinus maenas* Pennant, it can be shown that when adapted to brackish water, the amino acid content of the cell is lowered with respect to that observed in sea water (*127*).

Thus when the blood osmotic pressure increases, muscle and nerve fibers can prevent excessive water loss by the addition of nitrogenous substances, the process being reversible.

The question arises as to the origin of the amino acids. There are at least two possibilities: the amino acids could be of extracellular origin and transported (actively or not) in the cell; or they could come from within the cell.

On the basis of experiments performed on isolated nerve (*130*), it has been shown: (*a*) that the regulation of intracellular osmotic pressure is not dependent on hormonal mechanism; (b) that the amino acids contributing to the total osmotic pressure are of intracellular origin; and

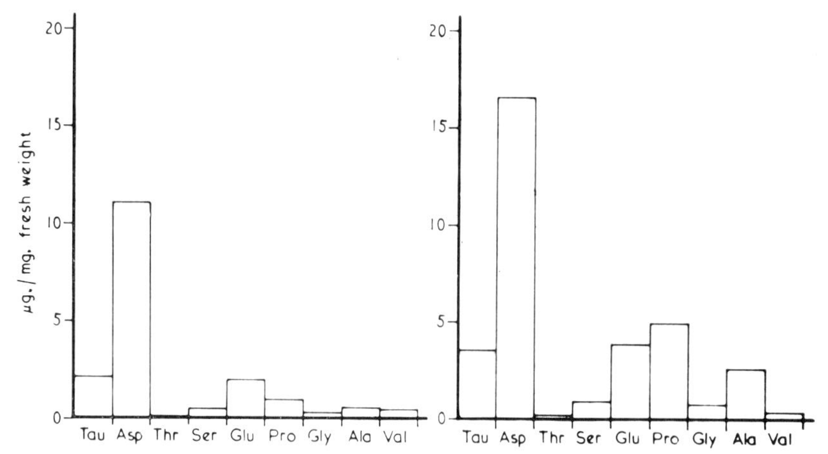

FIG. 9. *Eriocheir sinensis* Milne Edwards. Free amino acid in nerve fibers isolated from animals kept in fresh water (left) and sea water (right). Ordinate: micrograms per milligram fresh weight.

(*c*) that the osmotic pressure per se is not responsible for the increase in amino acid concentration; the presence of Na or K is necessary.

These results leave anyhow another question unanswered. The regulation of the intracellular pool of amino acids could indeed be mainly dependent on the turnover rate of some proteins or result from a balance between synthesis and breakdown of amino acids. Osmotic adaptation is paralleled by a modification of nitrogen excretion which increases when transferred to dilute medium and decreases during the adaptation to hypertonic medium. This has been demonstrated for *Carcinus maenas* (*131*) and *Eriocheir sinensis* (*132*). It is therefore likely that the regulation of the intracellular amino acid pool depends on a balance between synthesis and breakdown of amino acids.

We thus postulate that the rate of amino acid production, as well as the rate of transamination and dehydrogenation, are directly dependent on the ionic composition of the intracellular liquid. There are experimental arguments in favor of this view.

In a series of experiments carried out in collaboration with R. Gilles, we have studied the incorporation of C^{14} from glucose and pyruvate in the free amino acids of the isolated nervous chain of the lobster *Homarus vulgaris* L. Our aim was to use experimental conditions known to affect the ionic distribution in the intracellular space. We have thus chosen two pharmacological agents, veratrine and cocaine, the action of which is generally interpreted in terms of an effect on the permeability of the cell membrane (*133, 133a*). As a result there is a shift in the ionic distribution between the cell and its surroundings.

TABLE XV

ISOLATED VENTRAL NERVE CHAIN OF *Homarus vulgaris* L.: EFFECT OF VERATRINE, COCAINE, AND ELECTRICAL STIMULATION ON THE INCORPORATION OF C^{14} FROM GLUCOSE AND PYRUVATE IN FOUR AMINO ACIDS[a]

	Glucose-U-C^{14}		Pyruvate-1-C^{14}	
Amino acid	Control	Veratrine, 4 μM	Control	Veratrine, 4 μM
Alanine	50.84	106.43	481.46	489.11
Glycine	16.39	20.18	94.99	96.30
Glutamic acid	11.88	15.04	16.04	23.76
Aspartic acid	7.42	8.91	19.60	37.13
	Control	Cocaine, 4 mM	Control	Cocaine, 4 mM
Alanine	114.32	129.17	401.49	643.24
Glycine	11.15	13.72	7.74	15.55
Glutamic acid	13.88	10.24	20.05	13.81
Aspartic acid	11.57	8.73	18.46	11.14
	Control	Stimulation 10 sec.$^{-1}$	Control	Stimulation 10 sec.$^{-1}$
Alanine	108.54	187.19	129.11	141.22
Glycine	16.95	19.23	4.73	4.88
Glutamic acid	12.98	16.37	4.01	4.11
Aspartic acid	12.24	17.22	5.34	11.65

[a] Gilles and Schoffeniels (*135*).

[b] Stimulation and compounds were applied for 1 hour.

We have also stimulated the nerve, since electrical activity is accompanied with ionic exchange between intra- and extracellular fluid (*134*).

Our results using glucose-U-C^{14} and pyruvate-1-C^{14} and -2-C^{14} show that the labeling of amino acids can be affected by our experimental conditions (Table XV).

It can be seen that the values of the control are different if we use glucose-U-C^{14} or pyruvate-1-C^{14} as substrate. This is also true with pyruvate-2-C^{14}, and this aspect of the problem is discussed in full detail elsewhere (*135*).

It is also evident that the results obtained with veratrine and during electrical stimulation are identical since in both conditions we find an increase in the labeling of the four amino acids isolated. This seems to indicate a similar mode of action. We thus have measured the Na and K content of the lobster ventral nervous chain before and after application of veratrine. The results are given in Table XVI.

TABLE XVI
EFFECT OF VERATRINE (4 μM) ON THE NA AND K CONTENT OF THE ISOLATED VENTRAL NERVE CHAIN OF *Homarus vulgaris* L.[a,b]

Sample	Na	K
Control	240	103
Veratrine	278	68.7
Control	249	100
Veratrine	301	65

[a] Gilles and Schoffeniels (*135*).
[b] Concentration given in microequivalents per gram fresh weight.

Despite the fact that the figures do not give the true values of the cation content of the intracellular fluid, the values obtained after application of veratrine are significantly different and thus support the conclusion that veratrine at the concentration used affects the cation distribution in the same way as the stimulation does, i.e., increase in intracellular Na concentration, decrease in intracellular K concentration.

Moreover, the results are consistent with our general assumption that the metabolism of intracellular amino acids is directly dependent on the ionic composition of the intracellular fluid.

The above results were obtained with a stenohaline species *Homarus vulgaris* L. It is, however, interesting to consider them in relation to the problem of the osmoregulatory function of amino acids in euryhaline species. If the total amount of free amino acid within a cell is directly related to the ionic composition of the intracellular liquid, at what level should we search for the difference between eury- and stenohaline species?

In Table XVII we give the total amount of free amino acid (expressed as micrograms leucine per milligram fresh weight) found in an isolated nervous ventral chain of *Homarus vulgaris* L. incubated for 2 hours in the presence or absence of veratrine. The results show that there is no modification in the total concentration of free amino acids found in the intracellular liquid under the influence of veratrine. Thus despite the

TABLE XVII
TOTAL AMINO ACID CONTENT OF ISOLATED VENTRAL NERVE CHAIN INCUBATED 2 HOURS IN THE PRESENCE OF VERATRINE (4 μM)

Group	Control	Veratrine
1	26.8	26.11
2	14.5	14.6

[a] Results are expressed as micrograms leucine per milligram fresh weight. In 1 the results are the mean of 6 experiments; in 2 half a chain was used as a control, the other half for the experiment.

fact that the rate of synthesis of some amino acids is increased under the influence of veratrine, the total amount of free amino acids remains unchanged. This could mean that the rate of catabolism is also increased, the net result being an acceleration of the turnover rate with no final change in concentration. Or the rate of synthesis of some amino acids could be increased with a parallel increase in the rate of breakdown of other amino acids.

Whatever the answer, we may formulate the following hypothesis to explain the difference between steno- and euryhaline species. It could be suggested that, under intracellular ionic conditions of increased production of free amino acids, there is no parallel increase in breakdown of amino acids in a euryhaline species, thus leading to an increase in total amount of intracellular free amino acids. On the contrary, in a stenohaline species, any increase in free amino acid production would be accompanied by a concomitant increase in free amino acid catabolism, the net result being an increase in turnover rate without change in final concentration. The possibility for an invertebrate to adapt itself in medium of various dilutions would then be the result of the acquisition of a mechanism enabling the cell to control independently the production and breakdown of amino acids. In a stenohaline species the level of the free amino acid pool being genetically determined, there must be some sort of relationship between amino acid production and breakdown since the pool has to remain constant: these intracellular conditions leading to an accelerated production must also affect the rate of catabolism in such a way that the total concentration in free amino acids remains unchanged.

This working hypothesis is easily accessible to experimental verifications and work along this line is now under progress in this laboratory.

To test this hypothesis, we have undertaken a study of the effect of various cations on the rate of activity of the enzymes of the nitrogen pool. In the following we shall deal essentially with some preliminary results obtained using the L-glutamic acid dehydrogenase extracted from the muscles of a euryhaline species, the crayfish *Astacus fluviatilis* F. and from a stenohaline species, the lobster *Homarus vulgaris* L. (*135a*).

The L-glutamic acid dehydrogenase is studied by measuring at 340 mμ the rate of disappearance of DPNH (reduced diphosphopyridine nucleotide) in the presence of α-ketoglutarate and NH_4Cl.

Figure 10 gives the results obtained with crayfish muscle when comparing the rate of oxidation of DPNH in various experimental conditions. It is clear that the oxidation of DPNH is enhanced by the presence

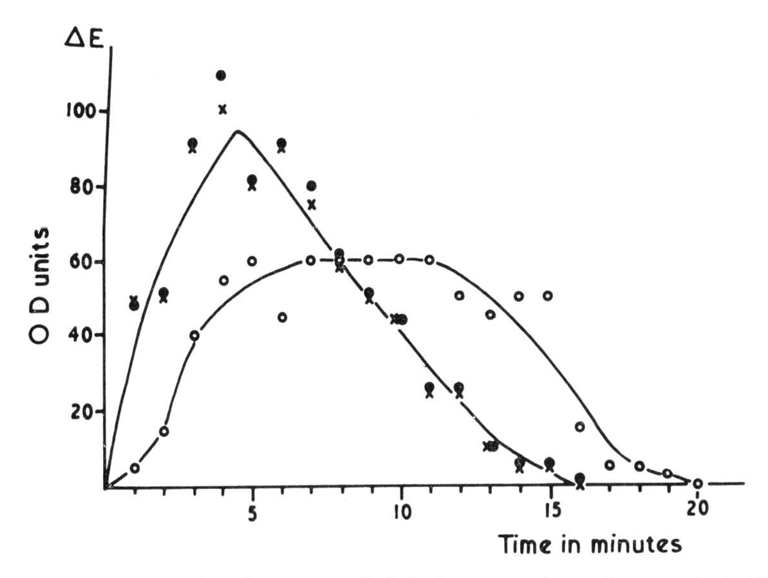

FIG. 10. Activity of L-glutamic acid dehydrogenase from *Astacus fluviatilis* F. in the presence of distilled water ○, 400 m*M* of Na ×, 400 m*M* of K ●. The activity is expressed in terms of the variation of optical density per minute (ΔE) as a function of time. Temperature of incubation 30° C. (*135a*).

of monovalent cations, thus indicating an activation of the L-glutamic acid dehydrogenase. The maximum effect is obtained about 3 minutes after the beginning of the reaction and there does not seem to be much difference between Na and K.

The importance of the concentration in monovalent cations of the incubating medium may be well demonstrated if we consider the ratio of activity in the presence of monovalent cations over activity in the absence of monovalent cation, for various concentrations of salts.

On Table XVIII we give the values of such ratios for concentrations in Na and K varying between 50 and 1000 m*M*. The results indicate that

TABLE XVIII
ACTIVITY OF L-GLUTAMIC ACID DEHYDROGENASE EXTRACTED FROM CRAYFISH MUSCLE[a]

	Na							K						
	50	100	200	400	500	750	1000	50	100	200	400	500	750	1000
1	1.5	2.5	3.5	4.5	—	—	—	1.5	2.5	3.4	4.4	—	—	—
2	—	—	—	2.7	2.5	1.5	1.3	—	—	—	2.7	2.2	1.5	1.2

[a] Values of the ratio of activity in the presence of monovalent cations over activity in the absence of monovalent cation. The values are calculated from the variations in optical density between 0 and 4 minutes of incubation at 30° C. Na and K concentration expressed in m*M*; pH of the reaction mixture 7.8 (*135a*).

the optimal concentration in monovalent cations is somewhere around 400 m*M*. There does not seem to be much difference between Na and K, at least in our experimental conditions.

That the results observed are not due to an unspecific effect of the ionic strength of the incubating medium is well demonstrated by the

TABLE XIX
ACTIVITY OF L-GLUTAMIC ACID DEHYDROGENASE IN CRAYFISH AND LOBSTER MUSCLE[a]

	Concentrations in cations (m*M*)		
Na	200	400	0
K	200	0	400
	Ratio		
Crayfish	1.3	2.9	3.0
Lobster	1.2	1.7	1.7

[a] Values of the ratio of activity in the presence of monovalent cation over activity in the absence of monovalent cation. The figures are calculated from the variations in optical density between 0 and 4 minutes of incubation at 30° C (*135a*).

fact that equivalent amounts of Na or K, or an equivalent mixture of both salts, do not activate equally well the oxidation of DPNH in the presence of L-glutamic acid dehydrogenase. This is true for the enzyme extracted from crayfish as well as from lobster muscle (Table XIX). This conclusion is substantiated by the fact that Mg ions even at low concentration inhibit the activity of the enzyme (Table XX).

The above results are consistent with the hypothesis that the metabolism of amino acids is strongly dependent on the cationic content of the cell. In order to integrate our results on euryhalinity, we have been

TABLE XX
ACTIVITY OF L-GLUTAMIC ACID DEHYDROGENASE IN CRAYFISH MUSCLE[a]

	Mg concentration (mM)		
	5	10	16.6
Ratio	0.33 [2]	0.23 [2]	0.28 [3]

[a] Values of the ratio of activity in the presence of Mg ions over activity in the absence of alkaline earth. The values are calculated from the variation in optical density between 0 and 4 minutes of incubation at 30° C. Number of experiments indicated in brackets (*135a*).

looking for possible differences between euryhaline and stenohaline species by comparing L-glutamic acid dehydrogenase activity extracted from crayfish and lobster muscle. In Table XXI we give the values of the ratio of activity in the presence of cations over activity in the absence of cation. It can be seen that the values obtained with the crayfish are

TABLE XXI
ACTIVITY OF L-GLUTAMIC ACID DEHYDROGENASE EXTRACTED FROM CRAYFISH AND LOBSTER MUSCLE[a]

	Na (mM)			K (mM)		
	100	200	400	100	200	400
Crayfish	2.5	3.5	4.5	2.5	3.4	4.4
	2.5	3.2	4.0	2.4	3.4	4.1
	2.3	3.3	4.2	2.4	3.4	3.9
Lobster	2.0	3.0	3.5	1.5	2.5	3.5
	1.1	2.3	2.8	1.1	1.8	2.1

[a] Comparison of the values of the ratio of activity in the presence of cations over activity in the absence of monovalent cation. The values are calculated from the variation in optical density between 0 and 4 minutes of incubation at 30° C. Na and K concentration expressed in mM; pH of the reaction mixture 7.8 (unpublished results).

generally higher than those obtained with the lobster. However, since our experiments are still in progress, it is too early at this stage of the work to decide whether or not the differences observed are of ecological significance.

It is also worth noticing that the rates of the two possible reactions catalyzed by L-glutamic acid dehydrogenase are in our experimental conditions very different. If we compare the rate of the reaction

$$\text{Glu} + \text{DPN} \rightarrow \alpha\text{-Ketoglutarate} + NH_3 + \text{DPNH} \quad (1)$$

with the rate of the reverse reactions, it can be seen that the rate of reaction (1) is negligible (Table XXII). This is true for the enzyme extracted from both lobster and crayfish. Thus if the conditions of our

TABLE XXII
ACTIVITY OF L-GLUTAMIC ACID DEHYDROGENASE EXTRACTED FROM CRAYFISH AND LOBSTER MUSCLE[a]

	Crayfish		Lobster	
	Na 0 mM	Na 400 mM	Na 0 mM	Na 400 mM
DPNH	0.120	0.400	0.060	0.130
DPN	0.006	0.008	0.009	0.005
			0.012	0.006

[a] The variation of optical density between 0 and 4 minutes of incubation at 30° C is given for the reaction α-ketoglutarate→glutamate (DPNH) and for the reverse reaction glutamate → α-ketoglutarate (DPN); pH of the reaction mixture is 7.8 (unpublished results).

in vitro experiments apply to the situation *in vivo,* the synthesis of glutamate should be the essential step controlled by the cationic content of the cell.

Therefore, it may be proposed that, at the molecular level, euryhalinity be explained by a direct action of the intracellular cation concentration on the reaction rate of L-glutamic acid dehydrogenase. Thus a euryhaline crustacean, when introduced into brackish water or into fresh water, undergoes a reduction of the inorganic osmotic effectors of the cell. This change exerts an action on the activity of L-glutamic acid dehydrogenase. Consequently the intracellular amino acid pool is decreased, thus contributing to the isosmotic intracellular regulation and preventing the water from invading the cells and killing the animal.

This concept is in accord with the observations mentioned earlier which show that when *Carcinus maenas* or *Eriocheir sinensis* are transferred into diluted medium, the nitrogen excretion is increased for a certain period of time, while the opposite effect is observed when the crab is transferred into sea water.

It thus appears that the euryhalinity of marine invertebrates results from a combination of an anisosmotic extracellular regulation and of an isosmotic intracellular regulation, or from the latter alone. We tentatively propose to consider the isosmotic intracellular regulation as being the result of a differential influence of the ionic composition of the cell on the activity of the biochemical systems responsible for the production of amino acids, on the one hand, and for their discharge, on the other hand. As the differential action is lacking in the stenohaline species, a change in the ionic composition of the cell would only result in a modification of the turnover rate of the amino acid pool, but not of its concentration.

In vertebrates the intracellular pool of free amino acids seems to be related to the ionic composition of the intracellular fluid and various authors have shown that in K deficient animals the intracellular content of cationic amino acids increases (*136–141*).

As we have shown, amino acids seem to play an important part in the osmoregulation of invertebrates. In aquatic or semiaquatic vertebrates this role seems to belong to urea (*142, 143*).

VI. Hormones and Permeability Characteristics of Living Cellular Membranes

A. Neurohypophyseal Hormones

Two active hormonal substances, secreted by the neurohypophysis have been isolated and synthesized (*144*). Both are octapeptides. They are oxytocin and vasopressin. Two vasopressins are of natural occurrence: arginine-vasopressin and lysine-vasopressin. Besides its oxytocic action, oxytocin affects both Na and water flux across the amphibian skin and the urinary bladder while vasopressin appears to have no activity. The renal effects are also well known.

More recently another active principle has been isolated from the neurohypophysis of chicken (*145*), frog (*146*), and fish (*Gadus luscus* L.) (*147*). This principle seems to have the same structure as the arginine-vasotocin synthesized by Katsoyannis and du Vigneaud (*148*).

As already mentioned, in amphibian skin and urinary bladder neurohypophyseal extracts exert a very marked action on the net flux of water arising under the influence of an osmotic gradient.

The generally accepted opinion is that the hormone acts on the cellular membrane facing outward (i.e., mucosal side for the bladder), by increasing the permeability to water and to Na. Calcium plays an important role in this phenomenon since an excess of this ion inhibits the effect of the hormone (*149, 150*).

In the light of the behavior of water, before and after application of the hormone, a simple model membrane has been proposed. The theoretical approach used in Section II of this chapter is based on this model.

To initiate the discussion of the model, it may be appropriate to recall that the phenomenon of osmosis appears to be considered from two different points of view. The classical view as typified by the work of Starling and Landis and in more recent years by Ussing, holds that osmosis is a mass flow of the solvent through the pores of the membrane, arising when a mole fraction difference of the solvent exists by virtue of the presence of a substance impermeable or less permeable to the barrier. The other point of view argues exclusively for the diffusion of the solvent, that is a molecular-molecular random drift (*151*). In the experiments carried out on amphibian skin, it is possible to measure simultaneously the net flux of water arising under the influence of an osmotic gradient as well as the influx using labeled water. Knowing the influx, one may calculate the permeability coefficient to water since

$$M_{\text{in}} = P_1 c_{w(o)} \tag{9}$$

If we calculate now the permeability coefficient to water from the net flux value

$$\Delta_w = M_{\text{in}} - M_{\text{out}} = P_2 c_{w(o)} - P_2 c_{w(i)} = P_2(c_{w(o)} - c_{w(i)}) \tag{10}$$

It appears that the value of P_2 is nearly 16 times that for P_1, as shown by the results of Ussing on the toad skin (*152*).

This is also true with nonbiological systems, as demonstrated by the experiments of Mauro, in 1957, working with a collodion membrane. Here again, under the influence of a hydrostatic pressure, he was able to demonstrate that the diffusion component of the solvent flux is 1/730 of the total flux (*153*).

One is forced therefore to conclude that any pressure difference, osmotic or hydrostatic, applied, gives rise to a transfer of water which is predominantly nondiffusional in nature.

When dealing with living membranes the alternative to the active transport of water hypothesis has been the acceptance of pores in the membrane. If it is so, the flow of water in a porous membrane should produce a drag effect on the solute molecules permeating the membrane via the pores. It has thus been concluded from experiments carried out with the isolated toad skin (*Bufo bufo*) (*154*) that the flux ratio for acetamide and thiourea is very near unity, indicating that these molecules are not subjected to active transport. After application of neurohypophyseal hormone, the flux ratio is still unity, except if there is an osmotic gradient across the skin. In the latter case, the deviation from unity is generally taken as indicating a drag effect of the solvent on the solute molecules.

As pointed out independently by Pappenheimer (*155*) and Ussing

(*1*) the equivalent pore radius in the membrane may be determined from the study of the relative rates of water movement under osmotic pressure gradient. An equivalent membrane with uniform cylindrical pores is thus considered. If it is assumed that the only force available for the transfer of water is the difference of osmotic pressure across the membrane, the diameter of the pores may be calculated using the well-known Poiseuille equation.

In various cells measurements have led to a calculated pore radius around 4 Å. Since the calculations rest upon the macroscopic laws of Poiseuille and of Fick, Solomon and associates (*156–158*) have checked the application of these laws to water flow and diffusion through pores of such small radii. According to Renkin (*159*) the laws apply to equivalent pore radii of 15–20 Å. In view of the problem raised by the small pore radius in cells, it is of importance to find an independent method of measuring the diameter of cell pores. Such a method is afforded from a consideration of the osmotic pressure developed across the membrane in the presence of solute which can cross the membrane. The osmotic pressure under these conditions differs from the classical van't Hoff osmotic pressure (*160*). The relationship of these osmotic pressures may be expressed in terms of a reflection coefficient σ, equal to OP_{obs}/OP_{theor} where OP_{obs} = osmotic pressure measured; OP_{theor} = osmotic pressure calculated according to van't Hoff.

σ may take on all values between 0, characteristic of a membrane with pores so large that they cannot discriminate between solvent and solute, and 1 the value for a membrane which can discriminate between solvent and solute.

When $\sigma = 0$, osmotic pressure disappears; if $\sigma = 1$, van't Hoff osmotic pressure will be developed. As shown by Solomon and his associates (*161, 162*) the determination of σ for a given solute may lead to a description of the cellular membrane in terms of its equivalent pore radius. The quantitative relationship between σ and the equivalent pore radius rests upon two equations. One relating σ to the apparent pore area for solute and solvent filtration, the other relating the apparent area for solute and solvent filtration to the equivalent pore radius and the radius of the solute molecule.

The results obtained show that the values for the pore radius are very close to 4.5 Å. for most of the cell studied; thus they are in fair agreement with the value derived from the analysis of water flux.

It should, however, be pointed out that there is still a possibility that the general agreement in the results is purely fortuitous. According to the theory, the expression for the flux ratio of an uncharged substances is (*1*)

$$\ln \frac{M_{\text{in}}}{M_{\text{out}}} = \ln \frac{a_o}{a_i} + \frac{D_w}{D} \int_0^{x_0} \frac{1}{A}\, dx \qquad (11)$$

where M_{in} and M_{out} are influx and outflux, α_o and α_i the chemical activities of the substance in the inside and outside media, D_w the net flux of water, D the free diffusion coefficient of the substance A the fraction of unit area available for diffusion, x_o the thickness of the membrane, and x the distance in the membrane from one boundary. As pointed out by Ussing this equation is valid only if the substance does not cross the membrane partly by dissolving in the membrane and if all pores are of the same shape and size. These conditions are rather unlikely for a biological membrane. Moreover another possibility may still be considered. Structural pores in the membrane may not adequately explain the nondiffusional water flux and the apparent drag effect observed would then be coincidental, the solute and solvent molecules, moving through separate structures in a more complex way than postulated in the currently accepted model of the pore membrane [see also (*163*)]. It would indeed seem exceptional for a solute to cross a cellular membrane without encountering chemical functions reactive to them. Even the smallest molecules used (water, methanol, formamide, urea, thiourea, etc.) are polar molecules and thus subjected to electrical field influences while crossing the membrane.

As pointed out above, Solomon and his associates have found apparent pore radii of similar magnitude, using different types of molecules (water, acetamide, urea, methylurea, propylene glycol, ethylene glycol, glycerol, etc.). This is obviously an interesting correspondence, but it still remains to be demonstrated that the compounds used enter the cell without interaction with the membrane (*109a*).

B. Other Hormones

The effects of the hormones secreted by the suprarenal glands have been extensively investigated by students in renal physiology (*164*). The cellular actions of these hormones have also been studied *in vitro* using various isolated cells or organs. Since these hormones act on the general metabolism of the cell and more specifically on the carbohydrate metabolism, it is rather difficult to decide without a careful analysis whether the ionic effects observed are due to a direct membrane action on the permeability characteristics or whether we are witnessing the consequences of an action taking place at some other level of anabolic or catabolic reactions. Moreover, when the published data seem to indicate a permeability effect, it remains difficult to decide whether we are dealing with an action on the active transport or on the passive permeability characteristics of the membrane. The hepatic uptake of α-aminoisobutyric acid and glycine is enhanced by the glucocorticoids (*165*). In yeast cell and red blood corpuscle, the corticoids seem to inhibit the extrusion of Na. This effect may be related to the decrease in intracellular K concentration observed in muscle fibers. In human red cell, the uptake of phosphate is inhibited by deoxycorticosterone, whereas cortisone decreases the uptake of fructose and glucose (*166*). In *Neurospora crassa* deoxycorticosterone inhibits the uptake of amino acids, sugars, and Rb (*167, 168*).

Insulin, growth hormone, estradiol, and stilbestrol have also been studied in relation to their effects on the permeability characteristics of living membrane (*168a–171*). The uptake of α-aminoisobutyric acid as well as glycine is increased in striated and smooth muscle by insulin, estradiol, and growth hormone. The uptake of amino acids is also enhanced in the Ehrlich ascites carcinoma cells in the presence of estradiol. On the contrary, stilbestrol suppresses, at low concentration, the glycine transport. This is, however, attributed to the effect of this hormone as a respiratory inhibitor (*172*).

In muscle the uptake of K is increased by insulin (*173, 174*).

The results presented in this section emphasize the multiplicity of transports that are affected by the same hormone. Passive permeability (including well-demonstrated mediated transport) as well as active transport of various substances are involved. This is to be related to previous observations concerning the effect of quaternary ammonium derivatives and other pharmacodynamically active agents on the permeability characteristics of living membranes. Since chemically related substances can affect various permeability characteristics not only in cells functionally different, but also in tissues belonging to zoological species far apart in the systematic classification, it could be proposed that the molecular architecture responsible for the various permeability characteristics of living membranes are chemically related, and that a common biochemical system could be responsible for all the permeability characteristics of living membranes. This would thus mean that we could consider the permeability characteristics as being a heterotypic expression of a common biochemical system (*49, 175*), this concept being used here in the sense defined by Mason (*176*).

VII. Alkaline Earths and Permeability Characteristics of Living Membranes

It is generally assumed that alkali metal ions have a well-defined role in the production of bioelectric potentials, while a possible interaction with cellular structure is seldom considered. On the contrary, this latter aspect is always considered when one studies the effect of alkaline earth on cellular functions. One has thus a biological classification of the cations corresponding to the periodic table of elements. This classification is also found if one considers the effect of cations on enzymatic reactions. It is observed that alkaline earths are fixed more or less firmly to the enzyme and often bind the substrate to the enzyme in the formation of the Michaelis-Menten complex, while alkali metal ions influence the reaction in a way not clearly understood. They do not form covalent bond or coordinate linkage. They may change the charge density at the surface of the enzyme affected by these cations. Schematically one may therefore say that the alkaline earths would play an essential role as fundamental elements in the molecular architecture of the cell while the alkali metal ions would be more directly related to phenomena involving the liquid phases of biological systems (see, however, Section VIII).

If this classification seems indeed to correspond to many observations, it is, however, not an absolute one, as within certain limits, fixation of alkaline earth are directly related to the presence of alkali metal ions. We may summarize our view in the following way. (*a*) Cellular structures are able to bind not only alkaline metal ions but also alkaline earths. (*b*) The various cations bound to the structure must be in a well-defined ratio if the functional integrity of the structure is to be optimum. (*c*) There is "competition"* between various cations for the cellular structures.

A. Passive Permeability

As shown above the electrical potential difference existing between the intracellular fluid and the extracellular space is due to the passive permeability characteristics of the membrane as well as the unequal distribution of ions between the two liquid phases. The unequal distribution of ions is the result of an active transport mechanism (mainly Na and K) requiring metabolic energy.

The molecular architectures responsible for the various permeability characteristics are differently affected not only by metabolic inhibitors but also by the ionic composition of the surrounding fluids, as shown by the following examples.

1. *Action of Calcium on Membrane Rectification*

The potential difference existing spontaneously across the giant axon membrane can be varied by passing an electrical current across it (*177*,

* No experimental evidence is available so far to decide whether or not we are dealing with a true competition as defined in enzymology.

178). The specific transverse resistance increases if the current is flowing inward; the reverse is true if the current flows in the opposite direction. The variations in specific resistance observed when the current is flowing are different for a same current density according to the direction of flow. Consequently the electrical potential difference is not a linear function of the current density and Ohm's law is not verified for many living membranes. The resistance being different according to the direction of current flow, it is said that the living membrane has rectifying properties. These electrical measurements thus show that the passive permeabilities of the membrane to Na and to K are different and that these permeabilities are differently affected by an electrical current.

Ca ions increase whereas Mg ions decrease the rectification properties of a membrane (*179*). In Ca-free medium rectification of the squid giant axon membrane disappears (*178*) and the specific transverse resistance is approximatively proportional to the Ca concentration in the outside medium (*180*). This change in resistance has to be related to the increase in Na influx and K efflux, observed in Ca-free medium (*134*). The above results clearly show that the molecular architectures responsible for the permeability characteristics of a living membrane—to Na and K especially—are directly influenced by the concentration of ionized Ca in the surrounding medium.

2. *The Resting Potential*

To assimilate a living cell and its surrounding medium to a simple physicochemical system is a rather naive assumption. It is evident that the chemical reactions of which the cell is the site, obey the laws of physicochemistry and more specifically the second law of thermodynamics. However, the physicochemical science has not yet defined laws enabling us to analyze and to define a biological function, considered at the molecular level, by integration of the chemical reactions in a sequence taking into account both physiological and morphological data. The study of the effect of the ionic composition on cellular structures has to be inserted in this task since such a study has for ultimate purpose a precise definition of these structures. As far as the cellular membrane is concerned we know that it is not the inert structure once postulated in earlier theories on permeability. It is the site of active transport mechanisms and is responsible for the generation of bioelectric potentials.

If the theory concerning the origin of electrochemical potential is of great help in our understanding of bioelectric potentials, experimental data show that this theory has to be applied to a biological system with great caution. In the Nernst formulation, the membrane structure is not supposed to be altered by a modification of the ionic composition of the bathing fluid. It is now well established that a living membrane is affected by the ionic atmosphere: Ca-free or K-rich media decrease the nerve specific transverse resistance (*181–182*). A change in membrane resistance may reflect an alteration in ionic fluxes or a structural reorganization of the membrane. The problem is thus to define at the molecular level the relations existing between a membrane and its surroundings. This has been considered in some detail in a previous volume of this series (Volume II, Chapter 10) as well as in another book (*95*).

The general conclusion to be drawn is that the structure of the membrane is different according to the ionic composition of the bathing fluid and is directly related to the concentration ratios of the various cations. The reader is thus referred to the above-mentioned publications for a more complete discussion of this matter (see also reference *182a*).

3. *Action Potential*

The effect of Ca on the action potential is rather well known (*183*). An elevation in Ca concentration augments the threshold, increases the specific resistance, and accelerates the accommodation, whereas a decrease in Ca concentration results in opposite effects and eventually brings the nerve fiber to a state of spontaneous activity (*180, 181, 184, 185*).

If one studies the relationships between outside concentration and electrical activity in the squid giant axon (*186*), it can be shown that, at low Ca concentration, there is an increase in K permeability and a subsequent depolarization. Sodium influx increases. Thus the passive permeability of the membrane to Na and K is directly related to Ca concentration. In Ca-free medium, the increase in Na conductance leading to an action potential is accelerated under the cathode, the reverse being true at the anode. In the same conditions the increase in K conductance at the cathode is also accelerated. These results show clearly the particular importance devolved upon Ca ions in the generation of an action potential. This is also well demonstrated by the fact that in Ca-free medium the K conductance increases and the electrical activity is abolished. Magnesium behaves, as far as the giant axon of the squid is concerned, like Ca but is nevertheless less effective. This could be explained if one considers that the affinity of Ca for the cellular structure involved is greater than that for Mg.

The above results may be summarized by saying that an increase in Ca concentration is equivalent to a hyperpolarization, a decrease in Ca concentration is equivalent to a depolarization.

That is why it has been suggested that the first step in the generation of an action potential could be a release of Ca bound in the membrane (*95, 187;* see also Volume II, Chapter 10).

4. *Passive Flux of Sodium and Potassium in Nonconducting Cells*

Calcium ions play also an important role in determining the passive permeability characteristics of nonconducting cells. In Ca-free medium the passive permeability to cations increases considerably in erythrocytes from the turtle (*188*), the snapping turtle *Chelydra serpentina* (*189*), fishes (*190*), and man (*191, 192*). *Acanthamoeba* in Ca-free medium loses about 8.5% of its total K within 5–10 minutes (*193*), K influx being 1.84 $\mu\mu$moles cm.$^{-2}$ sec.$^{-1}$, while the efflux is 4.74 $\mu\mu$moles cm.$^{-2}$ sec.$^{-1}$.

In the presence of 10 m*M* Ca, the influx decreases by 19% while the efflux decreases by 32%.

These results seem to indicate that divalent cations, and more particularly Ca, are bound at the cell surface to the molecular architecture responsible for the passive permeability characteristics of the membrane.

B. Active Transport

Without a careful analysis of the experimental conditions, it is rather difficult to demonstrate a direct effect of a substance on the mechanism of active transport of an ion. The flux of an ion across a living membrane is indeed the result of various mechanisms, and even if we are dealing with an active transport, passive permeability may be a limiting step.

To illustrate this point let us return to the frog skin. As shown in Section III, Na is actively transported from the epithelial side to the dermal side, the mechanism of active transport being located at the inner boundary of the epithelial cells. The outer boundary is specifically permeable to Na ions (*104*). There is good experimental evidence that the intracellular Na concentration sets the rate of the active transport mechanism. On the other hand, the intracellular Na concentration is related, among other things, to the Na passive permeability at the outer border of the cells. Thus if we modify the passive permeability to Na, we could influence the active transport of Na through a modification of intracellular Na concentration, without affecting directly the mechanism responsible for active transport (*100, 102, 108, 194*). This example shows how difficult it is to interpret the action of Ca and Mg on the active transport of ions.

Mullins (*195*) has shown that if the Ca concentration of a Ringer solution is doubled, the absorption of PO_4 by the isolated frog sciatic decreases by 33%. According to Huf *et al.* (*195a*) Ca-free Ringer is without any effect on the active transport of Na across the frog skin.

However, in this condition the skin continuously loses Ca. Bourguet *et al.* (*196, 197*) have therefore reexamined this problem using EDTA (ethylenediamine tetraacetate). The results obtained are difficult to interpret in terms of a direct action of Ca on the active transport mechanism. More recently Curran *et al.* (*198*) have shown that, in the presence of EDTA, the conductance of the isolated frog skin increases. As a result the potential difference and the short-circuited current decreases. They have shown that the outflux of Na, Cl, and SO_4 increase, while the influx of Na remains unchanged. The decrease in short-circuit current is thus completely explained by the increase in Na efflux. The results show therefore that the Ca has no effect on the active transport mechanism for Na. The effects observed can be explained in terms of an action on the passive permeability characteristics of the cellular membranes (*109*).

As far as human erythrocytes are concerned, Kahn (*199*) has shown that a decrease in Ca concentration is without effect on the K influx while an increased concentration inhibits, at least partially, the influx of K. Strontium and magnesium are without effect, thus demonstrating the specificity of the action.

C. Possible Mechanism of Action

A simple way of interpreting the action of alkaline earths is to postulate that they are bound to anionic sites in the membrane to form salt in equilibrium with the ion. It can be stated that (see also ref. *181*)

$$CaX = Ca^{2+} + X^{2-} \tag{12}$$

In the case of a polyvalent electrolyte, e.g., a protein, one has

$$Ca_nP = Ca_{n-1}P^{2-} + Ca^{2+} \tag{13}$$

All these reactions are determined by a constant related to the difference in free energy and entropy of reactants and products in their standard state. One may therefore write

$$K = \frac{(Ca^{2+})(X^{2-})}{(CaX)} \tag{14}$$

where K is a dissociation constant.

If we use this simple scheme to interpret the role of cations in the determination of the passive permeability characteristics of living membranes, we have to postulate that X, the molecular architecture responsible for a permeability characteristic can be in the complex form CaX or in the dissociated form X^{2-}.

The ratio of the two forms determines the value of the permeability coefficient of the membrane to the ionic species considered.

The ratio X^{2-}/CaX is evidently a function of the Ca concentration in the medium and of the affinity of X^{2-} for Ca as defined by the constant K (Eq. 14).

If we consider the system just defined in its relationship with a complex medium, e.g., the extracellular fluid, different types of variations may be considered: (*a*) Another cation may, by true competition, form a complex with X^{2-}; or (*b*) this cation will form a complex with X^{2-} without occupying the sites of the alkaline earth, but with the result that displacement of the equilibrium defined by Eq. 14 occurs (noncompetitive inhibition); or (*c*) the value of K defined in Eq. 14 may be directly related to the ionic strength of the medium.

In the first case, we may define a new constant K' for any other alkaline cation, K for instance, and

$$K' = \frac{2(K^+)(X^{2-})}{(K_2X)} \tag{15}$$

Whatever the mechanism in effect, the amount of CaX will be directly related not only to the value of K and the Ca concentration, but also to the cationic composition of the medium bathing X^{2-}.

In order to illustrate these propositions, let us consider the case of *Elodea* cells (*200*). In a solution of NaCl or KCl they rapidly lose their Ca. By progressively adding Ca to the solution, it is possible to determine the concentration corresponding to a fixation of Ca by the cell. This occurs when the ratios Ca:Na are close to 200. With $MgCl_2$ the ratio has a value of about 20. That there is a fixation of Ca on a cellular structure is well demonstrated by the fact that the total amount of Ca present in the cell can be completely extracted only in the presence of citrate. Note that the minimum quantity of Ca which cannot be extracted without citrate is not very different when expressed in terms of membrane surface area, if we compare yeast cells, *Elodea* cells, or *Arbacia* eggs. It is also interesting to consider the results of Danielli (*201, 202*) showing that the ratio Na:Ca at the surface of many cells (red cells, leukocytes, *Asteria* eggs) is close to 1 while it is around 100 in the medium, thereby suggesting a different affinity of the cellular structures involved for the various cations.

This difference in affinity can be best explained if the ions form salts of various strength. The ion forming the weakest salt will be more readily bound. In the case of *Elodea,* Ca has an affinity 100 times greater than Na, or Na changes the affinity of the structure for Ca following one of the mechanisms described above.

With a monomolecular film of stearic acid, it is possible to show that, if the solution supporting the film contains Na and Ca in a concentration ratio of 100, Na exchanges for Ca in the film. These results are best explained if we postulate the formation of complexes having different dissociation constants according to the ion considered. This therefore explains satisfactorily the so-called balance required for the various cations.

VIII. Chemical Nature of the Structure Responsible for the Permeability Characteristics of Living Membranes

It is actually impossible to analyze quantitatively, in the light of the scheme presented in the preceding section, the results concerning the action of various compounds on the permeability characteristics of a living membrane. The chemical nature of X, i.e., the molecular architecture responsible for the permeability characteristics, is still unknown. This is one of the major obstacles over which we stumble.

From the results of indirect experiments, various compounds have been proposed as being part of the chemical architecture responsible for the permeability characteristics of the membrane. Cephalin and chondroitin sulfuric acid are able to form complexes with Ca: thus the amount of Ca bound would control the permeability (*203, 204*). This hypothesis finds an experimental support in the results obtained while studying the permeability of connective tissue of vertebrates under various conditions: the diffusion of PO_4 increases in the absence of Ca (*205*).

Nucleic acids have also been proposed as being responsible for the permeability characteristics of living membranes, on the basis of the following observations (*200*): (*a*) presence of ribonucleic acid at the surface of some cells; (*b*) ribonucleic acid complexes with Ca; (*c*) inhibitory action of ribonuclease on the fixation of Ca by *Elodea* cells.

Let us now examine, in the light of available experimental findings, how we could characterize the molecular architectures responsible for the permeability characteristics of a membrane. The substance subjected to transport is generally assumed to form a complex with some membrane component. A reactive site for transport must therefore be assumed. On the basis of the fact that nitrogen, argon, and other rare gases are concentrated in the swim bladder of some fishes, it has however been argued that such a step is not necessary, as the rare gases do not enter into any known chemical reactions because of the saturation of their electronic shells. However, it should be borne in mind that the concentration process in this case seems to result from a countercurrent system in the rete mirabile and from the removal of oxygen (*206*).

Before attempting to isolate the molecule bearing the transport sites, the question must be asked whether the number of molecules is so small as to make their isolation and identification impossible. On the basis of the calculation made by Solomon *et al.* (*207*) concerning the kinetics of ouabain inhibition of K transport, one site for every million square angstroms of cellular surface is postulated, while Glynn (*208*) estimates only one-tenth of this number of sites to be present. Thus 5 kg. of cells must be collected in order to obtain 1 μmole of a molecule carrying the active site.

For yeast cells Conway *et al.* (*209*) estimate from the rubidium-potassium competition that 130 μeq of a cation carrier should be found in 1 kg. of centrifuged cells.

If one postulates that inorganic ions are passing the membrane through aqueous channels, it is possible to estimate from water flow measurements the density of these channels. From the figures obtained, the amount of molecules responsible for the specific permeability characteristics of the membrane can be calculated.

It appears that about 0.02% of the total area of the membrane can be attributed to "pore" surface. This should be divided into patches of 4 Å. radius, i.e., for 1 cm.^{2} 0.4×10^{13} patches. If each patch contains 1 molecule carrying the transport site(s), 0.4×10^{13} molecules can be extracted from 1 cm^2 of membrane surface. Since 1 cm.^{2} corresponds to ca. 1.10^6 cells, this means that ca. 150 μmoles could be extracted from 1 kg. of cells.

This estimation gives, of course, the total number of molecules carrying active sites lining a water-filled "pore" in the membrane.

The next question to be asked is whether or not the transport system has the properties of an enzyme. *A priori* it is not necessary to assume that the active site is an integral part of an enzyme molecule. The fact that a molecule is able to bind a substance in one phase and to release it in another does not describe an enzyme. However, when we are dealing with active transport, we know that energy must be fed into the transporting system. There is good experimental evidence to show that ATP is the energy source. The most conclusive experiments on this matter have been made by Hodgkin and his colleagues (*210–213*) on the squid giant axon. The endogenous arginine phosphate and ATP levels are depleted by poisoning the axon with 2 m*M* cyanide. As a result Na efflux as measured with Na^{22}, diminishes. The subsequent injection of arginine phosphate, phosphoenol pyruvate, ATP, or ADP restores the Na efflux. Hodgkin concludes therefore that high-energy phosphate compounds are necessary for active transport of cations in the squid giant axon. If this conclusion is correct, part of the transport system must act as an adenosine triphosphatase.

An ATPase activity has indeed been ascribed to various cell membranes (*214–217*); more recently an ATPase activity sensitive to alkali metal ions, first isolated by Skou in 1957 (*118*) from crab nerves, has been demonstrated in many other cells (*218–224*).

These findings do not necessarily demonstrate that the ATPase isolated is the molecule directly responsible for the transfer of material across the membrane. Since ATP is generally assumed to be the important source of cellular energy, there must be various ATPases affected differently by the intracellular conditions in order to provide, in the right sequence, the energy required by all the anabolic functions of the cell. One possibility still remains to be considered in the more specific case of alkali metal ions transport: ATP being the energy source, the membrane ATPase sensitive to the cation concentration of both intracellular and extracellular liquids catalyzes the transfer of a high-energy bond to the molecular architecture more directly related to the handling of ions across the membrane. This would give the cell additional control of the cation content of the intracellular fluid.

Another important aspect of the problem to be considered is the nature of the intimate mechanism used by the cell in the transfer of ions or molecules across the barrier. Are we dealing with a shuttling carrier, or is the solute moving along sites on a fixed structure?

It is actually very difficult to answer this question. Many models have been proposed [see for instance (*225*)]. They are discussed adequately in the very important review written by Christensen (*226*). When dealing with this problem, however, one has the impression that the only thing to be challenged is the imagination of the writer: any model thermodynamically possible is indeed acceptable since we do not have any experimental argument favoring one specific model more than another.

So far the active sites have been studied along two principal lines of investigation:

(*a*) The behavior of analogs of the solute is studied on the intact cell to find the structural modification which abolishes the transport. The chemical function responsible for the effect observed can sometimes be identified by examining the structure of the various compounds known to affect in the same way the permeability characteristics of the membrane (*48, 100–102, 106, 107, 109, 110, 175, 194*). On the basis of molecular complementarity a mirror image of the substrate can be proposed, thus giving the possible nature and configuration of the active site(s) on the molecule. This method has been used successfully in enzyme chemistry (*227–230*) and has tentatively been applied to resolve some problems on membrane permeability (*231*).

(*b*) The other approach deals essentially with attempts to identify some cellular extractable material with the molecular architecture responsible for some of the permeability characteristics of the membrane. There are interesting attempts to isolate and identify the structure involved in the permeability of cellular membranes.

Chagas (*232, 233*) in Rio de Janeiro and Ehrenpreis (*234, 235*) in Nachmansohn's laboratory in New York have claimed to have isolated the acetylcholine receptor from the electric organ of *Electrophorus electricus* L.

Woolley (*236*) has also tried to isolate a receptor reacting with 5-hydroxytryptamine in the presence of Ca. Beumer (*237*) extracted from *Shigella* substances able to combine with phages in the same way as the intact bacterial cell, in that both have the same requirements in Na and Ca for maximum binding. Hokin *et al.* (*238*) propose phosphatidic acid as the sodium carrier.

On the basis of the results published by the above authors, it appears to be very difficult to ascribe a well-defined physiological role to the material extracted. Some important properties found with the intact cell cannot always be demonstrated on the extract. In the case of the so-called acetylcholine receptor, curare binding could not be significantly reduced in the presence of carbamylcholine, a type of competition well demonstrated in various *in vivo* systems.

We have also found that material extracted, according to the technique of Ehrenpreis, from nonconducting tissues (gills of crab, red cells) (unpublished results) possesses at least some of the properties already described for the protein(s) isolated by Ehrenpreis. These results must therefore be interpreted with the greatest caution, until we have more criteria available, before deciding that an extract might be of physiological significance in cellular permeability (*239*).

IX. Conclusions

We are just beginning to have some indication of the possible relationships existing between the various functions of a membrane as well as their connection with the general metabolism of the cell.

Thus it seems reasonable to assume that the active transport of cations is essentially devoted to the regulation of cell volume. That we are dealing with a very primitive cellular function seems to be indicated by the fact that the active transport of cations is possible in the absence of amino acids, sugars, and fatty acids, while the converse is not verified. In this context, it could hardly be suggested that the ionic composition of the intracellular phase, i.e., a medium rich in potassium and poor in sodium, is an adaptation to the impelling necessity of enzymatic activity.

On the contrary, it appears that the limitation of enzymatic activity to such a medium would be a secondary adaptation to a primitive condition. This would also be the case for the mechanism generating an action potential, since it utilizes the free energy accumulated as ionic gradients to produce an electric current.

This general hypothesis may also explain why the active transport of organic ions and molecules is possible only in the presence of adequate amounts of inorganic cations. Scheme I may therefore be proposed to illustrate the relationships existing between the various functions of a living membrane and the general cellular metabolism.

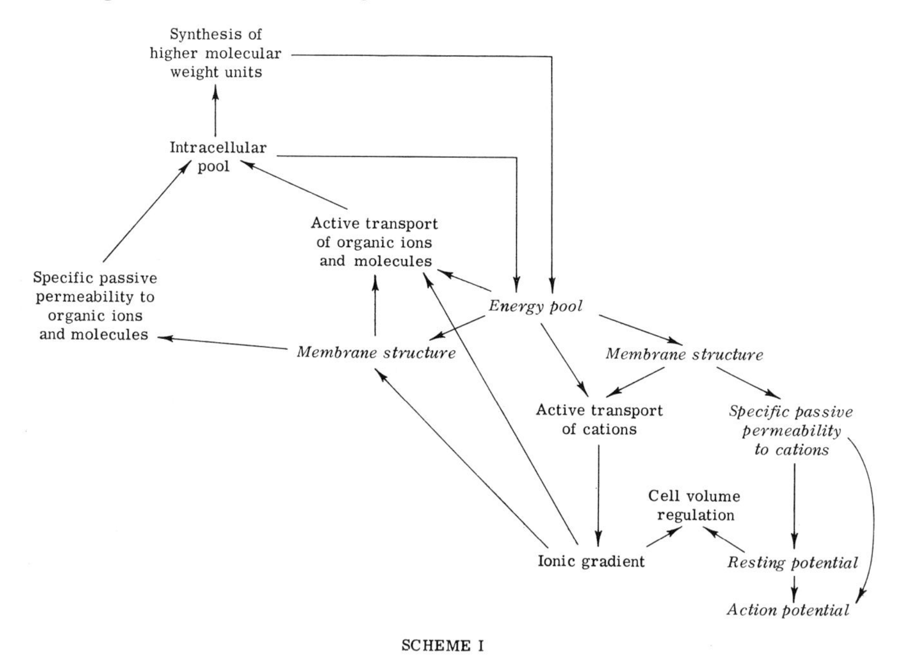

SCHEME I

It is obvious from this scheme that it is possible to modify one function of the membrane without a direct action on the mechanism directly responsible for this function. We may therefore expect a diversity in the sites of action of the various substances known to affect the permeability characteristics, and this invites us to be cautious in interpreting the results obtained.

As a corollary it is evident that the identification of the molecular architecture responsible for a permeability characteristic ("carrier," acetylcholine receptor, and so on) cannot be based solely on studies of the binding properties of the material extracted for various substances known to affect the function of the membrane *in vivo*.

In most of the studies dealing with the transfer of ions or molecules we do not encounter too much difficulty in demonstrating the metabolic dependence of a transport. We find, however, a challenging problem when we try to give a physical meaning to the various constants appearing in our flux equations. A simple model, the pore membrane, has been proposed on the basis of these equations. However, it is still a fact that this model is far from being completely satisfactory. Such a mechanistic model might be inadequate to explain the apparently simple behavior of water, urea, thiourea, and so on.

Finally, it may be proposed that the comparative study of membrane permeability illustrates two useful concepts in comparative biochemistry. It has been pointed out that in the field of membrane permeability, the differentiation seems to be achieved mainly through a spatial arrangement of permeability characteristics at the cell surface. This therefore constitutes a good example of physiological radiation.

On the other hand, in the light of available data, we may speculate on the chemical nature of the molecular architecture responsible for the various permeability characteristics. It may tentatively be proposed that the biochemical systems involved are closely related chemically. The permeability characteristics of living membranes could then be considered as heterotypic expressions of a common biochemical system.

References

1. V. Koefoed-Johnsen and H. H. Ussing, *Acta Physiol. Scand.* **28,** 60–76 (1953).
2. H. H. Ussing and K. Zerahn, *Acta Physiol. Scand.* **23,** 110–127 (1951).
3. E. Schoffeniels, *Arch. intern. physiol. et biochem.* **63,** 361–365 (1955).
4. D. D. Van Slyke and G. M. Meyer, *J. Biol. Chem.* **16,** 197–233 (1913).
5. D. L. Oxender and H. N. Christensen, *J. Biol. Chem.* **234,** 2321–2324 (1959).
6. E. F. Gale, *Advances in Protein Chem.* **8,** 285–391 (1953).
7. H. N. Christensen, T. R. Riggs, and N. E. Ray, *J. Biol. Chem.* **194,** 41–51 (1952).
8. E. Negelein, *Biochem. Z.* **323,** 214–234 (1952).
9. R. M. Johnstone, *Can. J. Biochem. and Physiol.* **37,** 589 (1959).
10. H. N. Christensen, M. K. Cushing, and J. A. Streicher, *Arch. Biochem.* **23,** 106–110 (1949).
11. H. N. Christensen, T. R. Riggs, H. Fischer, and I. M. Palatine, *J. Biol. Chem.* **198,** 15–22 (1952).
12. T. R. Riggs, B. A. Coyne, and H. N. Christensen, *J. Biol. Chem.* **209,** 395–411 (1954).
13. H. N. Christensen and T. R. Riggs, *J. Biol. Chem.* **220,** 265–278 (1956).
14. G. Wiseman, *J. Physiol.* (*London*) **120,** 63–72 (1953).
15. H. Akedo, T. Sugawa, S. Yoshikawa, and M. Suda, *J. Biochem.* (*Tokyo*) **47,** 124–130 (1960).
16. M. Baillien and E. Schoffeniels, *Biochim. et Biophys. Acta* **53,** 521–536 (1961).
17. H. N. Christensen and T. R. Riggs, *J. Biol. Chem.* **194,** 57–68 (1952).
18. L. M. Birt and F. J. R. Hird, *Biochem. J.* **70,** 277–286 (1958).

19. V. G. Allfrey, R. Meudt, J. W. Hopkins, and A. E. Mirsky, *Proc. Natl. Acad. Sci. U. S.* **47,** 907–932 (1961) and personal communication from Dr. Allfrey.
20. T. H. Wilson and G. Wiseman, *J. Physiol.* (*London*) **123,** 116–125 (1954).
21. E. W. Clarke, Q. H. Gibson, D. H. Smyth, and G. Wiseman, *J. Physiol.* (*London*) **112,** 46P (1951).
22. H. Hagihira, M. Ogata, N. Takedatsu, and M. Suda, *J. Biochem.* (*Tokyo*) **47,** 139–143 (1960).
23. E. L. Jervis and D. H. Smyth, *J. Physiol.* (*London*) **149,** 433–441 (1959).
24. R. P. Spencer and A. H. Samiy, *Am. J. Physiol.* **199,** 1033–1036 (1960).
25. E. C. C. Lin and T. H. Wilson, *Am. J. Physiol.* **199,** 127–130 (1960).
26. C. M. Paine, H. J. Newman, and M. W. Taylor, *Am. J. Physiol.* **197,** 9–12 (1959).
27. A. Gagnon, *Rev. can. biol.* **20,** 7–14 (1961).
28. D. M. Matthews and D. H. Smyth, *J. Physiol.* (*London*) **116,** 20–21P (1952).
29. W. T. Agar, F. J. R. Hird, and G. S. Sidhu, *Biochim. et Biophys. Acta* **22,** 21–30 (1956).
30. J. Pinsky and E. Geiger, *Proc. Soc. Exptl. Biol. Med.* **81,** 55–62 (1952).
31. G. Wiseman, *J. Physiol.* (*London*) **127,** 414–422 (1955).
32. K. H. Beyer, L. D. Wright, H. R. Skeggs, H. F. Russo, and G. A. Shaner, *Am. J. Physiol.* **151,** 202–210 (1947).
33. H. Kamin and P. Handler, *Am. J. Physiol.* **164,** 654–661 (1951).
34. J. L. Brown, A. H. Samiy, and R. F. Pitts, *Am. J. Physiol.* **200,** 370–372 (1961).
35. W. A. Webber, J. L. Brown, and R. F. Pitts, *Am. J. Physiol.* **200,** 380–386 (1961).
36. E. B. Robson and G. A. Rose, *Clin. Sci.* **16,** 75–91 (1957).
37. C. E. Dent and G. A. Rose, *Quart. J. Med.* **20,** 205–219 (1951).
38. M. W. Neil, *Biochem. J.* **71,** 118–124 (1959).
39. Q. H. Gibson and G. Wiseman, *Biochem. J.* **48,** 426–429 (1951).
40. M. D. Milne, A. Asatoor, and L. W. Loughbridge, *Lancet* **280,** 51–52 (1961).
41. H. W. Hagihira, E. C. C. Lin, A. H. Samiy, and T. H. Wilson, *Biophys. Biochem. Research Communs.* **4,** 478–481 (1961).
42. E. Schoffeniels, *in* "Biological Structure and Function" (T. W. Goodwin and O. Lindberg, eds.), Vol. II, pp. 621–631. Academic Press, New York, 1961.
43. D. Schachter and J. S. Britten, *Federation Proc.* **20,** 137 (1961).
44. D. Nathans, D. F. Tapley, and J. E. Ross, *Biochim. et Biophys. Acta* **41,** 271–282 (1960).
45. L. R. Finch and F. J. R. Hird, *Biochim et Biophys. Acta* **43,** 278–287 (1960).
46. T. R. Riggs, L. M. Walker, and H. N. Christensen, *J. Biol. Chem.* **233,** 1479–1484 (1958).
47. E. Schoffeniels, *in* "Bioelectrogenesis" (C. Chagas and A. Paes de Carvalho, eds.), pp. 147–165. Elsevier, Amsterdam, 1961.
48. E. Schoffeniels and D. Nachmansohn, *Biochim. et Biophys. Acta* **26,** 1–15 (1957).
49. E. Schoffeniels, *Arch. intern. physiol. et biochem.* **68,** 1–151 (1960).
50. H. N. Christensen, *in* "Amino Acid Metabolism" (W. D. McElroy and B. Glass, eds.), p. 63. Johns Hopkins Press, Baltimore, Maryland, 1955.
51. E. Heinz and H. Mariani, *Federation Proc.* **14,** 224 (1955).
52. E. Heinz, *J. Biol. Chem.* **225,** 305–315 (1957).
53. S. R. Elsden, *J. Exptl. Biol.* **22,** 51–62 (1945).

54. J. Barcroft, R. A. McAnally, and A. T. Phillipson, *J. Exptl. Biol.* **20**, 120–129 (1944).
55. E. Gray, A. F. Pilgrim, and R. A. Weller, *J. Exptl. Biol.* **28**, 74–82 (1951).
56. E. Gray and A. F. Pilgrim, *J. Exptl. Biol.* **28**, 83–90 (1951).
56a. W. D. Kitts, M. C. Robertson, B. Stephenson, and I. McT. Cowan, *Can. J. Zool.* **36**, 279–285 (1958).
56b. A. B. Stevenson, W. D. Kitts, A. J. Wood, and I. McT. Cowan, *Can. J. Zool.* **37**, 9–14 (1959).
57. R. B. Johnson and D. A. Peterson, *Federation Proc.* **19**, 321 (1960).
57a. A. Cools and Ch. Jeuniaux, *Arch. intern. physiol. et biochem.* **69**, 1–8 (1961).
58. D. H. Smyth and C. B. Taylor, *J. Physiol.* (*London*) **141**, 73–80 (1958).
59. J. M. Johnston, *J. Biol. Chem.* **234**, 1065–1067 (1959).
59a. B. J. Parsons, D. H. Smyth, and C. B. Taylor, *J. Physiol.* (*London*) **144**, 387–402 (1958).
60. F. Ponz, R. Parès, and M. Lluch, *Bull. soc. chim. biol.* **39**, 55–65 (1957).
61. E. Riklis and J. H. Quastel, *Can. J. Biochem. and Physiol.* **36**, 347–362 (1958).
62. R. K. Crane, D. Miller, and I. Bihler, *in* "Symposia Csav: Membrane Transport and Metabolism" (A. Kleinzeller and A. Kotyk, eds.), pp. 439–449. Czechoslovak Acad. Sci. Publ., Prague, 1961.
63. X. J. Musacchia, *Federation Proc.* **20**, 244 (1961).
64. T. Z. Csaky and M. Thale, *J. Physiol.* (*London*) **151**, 59–65 (1960).
65. A. M. Fox and X. J. Musacchia, *Federation Proc.* **19**, 182 (1960).
66. M. Burger, L. Hejmova, and A. Kleinzeller, *Biochem. J.* **71**, 233–242 (1959).
67. V. P. Cirillo, *Bacteriol. Proc.* p. 108 (1959).
68. E. J. Conway and M. Donney, *Biochem. J.* **47**, 347–355 (1950).
69. A. Rothstein, *Symposium Soc. Exptl. Biol.* **8**, 165–201 (1954).
70. A. Rothstein, *Protoplasmatologia* **2**, 1 (1954).
71. A. Rothstein, *Discussions Faraday Soc.* **21**, 229–238 (1956).
72. V. P. Cirillo, *in* "Symposia Csav: Membrane Transport and Metabolism" (A. Kleinzeller and A. Kotyk, eds.), pp. 343–351. Czechoslovak Acad. Sci. Publ., Prague, 1961.
73. H. Levi and H. H. Ussing, *Acta Physiol. Scand.* **16**, 232–249 (1948).
74. L. Lacko, M. Burger, L. Hejmova, and J. Reinkova, *in* "Symposia Csav: Membrane Transport and Metabolism" (A. Kleinzeller and A. Kotyk, eds.), pp. 399–408. Czechoslovak Acad. Sci. Publ., Prague, 1961.
75. W. Wilbrandt, *in* "Symposia Csav: Membrane Transport and Metabolism" (A. Kleinzeller and A. Kotyk, eds.), pp. 388–398. Czechoslovak Acad. Sci. Publ., Prague, 1961.
76. H. V. Rickenberg and J. J. Maio, *in* "Symposia Csav: Membrane Transport and Metabolism" (A. Kleinzeller and A. Kotyk, eds.), pp. 409–422. Czechoslovak Acad. Sci. Publ., Prague, 1961.
77. H. E. Morgan, R. L. Post, and C. R. Park, *in* "Symposia Csav: Membrane Transport and Metabolism" (A. Kleinzeller and A. Kotyk, eds.), pp. 423–430. Czechoslovak Acad. Sci. Publ., Prague, 1961.
78. P. J. Randle, *in* "Symposia Csav: Membrane Transport and Metabolism" (A. Kleinzeller and A. Kotyk, eds.), pp. 431–438. Czechoslovak Acad. Sci. Publ., Prague, 1961.
79. R. Levine and M. S. Goldstein, *Recent Progr. in Hormone Research* **11**, 343–380 (1955).
80. C. R. Park, J. Bornstein, and R. L. Post, *Am. J. Physiol.* **182**, 12–16 (1955).

81. P. J. Randle and G. H. Smith, *Biochem. J.* **70,** 490–500 (1958).
82. P. J. Randle and G. H. Smith, *Biochem. J.* **70,** 501–508 (1958).
83. H. E. Morgan, P. J. Randle, and D. M. Regen, *Biochem. J.* **73,** 573–579 (1959).
84. G. Bhattacharya, *Nature* **183,** 324–325 (1959).
85. A. Rothstein, *Bacteriol. Revs.* **23,** 175–201 (1959).
86. R. Lorente de No, *Harvey Lectures Ser.* **42,** 43–105 (1946–1947).
87. R. Lorente de No, "A Study of Nerve Physiology." Studies from the Rockefeller Institute for Med. Research, Vols. 131 and 132, 1947.
88. R. Lorente de No, *Cold Spring Harbor Symposia Quant. Biol.* **17,** 299–315 (1952).
89. T. L. Jahn, *J. Theoret. Biol.* **2,** 129–138 (1962).
90. E. J. Lund, *J. Exptl. Zool.* **51,** 265–290 (1928).
91. P. A. Kometiani, *in* "Symposia Csav: Membrane Transport and Metabolism" (A. Kleinzeller and A. Kotyk, eds.), pp. 180–192. Czechoslovak Acad. Sci. Publ., Prague, 1961.
92. M. Gerebtzoff and E. Schoffeniels, *in* "Comparative Biochemistry" (M. Florkin and H. S. Mason, eds.), Vol. II, pp. 519–544. Academic Press, New York, 1961.
93. D. E. Goldman, *J. Gen. Physiol.* **27,** 37–60 (1943).
94. L. J. Mullins, *Ann. N. Y. Acad. Sci.* **94,** 390–404 (1961).
95. E. Schoffeniels and Z. M. Bacq, *in* "Les ions alcalino-terreux en biologie" (Z. M. Bacq, ed.), "Handbuch der experimentellen Pharmakologie: "Ergänzungswerk," Vol. XVII. Springer, Berlin, 1963.
96. D. C. Tosteson and J. F. Hoffman, *J. Gen. Physiol.* **44,** 169–194 (1960).
97. M. Florkin, *Bull. soc. chim. biol.* **45,** 653–680 (1963).
98. M. Florkin, *Proc. 5th Intern. Congr. Biochem., Moscow, 1961* Preprint 202.
99. L. B. Kirschner, *J. Cellular Comp. Physiol.* **45,** 89–102 (1955).
100. J. C. Skou and K. Zerahn, *Biochim. et Biophys. Acta* **35,** 324–333 (1959).
101. E. Schoffeniels, *Arch. intern. physiol. et biochem.* **68,** 231–232 (1960).
102. E. Schoffeniels and M. Baillien, *Arch. intern. physiol. et biochem.* **68,** 376–377 (1960).
103. E. Schoffeniels, *Arch. intern. physiol. et biochem.* **63,** 513–530 (1955).
104. V. Koefoed-Johnsen and H. H. Ussing, *Acta. Physiol. Scand.* **42,** 298–308 (1958).
105. L. Engbaek and T. Hoshiko, *Acta Physiol. Scand.* **39,** 348–355 (1957).
106. R. R. Tercafs and E. Schoffeniels, *Arch. intern. physiol. et biochem.* **69,** 604–605 (1961).
107. R. R. Tercafs and E. Schoffeniels, *Arch. intern. physiol. et biochem.* **70,** 129–130 (1962).
108. E. Schoffeniels and R. R. Tercafs, *Biochem. Pharmacol.* **11,** 769–778 (1962).
109. E. Schoffeniels, R. Gilles, and G. Dandrifosse, *Arch. intern. physiol. et biochem.* **70,** 335–344 (1962).
109a. E. Schoffeniels, *Gen. Comp. Endocrinol.* **3,** 73i (1963).
110. R. R. Tercafs and E. Schoffeniels, *Science* **133,** 1706 (1961).
111. A. Leaf and H. S. Frazier, *Progr. in Cardiovascular Diseases* **4,** 47–64 (1961).
112. H. S. Frazier, E. F. Dempsey, and A. Leaf, *J. Gen. Physiol.* **45,** 529–543 (1962).
113. M. Baillien and E. Schoffeniels, *Biochim. et Biophys. Acta* **53,** 537–548 (1961).

114. T. W. Clarkson, A. C. Cross, and S. Toole, *Nature* **191,** 501–502 (1961).
115. M. Baillien and E. Schoffeniels, *Arch. intern. physiol. et biochem.* **70,** 140–141 (1962).
116. J. Orloff and J. J. Handler, *Biochem. Biophys. Research Communs.* **5,** 63–66 (1961).
117. H. N. Christensen, T. R. Riggs, H. Fischer, and I. M. Palatine, *J. Biol. Chem.* **198,** 1–14 (1952).
118. J. C. Skou, *Biochim. et Biophys. Acta* **23,** 394–401 (1957).
119. J. T. Holden, *in* "Amino Acid Pools" (J. T. Holden, ed.), pp. 566–594. Elsevier, Amsterdam, 1962.
120. M. Florkin, *Proc. Intern. Congr. Biochem. 4th Congr., Vienna, 1958,* Vol. **12,** 63–77.
121. L. Fredericq, *Bull. acad. Belg., Classe sci.* p. 428 (1901).
122. M. N. Camien, H. Sarlet, Gh. Duchâteau, and M. Florkin, *J. Biol. Chem.* **193,** 881–885 (1951).
123. Gh. Duchâteau, H. Sarlet, M. N. Camien, and M. Florkin, *Arch. intern. physiol.* **60,** 105–106 (1952).
124. Gh. Duchâteau and M. Florkin, *Arch. intern. physiol. et biochim.* **63,** 213–221 (1955).
125. Gh. Duchâteau and M. Florkin, *Arch. intern. physiol. et biochim.* **63,** 249–251 (1955).
126. Gh. Duchâteau and M. Florkin, *J. physiol.* (*Paris*) **48,** 520 (1956).
127. Gh. Duchâteau, M. Florkin, and Ch. Jeuniaux, *Arch. intern. physiol. et biochim.* **67,** 489–500 (1959).
128. S. Bricteux-Grégoire, Gh. Duchâteau, Ch. Jeuniaux, and M. Florkin, *Arch. intern. physiol. et biochim.* **70,** 273–286 (1962).
129. M. Florkin, *Bull. acad. roy. Belg. Classe sci.* **48,** 687–694 (1962).
130. E. Schoffeniels, *Arch. intern. physiol. et biochim.* **68,** 696–698 (1960).
131. A. E. Needham, *Physiol. Comp. Oecol.* **4,** 209 (1957).
132. Ch. Jeuniaux and M. Florkin, *Arch. intern. physiol. et biochim.* **69,** 385–386 (1961).
133. A. Wollenberger, *Biochem. J.* **61,** 77–80 (1955).
133a. M. Kini and J. H. Quastel, *Science* **131,** 413–414 (1960).
134. A. L. Hodgkin, *Biol. Revs.* **26,** 339–409 (1951).
135. R. Gilles and E. Schoffeniels, *Biochim. et Biophys. Acta* **82,** 525–537 (1964).
135a. E. Schoffeniels and R. Gilles, *Life Sciences* **11,** 834–839 (1963).
136. C. Terner, L. V. Eggleston, and H. A. Krebs, *Biochem. J.* **47,** 139–149 (1950).
137. P. R. Cannon, L. E. Frazier, and R. H. Hughes, *Metabolism Clin. and Exptl.* **1,** 49–57 (1952).
138. R. E. Cooke, W. E. Segar, D. B. Cheek, F. E. Coville, and D. C. Darrow, *J. Clin. Invest.* **31,** 798–805 (1952).
139. E. Muntwyler, G. E. Griffin, and R. L. Arends, *Am. J. Physiol.* **174,** 283–288 (1953).
140. R. E. Eckel, C. E. Pope, II, and J. E. C. Norris, *Arch. Biochem. Biophys.* **52,** 293–294 (1954).
141. M. Iacobellis, E. Muntwyler, and C. I. Dogben, *Am. J. Physiol.* **185,** 275–278 (1956).
142. M. S. Gordon, K. Schmidt-Nielsen, and H. M. Kelly, *J. Exptl. Biol.* **38,** 659–678 (1961).
143. R. R. Tercafs and E. Schoffeniels, *Life Sci.* **1,** 19–23 (1962).

144. V. du Vigneaud, *Harvey Lectures* **50,** 1–26 (1954–1955).
145. R. Acher, J. Chauvet, and M. T. Lenci, *Biochim. et Biophys. Acta* **38,** 344–345 (1960).
146. R. Acher, J. Chauvet, M. T. Lenci, F. Morel, and J. Maetz, *Biochim. et Biophys. Acta* **42,** 379–380 (1960).
147. R. Acher, J. Chauvet, M. T. Chauvet, and D. Crepy, *Biochim. et Biophys. Acta* **51,** 419–420 (1961).
148. P. G. Katsoyannis and V. du Vigneaud, *J. Biol. Chem.* **233,** 1352–1354 (1958).
149. G. Whittembury, N. Sugino, and A. K. Solomon, *Nature* **187,** 699–701 (1960).
150. M. J. Petersen and I. S. Edelman, *Federation Proc.* **21,** 146 (1962).
151. F. P. Chinard, *Am. J. Physiol.* **171,** 578–586 (1952).
152. H. H. Ussing, *Colston Papers* **7,** 33–41 (1954).
153. A. Mauro, *Science* **126,** 252–253 (1957).
154. B. Andersen and H. H. Ussing, *Acta Physiol. Scand.* **39,** 228–239 (1957).
155. J. R. Pappenheimer, E. M. Renkin, and L. M. Borrero, *Am. J. Physiol.* **167,** 13–46 (1951).
156. V. W. Sidel and A. K. Solomon, *J. Gen. Physiol.* **41,** 243–257 (1957).
157. C. V. Paganelli and A. K. Solomon, *J. Gen. Physiol.* **41,** 259–277 (1957).
158. R. P. Durbin, *J. Gen. Physiol.* **44,** 315–326 (1960).
159. E. M. Renkin, *J. Gen. Physiol.* **38,** 225–243 (1954).
160. A. J. Staverman, *Rec. trav. chim.* **70,** 344 (1951).
161. R. P. Durbin, H. Frank, and A. K. Solomon, *J. Gen. Physiol.* **39,** 535–551 (1956).
162. D. Goldstein and A. K. Solomon, *J. Gen. Physiol.* **44,** 1–17 (1960).
163. E. Robbins and A. Mauro, *J. Gen. Physiol.* **43,** 523–532 (1960).
164. F. Morel, *Compt. Rend. 4e Réunion d'Endocrinologie* pp. 47–88 (1957).
165. H. N. Christensen, *in* "Symposia Csav: Membrane Transport and Metabolism" (A. Kleinzeller and A. Kotyk, eds.), pp. 465–469. Czechoslovak Acad. Sci. Publ., Prague, 1961.
166. A. Pletscher, P. Van Planta, and W. A. Hunzinger, *Helv. Physiol. Pharmacol. Acta* **13,** 18–24 (1955).
167. G. Lester, D. Stone, and O. Hechter, *Arch. Biochem. Biophys.* **75,** 196–214 (1958).
168. G. Lester and O. Hechter, *Proc. Natl. Acad. Sci. U. S.* **45,** 1792 (1959).
168a. M. E. Krahl, "The Action of Insulin on Cells." Academic Press, New York, 1961.
169. H. E. Morgan, R. L. Post, and C. R. Park, *in* "Symposia Csav: Membrane Transport and Metabolism" (A. Kleinzeller and A. Kotyk, eds.), pp. 423–430. Czechoslovak Acad. Sci. Publ., Prague, 1961.
170. D. M. Kipnis and M. W. Noall, *Biochim. et Biophys. Acta* **28,** 226–227 (1958).
171. R. M. C. Dawson, *Biochem. J.* **47,** 386–391 (1950).
172. A. Tenenhouse and J. H. Quastel, *Can. J. Biochem. and Physiol.* **38,** 1311–1317 (1960).
173. E. Fluckiger and F. Verzar, *Helv. Physiol. Acta* **12,** 50–56 (1954).
174. K. Zierler, *Science* **126,** 1067–1068 (1957).
175. E. Schoffeniels, *Arch. intern. physiol. et biochem.* **67,** 517–519 (1959).
176. H. S. Mason, *Advances in Enzymol.* **16,** 105–184 (1955).
177. K. S. Cole, *J. Gen. Physiol.* **25,** 29–51 (1941).

178. A. L. Hodgkin, A. F. Huxley, and B. Katz, *Arch. Sci. Physiol.* **3**, 129–150 (1949).
179. H. B. Steinbach, S. Spiegelman, and N. Kawata, *J. Cellular Comp. Physiol.* **24**, 147–154 (1944).
180. K. S. Cole, *Arch. sci. physiol.* **3**, 253–258 (1949).
181. F. Brink, *Pharmacol. Revs.* **6**, 243–298 (1954).
182. A. L. Hodgkin and R. D. Keynes, *J. Physiol. (London)* **128**, 61–88 (1955).
182a. R. I. Macey and S. Myers, *Am. J. Physiol.* **204**, 1095–1099 (1963).
183. J. Cerf, *in* "Les ions alcalino-terreux en biologie" (Z. M. Bacq, ed.), "Handbuch der Experimentellen Pharmakologie: Ergänzungswerk," Vol. XVII. Springer, Berlin, 1963.
184. E. D. Adrian and S. Gelfan, *J. Physiol. (London)* **78**, 271–287 (1933).
185. A. Arvanitaki, *Arch. intern. physiol.* **49**, 209–256 (1939).
186. B. Frankenhaeuser and A. L. Hodgkin, *J. Physiol. (London)* **137**, 218–244 (1959).
187. A. L. Hodgkin and B. Katz, *J. Physiol. (London)* **116**, 424–448 (1952).
188. M. Maizels, *J. Physiol. (London)* **132**, 414–441 (1956).
189. R. A. Lyman, *J. Cellular Comp. Physiol.* **25**, 65–73 (1945).
190. E. C. Black and L. Irving, *J. Cellular Comp. Physiol.* **12**, 255–262 (1938).
191. M. Maizels, *Nature* **184**, 366 (1959).
192. U. Bolingbroke and M. Maizels, *J. Physiol. (London)* **149**, 563–585 (1959).
193. R. L. Klein, *J. Cellular Comp. Physiol.* **53**, 241–258 (1959).
194. E. Schoffeniels, *Abstr. Commun. 21st Intern. Congr. Physiol. Sci., Buenos Aires, August, 1959.*
195. L. J. Mullins, *J. Cellular Comp. Physiol.* **44**, 77–86 (1954).
195a. E. G. Huf, J. Parrish, and C. Weatherford, *Am. J. Physiol.* **164**, 137–142 (1951).
196. J. Bourguet, *Compt. rend. soc. biol.* **151**, 1782–1783 (1957).
197. J. Bourguet and W. Van Rossum, *J. physiol. (Paris)* **50**, 189–192 (1958).
198. P. F. Curran, J. Zadunaisky, and R. Gill, *Biochim. et Biophys. Acta* **52**, 392–395 (1961).
199. J. B. Kahn, *J. Pharmacol. Exptl. Therap.* **123**, 263–268 (1958).
200. D. Mazia, *Cold Spring Harbor Symposia Quant. Biol.* **8**, 195–203 (1940).
201. J. F. Danielli, *J. Exptl. Biol.* **20**, 167–176 (1944).
202. J. F. Danielli, "Cell Physiology and Pharmacology." Elsevier, Amsterdam, 1950.
203. E. E. Alexander, T. Teorell, and C. G. Aborg, *Trans. Faraday Soc.* **35**, 1200–1205 (1939).
204. M. B. Martin, *Arch. Biochem.* **43**, 181–193 (1953).
205. E. Schoffeniels, *Arch. intern. physiol. et biochem.* **63**, 366–375 (1955).
206. J. Wittenberg, *J. Gen. Physiol.* **41**, 783–804 (1958).
207. A. K. Solomon, T. J. Gill, and G. L. Gold, *J. Gen. Physiol.* **40**, 327–350 (1956).
208. I. M. Glynn, *J. Physiol. (London)* **136**, 148–173 (1957).
209. E. J. Conway and F. Duggan, *Biochem. J.* **69**, 265–274 (1958).
210. P. C. Caldwell, *J. Physiol. (London)* **132**, 35P (1956).
211. P. C. Caldwell, *in* "The Method of Isotope Tracers Applied to the Study of Active Ion Transport" (J. Coursaget, ed.), p. 88. Pergamon Press, New York, 1958.

212. P. C. Caldwell and R. D. Keynes, *J. Physiol.* (*London*) **148,** 8P–9P (1959).
213. A. L. Hodgkin, *Symposia and Special Lectures, 21st Intern. Congr. Physiol. Sci., Buenos Aires* p. 168 (1959).
214. B. Libet, *Federation Proc.* **7,** 72 (1948).
215. A. Rothstein and R. Meier, *J. Cellular Comp. Physiol.* **32,** 77–103 (1948).
216. E. M. Clarkson and M. Maizels, *J. Physiol.* (*London*) **116,** 112–128 (1952).
217. G. Acs, T. Garzo, G. Grosz, J. Molnar, O. Stephaneck, and F. B. Straub, *Acta Physiol. Acad. Sci. Hung.* **8,** 269 (1955).
218. R. L. Post, C. R. Merritt, C. R. Kinsolving, and C. D. Albright, *J. Biol. Chem.* **235,** 1796–1802 (1960).
219. D. C. Tosteson, R. H. Moulton, and M. Blaustein, *Federation Proc.* **20,** 128 (1961).
220. E. T. Dunham and I. M. Glynn, *J. Physiol.* (*London*) **156,** 274–293 (1961).
221. J. C. Skou, *Biochim. et Biophys. Acta* **58,** 314–325 (1962).
222. R. W. Albers and G. J. Koval, *Life Sci.* **5,** 219–222 (1962).
223. I. M. Glynn, *J. Physiol.* (*London*) **160,** 18P–19P (1962).
224. E. Schoffeniels, *Life Sci.* **9,** 437–440 (1962).
225. J. F. Danielli, *Symposia Soc. Exptl. Biol.* **8,** 502–516 (1954).
226. H. N. Christensen, *Advances in Protein Chem.* **15,** 239–314 (1960).
227. I. B. Wilson, *J. Biol. Chem.* **190,** 111–117 (1951).
228. I. B. Wilson, *J. Biol. Chem.* **199,** 113–120 (1952).
229. I. B. Wilson, *J. Biol. Chem.* **197,** 215–225 (1952).
230. I. B. Wilson, *in* "The Mechanism of Enzyme Action" (W. D. McElroy and B. Glass, eds.), p. 642. Johns Hopkins Press, Baltimore, Maryland, 1954.
231. D. Nachmansohn, "Chemical and Molecular Basis of Nerve Activity." Academic Press, New York, 1959.
232. C. Chagas, E. Penna-Franca, A. Hasson, C. Crocker, K. Nishie, and E. J. Garcia, *Ann. acad. brasil. sci.* **29,** 53 (1957).
233. C. Chagas, E. Penna-Franca, K. Nishie, and E. J. Garcia, *Arch. Biochem. Biophys.* **75,** 251–259 (1958).
234. S. Ehrenpreis, *in* "Bioelectrogenesis" (C. Chagas and A. Paes de Carvalho, eds.), pp. 379–396. Elsevier, Amsterdam, 1961.
235. S. Ehrenpreis, *Biochim. et Biophys. Acta* **44,** 561–577 (1960).
236. D. W. Woolley and N. K. Campbell, *Biochim. et Biophys. Acta* **40,** 543–544 (1960).
237. J. Beumer, *Mém. acad. roy. med. Belg.* [2] **4,** 47 pp. (1961).
238. L. E. Hokin and M. R. Hokin, *Nature* **184,** 1068–1069 (1959).
239. E. Schoffeniels, *Arch. intern. physiol. et biochem.* **70,** 423–425 (1962).

CHAPTER 4

The Hormones and Behavior

William C. Young*

Oregon Regional Primate Research Center, Beaverton, Oregon, and Department of Anatomy, University of Oregon Medical School, Portland, Oregon

I. Introduction

Inquiry into the manner in which the behavior of animals is influenced by hormones has had a course resembling in many ways the inquiry into the relationship between other vital activities and the hormones. Descriptive studies of behavior corresponding to the examination of tissue structure preceded experimentation, the first hints at "cause-and-effect" followed glandular ablation and the transplantation of the various endocrine organs and tissues, more precise information was obtained when purified hormones became available, and currently interest is being focused on the mechanisms by which the hormones "condition" tissues to respond to the stimuli which elicit the types of behavior associated with hormonal action. A difference in the development of the subjects is that at all times the acquisition of information about the hormones and behavior has lagged behind—often by years—

* Support of the investigations conducted at the University of Kansas and the Oregon Regional Primate Research Center was provided by research grant M-504 from the National Institute of Mental Health of the National Institutes of Health.

the acquisition of information about the hormones and the other responses they stimulate.

Explanations for this fact may be that until recently relatively few investigators were interested in the hormones and behavior, and that few investigators trained to probe into the biochemical aspects of the subject have chosen to do so. The invitation to prepare this chapter is taken as a sign of unfolding interest on the part of the latter group. Acceptance of the invitation may be taken as an expression of confidence that, if an overall view can be presented, a larger number of biochemists will be stimulated to join forces with the psychologists, ethologists, physiologists, and morphologists in their investigation of the many problems pressing for solution.

Behavior is mediated by tissues, much if not most of it by the highly specialized neural and muscular tissues. It is not surprising therefore that methods for the study of the hormones and behavior have much in common with the methods for the study of the hormones and any tissue responses, that many of the same safeguards and precautions must be taken, and that in certain important instances the rules of action of the hormones appear to be the same. For example, in females of a number of species, the preparation of the genital tract and of the neural tissues mediating mating behavior for full functioning depends on the synergistic action of estrogen and progesterone. Whether behavior or some other activity of the organism is being studied, allowance must be made for differences in the age and sex of the animals, for species differences, strain differences, and differences between individuals. The nutritional state, manner of confinement, temperature, character of the illumination in the case of species normally nocturnal in their habits (*1*), season, stage in the reproductive cycle, and general health of the animal including the possibility of even rather subtle endocrine imbalance must be considered. Also important for research in these two fields of endocrinology arc glandular ablation prior to hormone administration, the manner of hormone administration (*1a*), the use of pure preparations, accurate measurement of the administered hormones, attention to thresholds, and the use of physiological rather than pharmacological dosages. The influence of tissue responsiveness must be evaluated. Hormone antagonisms, synergisms, and facilitation often are the same, whether effects on behavior or effects on other vital activities are being followed. As we will see later when more of the background has been established, these similarities are of more than ordinary importance. When for some reason clarification is not given by data obtained from behavioral studies, and interpretation is difficult, the gap may be filled by referring to data obtained from morphological studies, and vice versa.

The other side of the coin for investigators of the hormones and behavior are the problems that are not encountered or, perhaps more accurately, are encountered in a very different form in studies of such tissue responses as secretion, growth, muscular contraction, fluid balance, etc. There is the problem of distinguishing between the hormones which influence behavior directly and those with actions which are merely supportive; its counterpart is the behavior which is subject to hormonal influence. One of the oldest problems, and one that is still very much with us, centers around the recording and measurement of behavior. The opinion was once held by many endocrinologists and morphologists, that the end points of behavior are not sufficiently sharp to be useful in experimental studies. The dominance of this belief may well have discouraged biochemists from entering this field of investigation. However, as we show, as the behavior characterizing members of each phylum is described, the contrary is true; indeed the nature of the end points has been the means to insights not easily gained from the other responses. Phyletic, generic, species, and even strain differences are the evidence that an evolution of behavior has occurred, but in the complex of the relationships we are discussing what has evolved—the endocrine system producing these hormones or the character of the tissues on which the hormones act? Other problems are more conventionally endocrinological: e.g., the identification, nature, and origin of the hormones which influence behavior; the place and manner of action of these hormones in bringing to expression the behavior with which their action is associated; and the temporal relationships. The problems mentioned thus far are common to all animals displaying behavior which is subject to hormonal control. For this reason it seems well to elaborate on them before turning to a discussion of the many specific relationships that have been revealed.

II. The Hormones Influencing Behavior and the Behavior Most Subject to Hormonal Influence and Control

The many relatively recent reviews and discussions of the hormones and behavior (*2–9*) have dealt largely with the relationships between steroid hormones and particularly between the gonadal hormones and behavior. Other reviews and original articles deal with the hormones associated with growth and pupation in insects, including their behavior during metamorphosis (*10–15*). Except for the suggestion that the active principles of the prothoracic gland are unsaturated ketones (*16, 17*), the chemical nature of the insect hormones is largely unknown. The subject is discussed briefly in a review which contains a characterization of the prothoracic gland hormone, ecdysone (*17a*).

In lower vertebrates much of reproductive behavior, including aggressive and submissive behavior, territorial defense, and locomotor behavior associated with reproduction, is dependent on gonadal hormones. These hormones are of less importance or have no direct action in conditioned responses and learning (*2*), but see Douglas *et al.* (*18*). The latter reported that injections of estradiol benzoate into rats were followed by an increase in time taken to run a goal-gradient alley. The weakening of the response was regarded possibly as an alteration in the functional equilibration of the central nervous system shown by changes in water balance and by changes in the threshold to some environmental patterns of stimulation. Throughout the vertebrate phyla hormones of the embryonic and fetal gonads are important for the patterning of the behavior displayed after the attainment of adulthood in fishes (*19–24*), amphibians (*25–30*), domestic fowl (*31*), the guinea pig (*32, 33*), and probably the rhesus monkey (*33a*). In the rat which has a short gestation, the testes have this role for approximately the first 5 to 10 days postnatally (*33a*). The role of gonadal hormones in man is controversial (*6, 8, 34–36*), but not excluded, in the opinion of this reviewer, is the possibility that the vigor of sexual behavior is influenced by these substances.

In subhuman vertebrates and in man the hormones secreted by the adrenal cortex, thyroid, parathyroid, and islands of Langerhans are regulatory (*37–41*) or supportive in the sense that they help to maintain the metabolic balance without which a normal functioning of the tissues mediating behavior is impossible. (*42*). No direct action similar to that of the gonadal hormones has been demonstrated.

The hypophysis may perhaps occupy an intermediate position. Its secretions are directly or indirectly supportive, but one substance, prolactin, has been closely associated with the migration of certain salamanders from land to water (*43–46*) and with parental behavior in birds and the laboratory rat (*47–50*). Doubt that the latter relationship is direct was expressed by the discussants of Dr. Riddle's paper in 1937, and the basis for cautious reservation is contained in the articles by Leblond (*51, 52*) and Leblond and Nelson (*53, 54*) and in the thoughtfully prepared reviews by Eisner (*5*) and Lehrman (*7*). The possibility that oviposition and spawning of the killifish *Fundulus* are associated with neurohypophyseal hormones was suggested by the observation that vibrating flexures of the body identical with those shown by spawning males and females are exhibited following the injection of natural vasopressin or oxytocin into intact, hypophysectomized or gonadectomized subjects (*55, 56*). As the comment by Aronson (*57*) indicates, the specific relationship of these vibrations to reproductive behavior has yet to be demonstrated. Hoar (*58*) makes a strong case for the participation of hypophyseal hormones in the regulation of nest building, courtship, and agonistic behavior of the male stickleback, *Gasterosteus aculeatus*, but the identity of the hormones has not been established. The relationship is synergistic and more evident in nest building and courtship than in the initial development of aggressive behavior.

III. The Recording and Measurement of Behavior

The methods of recording and measuring behavior—reviewed by Denenberg and Banks (*59*) for the domestic animals—vary from species to species. Many factors account for this. The technical problems imposed by the behavior of the species selected for study are usually peculiar to that species; they are never common to all. In most species the behavior displayed by the two sexes tends to be strongly dimorphic and requires different methodologies. The development of methods has been influenced by the background, interests, and goals of the investigator. In a general way methods have ranged from the relatively simple procedures developed by investigators who have used laboratory mammals—many references are contained in the review by Young (*9*)—to the elaborate schema prepared by the psychologists and ethologists who have followed the sequences or reaction chains in many fishes, birds, and insects, e.g., Baerends *et al.* (*60*), Barrass (*61*), Fabricius and Lindroth (*62*), Gabbutt (*63*), Hinde (*64, 65*), Lind (*66*), Morris (*67*), Moynihan and Hall (*68*), Skard (*69*), Spieth (*70*), and Wood-Gush (*71*). To be sure, not all the behavior described by these investigators has been related to hormonal activity, but diagrams of the type they have prepared are an aid in any analysis that is attempted.

Quite apart from the variations in methods imposed by differences between species and sexes are those assignable to differences in the training, technical skill, and purposes of the investigator. Furthermore, over a period of time the methods employed by individual investigators have changed, for experience with a species leads inevitably to a finer discernment of the many elements or measures composing the patterns characteristic of that species. This is well illustrated in the articles by Beach, Stone, Young, and their associates written during the period spanning the 1920's through the 1950's.

In any study of the hormones and behavior, allowance must be made for a number of factors which are less relevant for the student of the common morphological and physiological responses to hormonal action. Captivity and confinement influence behavior (*72–75*) and in all likelihood endocrine functioning. As a result, deviations in behavior may be anticipated in many species transferred from the wild state to that of confinement. Whatever the species, environmental control at the time of the observation or test must be rigid. Uncomfortably high or low temperatures and unusual sounds should be avoided. Animals should be accustomed to being handled and they should be cage adapted, that is placed in the cage, enclosure, or apparatus where the test is to be given a few minutes before it begins. In mating tests this is more important for the male than for the female, and investigators have long been aware that the female should be brought to the cage of the male (*76, 77*). The recency of sexual activity is important, particularly when males are being used. A number of the newer articles in which the relationships between the sexual act and subsequent behavior is described are cited by Young (*9*). The phase of the cycle in females should be known, not only because of the direct relationship of the phase to sexual behavior, but also because the females of some species display aggressive behavior during the diestrum and are cyclic in this respect (*78–80*).

The behavioral literature of the last decade is replete with reports of what are often lumped together as experiential factors and their influence on behavior. Included are various types of sensory deprivation, social isolation during infancy, maintenance in enriched and restricted environments, immobilization, crowding, exposure to noxious stimuli such as electric shock, high and low temperatures, noise, and handling or gentling. Selected fishes, birds, and mammals, including monkeys and chimpanzees, have been used. Much of the literature is cited by Denenberg (*81*), and other articles have appeared more recently (*75, 82–90*). Many of the results are equivocal if not contradictory; nevertheless, the evidence is impressive that in birds and mammals life experiences, and particularly those during infancy and the juvenile period, do much to shape the character of behavior displayed later. The point is especially important for the investigator as he selects animals for studies of the relationships between the hormones such as those from the thyroid, adrenal cortex, and gonads, the secretion of which is regulated by hypothalamic-hypophyseal activity.

In the development of methods for studying the relationships between the hormones and behavior, the investigator must be on guard, again against factors many of which are less important for the student of other responses to hormonal action. Much of the behavior influenced by hormones is complex, much is displayed in a rapid succession of movements, much cannot be observed and recorded except by watching the animals, and within a species much is extremely variable from individual to individual. Under such circumstances, the matter of observer reliability is important and is a point over which scrupulous watch should be kept.

The complexity of the patterns of behavior is an obstacle to the development of satisfactory systems for scoring behavior (*9*). Ideally, a score should reveal precisely and at a glance what happened during a test, but unfortunately, as Clark and Aronson (*91*), Valenstein *et al.* (*92*), and Larsson (*93*) emphasized, it does not always do so. The score obtained in a test bears some resemblance to the score in a baseball game. A score of 1 to 0 tells a reader nothing about the combination of hits, walks, and errors which produced the run, but it does reveal that the character of the game was very different from that in which the score was 7 to 6 or 15 to 1. The score in the behavioral test as it has been developed by investigators working with fishes, birds, and mammals has just this role. As long as the limitations are recognized, methods of scoring will have an important place in the quantification of behavior.

The variability of behavioral display from individual to individual is a problem in itself. The variability is explained partly by the circumstance that patterns of behavior are composed of many elements or measures, each of which usually varies greatly and independently of the variations in the other elements of the pattern. The existence of these many elements and their variability may complicate the recording and analysis of behavior [see Denenberg (*81*) for a description of methods for recording, coding, and correlating these elements of a complicated pattern], but these features can be turned very easily to the advantage of the investigator of the hormones and behavior. The variability is a means by which the maturity or immaturity of a pattern can be revealed; in male mammals, for example, a variable in the form of an incomplete pattern is observed in prepuberal subjects (*94–97*). Familiarity with the variability displayed within a group of animals and with the fact that many individuals tend to display the same pattern from cycle to cycle, led to an analysis of the role of tissue responsiveness in the action of gonadal hormones in bringing mating behavior to expression (*98, 99*).

This tendency of individuals to display the same pattern of behavior can be useful to the endocrinologist or biochemist interested in behavior. If the establishment of the character of these patterns of behavior in intact animals is a part of the methodology of the experiment, and therefore if the animal is allowed to be its own control, the possibility exists that the effectiveness of hormones administered in a replacement therapy can be determined most accurately by comparing the character of the behavior displayed postoperatively and under experimental conditions with that displayed preoperatively. An example of the procedure is provided by experiments on the male guinea pig in which quantitative and qualitative tests were made of the action of testosterone, estradiol, and estrone (*99, 100*).

IV. Fishes

Detailed and careful descriptions of behavior believed to be hormone dependent have been given for many fishes and need not be repeated here. A few articles and reviews which would lead a reader into the literature in this field are cited (*57, 60, 67, 91, 101–107*). The behavior described is courtship, mating in the viviparous species, spawning, nest building, territorial fighting, and parental behavior including fanning the eggs, guarding the eggs, and feeding activities. The suggestion has been made that hypothalamic, hypophyseal, thyroid, and gonadal hormones participate in different ways in the regulation of migratory behavior, but it is evident from reviews by investigators active in the field (*37, 58, 108*) that we are far from an understanding of the internal mechanisms and external stimuli by which this latter behavior is regulated.

Methods of measuring these types of behavior have been described: fighting, nest building, courtship, spawning, and parental behavior in the three-spined stickleback, *Gasterosteus aculeatus* (*58, 107, 109*); courtship and mating behavior by the swordtail, *Xiphophorus helleri* (*105, 110*); courtship and mating behavior of *Platypoecilus* sp. (*124, 105*); fighting and nesting behavior of the Siamese fighting fish, *Betta splendens* (*111, 112*); nest building, spawning, and "incubation" behavior of the African mouthbreeder, *Tilapia macrocephala* (*101, 113*); courtship and mating behavior of the guppy, *Lebistes reticulatus* (*60, 91*); spawning behavior of the whitefish, *Coregonus lavaretus* (*62*); spawning behavior of the gobiid *Bathygobius soporator* (*114*); fanning behavior of the river bullhead, *Cottus gobio* (*115*); swimming activity of the goldfish *Carassius auratus* (*116*); swimming speed, territorial defense, and schooling behavior of the Pacific salmon, *Oncorhynchus* sp. (*117, 118*); swimming movements of the three-spined stickleback (*37, 119*).

In fishes, although quantitative differences exist (*101, 111*), many of the elements enumerated above are displayed by both sexes (*57, 62, 101, 104, 106, 112, 120–122*). In at least one species, *Tilapia macrocephala,* none of the patterns of reproductive behavior thus far investigated is entirely characteristic of either sex. These observations can only mean that fish of one sex commonly possess the nervous mechanism capable of mediating the reproductive behavior of the opposite sex (*57, 120.*) In the other vertebrate phyla a greater dimorphism of behavior is shown (*101*). Although it is not complete (*2, 9, 65*), the difference is sufficient to suggest that a change in the direction of greater dimorphism of behavior has occurred as the higher vertebrates have evolved.

The relationship of gonadal hormones to the behavior of fishes has been the subject of many investigations (*123*), and in general the validity of the evidence for a direct effect is not questioned. Not even in cyclostomes and elasmobranchs (*124*) is there any reason for doubting that the gonads and secondary sexual characters are hormonally controlled. Aronson (*57*), reviewing the results reported following gonadectomy and the results reported following treatment with testosterone propionate, methyl testosterone, pregneninolone, estradiol, and a variety of hormonal and nonhormonal substances, is more reserved. The persistence of male behavior following castration was noted in a number of fishes and led to the suggestion that testicular secretions are more important for the ontogeny of this behavior than they are for its maintenance in the adult. A similar possibility for the ovarian hormones does not seem to have been considered.

The likelihood that the hormones produced by the gonads of fishes are steroids was long ago deduced from effects of artificial and mammalian steroids on the secondary sex characters of fishes, and from the effects of extracts of fish gonads on mammalian tissues normally responsive to steroids (*125–127*). Direct evidence was provided by the extraction of androgenic substances from the testes of silver salmon (*128*), chum salmon (*129*), and the dogfish *Scyliorhinus stellaris* (*130, 131*); and of estrogens from dogfish ova (*132*), of estrogenic substances and possibly progesterone from lungfish ovaries (*133*), and of estrogens from the ovaries of *Torpedo marmorata* (*130*). The estrogen obtained from the ova was identified as estradiol-17β, which is thought to be one of the principal estrogens secreted by the Graafian follicle in mammals; estrone is the other (*134*). The estrogens from the lungfish ovaries were estriol and estrone, with a trace of estradiol-17β, whereas those from *Torpedo ovaries* were estriol and estradiol-17β in a proportion of 2 to 1. The important generalization that the ovaries of all vertebrates produce estrogens seems justified (*133*).

The site of origin of the gonadal hormones of fishes is discussed in recent reviews (*126, 127, 130, 135, 136*). Forbes (*135*) and Hoar (*126, 127, 136*) especially stress the uncertainty with respect to the cellular origin of the male hormone and attribute this uncertainty to the failure of so many investigators to identify interstitial cells in the testes of certain fishes. The question seems to have been clarified by Marshall and Lofts (*137, 138*). They explain that two distinct endocrine arrangements occur in the testes of fishes. One is the typical interstitial cell pattern of vertebrates and has presented no problem. The other is a complex of perilobular connective tissue elements which undergo a cycle essentially similar to that of the interstitial cell cycle in seasonal birds. Functionally, both arrangements are considered similar to the permanent interstitial or Leydig cell unit present in most mammals. Histochemical properties associated with the secretion of androgens, i.e., the accumulation and disappearance of cholesterol-positive lipids in the cytoplasm of the cells, are common to all.

The structure of the fish ovary differs from that in other vertebrates (*135, 136, 139*); nevertheless, Hoar (*136*) states that an inner granulosa and an outer theca are probably potentially present in all. According to Hoar the theca interna probably produces estrogens, as in mammals. Ball (*140*), on the other hand, while acknowledging that decisive evidence of the endocrine function of any type of cell in the ovary of bony fishes has not been produced, points out that the cells of the theca do not contain lipid droplets or cholesterol and their appearance never approximates that of the cells of the theca interna of mammals and birds, which probably are estrogen-secreting elements in members of these phyla. He marshals impressive evidence for the suggestion, originally made by Kinoshita (*141*) and by Bretschneider and Duyvené de Wit (*142*), that granulosa cells in the atretic follicles (corpora atretica) are the source of ovarian steroid hormones. We presume from the histochemical observations reviewed by Chieffi (*130*) that not only are the granulosa cells in the preovulation corpora lutea of *Torpedo* a source of steroid hormones, but that the granulosa cells in the postovulation corpora lutea of *Scyliorhinus* also have this role.

Important in looking at the problem comparatively, are the facts that the cellular origin of ovarian steroids in mammals has not yet been resolved satisfactorily (*143–146*), but that prototypes of the elements considered as sources of these hormones in mammals are present in fishes.

V. Amphibians

Probably because of the conspicuous clasping reflex of male anurans during the breeding season, frogs and toads were among the first animals to be used in tests of the relationship between the gonads and mating behavior. Many of the early experiments are described in Lipschütz' *Internal Secretions of the Sex Glands* (*147*). Much of the work done more recently is cited by Dodd (*123*) in his review of the gonadal hormones and secondary sex characters in the lower vertebrates.

Descriptive accounts of the behavior of anura (*148–157*) and urodeles (*158–161*) are relatively numerous. Types of behavior associated with hormonal action are the breeding behavior and a migrating behavior from land to the ponds in which they breed. The former consists of vocalizations by both sexes, amplexus or clasping which is done by both sexes but which is subject to a strong seasonal modification in the male, oviposition, ejaculation by the male and his release of the female, and a recognizable estrous behavior by the female (*123, 152*). Methods of quantifying clasping behavior, duration of oviposition, ejaculatory movements of the male, and release of the female have been developed, particularly by Aronson and Noble (*148–152*) and by Russell (*162, 163*). Aggressive behavior and territorial defense have been reported in a number of species mentioned by Haubrich (*164*) in his study of hierarchial behavior in *Xenopus*, but no effort to relate this behavior to hormonal action is cited. Migrating behavior has been studied rather grossly, but by methods that were adequate to demonstrate the action of prolactin in stimulating this behavior in hypophysectomized, gonadectomized *Diemyctylus* and in species of *Triturus* (*43–46*). This action apparently is a direct effect of the hypophyseal hormone on behavior.

Dependence of mating behavior on the gonads is assumed from the reports of its disappearance following gonadectomy and its induction following treatment with extracts of testicular and hypophyseal tissue (*147, 165–167*). Despite the report by Burgos (*168*) that restoration of clasping behavior in castrated *Bufo* required a pituitary extract as well as testosterone, the assumption seems to be that steroid hormones are sufficient, as they certainly are in the maintenance and functioning of the reproductive tract and accessory tissues (*123, 135, 169*).

The chemical identity of these hormones and their cellular origin present problems, a number of which are discussed by Dodd (*123*). Within the male of the newt *Taricha torosa*, connective tissue cells surrounding each testicular lobule form a ring of lipid-filled cells surrounding the Sertoli elements. At the same time, these latter elements develop cell boundaries and become an inner ring of lipid-filled cells. This double-layered structure is believed to be glandular and a source of male sex hormone (*170*). In a more recent study of *Xenopus laevis*, after stimulation with gonadotropins, steroid-3β-ol-dehydrogenase activity indicative of steroid hormone production was demonstrated in the interstitial tissue and under the tunica albuginea (*171*). The circumstance that evidence of glandular activity was found in the "lobule-boundary" and Sertoli cells of one species and in the interstitial cells of another species is not disturbing; Lofts and Marshall (*138*) note that both arrangements seem to be associated with steroid hormone secretion. The identity of the hormone was not determined.

The situation in the female is less clear. Structural (*169*) and behavioral changes (*167*) following ovariectomy and replacement therapy are the evidence that the ovaries of amphibians produce estrogens. Chromatographic techniques enabled Gallien and Chalumeau-Le Foulgoc (*172*) to demonstrate the presence of steroids of the estrone-estradiol group in juvenile ovaries of *Xenopus*. Estrone and estradiol were found in adults. Pesonen and Rapola (*171*), on the other hand, could find no steroid dehydrogenase activity in the ovaries of *Xenopus laevis* and *Bufo bufo* and concluded that there is no appreciable production of steroids in the ovaries of these species. They suggest that such hormones originate in adrenal tissue in which there was invariably a distinct dehydrogenase activity. The inconsistency of their hypothesis with the isolation of estrogens by Gallien and Chalumeau-Le Foulgoc was recognized.

Another difficulty centers around the hormonal activity of the corpus luteum. Whether this structure is preovulatory (*142*) or postovulatory (*170, 173*), it forms from the follicular epithelium (granulosa cells) and is surrounded by a thin but compact capsule of thecal tissue. Bretschneider and Duyvené de Wit (*142*) believe that the granulosa cells produce a sex hormone which acts on the accessory reproductive organs. At this time the possibility that this substance is progesterone should not be rejected; indirect evidence has been obtained that progesterone or a close derivative is present about the time of ovulation in the ovaries of *Bufo arenarum* (*174*) and *Rana pipiens* (*175*).

When we look at the Amphibia it is only too obvious that many gaps must be filled before we will have a reasonably satisfying understanding of the relationship between the hormones and behavior. It seems clear, however, unless confirmation is given to the hypothesis that the adrenal cortex rather than the ovary is the main source of estrogens in the female (*171*), that no tissue relationship or hormone not represented in the other vertebrates is involved in the induction of reproductive behavior. The broad significance of the relationship of the hypophyseal hormone prolactin to the migration of efts to and from land and water (*43–46*) appears not to be known. The relationship could be a specialization peculiar to certain amphibians or it could be a variation of other relationships between the hypophysis and behavior which have appeared in other phyla.

VI. Reptiles

Dodd (*123*) reminds us in his discussion of the hormones and reproduction in reptiles that internal fertilization which has become universal in this group has involved the development of copulatory organs and specialized mating behavior. Despite these important developments, less is known about the relationship between the hormones and behavior in reptiles than in members of the other vertebrate phyla. Quantification can hardly be claimed to have been attempted, but from the descriptive studies of turtles and lizards (*176–187*) and from the many short reports in the herpetological journals, the patterns of aggressive, territorial, courtship, mating, oviposition, and brooding behavior (in the sense of incubation) seem to be quite definite and amenable to such treatment. What appears to be an early stage in the evolution of parental behavior is described by Dharmakumarsinhji (*188*) in his note on the copulatory behavior of the marsh crocodile. The interest of Noble and Mason (*185*) did not extend beyond the care of the eggs by the blue-tailed skink, *Eumeces fasciatus,* but they noted that one female in their series remained on the nest with the young for over 2 days after they were hatched.

Many of the structural changes which follow gonadectomy and hormonal treatment are described by Dodd (*123*), by Forbes (*135*), and by Kehl and Combescot (*189*) in their reviews. The assumption is justified that the relationship between the gonadal hormones and behavior is also close. Direct evidence is provided by the increased aggressiveness of turtles and lizards given testosterone propionate (*190–194*) and by the courtship and mating behavior displayed by gonadectomized male and female *Anolis carolinensis* following treatment with estradiol dipropionate and testosterone propionate (*186, 193, 194*). Presumptive evidence for the relationship between the testes and the behavior of the male is given by the correlation between the postspermatogenic steatogenesis and the autumnal sexuality of some vipers (*195*). Evans (*178, 196*) reported that ovarian hormone inhibits aggressiveness in female *Anolis carolinensis.* Intact individuals are not aggressive toward other females in the cage, but following ovariectomy they dominate females and smaller males. Greenberg and Noble (*182*), on the other hand, found no evidence for an inverse relationship between ovarian hormones and pugnacity. Furthermore, pugnacity was seen in fully spayed females whereas others did not fight. All this was the basis for the conclusion that aggressiveness in the female is a genetic trait not requiring hormonal activation. Unknown to Evans or to Greenberg and Noble was the fact that aggression and sexual receptivity are negatively related in at least a number of mammals (*78–80*). It may be that the entire subject should be reinvestigated.

Neither the identity of the gonadal hormones produced by reptiles nor their cellular origin has been established, but nothing in the extensive morphological and endocrinological literature suggests any deviation from the relationships in the other vertebrates. Interstitial tissue is present in the testes and, in most species, signs of activity in these cells are correlated with the secondary sex characters. As in the pike, frog, and birds, androgens may be present in the tubular lipid present following the postspermatogenic metamorphosis of unshed germinal epithelium (*195*).

Follicles containing follicular fluid develop in the ovary, as do corpora lutea which resemble those in mammals except for the absence of blood vessels in the central portion (*135, 197, 198*). The androgenic action of alcoholic extracts of testes from the snakes *Bothrops* and *Crotalus*, and the estrogenic action of alcoholic extracts of ovaries from these species were demonstrated by Valle and Valle (*199*). Extracts of corpora lutea from the same females gave a 2+ endometrial reaction in the McPhail assay for progesterone (*200*). Vaginal estrus in mice was induced by 4 daily injections of 0.1 ml. follicular fluid from *Crotalus* (*201*). A substance with progesterone-like activity was extracted from the plasma of two pregnant water snakes, *Natrix s. sipedon* (*202*). The concentration rose from 0.3–1.0 μg. equivalent of progesterone per milliliter of plasma in individuals with inactive ovaries or preovulatory follicles to 2 μg. following ovulation, to 4 μg. by mid-pregnancy, and to 8 μg. at full term.

VII. Birds

Interest in the relationship of the hormones to behavior in birds has a long history and is second only to that in mammals. For the most part, activity has been directed toward an elucidation of the role of the hypothalamicopituitary system and the gonadal hormones in the expression and control of reproductive behavior and migration. Professional and amateur ornithologists, endocrinologists, morphologists, psychologists, ethologists, and poultry husbandrymen have participated. A recounting of the enormous literature would be out of place here, but a number of recent reviews of descriptive and experimental studies contain references to species that have been studied, much about their behavior, and details of methodology by which quantification has become possible (*5, 7, 203–208*).

Many birds migrate, and in all except the parasitic species (*209–213*) the behavioral sequence which is a part of the reproductive process is commonly composed of territorial establishment and defense, nest building, courtship, mating, egg laying, incubation, and parental care. The sequence probably is more elaborate than any encountered in the other vertebrate phyla. Many factors such as seasonal and meteorological changes, food, nesting sites, nesting materials, and especially interpersonal relationships influence this behavior (*7*), but agreement is general that once the process starts at the beginning of the reproductive season, a certain endocrine readiness must exist before the next step will be taken.

The relationship of the hormones to migration is equivocal (*208, 214–218*). Experimental analysis of the problem is difficult, and conceptualization must be broad enough to cover the two sexes. Any theory must be adequate to account for postnuptial as well as prenuptial migration and for the fact that some species migrate from areas north of the equator whereas others start from south of the equator.

The results of early attempts to follow the activity of trapped birds after gonadectomy and release (*219–222*) were believed to support the view that migration is not associated with the state of the gonads, but Bullough (*214*) comments with good reason that these results are inconclusive. Measurement of the nocturnal restlessness, *Zugunruhe,* displayed twice a year by migratory birds (*217, 223, 224*) has been used widely in a laboratory approach to the problem. Attention has been given also to the accumulation of fat which precedes the development of *Zugunruhe* (*225, 226*). The extent to which these phenomena are concomitants of migration and the degree to which they are under hypothalamic, hypophyseal, and gonadal control are mooted points. Farner (*215, 227*) and Farner *et al.* (*223*) discount the role of gonads in favor of the notion that nongonadotropic effects of the anterior pituitary are primary. Marshall (*217*) doubts that rejection of the idea that the sex hormones are directly involved can be justified. He reminds us that fat deposition does not occur in all migratory species, that it can be induced by photostimulation, gonadotropins, and testosterone, and finally that certain critical experiments have not been performed, e.g., measurement of the nocturnal activity in hypophysectomized postnuptial migrants in the autumn, and of this activity in hypophysectomized light-stimulated prenuptial migrants in the spring.

The relationship of the hormones to mating behavior, aggressive behavior, and territorial defense in male birds is not controversial (*4, 228–231*). Except for aggressive behavior in the starling (*232*), these types of behavior disappear or are displayed in reduced strength following gonadectomy, and restoration follows administration of testosterone. The many correlations of interstitial cell development with seasonal activity (*230, 233*) and the evidence from histochemical studies (*230, 234*) are the basis for the conclusion that interstitial cells are the principal source of this androgen.

Unsolved problems exist, but they are not unlike those encountered in the other vertebrate phyla—the relatively slow decline in the strength of mating activity following castration (*235, 236*), the persistence of many elements of the pattern after castration (*235, 237–239*), the apparently complete pattern of masculine behavior exhibited by one gonadectomized hybrid pigeon (*240*), the site of hormone action, and the mechanism by which androgens exert their effects.

One problem may be more specific for birds, although it is encountered in other phyla. Males of some species normally perform or assist in tasks such as nest building, incubation, and care of the young, which in most species are performed by the female. Many examples of behavior of this sort are cited by Lehrman (7). He states that there are no data bearing on the relationship between nest building and male gonadal cycles to compare with those on the relationship of nest building to the female cycle.

The relationship between testicular hormone and incubation by the male is not clear. Again, citing cases from Lehrman's review (7), there is at least one species, the black-crowned night heron, *Nycticorax n. hoactli,* in which incubation by the male was induced by testosterone (*241*). In the ring dove incubation by the male was induced by progesterone (*242, 243*), and in the short-tailed shearwater the lipid metamorphosis of testis tubules associated with the production of progestins (*244*) coincides with the onset of incubation by the male (*245*). In cases of this latter type it should be ascertained whether progesterone acts directly or as an intermediary in the production of testosterone (*246*).

Care of chicks by the domestic cock is inhibited by testosterone (*7, 247*). Clearly therefore in males of this species the action of some other hormone is involved, and prolactin is indicated (*247, 248*). Nalbandov doubts, however, that prolactin in itself brings about broodiness. Recalling the old observations that capons readily accept the care of young chicks (*249*) and that prolactin inhibits secretion of follicle-stimulating hormone (FSH) (*250*), he devised experiments leading to the conclusion that prolactin, by shutting off the secretion of androgen, creates conditions whereby environmental stimuli essential for the brooding response can act. A recent reconsideration of the problem (*5*) is centered around the control of parental behavior in female birds, but the suggestions which emerge seem applicable to the male as well and in many respects are more satisfying than the explanation advanced by Nalbandov (*247*) and Lehrman (*7*). The most important is that there is no very precise hormonal condition which is a necessary prerequisite for parental behavior; at the most a facilitating action would be claimed. Eisner (*5*) notes after a thoughtful analysis of the problem, that the hormones which in one species or another have been found to facilitate parental behavior are prolactin, progesterone, deoxycorticosterone, luteinizing hormone (LH), androgen, and thyroxine. She suggests, however, that in the future attention should be given mainly to prolactin and progesterone.

The behavior characteristic of the female consists of such elements as oviposition, nest building, mating, incubation, and care of the young. Territorial defense, courtship behavior, song, and male-like mounting behavior, all of which are more often a part of the repertoire of the male, are also seen in many species and in wild species especially in the fall (*217, 230, 251–265*). Recent reviews (*5, 7*) and a sampling of the vast literature reveal that for no one of these elements can a clear story be given.

Under certain circumstances aggressive behavior and territorial defense are displayed by females of such diverse species as the ruffed grouse, Canada goose, domesticated fowl, canary, house wren, and black-headed gull (*266–270*). Inasmuch as androgens probably are produced by the ovaries of birds (*241, 265*), and aggressive behavior is displayed by some female birds following injections of testosterone propionate (*267, 271–274*), the inference might be that aggressive behavior in intact, untreated females is a response to the androgen. This may be true for aggressive behavior and for the other types of "masculine" behavior displayed by the female such as song in the mockingbird (*260*), male-like mounting (*253–255, 259, 262*), and courtship (*258*). On the other hand, we should not exclude the possibility that estrogens influence this behavior. They are effective stimulants of masculine behavior in cows (*275*), and estrogen followed by progesterone induces male-like mounting in female guinea pigs (*276*).

Knowledge about the relationship of ovarian hormones to mating behavior is deficient. Ovariectomy of the bird is difficult and in general does not seem to have been attempted by investigators interested in behavior. The castrated pullet or poulard is "negative" in her behavior (*4, 277*). She is described as being shy, inoffensive, and not showing any of the female reactions. From this observation and from the fact that nest building, mating, and ovular growth are closely correlated in time (*5, 7*), the role of an ovarian hormone or hormones would be assumed. Partial confirmation of this hypothesis was given by the display of female behavior following treatment of laughing gulls with an unspecified estrogen (*278*) and of chicks with estradiol benzoate (*279*). In experiments in which bilaterally gonadectomized hens were given estradiol benzoate, a strong squatting behavior was displayed (*279, 280*). Two other possibilities must be noted. Testosterone propionate rather than estrone was effective in stimulating female behavior in the black-crowned night heron (*241*). It should also be recalled that estrogen and progesterone are produced by hens (*281–284*) and no one seems to have used gonadectomized birds in an effort to ascertain whether estrogen and progesterone are required, as in some mammals (*9*). Adams and Herrick (*285*) did find that progesterone augmented the squatting behavior of intact 6-week-old chicks when it was administered following the injection of diethylstilbestrol.

Nest building and incubation behavior by the female are discussed by Lehrman (*7*). The generally close temporal relationship between ovarian follicular growth, sexual receptivity, and nest building suggests that in many species of birds the physiological conditions leading to nest building are the same as those associated with copulation and that females are prepared for both types of behavior by substances produced during maximum follicular growth. On the other hand, experimental studies have been few and they have not led to anything definitive or suggestive. Lehrman (*7*) induced nest building in intact female ring doves by injecting diethylstilbestrol. Testosterone propionate was not effective. What amounts to an opposite result was obtained by Noble and Wurm (*241*). Injections of testosterone propionate into intact and gonadectomized black-crowned night herons were followed by nest building and courtship by the females as well as by the males. No phase of the female behavior was induced by the preparations of estrone they used. Near-lethal levels of estradiol benzoate induced nest building in canaries during the nonbreeding season (*286*). The addition of progesterone or progesterone alone was without a detectable effect.

Incubation has long been associated with the hypophyseal hormone prolactin, but the belief that this is the hormone specifically concerned with the induction of incubation behavior (*49, 287*) has been questioned and largely replaced by the view that an ovarian hormone or hormones are more directly involved (*5, 7, 243, 288*). The basis for this change in opinion has a long history. The amount of prolactin in the pituitary glands of hens and ring-necked pheasants is small at the beginning of incubation and rises sharply as incubation progresses (*289–293*). This finding is given meaning by the insightful contribution of Patel (*294*). He showed (*a*) that the act of incubation in pigeons, rather than being induced by prolactin, actually stimulates the secretion of this hormone, and (*b*) that in males, at least, presence of the testes is necessary, not only for the initiation of sexual behavior, but also for the functioning of the pituitary as it produces prolactin in response to psychic stimulation.

Indications of the sequence of events in the female are provided by an examination of the temporal relationship between ovulation and egg laying, on the one hand, and incubation, on the other (*7*). Variation is shown from incubation starting with the laying of the first egg, as in most water birds and some songbirds such as the Florida Jay, *Cyanocitta coerulescens* (*295*), and graceful warbler, *Prinia gracilis* (*296*), to incubation which starts only after the last egg has been laid, as in the snow bunting, *Plectrophenax nivalis* (*297*), and cedar waxwing, *Bombycilla cedrorum* (*298*). Lehrman (*7*) notes, however, that with respect to hormonal changes associated with the last stages of follicular development and ovulation the variation is not great. In fowl (*281, 283, 284, 299*), as in mammals (*143, 146*), this is a time when estrogen and progesterone are being produced, and in fowl and in the ring dove, as in mammals, these hormones function synergistically to produce growth and secretory changes in the genital tract (*300–304*). A familiarity with this background and with the report that squatting behavior by female chicks was induced by diethylstilbestrol and progesterone together rather than by either substance alone (*285*), led Lehrman and Brody (*304*) to suggest that the normal cycle in the ring dove includes a period of estrogen secretion concurrent with nest building followed by a period of progesterone secretion associated with incubation behavior. Confirmation of this hypothesis was believed to be given by the display of a readiness to incubate within a few minutes after the birds injected with progesterone were placed with a mate in cages containing a nest with two eggs (*243*). No increase in crop weight was associated with the onset of this behavior or with the hormonal treatment which induced it, a fact which seemed to demonstrate that prolactin was not involved.

It is unfortunate that most of the data bearing on the relationship of the hormones to incubation in birds have been obtained from so few species. As Eisner (*5*) points out, it may not be assumed that the onset of incubation is mediated by progesterone in species other than doves. Furthermore, the fact that oviducal changes in birds are produced by the synergistic action of estrogen and progesterone suggests that, in some species, incubation may be induced by the successive action of these hormones. If progesterone alone is responsible for incubation, as the report by Lehrman (*243*) would lead us to believe, the action is unusual, for in birds and in mammals generally, when progesterone is effecting a reaction the relationship is synergistic with an estrogen. Despite these concerns, the important point is that incubation behavior was induced by an ovarian hormone without any evidence of prolactin participation. Increasing in amount as prolactin does with incubation, and decreasing sharply when the chicks are hatched (*290, 291*), the possibility must be considered that its production during incubation is in anticipation of some role in the preparation for parental care. As we stated above in connection with the relationship of the hormones to parental care by the male, this is something that cannot be excluded despite the developing opinion that any action is mainly facilitative (*5, 7*).

Many reports reviewed by Marshall (*230*), Parkes and Marshall (*208*), and van Tienhoven (*299*) indicate that androgenic, estrogenic, and gestagenic substances are produced by both males and females. Relative quantities in the sexes are not given. Progesterone has been detected on chromatograms of extracts of maturing and ruptured follicles from laying hens (*283*). Evidence based on chromatographic mobility, ultraviolet spectrophotometry, and chemical reaction indicates that the principal estrogens in ovarian tissues of the fowl are estrone, estradiol, and estriol (*305*). The formation of an insoluble digitomide in the phenolic steroid fraction from the droppings of fowl suggested that estrone is the biologically active form (*306*).

Much attention has been given to the cellular origin of the gonadal hormones in birds. As in the work with animals in other phyla, suggestive information was obtained from correlations between seasonal reproductive activity and the quantity and microscopic appearance of gonadal tissue. More recently reliance has been placed on histochemical studies. In general, steroid-secreting cells and steroid-containing substances are indicated by their content of osmophilic cholesterol-containing lipids. Qualitative distinctions are based on other criteria, for the most part the presence of cells in tissues known from physiologic or morphologic tests to be secreting estrogens, androgens, or gestagens, but also from supplementary chromatographic studies as in the work of Lofts and Marshall (*244*) on the content of the postnuptial testicular tubules, and from bioassays such as that developed by Hooker and Forbes (*307, 308*).

Within male birds, Leydig or testicular interstitial cells have long been considered to be the principal source of androgen (*230, 299*). The association of a Sertoli cell tumor near the gonadal area with the feminization of a Brown Leghorn capon was taken as evidence that Sertoli cells secrete estrogen (*309*). The source of the progesterone found in the plasma of cocks (*282*) is unknown. Participation of the tubules in the secretion of steroids has been demonstrated by investigators who have examined the testes of a number of species of birds at the conclusion of spermatogenesis and prior to the autumnal or postnuptial recrudescence of reproductive behavior. The latter is seen in males and females of many birds and is well described by several British colleagues (*233, 252, 256, 257, 261, 310–312*). In several widely unrelated species there is a massive cholesterol-positive steatogenesis in the seminiferous tubules. The tubules collapse, and the unshed germinal material and apparently the syncytial Sertoli cytoplasm are converted to cholesterol-positive lipids (*230, 245, 312*). Tests of the possibility that these metamorphosed tubules contain progestin which might have an endocrine function were made by Lofts and Marshall (*244*), who analyzed the tubular liquid by paper chromatography and by bioassay of the progestin content. As had been predicted, progestins appeared in the chromatograms of extracts from these tests. A role of this hormonal substance in incubation behavior and the feeding of the young and in the limited autumnal sexual activity has been suggested (*195, 233, 244*), but thus far these possibilities are only speculative. Corresponding changes do not occur in the female rook *Corvus frugilegus,* in which both sexes were studied (*261*, (*312*). Early in May when the seminiferous tubules were packed with cholesterol-positive lipids, follicular growth to a diameter of about 800 μ continued and each follicle involuted to form its quota of interstitial cells, which are believed to be estrogenic in function.

Uncertainty exists with respect to the cellular origin of the ovarian steroids. In addition to the reviews by Marshall (*230*), Parkes and Marshall (*208*), and van Tienhoven (*299*), the original investigations by Taber (*313*) and Marshall and Coombs (*312*) can be consulted for the background of older studies. The latter investigators present evidence for the view that "thecal gland cells," also called "ex-follicular cells" because of their origin, secrete estrogens and that "stromal gland cells" of interstitial origin are a source of androgen. The latter are called "female interstitial cells" and are believed to be homologous with the Leydig cells in the male. An ingenious experiment by Taber (*313*) involved the withdrawal of exogenous gonadotropic stimulation from the Brown Leghorn fowl which was accompanied by regression of the comb and the reappearance of lipid-filled interstitial cells in the testes of males and in the ovarian medulla of females. She concluded that the two types of cells are similar and are responsible for the secretion of androgen. Conclusive evidence with respect to the cellular origin of progesterone has not been obtained. Its origin from both developing and atretic follicles has been suggested (*312, 314*). If a corpus luteum is present (*197, 198, 312, 315*), it is short-lived.

A discussion of the relationship between the gonadal hormones and behavior in birds is an appropriate place to recall that the importance of the soma or substrate for the character of a response elicited by hormonal action may first have been noted in a report of the failure of implanted ovarian tissue to feminize the behavior of castrated male fowl (*316*). Variation in the relationships of the gonadal hormones to behavior is seen in birds which may be greater than that in any other phylum. Many examples of ambisexuality are called to our attention by Beach (*2*) and Lehrman (*7*): males and females build nests, share in incubation and in the care of the young. In the fall female British starlings, *Sturnus v. vulgaris,* display masculine behavior which is displayed in the spring only by males (*252*). Females of the woodpecker genus, *Dendrocopus,* may take the lead in pair formation in the fall and, by the courtship act of drumming attract a male to the winter territory (*259*). Some female British robins, *Erithacus rubecula melophilus,* sing and hold territories, although normally these roles are taken by males (*260*). A reversal of the roles is characteristic of some species. The female great crested grebe, *Podiceps cristatus,* actively courts the male (*258*). Reversal of the roles is complete in the red-necked phalarope, *Phalaropus lobatus.* The females defend territories and display on the breeding ground, the males incubate the eggs (*264*). There is a degree of bisexuality in the behavior of the black-crowned night heron, but in both sexes the behavior characteristic of the sex is induced by androgens. Estrogens alone did not stimulate any of the breeding behavior (*241*).

The significance of these deviant patterns is that all occur within a hormonal framework that is essentially similar—the same steroid substances produced by tissues that are homologous with the tissues which secrete these hormones in males and females in the other phyla. A survey of the relationship between the hormones and behavior in birds reveals additional evidence for the view that the locus of change as animals have evolved resides more in the tissues on which the hormones act than in the endocrine organs producing the hormones.

VIII. Mammals

The relationship between the hormones and reproductive behavior has been studied more intensively in mammals than in the members of any other vertebrate phylum. For this reason, conceptualization may be more advanced, but we are still far from an understanding of the mechanisms by which hormones prepare the organism for the behavior it displays. A number of reviews of descriptive and experimental investigations have appeared recently or should be cited because of their importance to workers in the field (*2, 4–7, 317–326*). Their substance will not be repeated except when this is necessary to relate the situation in mammals to that in the other vertebrate phyla.

Mating behavior including the increased activity encountered in many species at the time of mating has received more attention than other types of behavior known or suspected to be related to hormonal action, i.e., aggressive behavior, nest building, and parental behavior. Mating behavior can be divided rather arbitrarily into a preliminary or courtship phase and a copulatory phase, although often and especially under laboratory conditions or in controlled breeding situations, the copulatory phase is entered into rather directly. This is explained perhaps by the circumstance that males of these species tend to be used repeatedly. They are kept separate from females and are introduced into their cages or enclosures at frequent intervals and only when the latter are in heat. They know what is to come. During the courtship phase in the laboratory rat, guinea pig, cattle, sheep, goat, swine, horse, and cat, to select only a few examples, the males often sniff, lick, or bite the fur on various parts of the female's body. They may explore and nose the external genitalia of the female, and they may vocalize, particularly as they walk around the female or rub against her. Often the males mount or attempt to mount the female. Male rabbits and dogs will chase the female, almost playfully it would seem. The copulatory phase may be said to begin with intromission and ejaculation. Commonly ejaculation is preceded by several intromissions and in all the species mentioned except the guinea pig (and man) multiple ejaculations in rapid succession are the rule. Whatever the pattern in the male, measurement is possible and scoring procedures have been devised (*9, 320, 321, 324*).

Preliminary or courtship behavior in the sense of behavior which is stimulating to members of the opposite sex, is exhibited less by females than by males. Lethargic male guinea pigs are stimulated by mounting behavior of females which is common in this species (*276, 327*). Female sheep and goats will rub their necks and bodies against the males and stand still to receive them (*322*). Late in the proestrum many female swine show a special interest in the boar and nuzzle his scrotum and flanks. They will bite the ears lightly and occasionally mount the males. On the day prior to estrus females will pursue the males as well as other large objects (*323*). Female dogs frequently initiate spurts of running in which the males participate. During the proestrum some bitches will investigate the genital region of the males and mount them with the execution of a few pelvic thrusts (*320*). Female cats will crouch and posture and make treading movements which may be in response to and oriented toward the male (*325*). The copulatory behavior displayed when the female is in estrus and receptive is in the form of a lordosis or presentation to the male. The length of time lordosis can be elicited is measurable as is the intensity and duration of the single lordosis in the guinea pig. The use of the latter in estimating the strength of sexual behavior in the female was introduced by Dr. Goy (*328*).

Many investigators and observers of behavior have been struck by the great variability of the patterns displayed by individuals of a species. The late Alfred C. Kinsey made a point of this in many of his lectures and emphasized, particularly in the study of the human male (*34*), that the variation in behavior is much greater than that in structure. More important for the endocrinologist is the observation that patterns of behavior tend to characterize individuals and to be displayed from cycle to cycle in females and from test to test in males (*327, 329*). This feature of the response of individuals to hormones can be useful as an end point in tests of the specificity of hormonal action. The basis for a comparison of the effectiveness of a group of steroids might well be the faithfulness with which patterns characteristic of individuals are restored following glandular removal and replacement therapy (*99*).

Although questioned from time to time for lower mammals as well as for man (*35*), the hormonal basis of mating behavior is generally considered to be well established (*9*). Testicular androgen, presumably testosterone, is the effective hormone in the males of all species. Ovarian estrogen, presumably estradiol or a metabolite (*134*), is said to be effective in the cat, dog, ferret, goat, pig, and rhesus monkey. Progesterone in addition to estrogen is necessary for the normal display of estrus in the guinea pig, rat, mouse, hamster, and sheep, and it seems to participate along with estrogen in the induction of estrus in the cow and rabbit. The mechanism of the action of progesterone is not known (*330*). The suggestion found in the older as well as in the contemporary literature that androgens and estrogens of adrenal cortical origin function in maintaining the level of sexual behavior has not been demonstrated by the results of investigations designed to test the point (*9*). This is consistent with the conclusions that in adult males adrenal androgens are much weaker than testicular androgens in the usual biological tests and appear to be of little significance for the reproductive tract as substitutes for gonadal hormones, and that in females the stimulus of ovariectomy is not associated with any grossly detectable substitution by the adrenals (*331*).

A number of aspects of the relationship between the hormones and behavior in mammals have not yet been explained, although in no instance do substances different from those encountered in the other vertebrate phyla seem to be involved. In male mammals there is commonly a slow decline in reproductive vigor following castration (*9*) whereas in females, except in some ovariectomized rabbits (*332–334*), estrous behavior is not displayed after this operation. A number of male fishes (*57, 335, 336*), an amphibian (*160*), and several birds (*235, 237–239*) resemble mammals in this respect.

In most mammals in which estrogen and progesterone participate in the preparation of the female for estrus, the relationship is synergistic in the sense that normal behavior is not displayed unless progesterone has been preceded by an action of estrogen. The sheep is different, endogenous or exogenous estrogen must be preceded by progesterone (*337–344*). No other example of its kind has come to the reviewer's attention at any phylogenetic level; it would seem that the existence of a mechanism of action fundamentally different from that in the other vertebrates must be postulated.

The relationship between the hormones and reproductive or erotic behavior in primates is not clear and the subject has long been controversial (*2, 6, 8, 9, 34–36*). As far as the male is concerned, the tendency to discount the role of testicular hormones has its basis in part on the persistence of erotic behavior following castration. This, however, is not peculiar to man or even to primates. As we have just seen, sexual behavior declines slowly following the castration of male fishes, amphibians, and birds that have been studied. Beach (*345*) notes briefly that there are some dogs in which there is no detectable loss of sexual responsiveness or ability to copulate up to two years after castration. In female primates the change is well documented (*9*). Within the chimpanzee, receptivity coincides with most of the long follicular phase of the cycle, and in the human female it is coextensive with the entire cycle. Tentatively Beach (*345, 346*) attributes this change to the greater degree of cortical control over sexuality in these species and the greater extent to which the sexual arousal mechanism is affected by symbolic factors. In this place it is important to note that the change is postulated to have occurred within the nervous rather than within the endocrine system.

Discussion of the identification and cellular origin of gonadal hormones in mammals has been facilitated by the appearance of several comprehensive reviews within the last year (*143–146, 347*). The use of modern methods has revealed what was long suspected from bioassays and tissue responses, namely that the hormones are identical chemically with the gonadal hormones of the lower vertebrates. Testosterone is the most active hormone secreted by the testis, and estradiol-17β and estrone, encountered as the predominant hormones in female fishes, amphibians, reptiles, and birds, are the most active hormones secreted by the mammalian ovary. Testosterone is generally believed to be synthesized by interstitial or Leydig cells. No satisfactory evidence has been obtained in support of the view advanced in the early 1940's that testicular estrogens are produced by Sertoli cells. With respect to the ovary uncertainty exists. The specific suggestions have been made that estrogens are secreted by cells of the theca interna and interstitial cells, that androgens are secreted by interstitial cells and by hilus cells located along the unmyelinated nerve and blood vessels of the ovarian medulla and mesovarium (*348*), and that progesterone is secreted by granulosa lutein cells. More recently evidence has been presented that 20α-hydroxypregn-4-en-3-one rather than progesterone is the principal gestagen produced by the ovary of the New Zealand white rabbit and that it is synthesized by the interstitial cells which in this and other breeds of rabbits resemble luteal tissue (*348a*). A view encompassing all these suggestions is expressed by Eckstein (*143*), who stated that hormone production may be an inherent property of the four major elements—the granulosa, theca interna, corpus luteum, and interstitial cells. Either conclusion would be consistent with the opinions expressed by those who have looked into the corresponding problem in the lower vertebrates, and which are summarized in the earlier parts of this chapter.

Other types of behavior in mammals which at one time or another have been associated with gonadal hormone activity are aggressiveness, nest building, and parental behavior. Aggressiveness has been studied in several of the rodents, a group of rhesus monkeys, and the chimpanzee. Only in the rhesus monkey was the administration of gonadal hormones without effect on the hierarchy or dominance relations (*349*). This may perhaps be accounted for, Mirsky states, by the unusually violent aggressiveness which characterizes this species. In the case of the other species, the results from the many well-controlled experiments were uniform in revealing the influence of androgens and estrogens—depending on the situation—on the display of aggressive or dominance behavior. At the time of maximal genital swelling or following treatment of ovariectomized individuals with estradiol benzoate, female chimpanzees were dominant in competitive trials for a food reward (*350–353* and several older reports from the Yerkes Laboratory of Primate Biology). A castrated male receiving the same estrogen became subordinate, but when he was given methyl testosterone at a time when he was the dominant member of a pair, his dominance became enhanced (*350*). After similar treatment a subordinate female obtained most of the food. The aggressiveness of male rats and mice largely disappeared following castration (*354–358*) and it was increased or restored by injections of testosterone propionate (*355–357, 359, 360*). The manner of action of androgens and estrogens in producing these varied effects is not known. The problem is complicated by the sudden remission of aggressive behavior at the time of estrus in female guinea pigs, hamsters, short-tailed shrews, and probably many other mammals (*78–80*) when estrogen levels are thought to be at their highest. The observation by Kislak and Beach (*80*) that the administration of progesterone to an estrogen-conditioned and aggressive female hamster is followed immediately by a loss of the aggressiveness is an important lead, but its relevance for the broader problem is not now apparent.

The relationship of the hormones to nest building and parental behavior has been reviewed (*7*). The subject is complex, many of the results are contradictory, and no more than tentative conclusions are justified. Two points made early in the review are important and will be repeated here. The temporal relationships between ovulation, on the one hand, and mating, nest building, and parental behavior, on the other, are different in birds and mammals. In birds nest building, mating, and ovulation are closely associated in time, a period of incubation follows, and after hatching, parental behavior is displayed. In mammals any nest building that is a part of reproduction is separated from mating and ovulation by pregnancy and tends to be associated with parturition. For nest building therefore the ovarian conditions are greatly different in the two phyla and the difference in the hormonal control that is reported need not be surprising. The second point is that many mammals build shelters or nests which do not necessarily serve for reproduction. Nests of this type built by domestic mice have been designated "Schlafnester" or "sleeping nests," those built by pregnant mice "Brutnester" or "brood nests" (*361, 362*). Corresponding types built by rabbits are called "straw" and "maternal" nests (*363*). The construction of both may be influenced by hormonal action, the latter as we shall see, by ovarian hormones, and the former as an indirect response to a deficiency of thyroid hormone when there is a need for regulation of the body temperature (*39, 362*).

The relationship between the hormones and construction of the brood or maternal nest seems to have been studied only in the rabbit and mouse. In the former species this type of nest is built prior to or at parturition by lining the straw nest with fur plucked from the rabbit's own body (*364*). At this time the progesterone:estrogen ratio is reversed (*365*). Experimentally, maternal nest-building behavior has been induced by removal of the corpora lutea (*332, 366*), removal of the gravid uterus which led to an involution of the corpora lutea (*367*), removal of the conceptus mass between days 20 and 27 of gestation, and by ovariectomy between days 20 and 24 (*363*). Parturition and all of these procedures result in what Zarrow and his associates (*363*) call a "hormonal upset," but beyond indicating that estradiol, progesterone, and possibly prolactin are involved, there seems to be little that can be added.

Nonpregnant mice provided with hay will build a nest each night which can be removed and weighed the following morning. The amount used by the mice in Koller's (*361, 363*) experiments weighed from 7 to 11 grams. Pregnant females, on the other hand, build much larger nests starting abruptly the 4th to 5th day of pregnancy, which is the time the corpus luteum of pregnancy becomes histologically demonstrable. Confirmation of the belief that progesterone is involved was given by the marked increase in the nesting material used by intact nonpregnant and gonadectomized mice after 2 or 3 daily injections of this hormone. Koller (*361, 362*) reported also that the introduction of young mice into the cage with an adult female induced an abrupt increase in nest-building activity. As Lehrman (*7*) notes, this ability of young mice to stimulate nest-building behavior might be attributed to a hormonal change induced by stimuli coming from the young, but he excludes this possibility by recalling the finding of Leblond and Nelson (*53, 54*) this this behavior was induced in hypophysectomized female and male adults caged with young mice. Lehrman (*7*) adds that stimuli from the young and the effect of progesterone may perhaps be complementary mechanisms for maintaining nest building during the period when such behavior is adaptive.

Retrieving of the young is characteristic of many mammals; being measurable, it is a type of parental behavior which has been studied by investigators interested in the relationship of the hormones to parental behavior. Domestic mice, rats, cats, golden hamsters, and the vole *Microtus arvallis* have been used. Again the data are confused, chaotic, and in many cases contradictory. Unanimity exists that the tendency to retrieve young is most intense just after parturition and continues during much of the lactation period (*368–371*), but it has also been reported that often voles and about 20% of domestic rats retrieve young, regardless of their reproductive state or sex (*50–52, 371–373*). Prolactin and pituitary LH given to intact or gonadectomized female and male rats increased retrieving behavior substantially (*49, 50, 373*). Prolactin and the luteinizing hormone that was used were more effective in gonadectomized than in intact animals (*50*). Cats normally retrieve their litters; Allan and Wiles (*374*) reported that nine cats hypophysectomized toward the end of pregnancy gave birth to normal young, but did not "take care of them" except in one instance for 2 days. In experiments with rats hypophysectomy did not altogether prevent (*50*) or interfere (*53, 375*) with retrieving behavior. Retrieving behavior does not depend on lactation in the mouse and hamster (*52, 376*). Retrieving was reported to have been suppressed by estrone (*50, 373, 377*), although not in hypophysectomized animals (*373*). Male mice, on the other hand, displayed retrieving behavior following treatment with estrogen (*51*). The retrieval of pups by intact female rats following injections of progesterone (*50*) was not seen by Lott (*378*) in female rats and hamsters.

Motivation of females to nurse their young seems to have been assumed during the early studies of prolactin and mating behavior in the rat (*48–50*) and to be implied in studies showing that in domestic rats and rabbits the prolactin content of the pituitary gland is increased by suckling (*379, 380*). Again, though, there are difficulties to be resolved. Collip *et al.* (*375*) hypophysectomized lactating rats and found that although the mammary gland regressed, nursing and other maternal behavior were not impaired and the young continued to suckle until they died.

IX. Role of Hormones in the Patterning of Behavior

The discussion of the relationship between the hormones and behavior presented thus far has been focused on the action of these substances in mature animals in which the effect is one of activation, that is the tissues mediating specific types of behavior are so affected that the threshold for behavioral responses is lowered. Males display courtship behavior and mate, females go into estrus, etc. At earlier ages, at least in the guinea pig and rat, gonadal hormones have an organizing action, that is they determine the responsiveness that will later be shown to specific hormonal substances and the nature of the response, whether for example it be masculine or feminine (*33, 33a*). Experimental embryologists and endocrinologists have long been aware of this dual role of gonadal hormones in the differentiation of the genital tracts in developing males and females and in the functioning of the tracts after the attainment of adulthood (*381–386*). Evidence that gonadal hormones have corresponding relationships with the tissues mediating reproductive behavior has also long existed, but it has not heretofore been considered comparatively.

Data exist for several species of fishes, amphibians, birds, and mammals. In many cases it is known that following androgenic treatment of young females or estrogenic treatment of young males the treated individuals take on the role of the opposite sex, but investigations of the guinea pig and rat have been extended somewhat further. The relationships in these species will be considered first. The injection of testosterone or testosterone propionate into the amniotic cavity of 20–27 day fetuses (*32, 387–389*), and the injection of pregnant guinea pigs with testosterone propionate, have profound effects on the development of the genital tracts and on behavior (*33*). Females become pseudohermaphroditic with masculinized external genitalia, hypertrophied Wolffian ducts, frequent failure of Müllerian duct-urogenital sinus fusion, and ovarian dysfunction. When individuals gonadectomized as adults were tested, there was found to be a suppression of the capacity for displaying the feminine measures of behavior (duration of heat and maximum duration of lordosis) accompanied by a lowered responsiveness to estradiol benzoate and progesterone, and an intensification of the masculine component (male-like mounting) accompanied by an increased responsiveness to testosterone propionate. The results of tests at 11–12 months of age indicated that the effects are permanent. At the most the male siblings were affected only slightly, and then only when the prenatal treatment was followed by postnatal treatment (*390*). Administration of the androgen between days 30 and 35 of gestation was most effective (*391*). Testes of 26- to 31-day female guinea pigs secrete androgen at this time (*392*). In the rat the period of maximum susceptibility is about the same, but because of the short gestation period it appears from presently recorded data to be postnatal rather than prenatal (*392a,b*). Detailed reports of the behavior of female rats to which testosterone was administered during the period of maximum susceptibility have not appeared, but in general the alterations were similar to those described for the guinea pig. Enhancement of the capacity to display masculine behavior and suppression of the capacity to display feminine behavior were seen (*392a,c,d,e*).

The fetal testicular substance having these effects on the developing genital tracts and neural tissues has not been identified. Had discovery of the suppressing action of testosterone propionate on the tissues mediating mating behavior in the female come first, the assumption would have followed that the hormone of the fetal testis is essentially similar to that of the adult testis. On the other hand, testosterone propionate, while stimulating development of the male genital tract and the organization of the neural tissues mediating sexual behavior in the male, does not have the suppressing action on the Müllerian ducts which Jost (*393–395*) believes is possessed by the fetal testis. However, see Wells' (*384*) discussion of the point. In an effort to account for this inconsistency the suggestion has been made that the hormone produced by fetal testes is different from that produced by adult testes (*384, 393, 396*).

During attempts to feminize male guinea pigs, it was found that exogenous estrogens terminate pregnancy (*388*). For this reason more information has come from investigations in which the rat was used. The substance of several reports indicates that male rats injected with estradiol benzoate at 5 days of age exhibited markedly diminished or even an absence of masculine behavior (*392c,d,e, 396a*). When placed with vigorous intact males, the males treated in infancy with estradiol displayed an appreciable degree of feminine behavior in the form of lordosis (*396a*). These data suggested feminization of the male by the estrogen, but recalling the embryological evidence that sexual differentiation is the result of stimulation by testicular rather than by ovarian hormones, Whalen (*396a*) suggested that the female-like behavior might have been a consequence of functional castration. Unknown to him, an experiment designed to test this possibility had just been completed by Grady and Phoenix (*33a, 396b*). Their results revealed that in the absence of testes during the first 5 days of infancy, the male rat develops a capacity to display strong feminine responses. The possibility that estrogen has a feminizing action that can be superimposed on the degree of feminization seen by Grady and Phoenix remains to be tested.

The results from many experiments indicate that estrogens and androgens organize patterns of behavior in fishes, amphibians, and birds. The "männliche Sexualinstinkt" was displayed by genetic female *Platypoecilus* sp. and the medaka, *Oryzias latipes,* raised from the day of hatching in aquarium water containing methyltestosterone (*20, 23, 24*). The sex-reversed XX female medakas took the role of males, mated with normal XX females, and were fertile producing female (XX) progeny. Genetic males (XY) were transformed into XY females by the addition of estrone or diethylstilbestrol to the aquarium water (*19, 21, 22*). Matings of the XY females with normal XY males were fertile. If the reversals were permanent, as the reader is left to infer, an organization of behavior occurred comparable with and actually more extensive than that obtained in the guinea pig and rat. The point can be ascertained with certainty only if the behavior of sex-reversed individuals is tested following gonadectomy and controlled replacement therapy. In this respect work with the guinea pig is more advanced than that with lower vertebrates.

The display of heterotypical sexual behavior must be assumed to occur when sex reversal in adults is spontaneous as it may be in the swordfish *Xiphophorus helleri* (*397–400*) and in several other species (*122, 135, 401*). Masculine behavior by females of a number of species is also reported after treatment of older animals with androgenic substances (*23, 24, 402–404*), after ovariectomy and the regeneration of testicular tissue (*405, 406*), and after ovariectomy and the implantation of testicular tissue (*403*). It would be interesting if we could know from this work on adults, whether the effects were permanent and whether there had been any alteration of the responsiveness to male or female hormones. The only hint that the effects were permanent and that the administered hormone had on organizing action is contained in the statement by Okada and Yamashita (*403*) that once formed, the acquired male characteristics do not disappear readily even after the implanted methyldihydrotestosterone must have lost its effectiveness. At the other extreme, a loss of plasticity is suggested by Laskowski (*23, 24*), who stated that adult female *Platypoecilus variatus* when treated with methyltestosterone exhibited only the preliminary male courtship patterns. Precopulatory and copulatory behavior were not seen.

The point should be noted that in all the reports of investigations in which adult fishes were studied, the reversal of behavior was from that of the female to that of the male. Not enough work has been done to reveal whether reversal in the opposite direction can be obtained with the same facility, is easier, or is more difficult. From the belief expressed by Gallien (*28*) that a relationship exists between the nature of the homogametic sex and that of the hormone producing sex reversal, and from the experience with domestic fowl (page 235), the last possibility would be predicted.

Important experiments have been performed on amphibian larvae and adults. Within this phylum, the possibility that androgenic and estrogenic substances have an organizing action seems likely, but as with the work on fishes critical tests have not been made. Equally important, the complexities of tissue responsiveness (*381, 407*) may apply to behavior as well; consequently caution in interpretation is indicated. An early attempt to reverse the sex in a species that would breed in the laboratory was rewarded when Humphrey (*25*) raised sex-reversed female Mexican axolotls in which testis preprimordia had been implanted into female larvae. The mating activity of these animals was typically masculine. Other investigators have obtained sex reversal by adding androgenic or estrogenic substances to the aquarium water at about the time the tadpoles begin eating. Genetic female *Rana temporaria* receiving testosterone propionate were transformed completely and permanently into individuals which functioned as males (*408*). The addition of estradiol benzoate to water containing the urodele *Pleurodeles waltlii* and the anuran *Xenopus laevis* resulted in the feminization of genetic males (*26–28, 407, 409*). In *Xenopus laevis* androgens interfere little with the development of the ovaries of genetic females, but the behavior is modified, and immediately after metamorphosis vigorous clasping behavior is shown (*29*). When male *Xenopus* tadpoles were exposed to estradiol benzoate, the entire animal was completely feminized. As was predicted, these sex-reversed males when bred with normal males produced only male offspring (*30*). Noting that the estradiol need be administered only during a short larval period, they added the important generalization that in the process of oogenesis and development of the female secondary sex characters including behavior, the genes play an active role only during a short and definite period. Beyond this point presumably the hormones become effective agents (*28, 407*).

With respect to birds, the only data bearing on the relationship of hormones administered during the embryonic period to the behavior displayed after hatching have been obtained by investigators who have used the domestic fowl. In most cases estrogens or androgens were injected into the allantoic or amniotic cavity, usually within the first 4 days of the incubation period. More recently eggs have been dipped for 5–20 seconds into a variety of steroids and then replaced in the incubator until hatching (*410*). Except for the Pincus and Hopkins (*410*) study in which the embryos were subjected to androgenic and estrogenic steroids, estrogens were used more commonly than androgens. For the most part when estrogens were administered to genetic males, a temporary feminization of behavior (*388, 410, 411*) or a weaker effect—better thought of as a lessening of the masculine responses—was reported (*31, 412, 413*). The behavior of one estrogenized bird (*414*) is not reported as being affected by the treatment. Premature attempts to crow are said to have followed injections of testosterone propionate into eggs of genetic females (*415*). Pincus and Hopkins (*410*) dipped eggs into testosterone, 17-methyltestosterone, progesterone, and Δ^5-pregnenolone and its glucoside. They reported simply that masculinization of the female was not accomplished as easily or to the same extent as feminization of the male.

It is clear that the results which followed the administration of estrogenic and androgenic substances into embryonic fowl do not give complete support to the suggestion that gonadal hormones present at that time have an organizing action on the tissues mediating sexual behavior in the adult. On the other hand, no data we have found would lead us to reject this possibility.

Consideration of the numerous reports on the effects of gonadal steroids administered before birth or hatching to representatives of four of the five large vertebrate phyla prompts the suggestion that in all a period exists during development when larval, embryonic, or fetal gonadal substances do much to determine the character of sexual behavior displayed during adulthood. For the two mammals for which information exists the evidence seems clear; for members of the other phyla it must be considered presumptive. If differences exist, suggesting an evolutionary trend (cf. Section X), they are not apparent from the data presently at hand. What seems justified are the hypotheses that this organizing action is more complete in some individuals and in some species than in others, and that the degree to which a pattern of behavior is displayed by the two sexes and the degree to which there is dimorphism in the responsiveness of adults to estrogens and androgens (*9*) vary accordingly. Investigation of the possibility would be time consuming, but when consideration is given to the importance of the character of the soma or substrate on which the hormones act for the behavior they elicit, more than an ordinary effort would seem to be justified.

Identification of the tissues on which these hormones act would be desirable. Presumably they are neural (*33*). This much had previously been suggested by Harris (*416*) in another context. Noting from the work of Pfeiffer (*417*) that prepuberal testis grafts in female rats produce a constant estrous state after puberty, and that ovaries grafted into adult males castrated at birth undergo cyclic changes, he postulated "that some neural structure in the male animal becomes differentiated and fixed in its function under the influence of androgens in early life." The suggestion was developed further following an investigation of the pattern of gonadotropin release in adult female and male rats injected at 5 days of age with testosterone propionate and estradiol benzoate, respectively (*392e*). Everett *et al.* (*418*), writing out of a background of experience with the neurogenic stimulation of gonadotropin secretion, were more definite. They agreed with Pfeiffer that the steadily secreting male-type hypophysis is determined by the action of androgen during infancy, but expressed the belief that the sex difference resides in the hypothalamus. Continuing, they wrote: "It appears that in rats during infancy the action of androgen conditions differentiation of the hypothalamic 'center' as an intrinsically acyclic mechanism. However, in an intact genetic female . . . , the 'center' differentiates as an intrinsically cyclic mechanism." As far as the control of gonadotropin secretion is concerned, the hypothalamus undoubtedly is the structure on which testicular hormones act during the formative period, but knowing as we do now that behavior as well as the type of gonadotropin secretion is involved, it may be well to avoid more than the generalization given by Harris (*392c,d, 416*) and Harris and Levine (*392e*).

X. Concluding Remarks

The presentation of comparative data leads almost inevitably from the subject of phyletic similarities and differences to evolution. In a survey of the relationships between the hormones and behavior the limitations of the data are such that we are pretty much restricted to reproductive behavior. Within this sphere the similarities outnumber the differences. The hormones are the same—testosterone in the males, estradiol-17β, estrone, and progesterone in the females. Testosterone seems essential for mating and courtship behavior and is important for the level of aggressiveness. A peculiarity of the action of this hormone which is encountered from fishes to man is the long persistence of its effects following castration. Estrogens are essential for mating behavior in all species and for nest building in the females in which this behavior is displayed. Progesterone appears to be important for incubation and parental behavior in birds and for mating behavior and nest building in a number of mammals. The possibility of pituitary involvement has been suggested for the courtship and nest-building behavior of at least one fish (*58*), for the land to water migration of certain salamanders, for the migratory and parental behavior of birds, for aggressive behavior of one bird (*232*), and for parental behavior of mammals. There is evidence that androgens and estrogens acting during the larval, embryonic, and fetal periods are influential in the patterning of the behavior displayed during adulthood.

These many actions of the same hormones are consistent with the importance that has been attached to the character of the tissues on which the hormones act. The information we have brought together reinforces the conclusions expressed by Florkin (*418a*) at the end of his chapter on the evolution of biochemical constituents, by Medawar (*419*) in his consideration of the evolution of viviparity, and by Beach (*420*) in his discussion of the evolution of the relationship between the gonadal and pituitary hormones and courtship and mating behavior in male animals. The substance of these conclusions was formulated by Florkin when he was writing about endocrine relationships to organ functioning: "L'évolution a souvent utilisé pour une nouvelle fonction une substance déjà existante en suscitant l'apparition d'un nouveau système biochimique récepteur de son action" (*418a*).

Beyond this generalization are several points which broaden the picture that has been created. We find for example, particularly in mammals but to some extent in birds (*7, 421–423*), an "intrusion" of psychologic influences, with the result that an investigator cannot always be sure where hormonal influences leave off and psychologic influences begin (*7, 53*). Such a development may well account for the difficulties in ascertaining the role of hormones in the induction of parental behavior (pages 218, 228–230). Something like this may contribute to the difficulty in arriving at an understanding of the relationship between the gonadal hormones and erotic behavior in man. It is very clear that in female primates an expanded period of receptivity has developed, first from the time of ovulation into the follicular phase and then into the luteal phase (*9, 424*). Beach (*317, 420,* e.g.) has discussed the problem in several places, stating that "evolutionary changes in the direction of increasing corticalization of sexual functions seem to be associated with increasing complexity and modifiability of the individual's sexual patterns, and also with a decreasing reliance upon gonadal hormones for sexual activation and performance."

The problem is presented by Bleuler and Stoll (*3*) in the discussion of the psychologic manifestations of hyper- and hypoactivity of the adrenal cortex in man. In writing about the highly variable and unpredictable emotional symptoms of patients with Cushing's syndrome and of patients treated with cortisone or ACTH they state: "We are not dealing simply with an expression of an endocrine stimulus or psychic function, but with highly personal reactions to this stimulus. These reactions depend not on the endocrine stimulus alone, but also on many other factors—the personal constitution, the personality development during the whole life, the present situation of the patient, and his intellectual and emotional evaluation of the situation . . . glucocorticoids (like other hormones) can influence the psychic life, but never is the psychic life or any aspect of it dominated by this hormonal influence alone."

We have noted that the endocrinologist probing into the relationship between gonadal hormones and reproductive behavior in lower mammals sees the beginning of this influence (*9*, pp. 1215–1221). In laboratory studies of lower mammals the relationships between the adrenal steroids and behavior have not been as apparent. Conceivably though direct relationships will be found, and it will be interesting to see if here too the beginning of an influence of psychologic or experiential factors cannot be detected.

Recently attention has been given to the role of prenatal gonadal hormones in the patterning of sexual behavior after the attainment of adulthood (*9, 33, 329*). Presumptive evidence that such an organizing action is a part of the development of sexuality in lower vertebrates is cited in the present discussion (Section IX). The suggestion is made here that the universal occurrence of dimorphism in the responsiveness of adults to estrogens and androgens and some of the ambisexual behavior may be consequences of this action during the embryonic and fetal period. Available data in the form of records of sex reversal in adult fishes, amphibians, and birds (*397–400, 425–428*) suggest that there is a greater plasticity in these phyla than in mammals and that in mammals the action of fetal gonadal hormones is more decisive. Psychiatrists and others would question this suggestion (see e.g., *6, 8, 34–36*). If they are correct, this would be another example of the "intrusion" of psychologic influences mentioned above. Data obtained from investigations of fishes, reptiles, and birds (*57, 62, 101, 104, 112, 120, 186, 193, 194, 241, 429*) suggest that the degree of specificity to estrogens and androgens may be less in members of these phyla than in mammals. Again, however, the suggestion has been made for man that androgens increase the sexual desire in the human female even more than estrogens (*430–438*).

A third example of an evolutionary change that may have taken place is in the degree of specificity to hormonal action within the individuals of a species and sex. Limited but carefully gathered data reveal that progesterone is quite highly specific in its estrus-inducing action in the female guinea pig (*439, 440*). The various estrogens and androgens should be tested similarly, as they have in the case of many tissue reactions.

A last subject has to do with the many similarities of the relationship between gonadal hormones to behavior and the relationship of the same hormones to the genital tracts. The similarities were noted during investigations of the role of testosterone propionate in the patterning of mating behavior in the guinea pig (*33*). They are discussed by Young (*9, 329*) and mentioned elsewhere in the present survey (Section IX). These responses of the fetal Wolffian ducts and neural tissues to androgens, and the responses of the adult female genital tract and neural tissues in some species to estrogen and progesterone are additional examples of the diverse uses to which hormones have been put. Within these tissues differentiation and organization, secretion, myometrial contraction, and stimulation leading to the expression of behavior are effects of the same hormones. In this place it would be appropriate to designate biochemical mechanisms by means of which these diverse end results are attained. Instead, we can only be reminded of the words of Boscott (*134*) in his general considerations on the mode of action of estrogens. The ability of estrogens to stimulate a wide variety of biochemical changes within the target tissues, he writes, makes it difficult to arrive at a unitarian mode of action. Many of the changes are related to growth processes and may therefore be common with the changes observed in growing tissues. Other changes may correspond to certain of the biochemical side effects of drug action cited by Knox *et al.* (*441*). Apropos of these alternatives, and for any phyletic level, it is difficult to think of the cumulative effect of androgens on the behavior of castrated males, and the estrogen or estrogen-progesterone-induced behavior in females as results of a "growth" process in the nerve cells which mediate this behavior. This difficulty may be a reason for looking at the second possibility proposed by Boscott (*134*) for the explanation students of the problem are seeking to obtain.

References

1. L. G. Browman, *J. Exptl. Zool.* **75**, 375–388 (1937).
1a. R. D. Lisk, *Can. J. Biochem. Physiol.* **38**, 1381–1383 (1960).
2. F. A. Beach, "Hormones and Behavior." Harper (Hoeber), New York, 1948.
3. M. Bleuler and W. A. Stoll, *in* "The Adrenocortical Hormones" (H. W. Deane, ed.), pp. 638–659. Springer, Berlin, 1962.
4. N. E. Collias, *in* "Steroid Hormones" (E. S. Gordon, ed.), pp. 277–329. University of Wisconsin Press, Madison, Wisconsin, 1950.
5. E. Eisner, *Animal Behav.* **8**, 155–179 (1960).
6. J. L. Hampson and J. G. Hampson, *in* "Sex and Internal Secretions" (W. C. Young, ed.), 3rd ed., pp. 1401–1432. Williams & Wilkins, Baltimore, Maryland, 1961.
7. D. S. Lehrman, *in* "Sex and Internal Secretions" (W. C. Young, ed.), 3rd ed., pp. 1268–1382. Williams & Wilkins, Baltimore, Maryland, 1961.
8. J. Money, *in* "Sex and Internal Secretions" (W. C. Young, ed.), 3rd ed., pp. 1383–1400. Williams & Wilkins, Baltimore, Maryland, 1961.

9. W. C. Young, *in* "Sex and Internal Secretions" (W. C. Young, ed.), 3rd ed., pp. 1173–1239. Williams & Wilkins, Baltimore, Maryland, 1961.
10. D. Bodenstein, *in* "Insect Physiology" (K. D. Roeder, ed.), pp. 879–931. Wiley, New York, 1953.
11. D. Gilmour, "The Biochemistry of Insects." Academic Press, New York, 1961.
12. H. Piepho, E. Boden, and I. Holz, *Z. Tierpsychol.* **17,** 261–269 (1960).
13. W. G. Van der Kloot and C. M. Williams, *Behaviour* **5,** 157–174 (1953).
14. V. B. Wigglesworth, "The Physiology of Insect Metamorphosis." Cambridge Univ. Press, London and New York, 1954.
15. C. M. Williams, *Biol. Bull.* **116,** 323–338 (1959).
16. P. Karlson, *Ann. sci. nat. Zool. et biol. animale* **18,** 125–137 (1956).
17. C. M. Williams, *Abstr., Proc. Am. Soc. Zoöl., Anat. Record* **120,** 743 (1954).
17a. P. Karlson, *in* "Progress in Comparative Endocrinology" (K. Takewaki, ed.), pp. 1–7. Academic Press, New York, 1962.
18. J. W. B. Douglas, D. A. Hanson, and S. Zuckerman, *J. Exptl. Biol.* **25,** 395–405 (1948).
19. T.-O. Yamamoto, *J. Exptl. Zool.* **123,** 571–594 (1953).
20. T.-O. Yamamoto, *J. Exptl. Zool.* **137,** 227–263 (1958).
21. T.-O. Yamamoto, *J. Exptl. Zool.* **141,** 133–153 (1959).
22. T.-O. Yamamoto, *Genetics* **44,** 739–757 (1959).
23. W. Laskowski, *Arch. Entwicklungsmech. Organ.* **146,** 137–182 (1953).
24. W. Laskowski, *Biol. Zentr.* **73,** 429–438 (1954).
25. R. R. Humphrey, *Am. J. Anat.* **76,** 33–66 (1945).
26. L. Gallien, *Compt. rend. acad. sci.* **231,** 919–920 (1950).
27. L. Gallien, *Bull. biol. France et Belg.* **90,** 163–183 (1956).
28. L. Gallien, *in* "Progress in Comparative Endocrinology" (K. Takewaki, ed.), pp. 346–355. Academic Press, New York, 1962.
29. C. Y. Chang and E. Witschi, *Proc. Soc. Exptl. Biol. Med.* **89,** 150–152 (1955).
30. C. Y. Chang and E. Witschi, *Proc. Soc. Exptl. Biol. Med.* **93,** 140–144 (1956).
31. L. V. Domm and D. E. Davis, *Physiol. Zoöl.* **21,** 14–31 (1948).
32. V. Dantchakoff, *Compt. rend. acad. sci.* **206,** 945–947 (1938).
33. C. H. Phoenix, R. W. Goy, A. A. Gerall, and W. C. Young, *Endocrinology* **65,** 369–382 (1959).
33a. W. C. Young, R. W. Goy, and C. H. Phoenix, *Science* **143,** 212–218 (1964).
34. A. C. Kinsey, W. B. Pomeroy, and C. E. Martin, "Sexual Behavior in the Human Male." Saunders, Philadelphia, Pennsylvania, 1948.
35. A. C. Kinsey, W. B. Pomeroy, C. E. Martin, and P. H. Gebhard, "Sexual Behavior in the Human Female." Saunders, Philadelphia, Pennsylvania, 1953.
36. M. Mead, *in* "Sex and Internal Secretions" (W. C. Young, ed.), 3rd ed., pp. 1433–1479. Williams & Wilkins, Baltimore, Maryland, 1961.
37. B. Baggerman, *in* "Progress in Comparative Endocrinology" (K. Takewaki, ed.), pp. 188–205. Academic Press, New York, 1962.
38. C. P. Richter, *Endocrinology* **17,** 73–87 (1933).
39. C. P. Richter, *Harvey Lectures Ser.* **38,** 63–103 (1942–1943).
40. C. P. Richter, *J. Comp. and Physiol. Psychol.* **40,** 129–134 (1947).
41. C. P. Richter, E. C. H. Schmidt, Jr., and P. D. Malone, *Bull. Johns Hopkins Hosp.* **76,** 192–219 (1945).
42. W. C. Young, *in* "Glandular Physiology and Therapy" (Council on Pharmacy and Therapy of the American Medical Association), 5th ed., pp. 515–534. Lippincott, Philadelphia, Pennsylvania, 1954.

43. C. S. Chadwick, *J. Exptl. Zool.* **86,** 175–187 (1941).
44. E. E. Reinke and C. S. Chadwick, *J. Exptl. Zool.* **83,** 223–233 (1940).
45. W. C. Grant, Jr. and J. A. Grant, *Biol. Bull.* **114,** 1–9 (1958).
46. H. Tuchmann-Duplessis, *Arch. Anat. Microscop. Morphol. Exptl.* **38,** 302–317 (1949).
47. O. Riddle, R. W. Bates, and E. L. Lahr, *Am. J. Physiol.* **111,** 352–360 (1935).
48. O. Riddle, *Cold Spring Harbor Symposia Quant. Biol.* **5,** 218–228 (1937).
49. O. Riddle, E. L. Lahr, and R. W. Bates, *Proc. Soc. Exptl. Biol. Med.* **32,** 730–734 (1935).
50. O. Riddle, E. L. Lahr, and R. W. Bates, *Am. J. Physiol.* **137,** 299–317 (1942).
51. C. P. Leblond, *Proc. Soc. Exptl. Biol. Med.* **38,** 66–70 (1938).
52. C. P. Leblond, *J. Genet. Psychol.* **57,** 327–344 (1940).
53. C. P. Leblond and W. O. Nelson, *Am. J. Physiol.* **120,** 167–172 (1937).
54. C. P. Leblond and W. O. Nelson, *Compt. rend. soc. biol.* **124,** 1064–1066 (1937).
55. A. E. Wilhelmi, G. E. Pickford, and W. H. Sawyer, *Endocrinology* **57,** 243–252 (1955).
56. G. E. Pickford and J. W. Atz, "The Physiology of the Pituitary Gland of Fishes." New York Zoological Society, New York, 1957.
57. L. R. Aronson, *in* "The Physiology of Fishes" (M. E. Brown, ed.), Vol. II, pp. 272–304. Academic Press, New York, 1957.
58. W. S. Hoar, *Animal Behav.* **10,** 247–266 (1962).
59. V. H. Denenberg and E. M. Banks, *in* "The Behaviour of Domestic Animals" (E. S. E. Hafez, ed.), pp. 201–243. Baillinière, London, 1962.
60. G. P. Baerends, R. Brouwer, and H. T. Waterbolk, *Behaviour* **8,** 249–334 (1955).
61. R. Barrass, *Behaviour* **15,** 185–209 (1960).
62. E. Fabricius and A. Lindroth, *Inst. Freshwater Research Drottningholm, Rept.* No. **35,** 105–112 (1954).
63. P. D. Gabbutt, *Brit. J. Animal Behav.* **2,** 84–88 (1954).
64. R. A. Hinde, *Behaviour* **7,** 207–232 (1955).
65. R. A. Hinde, *Ibis* **97,** 706–745 (1955); **98,** 1–23 (1956).
66. H. Lind, *Z. Tierpsychol.* **15,** 99–111 (1958).
67. D. Morris, *in* "L'Instinct dans le Comportement des Animaux et de l'Homme" (P.-P. Grassé, ed.), pp. 261–286. Masson, Paris, 1956.
68. M. Moynihan and M. F. Hall, *Behaviour* **7,** 33–76 (1955).
69. A. G. Skard, *Acta Psychol. Hague* **2,** 175–229 (1937).
70. H. T. Spieth, *Evolution* **1,** 17–31 (1947).
71. D. G. M. Wood-Gush, *Brit. J. Animal Behav.* **2,** 95–102 (1954).
72. E. C. Amoroso and F. H. A. Marshall, *in* "Marshall's Physiology of Reproduction" (A. S. Parkes, ed.), 3rd ed., Vol. I, Part II, pp. 707–831. Longmans, Green, New York, 1960.
73. H. Hediger, "Wild Animals in Captivity." Academic Press, New York, 1950.
74. W. A. Mason, *J. Comp. and Physiol. Psychol.* **53,** 582–589 (1960).
75. W. A. Mason, *J. Comp. and Physiol. Psychol.* **54,** 694–699 (1961).
76. C. P. Stone, *J. Comp. Psychol.* **2,** 95–153 (1922).
77. F. A. Beach, *J. Comp. Psychol.* **29,** 193–245 (1940).
78. W. C. Young, E. W. Dempsey, and H. I. Myers, *J. Comp. Psychol.* **19,** 313–335 (1935).
79. O. P. Pearson, *Am. J. Anat.* **75,** 39–93 (1944).

80. J. W. Kislak and F. A. Beach, *Endocrinology* **56**, 684–692 (1955).
81. V. H. Denenberg, *in* "The Behaviour of Domestic Animals" (E. S. E. Hafez, ed.), pp. 109–138. Baillière, London, 1962.
82. R. Bambridge, *Science* **136**, 259–260 (1962).
83. E. Cullen, *Abstr., Proc. Assoc. Study Animal Behav., Animal Behav.* **8**, 235 (1960).
84. V. H. Denenberg and J. R. C. Morton, *J. Comp. and Physiol. Psychol.* **55**, 242–246 (1962).
85. A. E. Fisher and E. B. Hale, *Behaviour* **10**, 309–323 (1957).
86. H. F. Harlow, *in* "The Central Nervous System and Behavior: Transactions of the Third Conference" (M. A. B. Brazier, ed.), pp. 307–357. Josiah Macy, Jr. Foundation, New York, 1960.
87. B. W. Lindholm, *J. Comp. and Physiol. Psychol.* **55**, 597–599 (1962).
88. W. A. Mason and P. C. Green, *J. Comp. and Physiol. Psychol.* **55**, 363–368 (1962).
89. J. T. Spence and B. A. Maher, *J. Comp. and Physiol. Psychol.* **55**, 247–251 (1962).
90. J. T. Spence and B. A. Maher, *J. Comp. and Physiol. Psychol.* **55**, 252–255 (1962).
91. E. Clark and L. R. Aronson, *Zoologica* **36**, 49–66 (1951).
92. E. S. Valenstein, W. Riss, and W. C. Young, *J. Comp. and Physiol. Psychol.* **47**, 162–165 (1954).
93. K. Larsson, *Acta Psychol. Gothoburgensia* **1** (1956).
94. C. P. Stone, *Am. J. Physiol.* **68**, 407–424 (1924).
95. G. T. Avery, *J. Comp. Psychol.* **5**, 373–396 (1925).
96. C. M. Louttit, *J. Comp. Psychol.* **9**, 293–304 (1929).
97. R. C. Webster and W. C. Young, *Fertility and Sterility* **2**, 175–181 (1951).
98. W. C. Young, E. W. Dempsey, H. I. Myers, and C. W. Hagquist, *Am. J. Anat.* **63**, 457–487 (1938).
99. J. A. Grunt and W. C. Young, *Endocrinology* **51**, 237–248 (1952).
100. H. R. Antliff and W. C. Young, *Endocrinology* **59**, 74–82 (1956).
101. L. R. Aronson, *Zoologica* **34**, 133–158 (1949).
102. G. P. Baerends, *in* "The Physiology of Fishes" (M. E. Brown, ed.), Vol. II, pp. 229–269. Academic Press, New York, 1957.
103. K. Fiedler, *Z. Tierpsychol.* **11**, 358–416 (1954).
104. D. Morris, *Behaviour* **4**, 233–261 (1962).
105. H. Schlosberg, M. C. Duncan, and B. H. Daitch, *Physiol. Zoöl.* **22**, 148–161 (1949).
106. W. N. Tavolga, *Bull. Am. Museum Nat. Hist.* **104**, 427–459 (1954).
107. J. J. A. van Iersel, *Behaviour* (*Suppl.*) **3** (1953).
108. M. Fontaine, *in* "L'Instinct dans le Comportement des Animaux et de l'Homme" (P.-P. Grassé, ed.), pp. 151–175. Masson, Paris, 1956.
109. K. Ikeda, *Japan. J. Zoöl.* **5**, 135–157 (1933).
110. M. C. Duncan, *J. Genet. Psychol.* **78**, 159–164 (1951).
111. J. C. Braddock and Z. I. Braddock, *Physiol. Zoöl.* **28**, 152–172 (1955).
112. J. C. Braddock and Z. I. Braddock, *Animal Behav.* **7**, 222–232 (1959).
113. L. R. Aronson, *Physiol. Zoöl.* **18**, 403–415 (1945).
114. W. N. Tavolga, *Physiol. Zoöl.* **28**, 218–233 (1955).
115. D. Morris, *Behaviour* **7**, 1–33 (1955).
116. L. L. Stanley and G. L. Tescher, *Endocrinology* **15**, 55–56 (1931).
117. W. S. Hoar, *J. Fisheries Research Board Can.* **8**, 241–263 (1951).

118. W. S. Hoar, D. MacKinnon, and A. Redlich, *Can. J. Zool.* **30,** 273–286 (1952).
119. B. Baggerman, *Arch. neerl. zool.* **12,** 105–317 (1957).
120. E. M. Barraud, *Brit. J. Animal Behav.* **3,** 134–136 (1955).
121. E. Butz and P. Kuenzer, *Z. Tierpsychol.* **14,** 204–209 (1957).
122. J. J. Duyvené de Wit, *S. African J. Sci.* **51,** 249–251 (1955).
123. J. M. Dodd, *in* "Marshall's Physiology of Reproduction" (A. S. Parkes, ed.), 3rd ed., Vol. I, Part II, pp. 417–582. Longmans, Green, New York, 1960.
124. J. M. Dodd, P. J. Evennett, and C. K. Goddard, *Symp. Zool. Soc. London* **No. 1,** 77–103 (1960).
125. W. S. Hoar, *Univ. Toronto Biol. Ser.* **No. 59;** *Pub. Ont. Fisheries Research Lab.* **No. 71,** 1–51 (1951).
126. W. S. Hoar, *Mem. Soc. Endocrinol.* **4,** 5–24 (1955).
127. W. S. Hoar, *in* "The Physiology of Fishes" (M. E. Brown, ed.), Vol. I, pp. 245–285. Academic Press, New York, 1957.
128. L. W. Hazleton and F. J. Goodrich, *J. Am. Pharmacol. Assoc.* **26,** 420–421 (1937).
129. G. D. Potter and W. S. Hoar, *J. Fisheries Research Board Can.* **11,** 63–68 (1954).
130. G. Chieffi, *in* "Progress in Comparative Endocrinology" (K. Takewaki, ed.), pp. 275–285. Academic Press, New York, 1962.
131. G. Chieffi and C. Lupo, *Nature* **190,** 169–170 (1961).
132. H. H. Wotiz, C. Botticelli, F. L. Hisaw, Jr., and I. Ringler, *J. Biol. Chem.* **231,** 589–592 (1958).
133. F. D. Dean and I. Chester Jones, *J. Endocrinol.* **18,** 366–371 (1959).
134. R. J. Boscott, *in* "The Ovary" (Sir S. Zuckerman, ed.), Vol. II, pp. 1–45. Academic Press, New York, 1962.
135. T. R. Forbes, *in* "Sex and Internal Secretions" (W. C. Young, ed.), 3rd ed., pp. 1035–1087. Williams & Wilkins, Baltimore, Maryland, 1961.
136. W. S. Hoar, *in* "The Physiology of Fishes" (M. E. Brown, ed.), Vol. I, pp. 287–321. Academic Press, New York, 1957.
137. A. J. Marshall and B. Lofts, *Nature* **177,** 704–705 (1956).
138. B. Lofts and A. J. Marshall, *Quart. J. Microscop. Sci.* **98,** 79–88 (1957).
139. L. L. Franchi, *in* "The Ovary" (Sir S. Zuckerman, ed.), Vol. II, pp. 121–142. Academic Press, New York, 1962.
140. J. N. Ball, *in* "Hormones in Fish" (I. Chester Jones, ed.), pp. 104–135. Symposium of the Zoological Society of London, No. 1, London, 1960.
141. Y. Kinoshita, *J. Sci. Hiroshima Univ. Ser. B, Div. 1,* **6,** 5–22 (1938).
142. L. H. Bretschneider and J. J. Duyvené de Wit, "Sexual Endocrinology of Non-mammalian Vertebrates." Elsevier, Amsterdam, 1947.
143. P. Eckstein, *in* "The Ovary" (Sir S. Zuckerman, ed.), Vol. I, pp. 311–359. Academic Press, New York, 1962.
144. R. J. Harrison, *in* "The Ovary" (Sir S. Zuckerman, ed.), Vol. I, pp. 143–187. Academic Press, New York, 1962.
145. F. Jacoby, *in* "The Ovary" (Sir S. Zuckerman, ed.), Vol. I, pp. 189–245. Academic Press, New York, 1962.
146. W. C. Young, *in* "Sex and Internal Secretions" (W. C. Young, ed.), 3rd ed., pp. 449–496. Williams & Wilkins, Baltimore, Maryland, 1961.
147. A. Lipschütz, "The Internal Secretions of the Sex Glands." Williams & Wilkins, Baltimore, Maryland, 1924.
148. L. R. Aronson, *Copeia,* pp. 246–249 (1943).

149. L. R. Aronson, *Am. Midland Naturalist* **29,** 242–244 (1943).
150. L. R. Aronson, *Am. Museum Novitates* **No. 1224** (1943).
151. L. R. Aronson, *Am. Museum Novitates* **No. 1250** (1944).
152. G. K. Noble and L. R. Aronson, *Bull. Am. Museum Nat. Hist.* **80,** 127–142 (1942).
153. A. N. Bragg, *Am. Naturalist* **74,** 322–349 (1940).
154. I. von Eibl-Eibesfeldt, *Behaviour* **2,** 217–236 (1950).
155. H. Heusser, *Z. Tierpsychol.* **17,** 67–81 (1960).
156. R. M. Savage, *Proc. Zool. Soc. London* pp. 55–70 (1934).
157. H. A. Shapiro, *J. Exptl. Biol.* **13,** 48–56 (1936).
158. E. O. Jordan, *J. Morphol.* **5,** 263–270 (1891).
159. P. H. Pope, *Ann. Carnegie Museum* **15,** 305–368 (1924).
160. R. E. Smith, *Copeia* pp. 255–262 (1941).
161. K. F. Stein, *Copeia* pp. 86–88 (1938).
162. W. M. S. Russell, *Behaviour* **7,** 113–188 (1955).
163. W. M. S. Russell, *Behaviour* **15,** 253–282 (1960).
164. R. Haubrich, *Animal Behav.* **9,** 71–76 (1961).
165. G. Brossard and P. Gley, *Compt. rend. soc. biol.* **101,** 757–758 (1929).
166. H. A. Shapiro, *J. Exptl. Biol.* **13,** 57–59 (1936).
167. H. A. Shapiro, *J. Exptl. Biol.* **14,** 38–47 (1937).
168. M. H. Burgos, *Rev. soc. arg. biol.* **26,** 359–371 (1950).
169. C. L. Smith, *Mem. Soc. Endocrinol.* **4,** 39–56 (1955).
170. M. R. Miller and M. E. Robbins, *J. Exptl. Zool.* **125,** 415–446 (1954).
171. S. Pesonen and J. Rapola, *Gen. Comp. Endocrinol.* **2,** 425–432 (1962).
172. L. Gallien and M.-T. Chalumeau-Le Foulgoc, *Compt. rend. acad. sci.* **251,** 460–462 (1960).
173. R. K. Burns, Jr., *J. Exptl. Zool.* **63,** 309–327 (1932).
174. C. Galli-Maïnini, *Compt. rend. soc. biol.* **145,** 131–133 (1951).
175. P. A. Wright, *Gen. Comp. Endocrinol.* **1,** 20–23 (1961).
176. F. R. Cagle, *Ecol. Monographs* **20,** 31–54 (1950).
177. L. T. Evans, *Copeia* pp. 3–6 (1935).
178. L. T. Evans, *J. Genet. Psychol.* **48,** 217–221 (1936).
179. L. T. Evans, *J. Genet. Psychol.* **48,** 88–111 (1936).
180. L. T. Evans, *Abstr., Proc. Am. Soc. Zoöl. Anat. Record* **94,** 395–396 (1946).
181. L. T. Evans, *Herpetologica* **9,** 189–192 (1953).
182. B. Greenberg and G. K. Noble, *Physiol. Zoöl.* **17,** 392–439 (1944).
183. J. M. Legler, *Lloydia* **18,** 95–99 (1955).
184. G. K. Noble and H. T. Bradley, *Ann. N. Y. Acad. Sci.* **35,** 25–100 (1933).
185. G. K. Noble and E. R. Mason, *Am. Museum Novitates* **No. 619** (1933).
186. G. K. Noble and B. Greenberg, *J. Exptl. Zool.* **88,** 451–479 (1941).
187. E. H. Taylor, *Univ. Kansas Sci. Bull.* **21,** 269–271 (1933).
188. K. S. Dharmakumarsinhji, *J. Bombay Nat. Hist. Soc.* **47,** 174–176 (1947).
189. R. Kehl and C. Combescot, *Mem. Soc. Endocrinol.* **4,** 57–74 (1955).
190. L. T. Evans, *Biol. Bull.* **79,** 371 (1940).
191. L. T. Evans, *Abstr., Proc. Am. Soc. Zool. Anat. Record* **94,** 405–406 (1946).
192. L. T. Evans, *Herpetologica* **8,** 11–14 (1952).
193. G. K. Noble and B. Greenberg, *Proc. Soc. Exptl. Biol. Med.* **44,** 460–462 (1940).
194. G. K. Noble and B. Greenberg, *Proc. Soc. Exptl. Biol. Med.* **47,** 32–37 (1941).
195. A. J. Marshall and F. M. Woolf, *Quart. J. Microscop. Sci.* **98,** 89–100 (1957).

196. L. T. Evans, *J. Genet. Psychol.* **49,** 49–60 (1936).
197. R. J. Harrison, *Biol. Revs. Cambridge Phil. Soc.* **23,** 296–331 (1948).
198. L. Harrison Matthews, *Mem. Soc. Endocrinol.* **4,** 129–144 (1955).
199. J. R. Valle and L. A. R. Valle, *Science* **97,** 400 (1943).
200. A. Porto, *Mem. Inst. Butantan (São Paulo)* **15,** 27–30 (1941).
201. L. Fraenkel and T. Martins, *Compt. rend. soc. biol.* **127,** 466–468 (1938).
202. D. E. Bragdon, E. A. Lazo-Wasem, M. X. Zarrow, and F. L. Hisaw, *Proc. Soc. Exptl. Biol. Med.* **86,** 477–480 (1954).
203. N. E. Collias, *in* "The Behaviour of Domestic Animals" (E. S. E. Hafez, ed.), pp. 565–585. Baillière, London, 1962.
204. A. M. Guhl, *in* "Sex and Internal Secretions" (W. C. Young, ed.), 3rd ed., pp. 1240–1267. William & Wilkins, Baltimore, Maryland, 1961.
205. A. M. Guhl, *in* "The Behaviour of Domestic Animals" (E. S. E. Hafez, ed.), pp. 491–530. Baillière, London, 1962.
206. E. B. Hale and M. W. Schein, *in* "The Behaviour of Domestic Animals" (E. S. E. Hafez, ed.), pp. 531–564. Baillière, London, 1962.
207. R. A. Hinde, *in* "Biology and Comparative Physiology of Birds" (A. J. Marshall, ed.), Vol. II, pp. 373–411. Academic Press, New York, 1961.
208. A. S. Parkes and A. J. Marshall, *in* "Marshall's Physiology of Reproduction" (A. S. Parkes, ed.), 3rd ed., Vol. I, Part II, pp. 583–706. Longmans, Green, New York, 1960.
209. H. Friedmann, "The Cowbirds. A Study in the Biology of Social Parasitism." Charles C Thomas, Springfield, Illinois, 1929.
210. H. Friedmann, *Bull. U. S. Natl. Museum* **No. 208** (1955).
211. W. Makatsch, "Der Brutparasitismus der Kuckucksvögel." Quelle & Meyer, Leipzig, Germany, 1937.
212. H. N. Southern, *in* "Evolution as a Process" (J. Huxley, A. C. Hardy, and E. B. Ford, eds.), pp. 219–232. Allen and Unwin, London, 1954.
213. M. W. Weller, *Ecol. Monographs* **29,** 333–365 (1959).
214. W. S. Bullough, *Biol. Revs. Cambridge Phil. Soc.* **20,** 89–99 (1945).
215. D. S. Farner, *in* "Recent Studies in Avian Biology" (A. Wolfson, ed.), pp. 198–237. University of Illinois Press, Urbana, Illinois, 1955.
216. S. C. Kendeigh, G. C. West, and G. W. Cox, *Animal Behav.* **8,** 180–185 (1960).
217. A. J. Marshall, *in* "Biology and Comparative Physiology of Birds" (A. J. Marshall, ed.), Vol. II, pp. 307–339. Academic Press, New York, 1961.
218. A. Wolfson, *in* "Comparative Endocrinology" (A. Gorbman, ed.), pp. 38–70. Wiley, New York, 1959.
219. G. J. Van Oordt and C. J. A. C. Bol, *Biol. Zentr.* **49,** 173–186 (1929).
220. W. Rowen, *Proc. Natl. Acad. Sci. U. S.* **18,** 639–654 (1932).
221. P. Putzig, *Vogelzug* **8,** 116–130 (1937).
222. H. W. Hann, *Bird Banding* **10,** 122–124 (1939).
223. D. S. Farner, L. R. Mewaldt, and J. R. King, *J. Comp. and Physiol. Psychol.* **47,** 148–153 (1954).
224. H. O. Wagner, *Z. Tierpsychol.* **18,** 302–319 (1961).
225. A. Wolfson, *Condor* **44,** 237–263 (1942).
226. R. D. McGreal and D. S. Farner, *Northwest Sci.* **30,** 12–23 (1956).
227. D. S. Farner, *Condor* **52,** 104–122 (1950).
228. L. V. Domm, *in* "Sex and Internal Secretions" (E. Allen, ed.), 2nd ed., pp. 227–327. Williams & Wilkins, Baltimore, Maryland, 1939.

229. J. Benoit, *in* "L'Instinct dans le Comportement des Animaux et de l'Homme" (P.-P. Grassé, ed.), pp. 177–260. Masson, Paris, 1956.
230. A. J. Marshall, *in* "Biology and Comparative Physiology of Birds" (A. J. Marshall, ed.), Vol. II, pp. 169–213. Academic Press, New York, 1961.
231. R. E. Phillips and F. McKinney, *Animal Behav.* **10**, 244–246 (1962).
232. D. E. Davis, *Science* **126**, 253 (1957).
233. A. J. Marshall, *Mem. Soc. Endocrinol.* **4**, 75–93 (1955).
234. J. D. S. Kumaran and C. W. Turner, *Poultry Sci.* **28**, 636–640 (1949).
235. C. R. Carpenter, *J. Comp. Psychol.* **16**, 25–27 (1933).
236. F. Caridroit, *in* "Nouveau Traité de Physiologie," Vol. VII, Book II. Presses Universitaires, Paris, 1946.
237. J. Benoit, *Arch. zool. exptl. et gén.* **69**, 217–499 (1929).
238. C. R. Carpenter, *J. Comp. Psychol.* **16**, 59–97 (1933).
239. H. M. Scott and L. F. Payne, *J. Exptl. Zool.* **69**, 123–136 (1934).
240. O. Riddle, *Brit. J. Exptl. Biol.* **2**, 211–246 (1925).
241. G. K. Noble and M. Wurm, *Endocrinology* **26**, 837–850 (1940).
242. O. Riddle and E. L. Lahr, *Endocrinology* **35**, 255–260 (1944).
243. D. S. Lehrman, *J. Comp. and Physiol. Psychol.* **51**, 142–145 (1958).
244. B. Lofts and A. J. Marshall, *J. Endocrinol.* **19**, 16–21 (1959).
245. A. J. Marshall and D. L. Serventy, *Proc. Zool. Soc. London* **127**, 489–510 (1956).
246. M. E. Davis and E. J. Plotz, *Fertility and Sterility* **8**, 603–618 (1957).
247. A. V. Nalbandov, *Endocrinology* **36**, 251–258 (1945).
248. A. V. Nalbandov and L. E. Card, *J. Heredity* **36**, 34–39 (1945).
249. H. D. Goodale, *J. Animal Behav.* **6**, 319–324 (1916).
250. R. W. Bates, O. Riddle, and E. L. Lahr, *Am. J. Physiol.* **119**, 610–614 (1937).
251. E. A. Armstrong, "Bird Display and Behaviour." Lindsay Drummond, London, 1947.
252. W. S. Bullough and R. Carrick, *Nature* **145**, 629 (1940).
253. L. V. Domm, *Abstr., Proc. Am. Soc. Zool., Anat. Record* **99**, 554 (1947).
254. A. M. Guhl, *Trans. Kansas Acad. Sci.* **51**, 107–111 (1948).
255. E. B. Hale, *Poultry Sci.* **34**, 1059–1067 (1955).
256. E. O. Höhn, *Proc. Zool. Soc. London* **117**, 281–304 (1947).
257. E. O. Höhn, *Brit. J. Animal Behav.* **1**, 48–58 (1953).
258. J. S. Huxley, *Proc. Zool. Soc. London* pp. 491–562 (1914).
259. L. Kilham, *Auk* **77**, 259–270 (1960).
260. D. Lack, *Proc. Zool. Soc. London Ser. A* **109**, 169–219 (1939).
261. A. J. Marshall and C. J. F. Coombs, *Nature* **169**, 261–264 (1952).
262. D. Morris, *Behaviour* **8**, 46–56 (1955).
263. R. S. Palmer, *Proc. Boston Soc. Nat. Hist.* **42**, 1–119 (1941).
264. N. Tinbergen, *Ardea* **24**, 1–42 (1935).
265. E. Witschi and R. A. Miller, *J. Exptl. Zool.* **79**, 475–487 (1938).
266. A. A. Allen, *Auk* **51**, 180–199 (1934).
267. N. E. Collias, *Physiol. Zoöl.* **17**, 83–123 (1944).
268. S. C. Kendeigh, *Illinois Biol. Monographs* **18**, #3 (1941).
269. M. Moynihan, *Behaviour (Suppl.)* **4** (1955).
270. H. H. Shoemaker, *Auk* **56**, 381–406 (1939).
271. W. C. Allee, N. E. Collias, and C. Z. Lutherman, *Physiol. Zoöl.* **12**, 412–440 (1939).
272. M. A. Bennett, *Ecology* **21**, 148–165 (1940).
273. W. R. Boss, *J. Exptl. Zool.* **94**, 181–209 (1943).

274. H. H. Shoemaker, *Proc. Soc. Exptl. Biol. Med.* **41**, 299–302 (1939).
275. J. Hammond, Jr., and F. T. Day, *J. Endocrinol.* **4**, 53–82 (1944).
276. W. C. Young and B. Rundlett, *Psychosomat. Med.* **1**, 449–460 (1939).
277. L. V. Domm, *J. Exptl. Zool.* **48**, 31–173 (1927).
278. G. K. Noble and M. Wurm, *Abstr., Proc. Am. Soc. Zool., Anat. Record* **78**, 50–51 (1940).
279. D. E. Davis and L. V. Domm, *Proc. Soc. Exptl. Biol. Med.* **48**, 667–669 (1941).
280. W. C. Allee and N. Collias, *Endocrinology* **27**, 87–94 (1940).
281. R. M. Fraps, C. W. Hooker, and T. R. Forbes, *Science* **108**, 86–87 (1948).
282. R. M. Fraps, C. W. Hooker, and T. R. Forbes, *Science* **109**, 493 (1949).
283. D. S. Layne, R. H. Common, W. A. Maw, and R. M. Fraps, *Proc. Soc. Exptl. Biol. Med.* **95**, 528–529 (1957).
284. I. M. Lytle and F. W. Lorenz, *Nature* **182**, 1681 (1958).
285. J. S. Adams and R. B. Herrick, *Poultry Sci.* **34**, 117–121 (1955).
286. R. P. Warren and R. A. Hinde, *Animal Behav.* **7**, 209–213 (1959).
287. E. L. Lahr and O. Riddle, *Am. J. Physiol.* **123**, 614–619 (1938).
288. E. Eisner, *Animal Behav.* **6**, 124–125 (1958).
289. W. H. Burrows and T. C. Byerly, *Proc. Soc. Exptl. Biol. Med.* **34**, 841–844 (1936).
290. Y. Saeki and Y. Tanabe, *Bull. Natl. Inst. Agr. Sci. (Japan) Ser.* **G8**, 101–109 (1954).
291. Y. Saeki and Y. Tanabe, *Poultry Sci.* **34**, 909–919 (1955).
292. W. Nakajo and K. Tanaka, *Poultry Sci.* **35**, 990–994 (1956).
293. R. P. Breitenbach and R. K. Meyer, *Proc. Soc. Exptl. Biol. Med.* **101**, 16–19 (1959).
294. M. D. Patel, *Physiol. Zoöl.* **9**, 129–152 (1936).
295. D. Amadon, *Am. Museum Novitates* **No. 1252** (1944).
296. K. E. L. Simmons, *Ibis* **96**, 262–292 (1954).
297. N. Tinbergen, *Trans. Linnean Soc. N. Y.* **5**, 1–94 (1939).
298. R. B. Lea, *Wilson Bull.* **54**, 225–237 (1942).
299. A. van Tienhoven, *in* "Sex and Internal Secretions" (W. C. Young, ed.), 3rd ed., pp. 1088–1169. Williams & Wilkins, Baltimore, Maryland, 1961.
300. R. Hertz, R. M. Fraps, and W. H. Sebrell, *Proc. Exptl. Biol. Med.* **52**, 142–144 (1943).
301. R. C. Mason, *Endocrinology* **51**, 570–573 (1952).
302. W. Bolton, *J. Agr. Sci.* **43**, 116–119 (1953).
303. J. W. A. Brant and A. V. Nalbandov, *Poultry Sci.* **35**, 692–700 (1956).
304. D. S. Lehrman and P. Brody, *Proc. Soc. Exptl. Biol. Med.* **95**, 373–375 (1957).
305. D. S. Layne, R. H. Common, W. A. Maw, and R. M. Fraps, *Nature* **181**, 351–352 (1958).
306. R. O. Hurst, A. Kuksis, and J. F. Bendell, *Can. J. Biochem. and Physiol.* **35**, 637–640 (1957).
307. C. W. Hooker and T. R. Forbes, *Endocrinology* **41**, 158–169 (1947).
308. C. W. Hooker and T. R. Forbes, *Endocrinology* **45**, 71–74 (1949).
309. W. G. Siller, *J. Endocrinol.* **14**, 197–203 (1956).
310. A. Morley, *Ibis* **85**, 132–158 (1943).
311. A. J. Marshall, *Proc. Zool. Soc. London* **121**, 727–740 (1952).
312. A. J. Marshall and C. J. F. Coombs, *Proc. Zool. Soc. London* **128**, 545–589 (1957).
313. E. Taber, *Endocrinology* **48**, 6–16 (1951).

314. R. M. Fraps, *Mem. Soc. Endocrinol.* **4,** 205–218 (1955).
315. D. E. Davis, *Anat. Record* **82,** 297–307 (1942).
316. H. D. Goodale, *Genetics* **3,** 276–299 (1918).
317. F. A. Beach, *Physiol. Revs.* **27,** 240–306 (1947).
318. F. A. Beach, *in* "Handbook of Experimental Psychology" (S. S. Stevens, ed.), pp. 387–434. Wiley, New York, 1951.
319. J. T. Eayrs and A. Glass, *in* "The Ovary" (Sir S. Zuckerman, ed.), Vol. II, pp. 381–433. Academic Press, New York, 1962.
320. J. L. Fuller and E. M. DuBuis, *in* "The Behaviour of Domestic Animals" (E. S. E. Hafez, ed.), pp. 415–452. Baillière, London, 1962.
321. E. S. E. Hafez and M. W. Schein, *in* "The Behaviour of Domestic Animals" (E. S. E. Hafez, ed.), pp. 247–296. Baillière, London, 1962.
322. E. S. E. Hafez and J. P. Scott, *in* "The Behaviour of Domestic Animals" (E. S. E. Hafez, ed.), pp. 297–333. Baillière, London, 1962.
323. E. S. E. Hafez, L. J. Sumption, and J. S. Jakway, *in* "The Behaviour of Domestic Animals" (E. S. E. Hafez, ed.), pp. 334–369. Baillière, London, 1962.
324. E. S. E. Hafez, M. Williams, and S. Wierzbowski, *in* "The Behaviour of Domestic Animals" (E. S. E. Hafez, ed.), pp. 370–396. Baillière, London, 1962.
325. J. S. Rosenblatt and T. C. Schneirla, *in* "The Behaviour of Domestic Animals" (E. S. E. Hafez, ed.), pp. 453–488. Baillière, London, 1962.
326. A. N. Worden and J. S. Leahy, *in* "The Behaviour of Domestic Animals" (E. S. E. Hafez, ed.), pp. 397–414. Baillière, London, 1962.
327. W. C. Young, E. W. Dempsey, C. W. Hagquist, and J. L. Boiling, *J. Comp. Psychol.* **27,** 49–68 (1939).
328. R. W. Goy and W. C. Young, *Behaviour* **10,** 340–354 (1957).
329. W. C. Young, *in* "Roots of Behavior" (E. L. Bliss, ed.), pp. 115–122. Harper (Hoeber), New York, 1962.
330. R. J. Boscott, *in* "The Ovary" (Sir S. Zuckerman, ed.), Vol. II, pp. 47–79. Academic Press, New York, 1962.
331. E. Howard and C. J. Migeon, *in* "The Adrenocortical Hormones" (H. W. Deane, ed.), pp. 570–637. Springer, Berlin, 1962.
332. M. Klein, *Ciba Found. Colloq. Endocrinol.* **3,** 323–337 (1952).
333. M. Klein, *Mem. Soc. Endocrinol.* **7,** 144–153 (1960).
334. M. Klein and E. Gagnière, *Compt. rend. soc. biol.* **150,** 1440–1442 (1956).
335. L. R. Aronson, A. Scharf, and H. Silverman, *Proc. Am. Soc. Zool. Anat. Record* **137,** 335 (1960).
336. G. K. Noble and K. F. Kumpf, *Abstr., Proc. Am. Soc. Zool. Anat. Record* (*Suppl. 1*) **67,** 113 (1936).
337. R. H. Dutt, *J. Animal Sci.* **12,** 515–523 (1953).
338. T. J. Robinson, *Endocrinology* **55,** 403–408 (1954).
339. T. J. Robinson, *J. Endocrinol.* **10,** 117–124 (1954).
340. T. J. Robinson, *J. Endocrinol.* **12,** 163–173 (1955).
341. T. J. Robinson, *in* "Reproduction in Domestic Animals" (H. H. Cole and P. T. Cupps, eds.), pp. 292–333. Academic Press, New York, 1959.
342. T. J. Robinson, N. W. Moore, and F. E. Binet, *J. Endocrinol.* **14,** 1–7 (1956).
343. P. G. Schinkel, *Australian J. Agr. Research* **5,** 465–469 (1954).
344. P. G. Schinkel, *Australian Vet. J.* **30,** 189–195 (1954).
345. F. A. Beach, *Ciba Found. Colloq. Endocrinol.* **3,** 3–17 (1952).

346. F. A. Beach, *in* "Nebraska Symposium on Motivation" (M. R. Jones, ed.), pp. 304–365. Williams & Wilkins, Baltimore, Maryland, 1961.
347. A. Albert, *in* "Sex and Internal Secretions" (W. C. Young, ed.), 3rd ed., pp. 304–365. Williams & Wilkins, Baltimore, Maryland, 1961.
348. W. H. Sternberg, *Am. J. Pathol.* **25**, 493–521 (1949).
348a. J. Hilliard, D. Archibald, and C. H. Sawyer, *Endocrinology* **72**, 59–66 (1963).
349. A. F. Mirsky, *J. Comp. and Physiol. Psychol.* **48**, 327–335 (1955).
350. G. Clark and H. G. Birch, *Psychosomat. Med.* **7**, 321–329 (1945).
351. G. Clark and H. G. Birch, *Bull. Can. Psychol. Assoc.* **6**, 15–18 (1946).
352. H. G. Birch and G. Clark, *Psychosomat. Med.* **8**, 320–331 (1946).
353. H. G. Birch and G. Clark, *J. Comp. and Physiol. Psychol.* **43**, 181–193 (1950).
354. F. A. Beach, *Physiol. Zoöl.* **18**, 390–402 (1945).
355. E. A. Beeman, *Physiol. Zoöl.* **20**, 373–405 (1947).
356. W. Bevan, G. W. Levy, J. M. Whitehouse, and J. M. Bevan, *Physiol. Zoöl.* **30**, 341–349 (1957).
357. J. P. Seward, *J. Comp. Psychol.* **38**, 175–197 (1945).
358. J. Uhrich, *J. Comp. Psychol.* **25**, 373–413 (1938).
359. J. P. Scott and E. Fredericson, *Physiol. Zoöl.* **24**, 273–309 (1951).
360. J. Tollman and J. A. King, *Brit. J. Animal Behav.* **4**, 147–149 (1956).
361. G. Koller, *Verhandl. deut. Zool. Ges. Freiburg* pp. 160–168 (1952).
362. G. Koller, *Zool. Anz.* (*Suppl.*) **19**, 123–132 (1956).
363. M. X. Zarrow, P. B. Sawin, S. Ross, V. H. Denenberg, D. Crary, E. D. Wilson, and A. Farooq, *J. Reprod. Fertility* **2**, 152–162 (1961).
364. P. B. Sawin, V. H. Denenberg, S. Ross, E. Hafter, and M. X. Zarrow, *Am. J. Physiol.* **198**, 1099–1102 (1960).
365. B. M. Schofield, *J. Physiol.* (*London*) **138**, 1–10 (1957).
366. M. Klein, *in* "L'Instinct dans le Comportement des Animaux et de l'Homme" (P.-P. Grassé, ed.), pp. 287–344. Masson, Paris, 1956.
367. M. X. Zarrow, P. B. Sawin, S. Ross, and V. H. Denenberg, *in* "Roots of Behavior" (E. L. Bliss, ed.), pp. 187–197. Harper (Hoeber), New York, 1962.
368. J. Labriola, *Proc. Soc. Exptl. Biol. Med.* **83**, 556–557 (1953).
369. E. Rabaud, *Bull. soc. zool. France* **46**, 73–81 (1921).
370. E. Raubaud, *J. Psychol. Norm. Pathol.* **18**, 487–495 (1921).
371. B. P. Wiesner and N. M. Sheard, "Maternal Behaviour in the Rat." Oliver and Boyd, London, 1933.
372. F. Frank, *Z. Tierpsychol.* **9**, 415–423 (1952).
373. O. Riddle, W. F. Hollander, R. A. Miller, E. L. Lahr, G. C. Smith, and H. N. Marvin, *Yearbook Carnegie Inst.* **41**, 203–211 (1942).
374. H. Allan and P. Wiles, *J. Physiol.* (*London*) **75**, 23–28 (1932).
375. J. B. Collip, H. Selye, and D. L. Thomson, *Nature* **131**, 56 (1933).
376. T. E. Rowell, *Animal Behav.* **9**, 11–15 (1961).
377. C. K. Weichert and S. Kerrigan, *Endocrinology* **30**, 741–752 (1942).
378. D. F. Lott, *J. Comp. and Physiol. Psychol.* **55**, 610–613 (1962).
379. J. Meites and C. W. Turner, *Endocrinology* **30**, 711–718 (1942).
380. J. Meites and C. W. Turner, *Research Bull. Mo. Agr. Exptl. Sta.* **No. 416**, (1948).
381. R. K. Burns, *in* "Sex and Internal Secretions" (W. C. Young, ed.), 3rd ed., pp. 76–158. Williams & Wilkins, Baltimore, Maryland, 1961.
382. F. L. Hisaw and F. L. Hisaw, Jr., *in* "Sex and Internal Secretions" (W. C.

Young, ed.), 3rd ed., pp. 556–589. Williams & Wilkins, Baltimore, Maryland, 1961.

383. D. Price and H. G. Williams-Ashman, *in* "Sex and Internal Secretions" (W. C. Young, ed.), 3rd ed., pp. 366–448. Williams & Wilkins, Baltimore, Maryland, 1961.

384. L. J. Wells, *in* "The Ovary" (Sir S. Zuckerman, ed.), Vol. II, pp. 131–153. Academic Press, New York, 1962.

385. E. Wolff, *in* "The Ovary" (Sir S. Zuckerman, ed.), Vol. II, pp. 81–129. Academic Press, New York, 1962.

386. E. Wolff, *in* "The Ovary" (Sir S. Zuckerman, ed.), Vol. II, pp. 155–178. Academic Press, New York, 1962.

387. V. Dantchakoff, *Compt. rend. acad. sci.* **204,** 195–197 (1937).

388. V. Dantchakoff, *Compt. rend. soc. biol.* **127,** 1255–1258 (1938).

389. W. Dantschakoff, *Biol. Zentr.* **58,** 302–328 (1938).

390. A. A. Gerall, *J. Comp. and Physiol. Psychol.* **56,** 92–95 (1963).

391. R. W. Goy, W. E. Bridson, and W. C. Young, *J. Comp. and Physiol. Psychol.* in press (1964).

392. D. Price, E. Ortiz, and J. J. P. Zaaijer, *Am. Zool.* (*Abstr., Proc. Am. Soc. Zool.*) **3,** 553 (1963).

392a. R. W. Goy, C. H. Phoenix, and W. C. Young, *Anat. Record* (*Abstr., Proc. Am. Assoc. Anat.*) **142,** 307 (1962).

392b. C. Revesz, D. Kernaghan, and D. Bindra, *J. Endocrinol.* **25,** 549–550 (1963).

392c. G. W. Harris, *in* "Frontiers in Brain Research" (J. D. French, ed.), pp. 191–241. Columbia Univ. Press, New York, 1962.

392d. G. W. Harris, *J. Reprod. and Fertil.* (*Abstr., Proc. Specialist Sessions on the Physiology of Reproduction, Seventh International Conference on Planned Parenthood, Singapore*) **5,** 299–300 (1963).

392e. G. W. Harris and S. Levine, *J. Physiol.* (*London*) (*Abstr., Proc. Physiol. Soc.*) **163,** 42–43 (1962).

393. A. Jost, *Arch. Anat. Microscop. Morphol. Exptl.* **39,** 577–607 (1950).

394. A. Jost, *Recent Progr. in Hormone Research* **8,** 379–418 (1953).

395. A. Jost, *in* "Third Conference on Gestation" (C. A. Villee, ed.), pp. 129–171. Josiah Macy, Jr. Foundation, New York, 1956.

396. D. Price, *in* "Third Conference on Gestation" (C. A. Villee, ed.), pp. 173–186. Josiah Macy, Jr. Foundation, New York, 1956.

396a. R. E. Whalen, *J. Comp. and Physiol. Psychol.* in press (1964).

396b. K. L. Grady and C. H. Phoenix, *Am. Zool.* (*Abstr., Proc. Am. Soc. Zool.*) **3,** 482–483 (1963).

397. J. M. Essenberg, *Biol. Bull.* **51,** 98–111 (1926).

398. E. Friess, *Arch. Entwicklungsmech. Organ.* **129,** 255–355 (1933).

399. J. W. Harms, *Zool. Anz.* **67,** 67–79 (1926).

400. M.-T. Régnier, *Bull. biol. France et Belg.* **72,** 385–493 (1938).

401. H. Breider, *Biol. Zentr.* **62,** 187–195 (1942).

402. W. J. Eversole, *Endocrinology* **28,** 603–610 (1941).

403. Y. K. Okada and H. Yamashita, *J. Fac. Sci. Imp. Univ. Tokyo, Sect. IV* **6,** 383–427 (1944).

404. M.-T. Régnier, *Compt. rend. soc. biol.* **136,** 202–203 (1942).

405. P. Kaiser and E. Schmidt, *Zool. Anz.* **146,** 66–73 (1951).

406. G. K. Noble and K. F. Kumpf, *Abstr., Proc. Am. Soc. Zool. Anat. Record* **70,** 97 (1937).

407. L. Gallien, *Mem. Soc. Endocrinol.* **4**, 188–204 (1955).
408. L. Gallien, *Bull. biol. France et Belg.* **78**, 257–359 (1944).
409. L. Gallien, *Compt. rend. acad. sci.* **240**, 913–915 (1955).
410. G. Pincus and T. F. Hopkins, *Endocrinology* **62**, 112–118 (1958).
411. V. Dantchakoff, *Compt. rend. acad. sci.* **202**, 879–881 (1936).
412. L. V. Domm and D. E. Davis, *Proc. Soc. Exptl. Biol. Med.* **48**, 665–667 (1941).
413. L. Kaufman, *Ann. Univ. Mariae Curie-Sklodowska, Lublin-Polonia: Sect. E*, pp. 25–42 (1954); *Abstr., World's Poultry Sci. J.* **12**, 41–42 (1956).
414. V. Dantchakoff, *Compt. rend. acad. sci.* **202**, 1112–1114 (1936).
415. V. Dantchakoff, *Compt. rend. soc. biol.* **124**, 235–238 (1937).
416. G. W. Harris, "Neural Control of the Pituitary Gland." Arnold, London, 1955.
417. C. A. Pfeiffer, *Am. J. Anat.* **58**, 195–225 (1936).
418. J. W. Everett, C. H. Sawyer, and J. E. Markee, *Endocrinology* **44**, 234–250 (1949).
418a. M. Florkin, "L'évolution Biochimique." Masson, Paris, 1944.
419. P. B. Medawar, *Symposia Soc. Exptl. Biol.* **7**, pp. 320–338 (1953).
420. F. A. Beach, *in* "Behavior and Evolution" (A. Roe and G. G. Simpson, eds.), pp. 81–102. Yale Univ. Press, New Haven, Connecticut, 1958.
421. W. Craig, *J. Animal Behav.* **4**, 121–133 (1914).
422. M. W. Schein and E. B. Hale, *Animal Behav.* **7**, 189–200 (1959).
423. D. G. M. Wood-Gush, *Poultry Sci.* **37**, 30–33 (1958).
424. S. Altmann, *in* "Roots of Behavior" (E. L. Bliss, ed.), pp. 277–285. Harper (Hoeber), New York, 1962.
425. F. A. E. Crew, *Proc. Roy. Soc.* **B95**, 256–278 (1923).
426. F. A. E. Crew, *Quart. Rev. Biol.* **2**, 427–441 (1927).
427. K. Ponse, *Compt. rend. soc. biol.* **92**, 582–583 (1925).
428. O. Riddle, *Am. Naturalist* **58**, 167–181 (1924).
429. H. A. Carr, *Carnegie Inst. Wash. Publ.* **No. 257**, Vol. III (1919).
430. E. Shorr, G. N. Papanicolaou, and B. F. Stimmel, *Proc. Soc. Exptl. Biol. Med.* **38**, 759–762 (1938).
431. A. A. Loeser, *Brit. Med. J.* **1**, 479–482 (1940).
432. U. J. Salmon, *J. Clin. Endocrinol.* **1**, 162–179 (1941).
433. U. J. Salmon and S. H. Geist, *J. Clin. Endocrinol.* **3**, 235–238 (1943).
434. R. B. Greenblatt, *J. Am. Med. Assoc.* **121**, 17–24 (1943).
435. S. Abel, *Am. J. Obstet. Gynecol.* **49**, 327–342 (1945).
436. A. C. Carter, E. J. Cohen, and E. Shorr, *Vitamins and Hormones* **5**, 317–391 (1947).
437. G. L. Foss, *Lancet* **i**, 667–669 (1951).
438. S. E. Waxenburg, M. G. Drellich, and A. M. Sutherland, *J. Clin. Endocrinol. and Metabolism* **19**, 193–202 (1959).
439. R. Hertz, R. K. Meyer, and M. A. Spielman, *Endocrinology* **21**, 533–535 (1937).
440. F. A. Kincl and R. I. Dorfman, *Acta Endocrinol.* **38**, 257–261 (1961).
441. W. E. Knox, V. H. Auerbach, and E. C. C. Lin, *Physiol. Revs.* **36**, 164–254 (1956).

CHAPTER 5

The Comparative Biochemistry of Antibiosis and Antibiotics

MAURICE WELSCH

Laboratory of General and Medical Microbiology, University of Liège and C.N.P.E.M., Liège, Belgium

I. General Considerations

About 1942, the need was felt for a general name covering the many and diverse substances that were then being extracted in increasing number from microbial cultures and found to possess the capacity of either killing or inhibiting the growth of specific microorganisms. A particular designation was especially required as a heading for the section dealing with them in scientific abstracting journals.

The name antibiotic was proposed by Waksman (*1, 2*) and rapidly obtained wide recognition. In fact, none of the other names proposed, such as mycoines or fongines, ever was in serious competition with it.

Antibiotic, as a substantive, does not seem to have been used previously (*3, 4*), although, as an adjective, it appeared occasionally in the scientific literature and, in fact, was even defined in Gould's medical dictionary (*5*) as "pertaining to antibiosis, tending to destroy life."

A. ANTIBIOSIS

From its Greek roots (*αντι*: against; *βιος*: life), antibiosis might cover all the phenomena involving the very many and extremely diverse agents that can be harmful to life. Vuillemin (*6*), however, coined the word by analogy with symbiosis which, by general assent, covers only biological associations that are, or that we believe to be, useful to the partners involved. Similarly, antibiosis was meant to designate a kind of natural relationship which frequently exists between living beings and makes one of them harmful to the other. Even with this more restricted meaning, it still comprises a large number of different biological phenomena, ranging from the obvious destruction of living beings by others to more subtle and complex examples of competition at all levels of the biosphere.

So diverse are the manifestations of antibiosis, so different the mechanisms at play in each case, that the need for a common name covering all the possible phenomena involved was never acutely felt. In fact, antibiosis was, originally, more or less synonymous with biological competition, biological antagonism, struggle for life, and so on. None of these expressions ever won undisputed supremacy leading to the eradication of the others from scientific vocabulary. Antibiosis was probably even less used than any of the others.

And there were good reasons for this, since, from the very start, the word antibiosis was endowed with some vagueness and early interpreted differently by various biologists. Thus, for Vuillemin, close biological associations with harmful effects, such as those observed in many instances of parasitism, were not to be included in antibiosis. But, on the contrary, for Ward (*7*), who, some ten years later, adopted Vuillemin's word, antibiosis precisely designated more particularly the intimate and noxious associations between host and parasite and thus became the exact antonym of symbiosis in its strictest sense.

Little used between 1900 and 1928, the word antibiosis was then revived by Papacostas and Gaté (*8*), who gave it a much more restricted meaning. Discarding predation and parasitism, they used it to designate only those associations between microorganisms living side by side which result in harmful effects for one or several of the partners involved, whether it be their death, the inhibition of their growth and multiplication, or the impairment of any one of their "normal" activities. To the microbial associations which, conversely, result in so-called favorable effects, such as an increase of growth rate, of the total yield, or of any biochemical activity, they applied the name stimulation. Later on, probiosis was suggested as a better one and many new words were introduced to designate particular instances of either antibiosis or stimulation (*9*).

Papacostas and Gaté visualized antibiosis as a somewhat artificial phenomenon, occurring in culture media under experimental conditions. They thought that it was purely fortuitous and devoid of any biological significance. To them, the production by a microorganism of a chemical harmful to another microbe (a case of antibiosis) was in no way comparable to the production by a snake of the venom with which it kills its prey (a case of biological competition). Oddly enough, the same example of the venomous snake was one of those selected by Vuillemin to illustrate his own concept of antibiosis.

If Papacostas and Gaté did not speculate about the possible significance of antibiosis in nature, their medical training led them to investigate mixed infections in animals and man and, in particular, to examine the principles and mechanisms of bacteriotherapy, a practice for which some hope was held at the time. Although many of the *in vivo* experiments were initiated on the basis of antibiosis or stimulation as observed *in vitro*, the authors felt, inconsequentially as it may appear at first sight, that different words were needed to designate, respectively, those instances in which the introduction of an additional microorganism was either favorable or detrimental to the infected host. They were in fact aware that the outcome of a mixed infection, as compared to that of a pure one, is not simply the result of antibiosis or stimulation occurring *in vivo* as they may *in vitro*. Antagonism and synergism were thus introduced to indicate, respectively, the more and the less favorable outcome for the host when doubly rather than singly infected. This, sound as it may be in principle, was unfortunately a source of confusion. First, Papacostas and Gaté considered usefulness and harmfulness with respect to a microorganism when dealing with mixed cultures (stimulation *versus* antibiosis), but with respect to the host when studying mixed infections (antagonism *versus* synergism). Second, the word antagonism, borrowed from de Bary (*10*), had been used by Emmerich (*11*) with exactly the same meaning as antibiosis by Papacostas and Gaté.

It is evident that the word antibiosis was used by different scientists to cover observations of the same general biological significance, but that each author displayed a tendency to restrict somewhat its meaning in his own way. Thus, the rambling of a predaceous animal over its hunting grounds and the killing of its victims, the destruction of vegetal species by herbivorous animals, the laying of traps by carnivorous plants, ensnaring fungi, and various animal species, are clear examples of antibiosis in Vuillemin's sense of the word. And so must, therefore, be the corresponding activities when exercised by man and brought to their highest degree of efficiency thanks to his intellectual power, such as the use of more and more deadly weapons developed through ages for hunting and war (war, by the way, being an example of isoantibiosis) or of the ever more efficient machinery devised to destroy plant life for nutritional or industrial purposes.

But the production by a parasite of a poisonous substance that destroys the cells or tissues of its host or paralyzes its defense mechanisms, the elaboration by the host of agents, whether preexisting or specifically induced, that kill or impede the multiplication of a parasite, the secretion by a plant or a microorganism, whether in nature or in artificial culture, of chemicals that diffuse in its neighborhood and prevent its being invaded by some other organisms, either because they are killed or their growth is inhibited, are also biologically related phenomena falling within the general concept of antibiosis. And here again, there is no reason not to include the corresponding specifically human activities, such as the use of synthetic chemicals or industrially manufactured biological products to obtain the willful destruction of harmful parasites, disease-transmitting arthropods, or other undesirable plants and animals.

A comparative analysis of the diverse manifestations of antibiosis would thus include problems pertaining to extremely various fields of science, ranging from sociology, psychology, and animal behaviorism to animal and plant physiology and to microbial biochemistry. It is therefore obvious that, unfortunately, the time has not yet come to undertake a comparative study of the biochemical basis of antibiosis in its broadest sense.

B. Antibiotics

When the word antibiotic was used by Waksman and his co-workers, starting around 1942, it was with the explicit statement that the word, derived from Vuillemin's antibiosis, was to be applied only to certain naturally occurring antimicrobial substances having a biological origin.

The definition, as fully given for the first time in 1945, was not altogether satisfactory (*12*), and a better worded and more concise one was proposed two years later: "*Antibiotic* or *antibiotic substance.* A chemical substance produced by microorganisms which has the capacity to inhibit the growth of bacteria and other microorganisms and even to destroy them" (*13*).

Compared with Vuillemin's idea of antibiosis, the derived word antibiotic, as defined by Waksman, remains well within the limits conveyed by the original concept, but with a more restricted meaning. Whereas antibiosis was meant to cover harmful biological relationships without specifying the nature of the mechanism involved, antibiotic applies only to chemical agents. Whereas antibiosis was meant to cover harmful interrelationships between any kind of living beings, antibiotic, rather in keeping with Papacostas and Gaté's narrower use of the word antibiosis, applies only to substances produced by, and noxious for, microorganisms.

Antibiotic is thus originally a word which defines sharply and adequately a class of chemical substances produced by microorganisms.

Obviously, the choice of the word and the admission that it was inspired by Vuillemin's antibiosis, implied that, initially and at first sight at least, antibiotics were regarded, or could conceivably be regarded, as the chemical agents responsible for microbial antagonism. Although later on their actual role in nature was much questioned (*14*), it is now well known that some antibiotics are produced in the soil and play a role in the evolution of the microflora (*15*).

However, Waksman's definition cannot be taken literally, and, from the start, the notion of antibiotic was endowed with some unavoidable vagueness. Common products of microbial metabolism, such as alcohols, simple organic acids, and many other substances, are able, when in sufficient concentration, to suppress the growth of, or kill, certain microorganisms. Should these common biological products be called antibiotics? To avoid the difficulty, two additional properties were tentatively introduced into the definition of an antibiotic (*16*), namely, the capacity to act at a low concentration and selectivity of action. Unfortunately, these properties cannot be defined in a precise quantitative way and their use introduces a subjective element of appreciation which rather blurs the notion of antibiotic. It is therefore just as well to rely on common sense to discard from the class of antibiotics the "common" metabolic products, whatever this may mean, which have antimicrobial activities.

But more serious difficulties were soon encountered when it became obvious that substances having properties similar to those of the antibiotics, as defined by Waksman, were produced by macroscopic fungi, higher plants, and even animals, especially when it was established that identical antibiotics can be produced by widely different living beings, and further when antibiotics, in the strictest sense, were produced by chemical synthesis.

The meaning of antibiotic was therefore early stretched far beyond Waksman's definition. The notion of microbiological origin was replaced by the broader one of biological origin and the definition became: chemical substances possessing antimicrobial activities that are produced by higher plants or animals as well as by microorganisms. Then, taken literally, it includes among the antibiotics a number of agents, for instance plant products such as many alkaloids, which are unlikely to play any part in natural antibiosis. But this is a minor difficulty when compared with the fact that the new definition also includes in the class of antibiotics all the chemical armamentarium involved in the mechanisms directly operating against microorganisms in natural and acquired immunity. Although this inclusion brings us back closer to the original broad notion of antibiosis, it would probably be, at the present time, a troublesome cause of confusion, inasmuch as its unavoidable consequence would be a splitting of immunology into two parts according to whether the substances studied do or do not have, directly or indirectly, some antimicrobial property.

A further step was taken when the name antibiotic was applied not only to naturally occurring antimicrobial substances but also to synthetic chemicals exerting a noxious effect upon microorganisms, even though they were not copies of natural models (*17a*). Physicians have quite often adopted this meaning of the word while restricting it, on the other hand, to chemicals that have a low enough toxicity for animal cells and organs so that they can be used for the therapy of microbial diseases. Certainly, the inclusion in the class of antibiotics of substances artificially produced by man's unique intellectual abilities and used by him to destroy inimical organisms is well in keeping with the original broad concept of antibiosis.

The final step to be taken, after which nothing would be left of Waksman's definition except the all-important provision that antibiotics are chemical substances, was to replace the property of antimicrobial activity by the more general one of toxicity for any kind of cell or organism. After such a broadening of the definition, the whole of toxicology would fall within the province of antibiotics, among which would be included a large number of substances playing certainly no part in any natural manifestation of antibiosis. In practice, the use of the word was extended only to include substances able to destroy not only microorganisms, but animal parasites, viruses, or neoplastic cells as well. Although there is evidently no *a priori* reason for antimicrobial properties to be associated in a given chemical with antiviral or anticancer properties, the success of antibiotics in the chemotherapy of bacterial and fungal diseases was an incentive for the search of biologically produced agents potentially usable for the treatment of virus diseases (*17b*) and cancer (*17c*). If relatively few substances of practical importance have so far been thus obtained, the number of antiviral and anticancer agents already recognized is far from negligible.

Exactly as in the case of the word antibiosis, the word antibiotic has been used by various authors with widely different meanings. However, it has always been applied only to chemical substances of various origin, possessing a more or less extensive range of toxicity. Therefore, whether one considers either their production by, or their action upon, living beings, the problems involved are always essentially of a biochemical nature.

C. The Comparative Point of View

If antibiotics, in principle, are a fit subject for a comparative biochemical study, one should, however, recognize that a number of difficulties are to be expected, some of them being the result of the fragmentary character of our present knowledge but others being of a more fundamental nature.

The biochemical problems to be considered fall under two main headings: those pertaining to the action of antibiotics upon sensitive cells and those concerned with their biosynthesis.

1. *Action of Antibiotics*

The main point of interest is the comparative study of the biochemical mechanisms which, in each particular case, are responsible for the antibiotic effects observed. The study should be undertaken with a view to explain: first, modes of action in relation to the chemical nature of the antibiotic; second, effects observed in different organisms in relation to their cell structure and biochemical activities, the problems of specificity, or natural resistance, being here included.

Intimately connected with the main question, are the problems pertaining to the biochemical basis responsible for the acquisition of resistance. The many known examples of cross resistance should be stressed since they occur, not only between chemically related antibiotics, but also between substances that are structurally quite different, pointing probably, when such is the case, to a similarity in mode of action.

For such a study, the meaning of antibiotic could well be broadened to include synthetic antimicrobial agents, at least insofar as what is known about them is likely to throw additional light on the problems raised by the naturally occurring antibiotics.

The effects of antibiotics upon sensitive cells are many and diverse. They may vary not only with the nature of the antibiotic and that of the organism submitted to its action, but also, for a given system, with concentration and experimental conditions. A wealth of information is thus available, but unfortunately, it is extremely difficult to coordinate. Our knowledge of the modes of action of antibiotics, to say nothing of their mechanisms of action, is at present very sketchy. In fact, only a minor fraction of all the known antibiotics has been subjected to that type of investigation, and in a very few cases only has it been possible to recognize a primary biochemical lesion (*18, 19*).

It follows that the fundamental reasons why each antibiotic displays a characteristic spectrum of action remain generally poorly understood. Broadly speaking, natural resistance may be due to: (*a*) inactivation of the antibiotic—the penicillino-resistance of species or strains producing penicillinase is a case in point; (*b*) nonpenetration of the antibiotic into the cell or inability to reach the sensitive receptor; (*c*) absence from, or nonessentiality for, the cell of the specifically sensitive biochemical system.

Similarly, the biochemical variations primarily responsible for the specific acquisition of resistance to an antibiotic remain, on the whole, obscure although numerous biochemical differences have been reported between a sensitive mother strain and the derived resistant ones. On the contrary, the genetic aspect of the problem has progressed more satisfactorily. The occurrence of spontaneous mutation followed by selection is now an experimentally established fact, and the main assumptions required by the theory—variation of resistance by discontinuous steps and polygenic control of resistance—have been corroborated by direct transformation, transduction, and recombination experiments (*20–23*).

Much remains to be done, however, before one could hope to propose fundamental correlations either between the mode and specificity of action of antibiotics on the one hand, their chemical nature on the other, or between the sensitivity of cells to antibiotics and their biochemical structures and activities.

2. *Biosynthesis of Antibiotics*

A first problem of interest is the production of antibiotics in relation to taxonomy. Unfortunately, the search for antibiotics has been conducted quite unevenly among different groups of organisms. Relatively little is known of "animal" antibiotics, from which we exclude the antimicrobial agents generally studied by the immunologist. Although antibiotics have been extracted in great number from higher plants and large fungi, comparatively few of them have been chemically identified and studied. Even among microorganisms, some groups, for instance the actinomycetes and the bacilli, have been much more thoroughly explored than others and, on the whole, the antibiotics which they have yielded have been more adequately and minutely studied. But such a situation is not necessarily an indication that antibiotic production by actinomycetes or bacilli is more frequent than by other bacteria, by fungi, by higher plants, or by animals, but rather that the former organisms have thus far given more useful antibiotics than the latter.

The information available is thus so biased that any generalization that would be deduced from the facts gathered to date is apt to be rather misleading. However, it is permissible to stress a few important well-established points: (*a*) a given organism may well produce more than one antibiotic, either simultaneously or one at a time according to the prevailing environmental conditions; (*b*) a given antibiotic may be produced by different organisms, sometimes closely related but sometimes taxonomically very distant; (*c*) antibiotics belonging to a same chemical type are sometimes highly characteristic of a definite taxonomic group, but, in other cases, quite unrelated species produce very similar or even identical compounds. A comparative study of the biochemical steps involved in the biosynthesis of identical or related substances by different organisms would be of great interest, but few relevant data are as yet available.

A second point of interest is the comparison of the chemical structure of different antibiotics or, more fundamental no doubt, of the metabolic pathways leading to their biosynthesis. Such a study should obviously include biochemically related metabolites having no antibiotic activity. But this raises a fundamental difficulty, since such substances are possibly biosynthesized simultaneously with, or under suitable conditions instead of, the antibiotic but remain unnoticed because our techniques of detection are not fit to reveal their presence.

It is now well known, however, that many antibiotics occur as families of closely related compounds endowed with quantitatively, and sometimes qualitatively, different antimicrobial properties, the group often comprising also members devoid of biological activity.

The diversity of chemical structures found among antibiotics was long a subject of bewilderment until the efforts of Chain (*24*), of Regna (*25*), and of Abraham and Newton (*26*) succeeded in introducing order into chaos. They have shown that a great number of antibiotics can be related, in whole or in part, structurally or biogenetically, to the common building blocks of living matter such as sugars, amino acids, fatty acids, and heterocyclic compounds. Many of them have been related to important metabolites (*27*). Antibiotics have thus lost their somewhat mysterious character; according to Bu'Lock (*28*), they should be classified, together with innumerable biologically inert substances, among the secondary metabolites, these being defined as molecules characterized by their restricted distribution and the fact that they have no obvious function in general metabolism. Antibiotics thus appear as further examples of the extreme diversity of variations on a few fundamental themes which has been recognized in biochemical structures and processes since the pioneer work of Kluyver, founder of comparative biochemistry.

II. Comparative Study of Individual Antibiotics

Owing to the difficulties mentioned above, we shall not undertake a separate study of each one of the main points of interest described. Instead, we shall endeavor to stress the structural and biogenetic (established or assumed) similarities of various antibiotics, pointing out whenever possible the other known facts of interest to comparative biochemistry.

Antibiotic will be understood in agreement with Waksman's definition, slightly extended to include natural substances with antiviral or anticancer properties. However, occasional reference will be made to antibiotic agents not having a microbial origin and to metabolites possessing no antibiotic activities.

The complexity of the subject as well as the limited space available will suffice to explain that our review has not the ambition of being exhaustive. Lack of space also forbids us to cite in each case the complete list of producing organisms and the numerous synonyms in more or less current use. Similarly, we have been compelled to curtail direct reference to the original literature and shall refer the reader to standard treatises (*13, 29–35*) and recent reviews (*36–45a*) for complementary bibliographical information.*

A. Antibiotics Wholly or Partially Derivable from Sugars

Sugars and sugar derivatives are present in many antibiotics, some of which, all produced by streptomycetes, are in fact wholly made up of such substances and therefore akin to the oligosaccharides.

1. *Oligosaccharide Antibiotics*

Trehalosamine (I) is a typical disaccharide produced by a strain resembling *Streptomyces lavendulae.* Kanamycin (*45b*) and kanamycin B (II), from *S. kanamyceticus;* streptomycin (III), from *S. griseus, S. bikiniensis, S. olivaceus,* and *S. mashuensis;* dihydrostreptomycin, from *S. humidus;* and hydroxystreptomycin (reticulin), from *S. rubrireticuli* and *S. griseocarneus,* are trisaccharides. Streptomycin B (mannosidostreptomycin), from *S. griseus,* and paromomycin (IV), from *S. rimosus* f. *paromomyceticus,* are tetrasaccharides.

Numerous biochemical modifications have been reported in microorganisms submitted to the action of antibiotics from the streptomycin group. The fundamental mode of action of these agents remains, however, unknown. Recent work of Erdös and collaborators (*46, 47*) indi-

* The survey of literature pertaining to this essay was concluded in August, 1962.

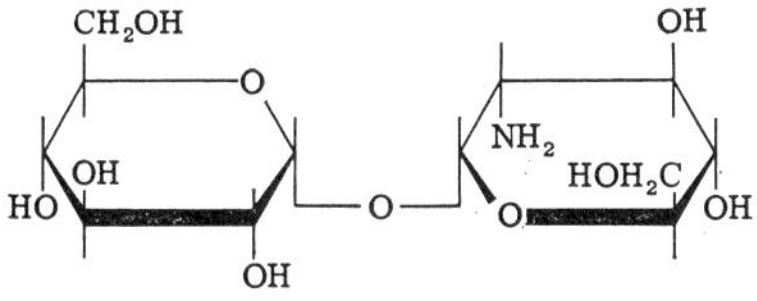

α-D-glucose α-D-glucosamine

Trehalosamine

(I)

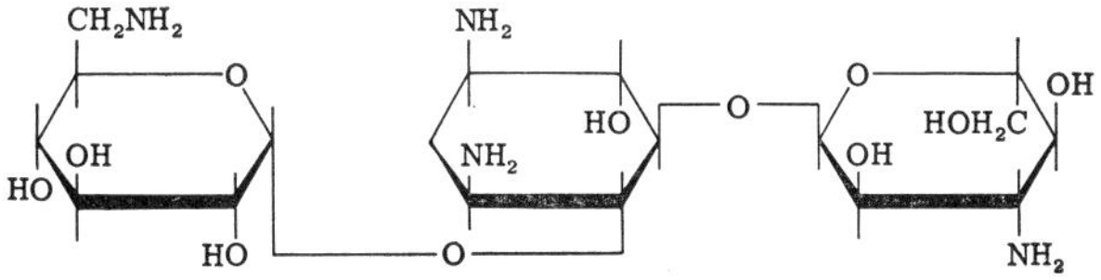

6-glucosamine 2-deoxystreptamine kanosamine

Kanamycin[a]

(II)

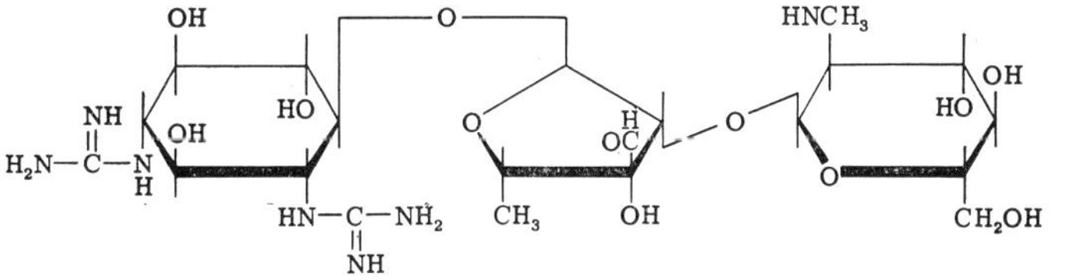

streptidine streptose *N*-methyl-L-glucosamine

streptobiosamine

Streptomycin[b]

(III)

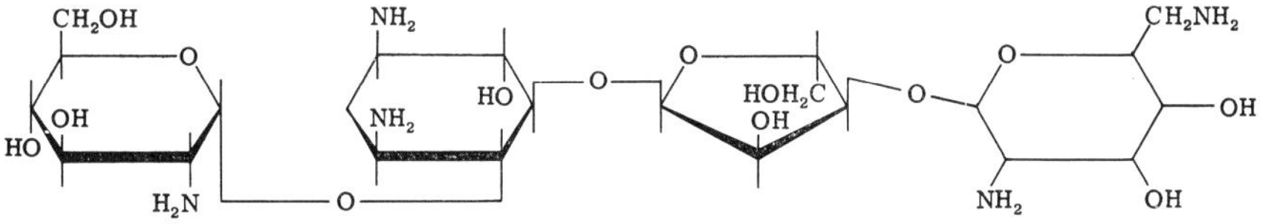

α-D-glucosamine 2-deoxystreptamine D-ribose paromose

paromamine paromobiosamine

Paromomycin

(IV)

[a] In kanamycin B, 6-glucosamine is replaced by an undetermined ninhydrin-positive compound.

[b] In dihydrostreptomycin, the CHO of streptose is replaced by CH_2OH and, in hydroxystreptomycin, its CH_3 is replaced by CH_2OH. In mannosidostreptomycin, β-D-mannose is linked to *N*-methyl-L-glucosamine.

cates that dihydrostreptomycin inhibits the transfer of amino acids from ribonucleic acid (RNA) to protein. However, according to Rosano *et al.* (*48*), streptomycin would interfere with RNA metabolism, with the result that treated cells excrete 5′-nucleotides. The same observation, reported by Anand *et al.* (*49*), is taken as evidence of damage to the cytoplasmic membrane, which may be fatal in itself (*50a*) or allow the penetration of the antibiotic into the cell with lethal consequences (*50b*). However, the leakage observed in streptomycin-treated *Escherichia coli* was not found, under similar conditions, in *Staphylococcus aureus* (*Micrococcus pyogenes* var. *aureus*), and the osmotic pressure of protoplasts from streptomycin-inhibited cells of *Escherichia coli* and *Bacillus megaterium* was not significantly different from that of normal cells (*51a*).

The bactericidal effect of streptomycin is much reduced under anaerobic conditions, but nothing indicates that the site of action of the antibiotic is a system more essential to cells growing aerobically than to cells growing anaerobically. It rather seems that the uptake of streptomycin is dependent upon aerobic respiration and there is a correlation between the amount of antibiotic irreversibly bound by the cell and its sensitivity (*51b*).

There is some evidence for the localization of streptomycin sensitivity in the ribosomes (*51c,d*), where the antibiotic might interfere with polypeptide synthesis (*51e*), possibly by "triggering" a depolymerization of ribonucleic acid (*51f*). This effect, which is obtained with low concentrations not only of streptomycin, but also of kanamycin and neomycin, is reversed by higher concentrations of the same antibiotics or by spermine. The protective action appears to be associated with the basicity of the substances used and is specifically antagonized by phosphate ions (*51g*). It seems, however, that ribonucleic acid breakdown is a secondary rather than a fundamental effect of streptomycin since its inhibition by magnesium does not simultaneously reverse the bactericidal action. It has been proposed that streptomycin would interfere with a function of intracellular magnesium and polyamines necessary to maintain the integrity of ribosomes (*51h*).

On the basis of observations showing that streptomycin-dependent mutants and sensitive (but not resistant) cells in the presence of the antibiotic excrete an excess of valine* and leucine, it has been suggested

* Bragg and Polglase have recently confirmed the excess production of L-valine by a streptomycin-dependent mutant of *Escherichia coli* growing aerobically in a glucose medium. They also found that this organism accumulated lactic acid when grown in a nitrogen atmosphere [P. D. Bragg and W. J. Polglase, *J. Bacteriol.* **84**, 370–374 (1962)].

that the antibacterial action of streptomycin might be explained by the blocking of CoA-SH which is known to play a part in the metabolism of the two amino acids. This assumption is also in agreement with the reversal of streptomycin action by pantothenate (*51i*).

Experiments showing an inhibitory effect of chloramphenicol upon the lethal action of streptomycin have led to the assumption that it is a two-stage process. The first phase, chloramphenicol-sensitive, would be the streptomycin-induced synthesis of a new protein necessary for bactericidal action (*51j*).

Neomycin B is associated with neomycin C in complexes variously known as neomycins, streptothricin B, fradiomycins, etc., produced by *S. fradiae, S. albogriseus,* and *Streptomyces* spp. (*51k*). Both contain a moiety, neomycin A or neamine, which comprises a diaminohexose and 2-deoxystreptamine (see II). In addition to neamine, they yield, upon degradation, a characteristic disaccharide, neobiosamine B or C, which is made up of D-ribose and a specific diaminohexose (neosamine B or C). They are therefore also tetrasaccharides. So, finally, is hydroxymycin, from *S. paucisporogenes,* which yields pseudo-neamine, itself made up of 2-deoxystreptamine and D-glucosamine, and another disaccharide comprising a pentose and a diaminohexose.

2. *Glycosidic Antibiotics*

In many other antibiotics, sugars and/or sugar derivatives are associated with an aglycon moiety of greater or lesser importance and of very variable nature.

For instance, it is a hydroxy fatty acid, saturated in ustilagic acids (V) from *Ustilago zeae* and pyolipic acid (VI) from *Pseudomonas pyocyanea,* unsaturated in nemotinic acid xyloside (VII) from basidiomycete B-841. In elaiomycin (VIII), from *Streptomyces gelaticus,* an amine is linked to methyl-2,4-dideoxy-2-aminotetroside. The aglycon moiety of homomycin (IX) and of the related or identical hygromycin A (*S. hygroscopicus, S. noboritoensis*) is a substituted cinnamic acid. In the related but simpler hygromycin B (*51l,m*), $C_{15}H_{28}O_{10}N_2$, one finds D-talose (IXb). The related sugar, 6-deoxy-L-talose, was found in the cell wall of *Actinomyces bovis* (*51n*), 6-deoxy-D-talose in a capsular polysaccharide from a gram-negative bacterium (*51p*), and 2-amino-2,6-dideoxy-L-talose in pneumosamine (*51q*).

Several antibiotics are typical nucleosides. They are supposed to interfere with synthesis of nucleic acids as a result of their competition for enzymes with the normal metabolites of which they are structural analogs (*52, 53a*). In some of them, adenine is linked to the sugar moiety: angustose or L-2-ketofucopyranose (X) in angustmycin A (S.

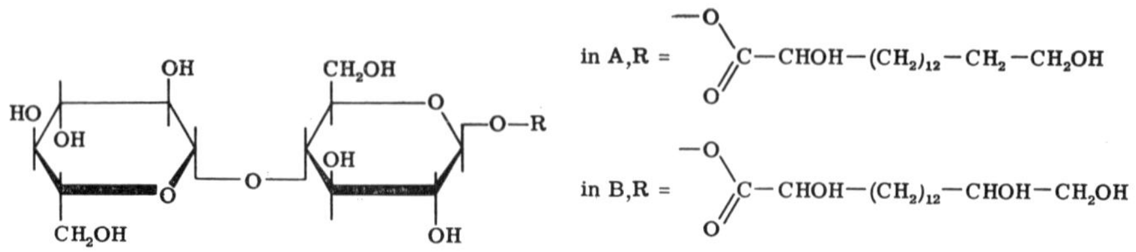

β-cellobiose

(ustilic acids)

Ustilagic acids A and B

(V)

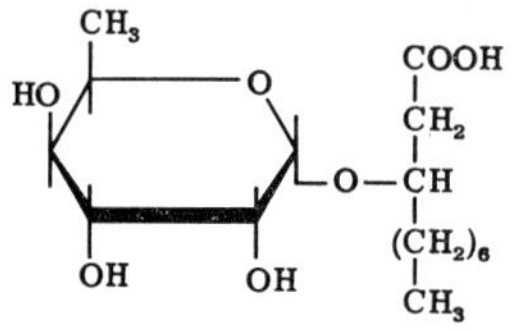

D-rhamnose

Pyolipic acid

(VI)

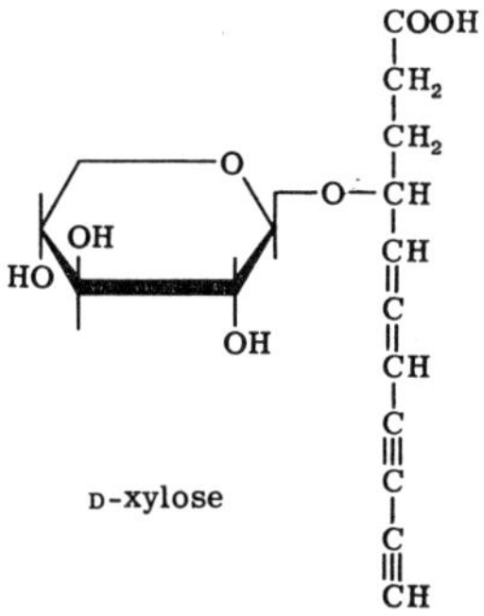

D-xylose

Nemotinic acid xyloside

(VII)

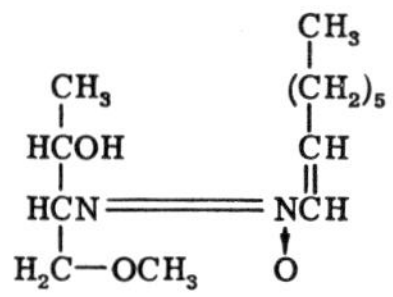

Elaiomycin

(VIII)

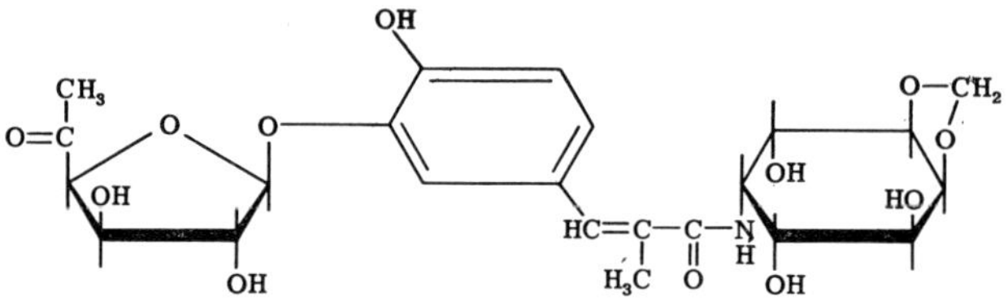

5-keto-6-deoxyarabohexose

neoinosamine-2
(with a methylene dioxy bridge)

Homomycin

(IX)

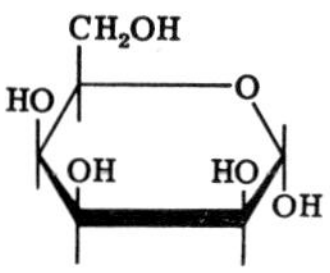

D-Talose

(IXb)

hygroscopicus, especially var. *angustmyceticus* and *decoyimine*); D-psicose (XI) in three closely related substances produced by streptomycetes —antibiotic U-9586, psicofuranine, and angustmycin C, the first two showing antibacterial and anticancer properties *in vivo* (*53b*), the last one being antibiotically inactive; cordycepose (XII) in cordycepin from

Cordyceps militaris; the sulfamic ester of an unidentified hexose ($C_6H_{10}O_5$—OSO_2NH_2) in nucleocidin from *Streptomyces calvus.* The common pentose D-ribose is linked to purine in nebularin, which is produced by *Agaricus nebularis* and several strains of streptomycetes, and to 4-aminopyrrolo-(2,3-*d*)-pyrimidine in the closely related streptomycete antibiotics tubercidin (XIII), toyocamycin (*54a*) from *S. albus* and *S. toyocaensis,* unamycin B from *S. fungicidicus,* monilin from *S. sakaensis,* and vengicide from *S. vendargensis.* In puromycin (XIV), from *S. alboniger,* 3-amino-3-deoxy-β-D-ribose is linked to 6-dimethylaminopurine (*54b*) and to *O*-methyl-L-tyrosine. This antiprotozoal and anticancer antibiotic is known to block a late stage of protein synthesis (*55a–55e*), possibly by competing with RNA-aminoacyl complexes and

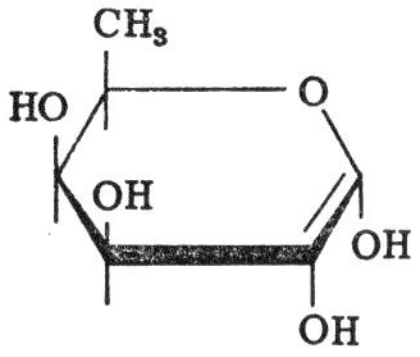

Angustose (X)

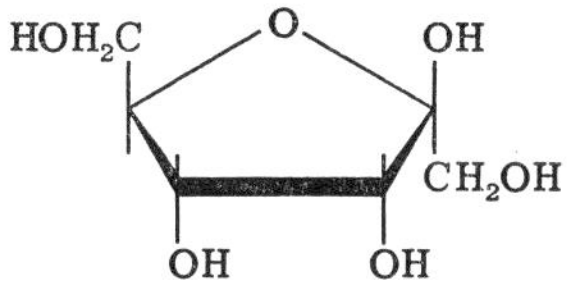

D-Psicose (XI)

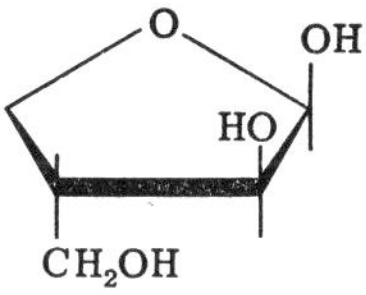

Cordycepose (XII)

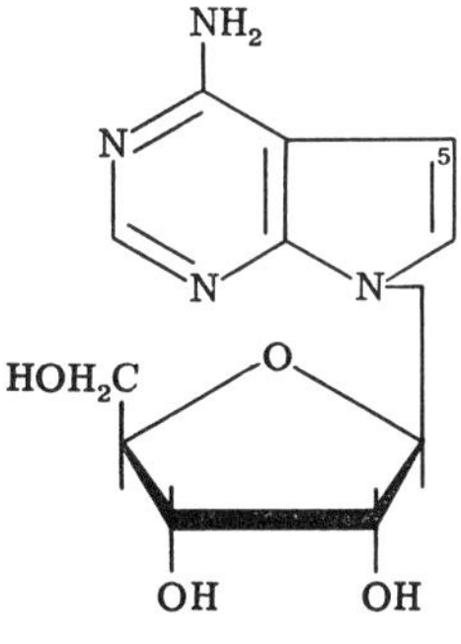

6-dimethylaminopurine

D-3-aminoribose

O-methyltyrosine

Tubercidin[a] (XIII)

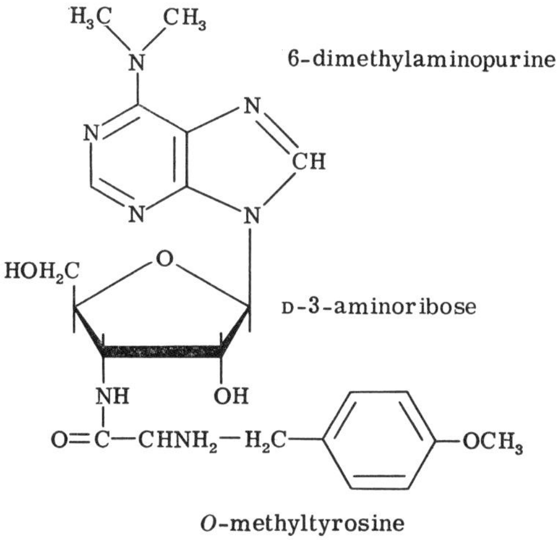

Puromycin (XIV)

[a] In the related toyocamycin, there is an additional CN group in position 5.

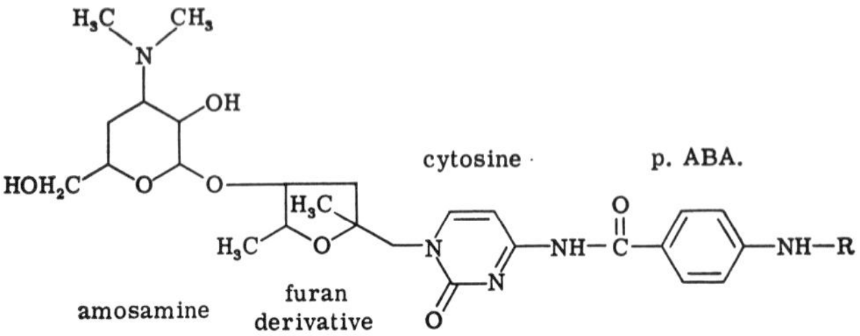

amosamine
furan derivative
cytosine
p. ABA.

Amicetin[a]
(XV)

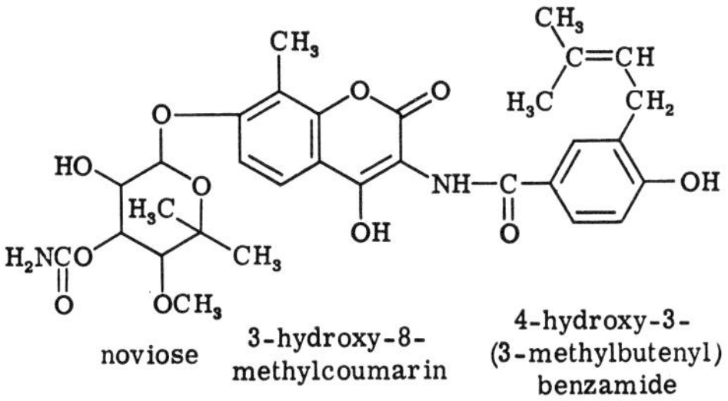

noviose
3-hydroxy-8-methylcoumarin
4-hydroxy-3-(3-methylbutenyl) benzamide

Novobiocin
(XVI)

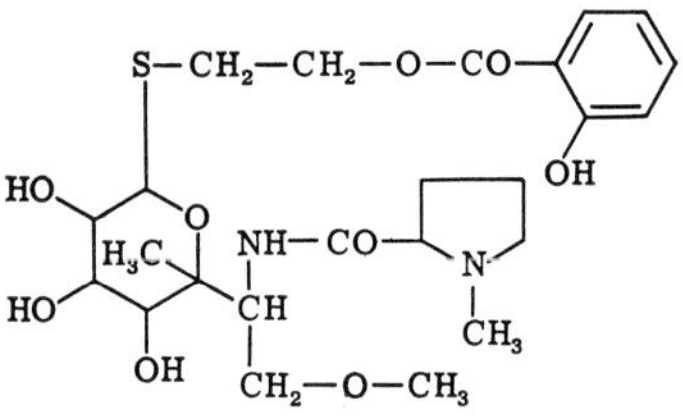

Celesticetin I
(XVII)

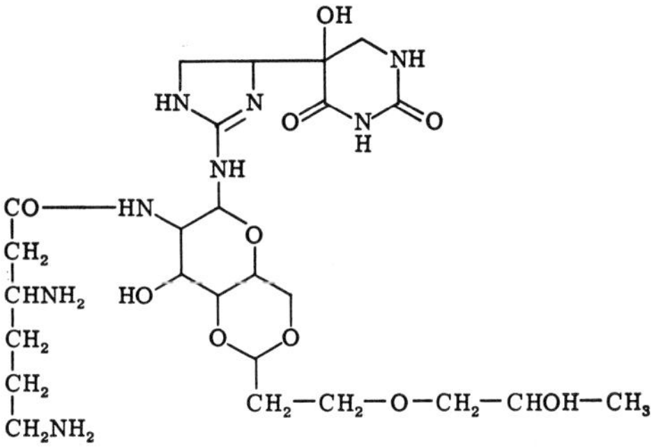

Racemomycin O
(XVIII)

[a] In amicetin A: R = CO—C(CH$_3$)NH$_2$—CH$_2$OH (α-methyl-D-serine). In amicetin B: R = H. Bamicetin is the same as amicetin A with a CH$_2$ less in the furan moiety.

thus preventing the liberation of activated amino acids and their assembly into peptide chains (*56a,b,c*). Many analogs, with slightly different activities, have been synthesized, and 3′-amino-3′-deoxyadenosine was recognized as an antitumor agent in cultures of *Helminthosporum* sp. (*56d*).

The aglycon fraction assumes a greater importance in streptomycete antibiotics such as amicetin (XV, *56e*), its precursor amicetin B and the related bamicetin, all from *S. plicatus*, novobiocin (XVI), from *S. sphaeroides*, *S. niveus*, etc., celesticetin I (XVII), from *S. caelestis*, and racemomycin O (XVIII). The antibiotic action of novobiocin (*57a,b*), analogs of which have been prepared biosynthetically (*57c*), has been explained either by its ability to uncouple the phosphorylations (*58*) or by its inhibitory effect upon cell wall biosynthesis, in a manner generally similar to that of the penicillins (*59*) or D-cycloserine (*60*), with leakage of cell constituents (*61*). More recently, its ability to complex magnesium ions has been regarded as its fundamental mechanism of action (*62*).

In a number of antibiotics produced by streptomycetes, sugars are associated to a polycyclic moiety. Thus, D-fucose and D-digitalose (XIX) are found in chartreusin (*62a*). Rhodosamine (XX) is present in η-pyrromycin, rhodomycins A and B, isorhodomycins A and B. An eight-carbon atom amino sugar, resembling mycaminose (XXI, *62b,c,d*) and amosamine (see XV), is found in aklavin and three as yet unidentified sugars are present in each of the cinerubins A and B, two being common to both whereas the third is characteristic of the particular antibiotic.

Unusual sugars are also important components of the macrolide antibiotics typically produced by streptomycetes. With the possible exceptions of tylosin and lankamycin, their presence in the molecule appears to be necessary for antibiotic activity.

Mycaminose (XXI) is a component of the newly described antibiotic acumycin, which, produced by *Streptomyces griseoflavus*, very likely belongs in the macrolide group (*62e*).

Mycaminose and mycarose (XXII, *62f,g*) are found together in carbomycins A and B and in tylosin. The latter sugar is associated with 2,3,4,6-tetradeoxy-4-dimethylaminohexopyranose (XXIII) and a third sugar in the foromacidins or spiramycins. Desosamine (*62h,i,j*) or picrocin (XXIV) is found in picromycin, methymycin, neomethymycin, and narbomycin. It is also present, together with cladinose (XXV), in erythromycins A and B, with an unidentified sugar, $C_7H_{13}O_3$, in erythromycin C, with L-oleandrose (XXVI) in oleandomycin. The last-cited sugar is also a component of the steroid glycoside oleandrin, which is found in the leaves of *Nerium oleander*.

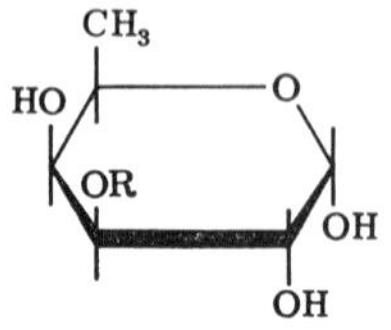

CH_3 HO O OR OH OH

D-Fucose (R = H)

(XIXa)

D-Digitalose (R = CH_3)

(XIXb)

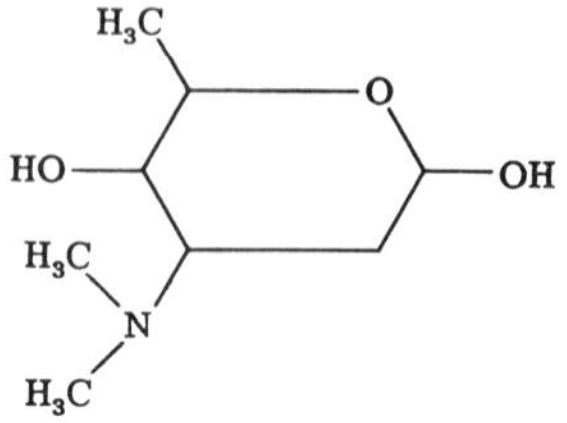

H_3C O HO OH H_3C N H_3C

Rhodosamine

(XX)

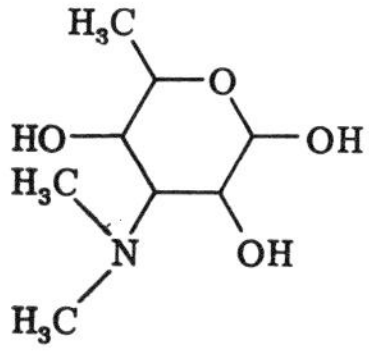

H_3C O HO OH H_3C N OH H_3C

Mycaminose

(XXI)

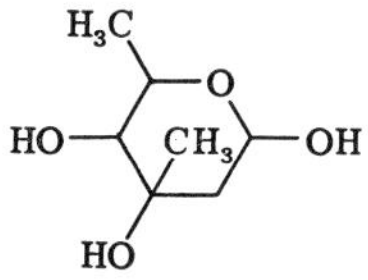

H_3C O HO CH_3 OH HO

Mycarose

(XXII)

H_3C CH_3 O N OH CH_3

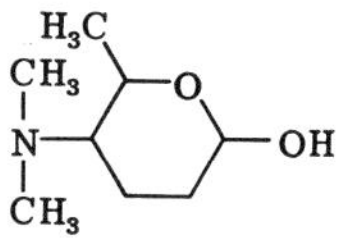

2,3,4,6-Tetradeoxy-4-dimethylamino-hexopyranose

(XXIII)

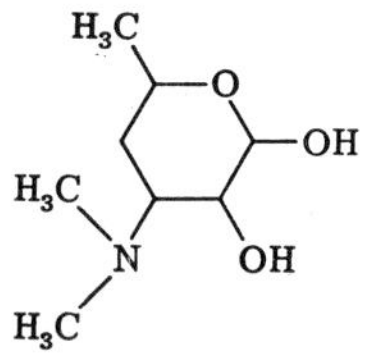

H_3C O OH H_3C N OH H_3C

Desosamine

(XXIV)

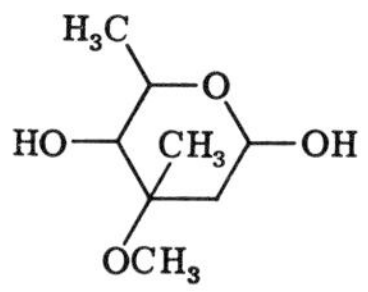

H_3C O HO CH_3 OH OCH_3

Cladinose

(XXV)

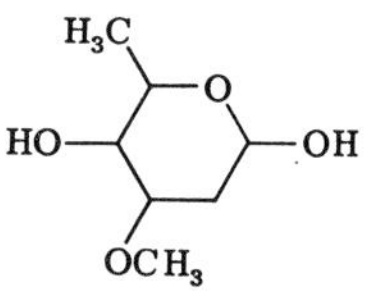

H_3C O HO OH OCH_3

L-Oleandrose

(XXVI)

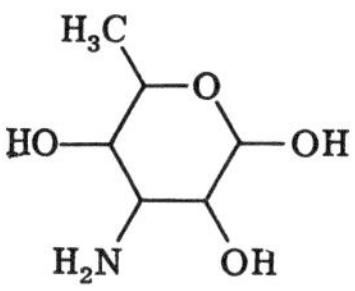

H_3C O HO OH H_2N OH

Mycosamine

(XXVII)

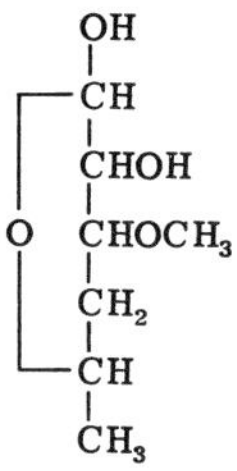

OH CH CHOH O $CHOCH_3$ CH_2 CH CH_3

Lankavose

(XXVIII)

OH CH CH_2 CH_3 O C OCH_3 $CHOCOCH_3$ CH CH_3

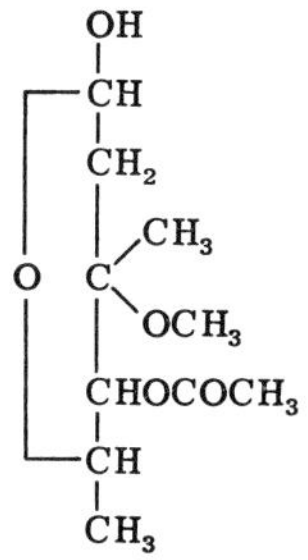

4-*O*-Acetylarcanose

(XXIX)

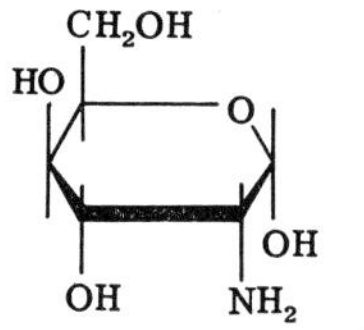

CH_2OH HO O OH OH NH_2

α-D-Gulosamine

(XXXa)

Mycosamine (XXVII) is a moiety of the heptaene macrolides amphotericin B and candidin, and of the tetraene macrolides pimaricin and nystatin. In fact, this amino sugar is thought to be present in most tetraene antibiotics. However, in PA-166, it is replaced by an unidentified amino sugar which is not of the deoxy type. Lankavose (XXVIII) and 4-*O*-acetylarcanose (XXIX) have been recently identified in lankamycin (*62k*). Lankavose is probably identical with chalcose, a degradation product from the antibiotic chalcomycin (*63*).

Finally, sugars are found in some of the polypeptide antibiotics of the streptothricin group produced by streptomycetes: glucosamine in roseomycin, α-D-gulosamine (XXXa) in the streptolins A and B and in streptothricin, an unidentified aminohexose in geomycin, and roseothricin A, a reducing sugar in racemomycin B.

3. *Occurrence and Biosynthesis of Sugars and Derivatives*

Sugars and sugar derivatives, common and unusual, are also found in other microbial products (*64*) besides antibiotics, notably in bacterial slimes, capsules, cell walls (*65a*) and substances (for instance antigens) more or less firmly bound to the latter structure. Among the common ones, glucose itself is rather rare while others are frequently found: D-ribose (very likely synthesized by way of the pentose phosphate cycle), D-deoxyribose (sometimes arising from direct reduction of the former), galactose, mannose, fucose, galacturonic acid, gluconic acid (all arising from D-glucose), D-glucosamine (formed either by glutamine amination of fructose 6-phosphate or by way of glucosone).

Most of the unusual sugars and derivatives seem to arise from a more "normal" parent, such as glucose, ribose, or glucosamine, through oxidation, reduction, decarboxylation, epimerization, etc., all these reactions occurring while the sugar is combined to a nucleotide. *N*-Methylation (frequently through methionine) and *N*-acetylation (generally involving acetyl coenzyme A) also occur frequently. Several of the sugar derivatives reviewed—for instance, 2-deoxystreptamine, streptidine, neoinosamine—are structurally related to the cyclic inositols. So is actinamine (XXXb), a degradation product (*65b,c*) of the antibacterial agent actinospectacin, from *Streptomyces spectabilis* (*65d,e*), for which the complete structure (XXXc) was recently proposed (*65f*). *Myo*-inositol has been shown to be a precursor of streptidine in streptomycin (*66a*). However, the biosynthesis of the inositols is as yet poorly understood. It is often said that they are probably formed by a direct cyclization of hexose. In fact, the conversion of glucose into inositol by parsley leaves has been recently demonstrated (*66b*).

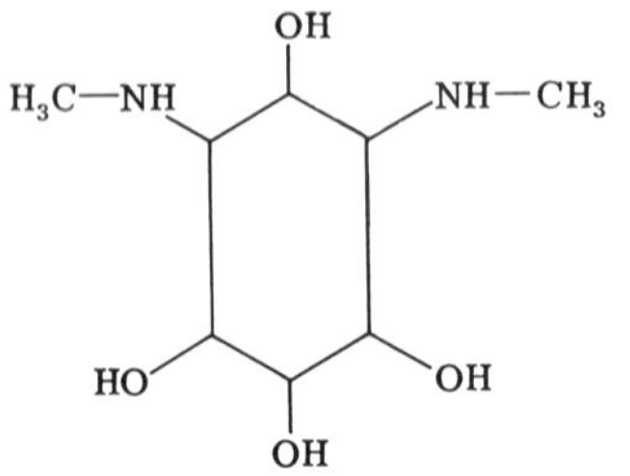

Actinamine

(XXXb)

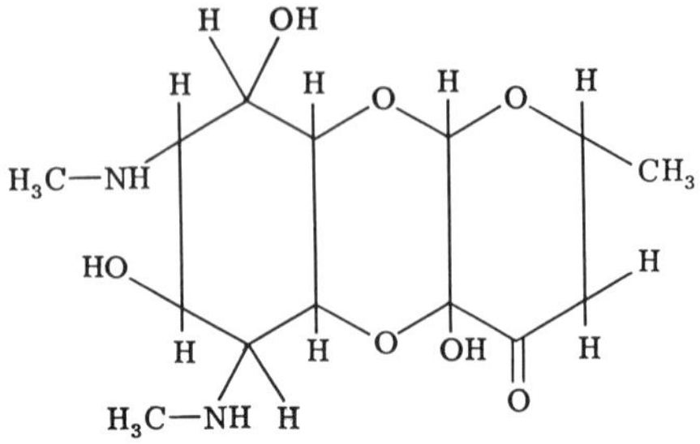

Actinospectacin

(XXXc)

B. Antibiotics Wholly or Partially Derivable from Amino Acids

A few antibiotics appear to be simple derivatives of single amino acids, and others contain an amino acid or related compound as an important moiety. Another group of antibiotics comprises oligopeptides and a larger group, polypeptides. Among the latter, some contain, in addition to the peptide chain, other constituents of variable importance, such as a heterocyclic chromophore group, as in the actinomycins, or hydroxy fatty acids, as in the peptolides. Colicins are believed to be, at least in part, of a protein nature (*67*); certain typical protein enzymes, able to kill sensitive species of microorganisms, are obviously to be included among antibiotics (*68a*). Some heterocyclic compounds with antibiotic properties, or which are part of an antibiotic, appear to be biosynthesized from aromatic amino acids or to stem from their metabolic pathway. Finally, purine and pyrimidine moieties are also biochemically linked to amino acid metabolism.

1. *Single Amino Acids and Derivatives in Antibiotics*

The presence of an amino acid or related moiety in some sugar-containing antibiotics has already been mentioned. For instance, *O*-methyl-L-tyrosine is a part of puromycin (XIV) and α-methyl-D-serine of amicetin A and bamicetin (XV).

Simple derivatives of amino acids, such as *O*-carbamylserine (XXXI), have been isolated from streptomycete cultures (*68b*) and some of them are endowed with antibiotic properties. Oxamycin or D-cycloserine (XXXII), from *S. orchidaceus, S. garyphalus, S. lavendulae, S. roseochromogenes,* and *S. nagasakiensis,* formally resembles D-serine and is possibly related biogenetically to alanine. It acts in a manner generally similar to that of the penicillins by interfering with cell wall biosynthesis. It appears to inhibit specifically the incorporation of D-alanyl residues

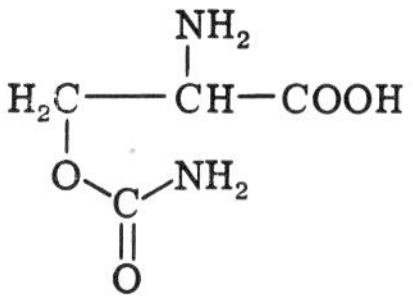

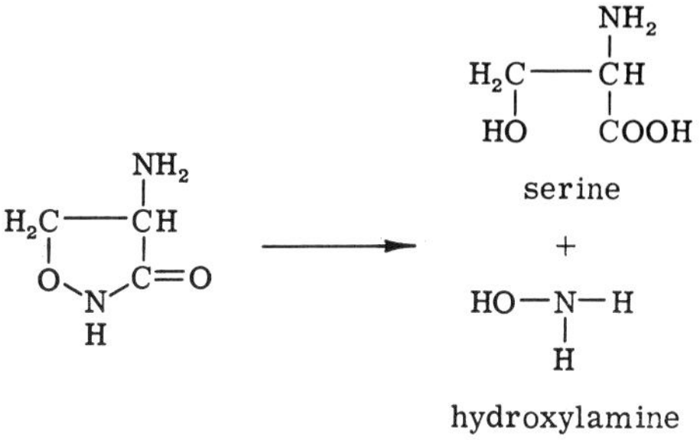

serine

+

hydroxylamine

O-Carbamyl-D-serine

(XXXI)

D-Cycloserine

(XXXII)

(*60, 68c,d*) into the polypeptide of the cell wall basal mucopeptide (*69a,b*). Associated with glycine or DL-alanine, it induces the transformation of streptocci into L forms, as does penicillin (*70*). The L isomer, obtained by synthesis, is less active and displays a different antibiotic spectrum. Its mode of action is certainly different, and it potentiates the activity of the natural D form (*71a,b*). Oxamycin and some of its derivatives (*71c*) are especially known as antituberculosis agents.

Upon prolonged hydrolysis, D-cycloserine yields DL-serine and hydroxylamine. It therefore may not be out of place to point here that amines have been found in some polypeptide antibiotics (hydroxylamine, ethanolamine, cadaverine) (see Table III), in elaiomycin (VIII), in aureothricin and related compounds (XLV). Let us also recall the antibacterial properties of polyamines, such as spermine and spermidine, isolated from animal tissues but found in many microorganisms as well, and the lytic effect on *Bacillus* spp. of cysteamine and related compounds (*72–75a*).

Azaserine from *S. fragilis* (XXXIII), possibly a serine derivative, is antagonized by phenylalanine (*75b,c*); 6-diazo-5-oxo-L-norleucine or DON (XXXIV) probably arises either from serine or leucine. It is produced by *S. aureus* and *S. phaeochromogenes.*

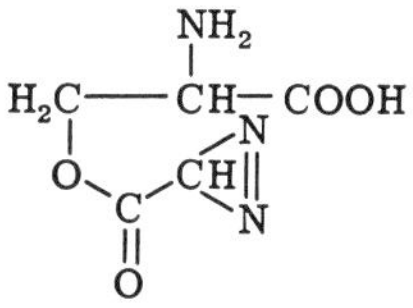

Azaserine

(XXXIII)

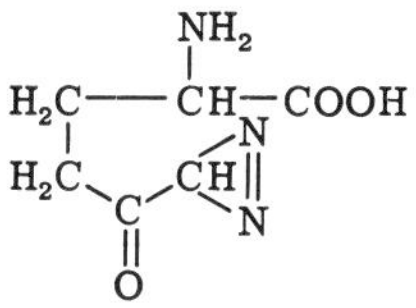

DON

(XXXIV)

All these substances show a formal resemblance to the non-nitrogen-containing sarcomycin (XXXV), from *S. erythrochromogenes,* which, however, is probably acetate derived. They have attracted interest especially in view of their specific toxicity for neoplastic cells. They

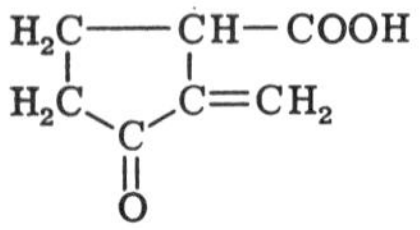

H_2C—CH—COOH
H_2C C=CH_2
C
O

Sarcomycin

(XXXV)

NH_2
H_2C—CH—COOH
H_2C NH_2
C
O

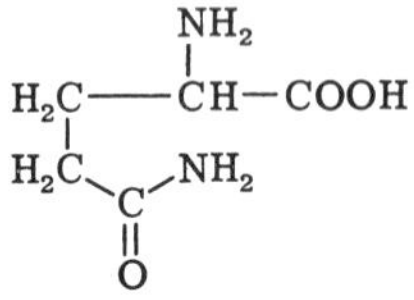

L-Glutamine

(XXXVI)

appear to inhibit the metabolism of purines, possibly by virtue of their structural analogy with glutamine (XXXVI), which is known to act as an aminating agent in the synthesis of purines and pyrimidines (*53a*). DON appears also to inhibit the incorporation of precursors into nucleic acids (*75d*).

2. *Oligopeptide Antibiotics*

The double-ring nucleus common to the penicillins (XXXVIIc) has long been regarded as a dipeptide. Studies devoted to the biosynthesis

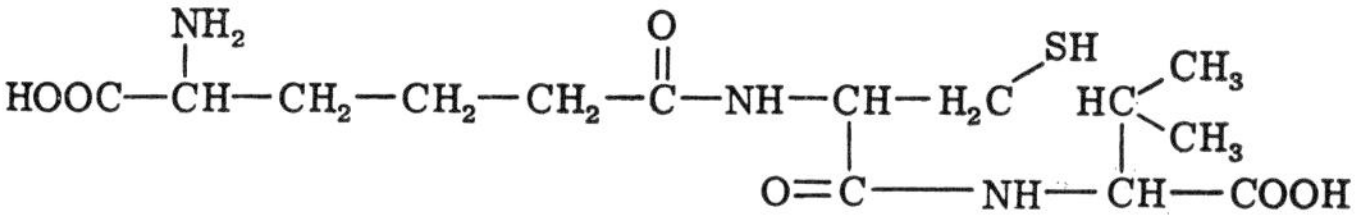

NH_2 O SH CH_3
HOOC—CH—CH_2—CH_2—CH_2—C—NH—CH—H_2C HC
CH_3
O=C—NH—CH—COOH

δ-(α-Aminoadipyl)cysteinylvaline

(XXXVIIa)

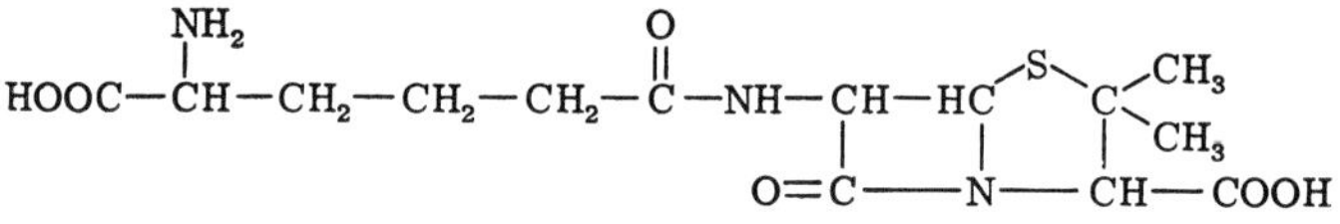

NH_2 O S CH_3
HOOC—CH—CH_2—CH_2—CH_2—C—NH—CH—HC C
CH_3
O=C—N—CH—COOH

Cephalosporin N

(XXXVIIb)

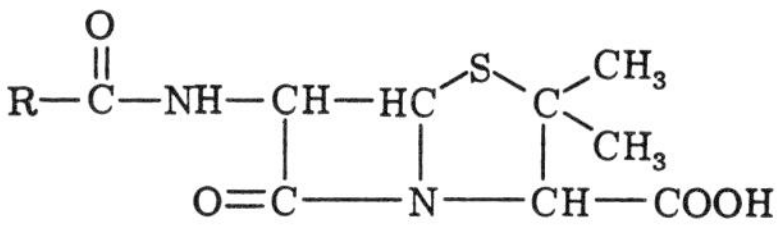

O S CH_3
R—C—NH—CH—HC C
CH_3
O=C—N—CH—COOH

Penicillins
(see Table I for significance of R)

(XXXVIIc)

of antibiotics of this family have confirmed the suggestion (*76, 77a,b*). A typical aliphatic tripeptide (XXXVIIa) was isolated from the mycelium of *Penicillium chrysogenum* (*78a*). Its cyclization through dehydrogenation would produce a particular member of the penicillin family (XXXVIIb), which is in fact synthesized in the cultures of *Cephalosporium salmosynnematum* (*37*), of some strains of *Paecilomyces persicinus* (*78b*) and of other fungi (*78c*), and variously known as cephalosporin N, synnematin B, or salmotin. Although this antibiotic has never been found as such in cultures of *Penicillium* spp. or of *Aspergillus flavus*, the producers of the other natural penicillins, it is nevertheless believed to be their common precursor from which they would be derived by transamidation (*79*).

It is well known that addition to the culture medium of a suitable precursor may favor the selective production of a given penicillin or even result in the elaboration of a new semisynthetic penicillin. It was even suggested that the biological significance of penicillin formation was that of a detoxication mechanism (*80*). New semisynthetic penicillins can also be prepared by chemical means from a natural one. This involves a reaction with either a functional group of the side chain from a natural penicillin, for instance hydroxybenzylpenicillin, or the amino group of 6-aminopenicillanic acid (*81–84b*). This substance* can now be obtained either directly from a suitable *Penicillium* culture (*85a,b, 86a*) or, through the action of an amidase, from phenoxymethylpenicillin or benzylpenicillin (*85b–86f*). The characteristic side chains of the natural penicillins and of a few of the innumerable semisynthetic ones are shown in Table I. Total or partial synthesis of the penicillins has also been achieved (*86g*).

The penicillins have a very wide spectrum of activity, provided that a sufficient concentration of the antibiotic is used. But each one of them has its own specificity of action, quantitatively different from that of the others (*87–92d*). They also differ as to their sensitivity to acids (*93*) and as to their capacity of acting either as substrate or inducer of the penicillinases (*94, 95, 96a–g*). However, they all appear to act according

* It has been recently reported that alkaline hydrolysis of penicillins yields a small amount of 6-aminopenicillanic acid [F. R. Batchelor and J. Cameron-Wood, *Nature* **195**, 1000 (1962)]. All preparations of this compound contain penicillin-like substances (factors 1, 2, and 3) that are sensitive to penicillinase. Factor 2 is biologically inert, but factor 1 is probably responsible for most of the activity against gram-positive organisms, but not against gram-negative ones, formerly attributed to 6-aminopenicillanic acid itself [F. R. Batchelor, M. Cole, D. Gazzard, and G. N. Rolinson, *Nature* **195**, 954–955 (1962)]. The penicillin-like substances are dialyzable and therefore distinct from the poly-6-aminopenicillanic acid described by N. H. Grant, D. E. Clark, and H. E. Alburn [*J. Am. Chem. Soc.* **84**, 876–877 (1962)].

to the same mechanism. A comparative study of the D and L diastereoisomers of α-phenoxyethylpenicillin shows a definite synergism of these compounds (*96h*).

The biochemical investigations of Park and Strominger (*97*) and the independent morphological observations of Lederberg (*98*), Hahn and

TABLE I
SIDE CHAINS OF DIFFERENT PENICILLINS

Penicillin	Significance of R in formula XXXVIIc
Natural penicillins	
Benzyl-P (G or II)	$C_6H_5-CH_2-$
p-Hydroxy-benzyl-P (X or III)	$HO-C_6H_4-CH_2-$
Δ^2-pentenyl-P (F, I, flavicidin or flavicin)	$CH_3-CH_2-CH=CH-CH_2-$
Δ^3-pentenyl-P	$CH_3-CH=CH-CH_2-CH_2-$
n-Amyl-P (dihydro-F or gigantic acid)	$CH_3-CH_2-CH_2-CH_2-CH_2-$
n-Heptyl-P (K)	$CH_3-CH_2-CH_2-CH_2-CH_2-CH_2-CH_2-$
Cephalosporin N (synnematin B, salmotin)	$HOOC-CH-CH_2-CH_2-CH_2-$ | NH_2
Examples of semisynthetic penicillins	
β-Chloroethyl-P	CH_2Cl-CH_2-
α-Bromoisobutyl-P	$(CH_3)_2-CH_2-CHBr-$
Allylmercaptoethyl-P (O)	$CH_2=CH-CH_2-S-CH_2-$
Phenoxymethyl-P (V)	$C_6H_5-O-CH_2-$
α-Phenoxyethyl-P	$C_6H_5-O-CH-$ | CH_3
α-Phenoxypropyl-P	$C_6H_5-O-CH-$ | C_2H_5
2,6-Dimethoxyphenyl-P	$(OCH_3)_2=C_6H_3-$
Aminobenzyl-P	C_6H_5-CH- | NH_2
3-Phenyl-5-methyl-4-isoxasolyl-P	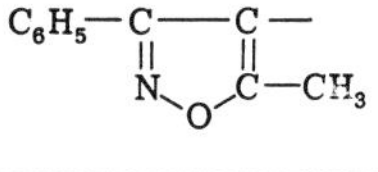 $C_6H_5-C——C-$ || || $N \diagdown_{O} \diagup C-CH_3$

Ciak (*99*), and Liebermeister and Kellenberger (*100*) have corroborated Duguid's (*101*) earlier suggestion that penicillin impairs the mechanical strength of the bacterial cell wall. Lacking the normal protection of its outer rigid envelope, the cell shows deformations and eventually bursts unless it is placed in an osmotically suitable environment where, instead of being lysed, it is converted into a fragile wall-less protoplast (*102–*

103b), or rather a wall-deficient spheroplast (*104*), sometimes capable of growth (*105a*).

This mode of action (*105b*) is similar to that observed in the case not only of other antibiotics such as novobiocin, D-cycloserine, bacitracin (*106*), vancomycin (*107a,b*), but also with other chemicals such as a particular sample of gentian violet (*108*), D-amino acids acting at low concentration (*109, 110*), L-amino acids, especially glycine and serine, at half molar or higher concentration (*111, 112*), uracil analogs (*113–115*), and even lithium chloride (*116a*) or potassium tellurite (*116b*).*

However, the precise step that is inhibited and the mechanism of inhibition are certainly different in each case. Alanine incorporation into the basal mucopeptide of the cell wall is prevented by D-cycloserine (*60, 71a, 117–120a*). The penicillins, possibly on account of a structural similarity (*120b*), appear to inhibit the transglycosidation thanks to which the *N*-acetylmuramic acid peptide is transferred from its uridine nucleotide to its definitive site in the cell wall, as shown by the accumulation of such nucleotides in penicillin-inhibited cultures (*97, 121–123e*). Similarly, the accumulation, in penicillin-treated staphylococcal cultures, of ribitol-containing cytidine nucleotides suggests that incorporation of ribitol into the teichoic acids of the cell wall is also inhibited by the antibiotic (*124, 125*).

Gentian violet prevents the addition to *N*-acetylmuramic acid nucleotide of the first amino acid of the peptide L-alanine (*108*). The site of action of amino acids remains uncertain, but it should be stressed that if glycine at molar concentration has no dissolving action on isolated cell walls (*126*), it nevertheless lyses (*127*) or, in the presence of a stabilizer such as 20% sucrose, converts into spheroplasts (*111*), the cells of resting but not of heat-killed bacterial suspensions. Its action is, however, much more pronounced on growing cells (*128, 129*). Uracil analogs act very likely as specific antagonists of uracil, and possibly of cytidine, which are part of the transferring coenzymes. Finally, it should be recalled that bacteriolysis or conversion into spheroplasts is also observed when suitable bacteria are so placed that they lack a specific growth factor indis-

* Lysis of gram-negative rods by SH-binding and oxidizing agents, but not by reducing substances, was recently reported. The residue is made up of impure cell walls. Treated cells are protected by a high osmotic pressure. The reagents have no visible effect on isolated cell walls or cytoplasmic membranes. Lysis is explained by an alteration of the cell envelopes, but whether it is a direct action, to be compared to that of lysozyme, or an indirect one of the same kind as that of penicillin, is left as an open question [M. Schaechter and K. A. Santomassino, *J. Bacteriol.* **84**, 318–325 (1962)].

pensable as a building block for the biosynthesis of their cell wall, e.g., diaminopimelic acid (*130, 131*) or lysine (*132*). Protoplast formation also occurs when galactose-sensitive mutants of *Salmonella* are submitted to the action of the sugar (*133*). All these observations are examples of unbalanced growth (*134–138a*).

Spheroplasts, whatever may be their origin, are thought to be the starting point of the L cycle of bacteria (*112, 138b, 139a,b*).

Although many biochemical effects produced by penicillin were reported earlier (*140–142*), it is widely accepted today that inhibition of cell wall synthesis truly represents the primary lesion responsible for antibiotic activity (*143–149*), inasmuch as many of the effects are not observed in media of high enough osmotic pressure (*150*). There is also a parallelism between the concentrations respectively needed to promote the conversion into spheroplasts and to inhibit the growth of a large number of species of widely different sensitivity (*112*).

However, it must be acknowledged that the theory now in favor does not explain all the known facts (*151*), for instance, the relative resistance of some highly aerobic nonpenicillinase-producing staphylococci (*152*).

Penicillin-promoted bacteriolysis has been explained by the induction of a particular enzyme (*153*), and it has been suggested that the conversion into spheroplasts is preceded by a more fundamental lethal action (*154, 155*).

Closely related to the natural penicillin known as cephalosporin N is another antibiotic, produced by the same *Cephalosporium salmosynnematum*, namely cephalosporin C (XXXVIII). Its double-ring nucleus,

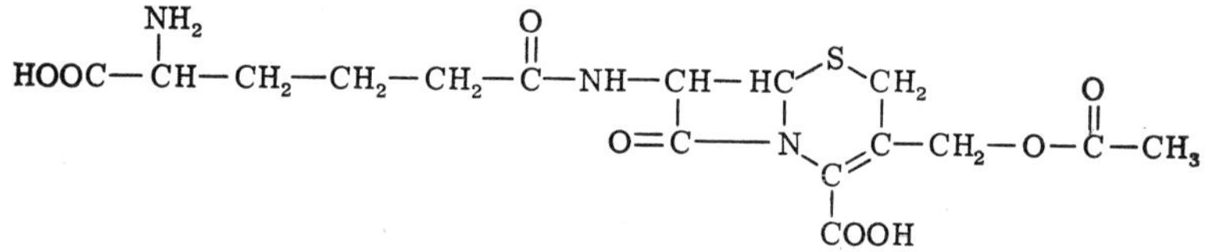

```
        NH2                     O
        |                       ||                 S
HOOC—CH—CH2—CH2—CH2—C—NH—CH—HC⁄ ⁀\CH2              O
                                 |    |      |                ||
                               O=C————N    C—CH2—O—C—CH3
                                        \C⁄⁼
                                         |
                                        COOH
```

Cephalosporin C

(XXXVIII)

7-aminocephalosporanic acid, differs from 6-aminopenicillanic acid in that the thiazolidine ring, fused with the β-lactam one in the latter, is replaced, in the former, by a dihydrothiazine ring bearing a side chain (*156–157b*) which is easily transformed or lost (*158–160b*). The differences in antibiotic spectrum and behavior toward penicillinases of these recently discovered compounds are of special interest for the study of the relations between molecular structure and biological activity (*161, 162a*). The biosynthesis of cephalosporin C is stimulated, rather specifically, by D-methionine (*162b*).

Alazopeptin is an anticancer agent produced by *Streptomyces griseoplanus* in which two moles of DON (XXXIV) are associated with one of alanine.

Other antibiotics of low molecular weight involving one or more amide bonds are, for example, netropsin (XXXIX), produced by several streptomycetes; lycomarasmine (XL) (*162c*) which is an analog and antagonist (produced by *Fusarium lycopersici*) of the growth factor

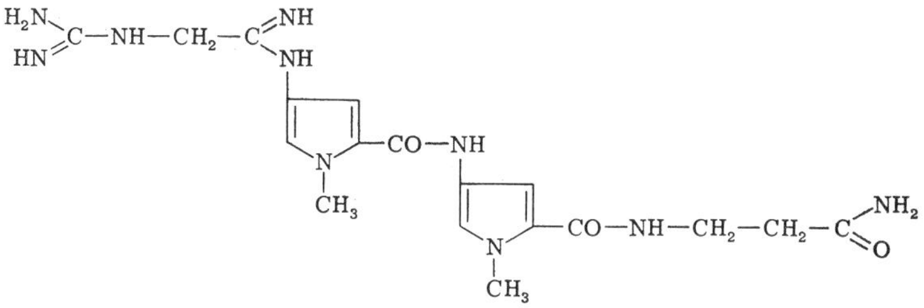

Netropsin

(XXXIX)

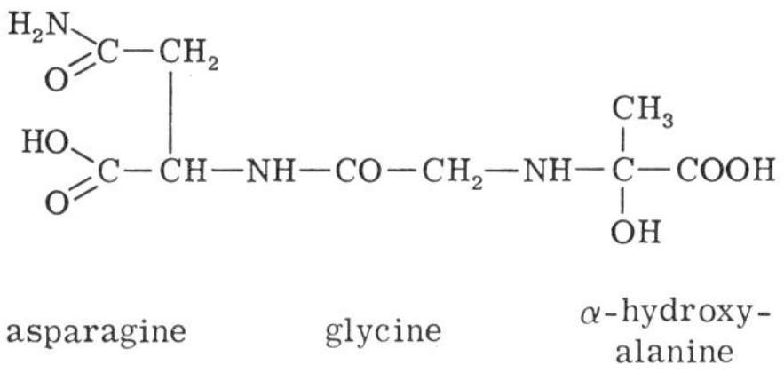

asparagine glycine α-hydroxy-alanine

Lycomarasmine

(XL)

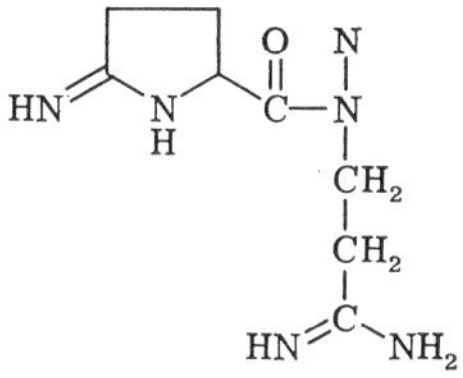

Noformicin

(XLI)

streptogenin, a tripeptide containing glutamic acid and glycine; noformicin (XLI) from *Nocardia formica;* nocardamine (XLII) from a species of *Nocardia* resembling *N. flavescens* (*163a*); eulicin (XLIII) from a species of *Streptomyces* resembling *S. parvus;* and amidinomycin (XLIV) from *Streptomyces* sp.

The four closely related streptomycete-produced antibiotics: holomycin (*S. griseus*), thiolutin (*S. albus, S. celluloflavus*), aureothricin (*S. thioluteus, S. farcinicus, S. celluloflavus, S. cyanoflavus*), and isobutyropyrrothine (*Streptomyces* sp.) have a common nucleus, holothin (XLV), which is obtainable from acid hydrolysis of holomycin and has some antibiotic activity of its own. Its *N*-methyl derivative, pyrrothine, is obtained, under the same conditions, from the three other antibiotics. Holothin and pyrrothine are weak amines with the structure of two fused heterocycles. They are combined, in the complete antibiotics, with an acetyl, propionyl, or isobutyryl radical (*163b*). The double ring is supposed to result from the cyclization of a glycylcystine intermediate,

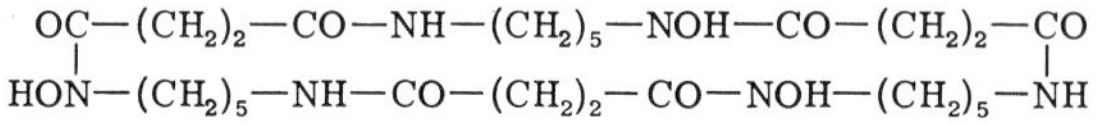

$$\begin{array}{l} OC-(CH_2)_2-CO-NH-(CH_2)_5-NOH-CO-(CH_2)_2-CO \\ | \qquad\qquad\qquad\qquad\qquad\qquad\qquad\qquad\qquad\qquad\qquad | \\ HON-(CH_2)_5-NH-CO-(CH_2)_2-CO-NOH-(CH_2)_5-NH \end{array}$$

Nocardamine

(XLII)

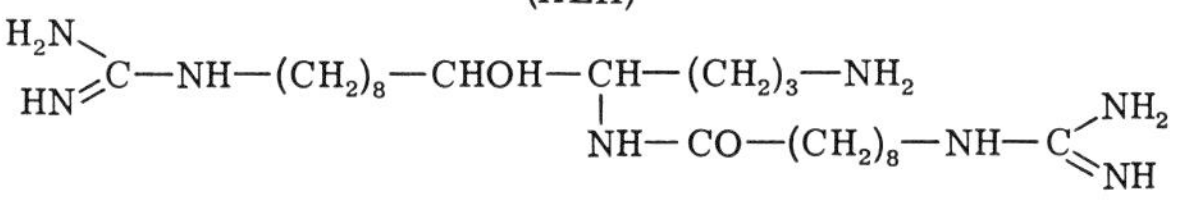

$$(H_2N)(HN{=})C-NH-(CH_2)_8-CHOH-CH(NH-CO-(CH_2)_8-NH-C({=}NH)NH_2)-(CH_2)_3-NH_2$$

Eulicin

(XLIII)

$$H_2N-C_5H_8-CO-NH-CH_2-CH_2-C({=}NH)NH_2$$

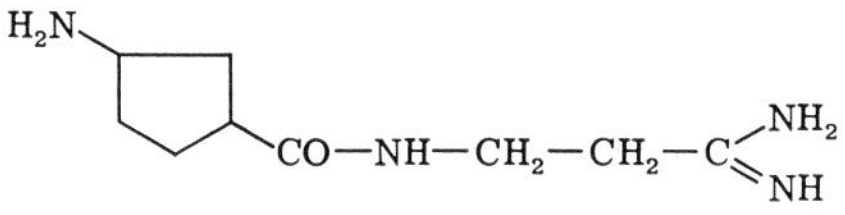

Amidinomycin

(XLIV)

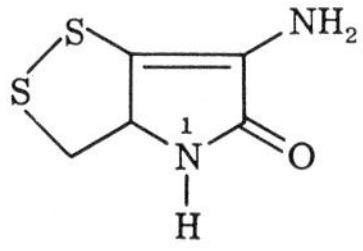

Holothin[a]

(XLV)

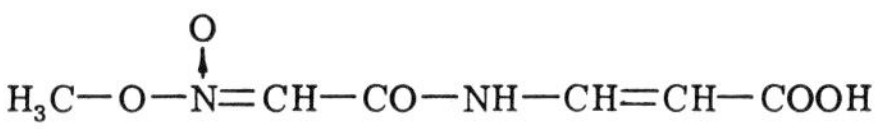

$$H_3C-O-N(\rightarrow O){=}CH-CO-NH-CH{=}CH-COOH$$

Enteromycin

(XLVb)

[a] In holomycin, the amine is combined to acetic acid. Pyrrothine is the N_1-methyl derivative of holothin. In thiolutin, aureothricin, and isobutyropyrrothine, the amine pyrrothine is combined, respectively, to acetic, propionic, and isobutyric acids.

in a manner reminiscent of the biosynthesis of the penicillins, with the loss of a three-carbon atom fragment, alanine or serine, from the cystine molecule.

In enteromycin (XLVb), from *Streptomyces albireticuli*, occurs the unusual 3-aminoacrylic acid (*164*), and it may be recalled that acrylic acid, which is abundant in *Phaeocystis pouchetii*, is held responsible for the antibiotic effects observed in polar marine animals using the alga as food (*165a*).

3. *Polypeptide Antibiotics**

A large number of antibiotics, mainly from streptomycetes and bacilli, are typical polypeptides of variable complexity. It is also known that certain polypeptides from animal tissues and cells have antimicrobial properties. Such is the case, for instance, for the so-called anthracocidal agent, which is a basic peptide rich in lysine, and for a fraction from calf thymus (*165b*).

Table II shows the products obtained from hydrolysis of some polypeptide antibiotics. It will be seen that they comprise the amino acids regularly found in protein hydrolyzates and a few less common ones, such as lanthionine, β-methyllanthionine, γ-aminobutyric and α,γ-diaminobutyric acids.

Several of the smaller polypeptide antibiotics have been more thoroughly studied; in many cases they were found to be cyclic peptides. Thus, gramicidins J1 and J2 (XLVI), from *Bacillus brevis*, are, respectively, hexa- and heptacyclopeptides. Gramicidin S (XLVII) and tyrocidins A and B (XLVIII), the latter two originally found associated with gramicidin D in the antibiotic complex tyrothricin, are cyclic decapeptides also produced by *B. brevis*. Mycobacillin (XLIX) is a cyclic tridecapeptide from *B. subtilis*.

In bacitracin A (L), one member of a complex of related antibiotics and biologically inert compounds (*165c*) produced by *B. subtilis* and *B. licheniformis* (ayfivin), a hexapeptide is cyclized by an amide bond between the α-carboxylic group of aspartic acid and the γ-amino group of lysine. It bears two side chains: one is asparagine, peptidically bound to lysine; the other is a straight-chain pentapeptide linked to lysine and with its two terminal amino acids, cysteine and isoleucine, conjugated in a thiazole ring. Divalent metal ions are necessary for bacitracin activity (*165d*). Its mode of action, although in many ways similar to that of penicillin, is not completely elucidated (*165e*).

* In the formulas illustrating Sections 3 and 4, the following abbreviations are used, in addition to the conventional ones for amino acids:

MeOct: (+)-6-methyloctanoic acid;
Dab: α,γ-diaminobutyric acid;
Hiv: α-hydroxyisovaleric acid;
Lac: lactic acid.

Peptide and ester bonds are represented by an arrow, the foot of which locates the carboxylic group, its head the amino or hydroxyl group, the latter being distinguished by the letter O. Whenever needed, a Greek letter indicates which one of several identical functional groups is involved.

TABLE II

COMPONENTS OF SOME POLYPEPTIDE ANTIBIOTICS

Polypeptide antibiotics	Producing organisms	Amino acids[a]																								
		Glycine	Alanine	Serine	Cystine	Lanthionine	β-Methyllanthionine	γ-Aminobutyric acid	Threonine	Methionine	Valine	Leucine	Isoleucine	Aspartic acid	Asparagine	Glutamic acid	α,γ-Diaminobutyric acid	Ornithine	Arginine	Lysine	Phenylalanine	Tyrosine	Tryptophan	Histidine	Proline	Hydroxyproline
Alvein	*Bacillus alvei*	−	−	−	−	−	−	−	−	−	−	−	−	−	−	−	−	−	+	−	−	−	−	−	−	−
Antibiotic B-456	*B. subtilis*	−	−	−	−	−	−	−	−	−	+	+	−	+	−	+	−	+	−	−	−	D	−	−	+	−
Antibiotic C-159	*Streptomyces canus*	+	+	−	−	−	−	−	+	−	−	−	−	+	−	−	−	−	−	−	−	−	−	−	−	−
Antibiotic Y-1	Yeast	+	+	−	−	−	−	−	−	−	+	+	−	−	−	+	−	−	−	−	−	−	−	−	−	−
Antibiotic Y-2	Yeast	+	+	−	−	−	−	+	−	−	+	+	−	−	−	+	−	−	−	−	−	−	−	−	−	−
Bacillomycin	*B. subtilis*	−	−	+	−	−	−	−	+	−	−	−	−	+	−	+	−	−	−	−	−	+	−	−	−	−
Bacillomycin B	*B. subtilis*	−	−	−	−	−	−	−	−	−	−	+	−	+	−	+	−	−	−	−	−	+	−	−	+	−
Bacillomycin C	*B. subtilis*	−	−	−	−	−	−	−	−	−	+	+	−	+	−	+	−	−	−	−	−	+	−	−	−	−
Bryamycin	*S. hawaiiensis*	+	+	−	+	−	−	−	+	−	−	−	+	−	−	−	−	−	−	−	−	−	−	−	−	−
Carzinocidin	*S. kitazawaensis*	+	−	−	+	−	−	−	−	−	−	−	−	−	−	+	−	−	−	+	−	−	−	−	−	−
Cephalomycin	*S. tanashiensis*	+	+	−	−	−	−	−	+	−	+	+	−	+	−	+	−	−	+	−	+	+	−	−	−	−
Cinnamycin	*S. cinnamomeus*	−	−	−	−	+	+	−	−	−	+	−	−	+	−	+	−	−	+	−	+	−	−	−	+	−
Coliformin	*Escherichia coli, Aerobacter aerogenes*	+	+	+	−	−	−	−	−	−	+	+	−	+	−	+	−	−	−	+	−	−	−	−	−	−
Comirin	*Pseudomonas antimycetica*	+	−	+	−	−	−	−	−	−	−	+	+	+	−	−	+	−	+	+	−	+	−	−	−	−
Diplococcin	Milk streptococci	−	−	−	−	−	−	−	−	−	−	−	−	−	−	−	−	−	+	−	−	−	−	−	−	−
Duramycin	*S. cinnamomeus*	+	−	−	−	+	+	−	−	−	+	−	−	+	−	+	−	?	−	−	+	−	−	−	+	?
Edein	*B. brevis*	+	−	−	−	−	−	−	−	−	−	−	−	+	−	+	−	−	+	−	−	+	−	−	−	−
Fungistatin	*B. subtilis*	−	+	+	−	−	−	−	+	−	+	−	+	+	−	−	−	−	−	+	−	+	+	−	+	−
Iturin[b]	*B. subtilis*	−	−	+	−	−	−	−	−	−	−	−	−	+	−	+	−	−	−	−	−	+	−	−	+	−
Licheniformins A, B	*B. licheniformis*	+	−	+	−	−	−	−	−	−	+	−	−	+	−	−	−	−	+	+	+	−	−	−	+	−
Melanomycin	*S. melanogenes*	−	+	−	−	−	−	−	−	−	+	+	−	−	−	+	−	−	−	−	+	−	−	+	+	−
Nisin A	*Streptococcus lactis, S. cremoris*	+	+	+	−	+	+	−	−	+	+	×	×	+	−	−	−	−	−	+	−	−	−	+	+	−
Nisins B, C	*Idem*	+	+	−	−	+	+	−	−	+	+	×	×	+	−	−	−	−	−	+	−	−	−	+	+	−
Nisin D	*Idem*	?	?	−	−	+	+	−	−	−	−	?	?	?	−	+	−	−	−	?	−	−	−	?	?	−
Phytoactin	*Streptomyces* sp.	+	+	+	−	−	−	−	−	−	+	×	×	−	−	−	−	−	+	−	−	−	−	−	+	−
Phytostreptin	*Streptomyces* sp.	+	+	+	−	−	−	−	−	−	+	×	×	−	−	−	−	−	+	−	−	−	−	−	+	−
Subtilin	*B. subtilis*	+	+	−	−	+	+	−	−	−	+	+	+	−	+	+	−	−	−	+	+	−	+	−	+	−
Telomycin	*Streptomyces* sp.	+	+	−	−	−	−	−	+	−	−	−	−	+	−	−	−	−	−	−	−	−	−	−	−	−

[a] + = Presence of amino acid; ? = possible occurrence of amino acid; × = leucine or isoleucine present; − = amino acid not present.

[b] Personal communication from L. Delcambe.

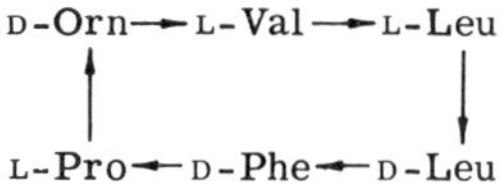

```
D-Orn → L-Val → L-Leu
  ↑                ↓
L-Pro ← D-Phe ← D-Leu
```

Gramicidin J1

(XLVIa)

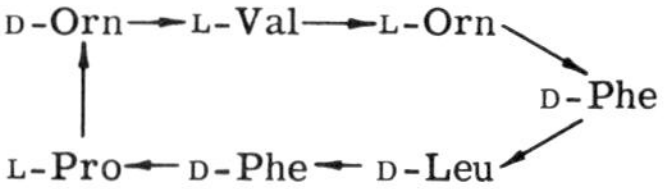

```
D-Orn → L-Val → L-Orn
  ↑                    ↘
  |                      D-Phe
  |                    ↙
L-Pro ← D-Phe ← D-Leu
```

Gramicidin J2

(XLVIb)

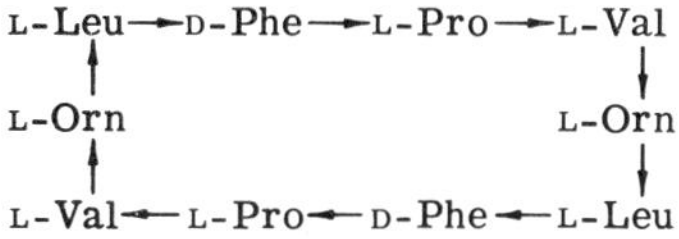

```
L-Leu → D-Phe → L-Pro → L-Val
  ↑                        ↓
L-Orn                    L-Orn
  ↑                        ↓
L-Val ← L-Pro ← D-Phe ← L-Leu
```

Gramicidin S

(XLVII)

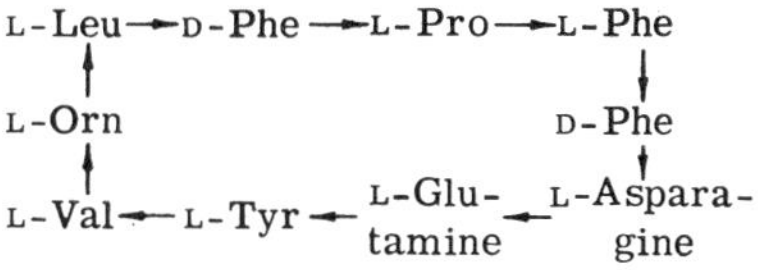

```
L-Leu → D-Phe → L-Pro → L-Phe
  ↑                        ↓
L-Orn                    D-Phe
  ↑                        ↓
L-Val ← L-Tyr ← L-Glu-  ← L-Aspara-
                tamine     gine
```

Tyrocidin A
(in Tyrocidin B, L-Try replaces L-Phe)

(XLVIII)

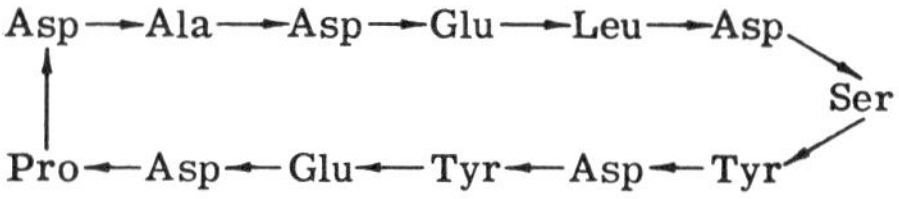

```
Asp → Ala → Asp → Glu → Leu → Asp
 ↑                                ↘
 |                                  Ser
 |                                ↙
Pro ← Asp ← Glu ← Tyr ← Asp ← Tyr
```

Mycobacillin

(XLIX)

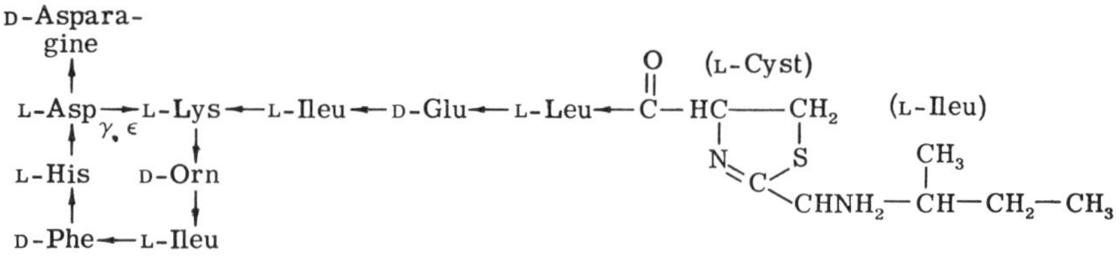

```
D-Aspara-
  gine
   ↑                                             O     (L-Cyst)
   |                                             ||
L-Asp → L-Lys ← L-Ileu ← D-Glu ← L-Leu ← C — HC —— CH2        (L-Ileu)
   ↑   γ, ε   ↓                                   |      |              CH3
L-His       D-Orn                                N      S              |
   ↑          ↓                                    ⩵ C ⟋
D-Phe  ←  L-Ileu                                       ⟍ CHNH2 — CH — CH2 — CH3
```

Bacitracin A

(L)

It appears, from the examples shown (XLVI–L), that common amino acids frequently occur in antibiotics under the unnatural or D configuration. D-Amino acids are also typical components of the mucopeptides from bacterial cell walls (*65a*), and it should be recalled here that the penicillins, D-cycloserine, novobiocin, vancomycin, and also bacitracin, apparently owe their antibiotic activity to their capacity of inhibiting cell wall biosynthesis. The biochemical peculiarities of bacterial cell walls have therefore been pointed out as an explanation of the low toxicity of certain antibiotics for animal cells, which would lack the

TABLE III

DEGRADATION PRODUCTS OF SOME POLYPEPTIDE ANTIBIOTICS[a]

Antibiotics	Producing microorganisms	Degradation products: Unknown reducing sugar	Unknown amino hexose	α-D-Glucosamine	Glucosamine	Loosely bound iron	Unknown base	Unknown fatty acid	Nonsaturated fatty acid	4-Isotridecenoic acid	Propionic acid	Guanidino compound	3-Methyluracil	Indole	Thiazole-containing fragments	2-Propionylthiazole-4-carboxylic acid	2-(1-Amino-2-methylpropyl)-thiazole-4-carboxylic acid	β-(2-Thiazole)-β-alanine	Geamine	Pipecolic acid	γ-Methylproline	Proline
Albomycin A	*Actinomyces subtropicus*	–	–	–	–	+	–	–	–	–	–	–	+	–	–	–	–	–	–	–	–	?
Antibiotic I. C. I. 13959	*Paecilomyces* sp.	–	–	–	–	–	–	–	–	–	–	–	–	–	–	–	–	–	–	–	+	–
Aspartocin	*S. griseus* var. *spiralis*, *S. violaceus*	–	–	–	–	–	–	–	+	–	–	–	–	–	–	–	–	–	–	D	–	1L
Bottromycin	*S. bottropensis*	–	–	–	–	–	–	–	–	–	–	–	–	–	–	–	–	+	–	–	–	–
Brevin	*B. brevis*	–	–	–	–	–	?	?	–	–	–	–	–	–	–	–	–	–	–	–	–	–
Ferrimycin A	*S. griseoflavus*, *S. galilaeus*, *S. lavendulae*	–	–	–	–	+	–	–	–	–	–	–	–	–	–	–	–	–	–	–	–	+
Geomycin	*S. xanthophaeus*	–	+	–	–	–	–	–	–	–	–	–	–	–	–	–	–	–	+	–	–	–
Glumamycin	*Streptomyces* sp.	–	–	–	–	–	–	–	–	+	–	–	–	–	–	–	–	–	–	D	–	L
Gramicidin D[b]	*B. brevis*	–	–	–	–	–	–	–	–	–	–	–	–	–	–	–	–	–	–	–	–	–
Grisein	*S. griseus*	–	–	–	–	+	–	–	–	–	–	–	+	–	–	–	–	–	–	–	–	–
Matamycin	*S. matensis*	–	–	–	–	–	–	–	–	–	–	–	–	–	–	–	–	–	–	–	–	–
Micrococcin P	*B. pumilus*	–	–	–	–	–	–	–	–	–	+	–	–	–	–	+	+	–	–	–	–	–
Mycothricins A and B	*S. lavendulae*, *Streptomyces* sp.	–	–	–	–	–	–	–	–	–	–	–	–	–	–	–	–	–	+	–	–	–
Pleocidin	*S. lavendulae*	–	–	–	–	–	–	–	–	–	–	–	–	–	–	–	–	–	+	–	–	–
Polypeptin	*B. krzemieniewski*	–	–	–	–	–	–	–	–	–	–	–	–	–	–	–	–	–	–	–	–	–
Racemomycin B	*S. racemochromogenus*	2	–	–	–	–	–	–	–	–	–	–	–	–	–	–	–	–	2	–	–	–
Roseomycin	*S. roseochromogenes*, *Streptomyces* sp.	–	–	–	+	–	–	–	–	–	–	–	–	+	–	–	–	–	–	–	–	–
Roseothricin A	*S. roseochromogenes*	–	+	–	–	–	–	–	–	–	–	–	–	–	–	–	–	–	1	–	–	–
Streptolins A and B	*S. lavendulae*, *S. griseus* f. *farinosus*	–	–	+	–	–	–	–	–	–	–	–	–	–	–	–	–	–	+	–	–	–
Streptothricin	*S. lavendulae*, *S. griseus* f. *farinosus*	–	–	+	–	–	–	–	–	–	–	–	–	–	–	–	–	–	+	–	–	–
Thiostrepton	*Streptomyces* sp.	–	–	–	–	–	–	–	–	–	–	–	–	–	+	–	–	–	–	–	–	–
Viomycin	*S. floridae*, *S. puniceus*, *S. vinaceus*, *S. californicus*, *S. abikoensum*, *S. olivoreticuli*, *S. griseus* var. *purpureus*	–	–	–	–	–	–	–	–	–	–	+	–	–	–	–	–	–	–	–	–	–

[a] Symbols: + = degradation product present; – = not present; ? = possible occurrence. Wherever possible, the plus sign is replaced by the letter D or/and L (indicating configuration) and a numeral (indicating the number of molecules of the amino acid in one of the polypeptide).

[b] However, see K. Okuda, C. S. Lin, and T. Winnick, *Nature* **195**, 1067–1069 (1962) for more recent information.

sensitive receptor, and as a possible clue for a rational approach in the search for chemotherapeutic agents (*135*).

The formation of D-alanine from L-alanine, and of other D-amino acids by transamination of suitable keto acids has been observed in *Bacillus licheniformis* (*165f*).

Table III shows the occurrence in some polypeptide antibiotics not only of common, if of the D form, amino acids, but also of unusual types of amino acids and derivatives (LI–LIV). It also draws the attention to the fact that iron is loosely bound to several peptides produced by

TABLE III (*Continued*)

Degradation products																													
Tryptophan	Tyrosine	β-Methylphenylalanine	Phenylalanine	β-Lysine	Arginine	1-Amino-5-hydroxyaminopentane	Cadaverine	Ornithine	α,γ-Diaminobutyric acid	α,β-Diaminobutyric acid	α,β-Diaminopropionic acid	Glutamic acid	β-Methylaspartic acid	Aspartic acid	Isoleucine	β-Hydroxyleucine	Leucine	δ-Aminovaleric acid	Valine	Threonine	α-Aminoisobutyric acid	Cysteic acid	Cysteine	Serine	β-Alanine	Alanine	Ethanolamine	Glycine	Hydroxylamine
−	−	−	−	−	−	+	−	+	−	−	−	?	−	−	−	−	−	−	−	−	−	−	−	+	−	?	−	?	+
−	−	−	−	−	−	−	−	−	−	−	−	−	−	−	−	+	L	−	−	−	+	−	−	−	+	−	−	−	−
−	−	−	−	−	−	−	−	−	−	+	−	−	L	4L	−	−	−	−	1L	−	−	−	−	−	−	−	−	2	−
−	−	+	−	−	−	−	−	−	−	−	−	−	−	−	−	−	−	−	+	−	−	−	−	−	−	−	−	+	−
−	+	−	−	−	−	−	−	−	−	−	−	−	−	+	−	−	−	−	−	−	−	−	−	+	−	−	−	+	−
−	−	−	−	−	−	+	+	−	−	−	−	−	−	−	−	−	−	+	−	−	−	−	−	−	−	−	−	−	−
−	−	−	−	+	−	−	−	−	−	−	−	+	−	+	−	−	−	−	−	+	−	−	−	+	−	+	−	+	−
−	−	−	−	−	−	−	−	−	−	+	−	−	−	L	−	−	−	−	L	L	−	−	−	−	−	−	−	+	−
4L	−	−	−	−	−	−	−	−	−	−	−	−	−	−	−	−	4D	−	{2L, 2D}	−	−	−	−	−	−	2L	1	1	−
−	−	−	−	−	−	−	−	−	−	−	−	+	−	−	−	−	−	−	−	−	−	−	−	−	−	−	−	−	+
−	−	−	−	−	+	−	−	−	−	−	−	−	−	−	−	−	−	−	−	−	−	+	−	+	−	+	−	+	−
−	−	−	−	−	−	−	−	−	−	−	−	−	−	−	−	−	−	−	−	+	−	−	−	−	−	−	−	−	−
−	−	−	−	+	−	−	−	−	−	−	−	−	−	−	−	−	−	−	−	−	−	−	−	+	−	−	−	−	−
−	−	−	−	+	−	−	−	−	−	−	−	−	−	−	−	−	−	−	−	−	−	−	−	−	−	−	−	−	−
−	−	−	1D	−	−	−	−	−	3	−	−	−	−	−	1L	−	2L	−	1D	1L	−	−	−	−	−	−	−	−	−
−	−	−	−	3	−	−	−	−	−	−	−	−	−	−	−	−	−	−	−	−	−	−	−	−	−	−	−	−	−
−	−	−	−	−	−	−	−	−	−	−	−	−	−	−	−	−	−	−	−	−	−	−	−	−	−	−	−	−	−
−	−	−	−	1	−	−	−	−	−	−	−	−	−	−	−	−	−	−	−	−	−	−	−	−	−	−	−	−	−
−	−	−	−	L	−	−	−	−	−	−	−	−	−	−	−	−	−	−	−	−	−	−	−	−	−	−	−	−	−
−	−	−	−	L	−	−	−	−	−	−	−	−	−	−	−	−	−	−	−	−	−	−	−	−	−	−	−	−	−
−	−	−	−	−	−	−	−	−	−	−	−	−	−	−	L	−	−	−	−	L	−	−	D	−	−	L	−	−	−
−	−	−	−	+	−	−	−	−	−	−	+	−	−	−	−	−	−	−	−	−	−	−	−	L	−	−	−	−	−

streptomycetes: albomycin (*166a,b*), ferrimycin (*167a–168*), grisein A, which, together with other less well known iron-containing antibiotics, have been grouped under the collective name sideromycins (*169*). They are believed to act as specific inhibitors of iron-containing growth factors (*170a*) constituting the group of sideramines (*170b, 171, 172a*). The compound 1-amino-5-hydroxylaminopentane occurs in acid hydrolyzates of several sideramines and sideromycins (*172b*) as well as in the antibiotic nocardamine (XLII) (*172c*) which, iron-complexed, is identical with ferrioxamine E (*163a*). The related 1-amino-5-hydroxylaminopentan-1-oic acid is a component of mycobactin, a growth factor for *Mycobacterium johnei* biosynthesized by *M. phlei* (*172d*). Table III also indicates the possible occurrence of moieties unrelated to amino acids, such as thiazole fragments (LV), sugars (streptothricin group), and fatty acids (*172e*).

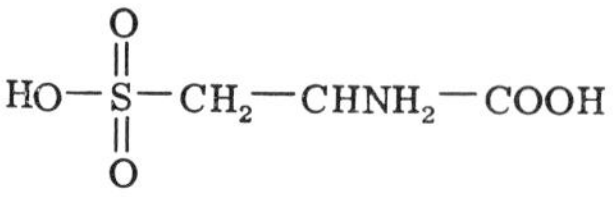

$$HO-S(=O)_2-CH_2-CHNH_2-COOH$$

Cysteic acid

(LI)

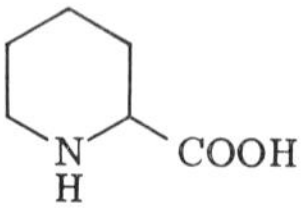

COOH

Pipecolic acid

(LII)

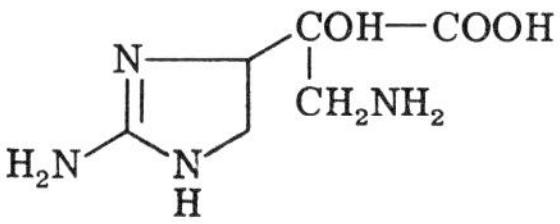

COH—COOH
CH$_2$NH$_2$
H_2N

Geamine

(LIII)

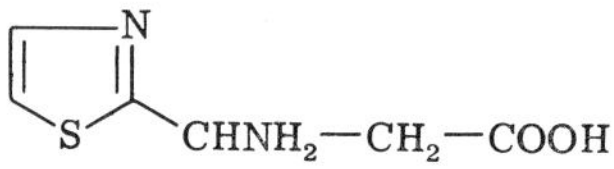

CHNH$_2$—CH$_2$—COOH

β-(2-Thiazole)-β-alanine

(LIV)

HOOC
CH$_3$
CHNH$_2$—CH—CH$_3$

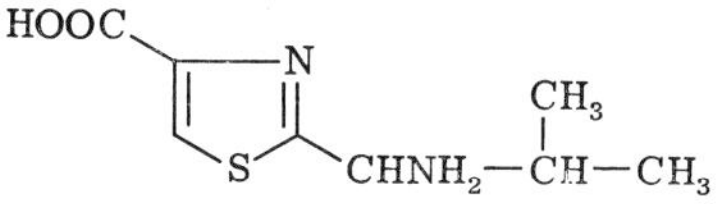

2-(1-Amino-2-methylpropyl)thiazole-4-carboxylic acid

(LV)

The latter type of compound assumes a greater importance in some microbial metabolites. Thus DL-fumarylylalanine is a metabolic product of *Penicillium resticulosum;* 3-oxydecanoic acid is bound to serine in

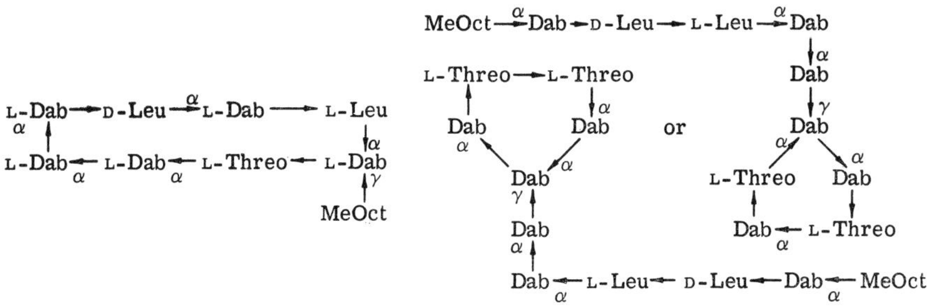

L-Dab → D-Leu →(α) L-Dab → L-Leu
L-Dab ← L-Dab ← L-Threo ← L-Dab
MeOct

MeOct →(α) Dab → D-Leu → L-Leu →(α) Dab
L-Threo → L-Threo Dab
Dab Dab or Dab
Dab L-Threo Dab
Dab Dab ← L-Threo
Dab ← L-Leu ← D-Leu ← Dab ← MeOct

(according to Kurihara and Suzuki) (according to Dautrevaux and Biserte)

Proposed structures for colistin

(LVI)

serratamic acid from *Serratia* spp. and to an open-chain peptide in viscosin from *Pseudomonas viscosa:* 3-oxydecanoic acid → Leu → Gly → Ser → Val → Threo → Leu. More important is (+)-6-methyloctanoic acid (MeOct), found as a side chain in several cyclic polypeptides in which it is combined to the γ-amino group of α,γ-diaminobutyric acid (Dab). Such is the case in colistin (LVI), or rather colistins (*172f*), from *B. colistinus* (*173a*), in the circulins A and B (LVII), from *B.*

L-Dab $\xleftarrow{\alpha}$ L-Dab ⟶ D-Leu ⟶ L-Ileu
α ↑ ↓ α
L-Threo L-Dab
↑ ↓ α
L-Dab $\xleftarrow[\alpha]{}$ L-Threo ⟵ L-Dab* $\xleftarrow[\alpha]{}$ L-Dab
↑ γ
MeOct

Circulin A
(in circulin B, MeOct is bound to the starred Dab)
(LVII)

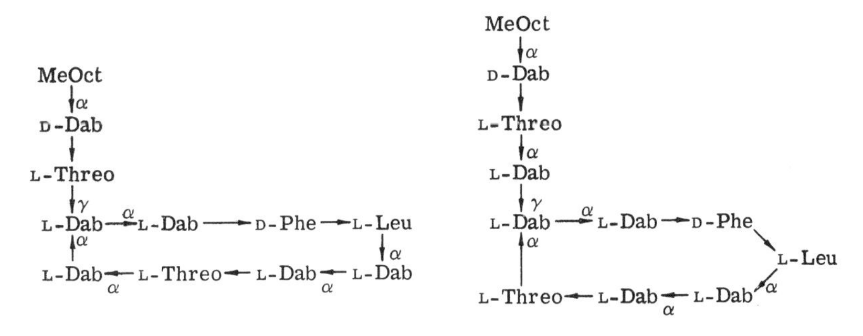

Two proposed structures for polymyxin B_1
(LVIII)

circulans, and in the polymyxins, from *B. polymyxa* (*173b, 174a*), of which six are known: A, sometimes called aerosporin since it is produced also by *B. aerosporus*, B_1, B_2, C, D, and E (Table IV). Two alternative structures (LVIII) have been proposed for polymyxin B_1. The polymyxin group of antibiotics is endowed with the property, quite unusual for polypeptide antibiotics, of being much more active against gram-negative than gram-positive bacteria. Nuclear lesions observed in colistin-treated *Escherichia coli* or *Pseudomonas aeruginosa* are different from those similarly induced in *Bacillus megaterium* (*174b*).

The gramicidins, tyrocidins, polymyxins, and subtilin inhibit the phosphorylations and promote the leakage of cell constituents. They are believed to induce damage to the cytoplasmic membrane by virtue of their tensioactive properties. Newton's experiments (*174c*), realized with an antibiotically active fluorescent derivative of polymyxin B obtained by coupling the γ-amino group of the α,γ-diaminobutyric acid of the anti-

TABLE IV
COMPOSITION OF THE POLYMYXINS[a]

Component found in hydrolyzate of polymyxins	Polymyxin					
	A	B_1	B_2	C	D	E
D-Serine	−	−	−	−	+	−
L-Threonine	+	2	2	+	+	+
Leucine	D	1L	1L	−	+	D
α,γ-Diaminobutyric acid	L	5L, 1D	5L, 1D	L	L	L
D-Phenylalanine	−	1	1	+	−	−
(+)-6-Methyloctanoic acid	+	1	−	+	+	+
Unidentified octanoic acid	−	−	1	−	−	−

[a] Symbols: + = component present; − = component absent. Wherever possible, the plus sign is replaced by D or/and L (indicating configuration) and/or a numeral (indicating the number of molecules of the amino acid in one of the polypeptide.

biotic with 1-dimethylaminonaphthalene 5-sulfonyl chloride, have conclusively demonstrated its specific fixation on the cell membrane of *Bacillus megaterium*. Gramicidin D and S and tyrocidins, but not polymyxin B and colistin, inhibit the ATP-reversal of reduced glutathione-induced mitochondrial swelling (*174d*).

The reasons explaining why such polypeptides have antibiotic properties and why they display a characteristic spectrum of activity are still obscure. However, studies bearing on the antimicrobial properties of animal and synthetic peptides (*175, 176*), some of which are analogs of polymyxins (*177a,b*), tyrocidins, and gramicidin S (*178–181*), are likely to help resolve the problem of the relations between structure and biological activity (*182, 183*).

An interesting feature of peptide antibiotics is observed in the actinomycins, red pigments produced by several species of streptomycetes as complex mixtures of different but closely related substances. A number of natural actinomycins have been isolated and characterized. Many more semisynthetic actinomycins (series E and F) have been obtained by addition to the culture medium of suitable amino acids, or even other substances, e.g., pipecolic acid, which are then preferentially incorporated into the antibiotic. Table V shows the origin and composition of several of the actinomycins (Brockmann's nomenclature). The presence of sarcosine and *N*-methylated amino acids is quite characteristic and it

TABLE V
COMPOSITION OF SOME OF THE ACTINOMYCINS

Actinomycins	Producing organisms[a]					Amino acids[b]											
	S. antibioticus	*S. chrysomallus*	*S. parvulus*	*S. fradiae*	*Streptomyces* sp.	Sarcosine	*N*-Methylalanine	Valine	*N*-Methylvaline	Isoleucine	Alloisoleucine	*N*-Methylisoleucine	Threonine	Proline	Hydroxyproline	Allohydroxyproline	Oxoproline
Natural																	
C 1	+	+	+	−	−	2	−	2D	2L	−	−	−	2L	2L	−	−	−
C 2	−	+	−	−	−	2	−	1D	2L	−	1D	−	2L	2L	−	−	−
C 3	+	+	−	−	−	2	−	−	2L	−	2D	−	2L	2L	−	−	−
X 0β	−	+	−	+	−	2	−	2	2	−	−	−	2	1	1	−	−
X 0γ	−	+	−	+	−	3	−	2	2	−	−	−	2	1	−	−	−
X 0δ	−	+	−	+	−	2	−	2	2	−	−	−	2	1	−	1	−
X 1a	−	+	−	+	−	3	−	2	2	−	−	−	2	−	−	−	1
X 2	−	+	−	−	−	2	−	2	2	−	−	−	2	1	−	−	1
X 3	−	−	−	+	−	+	−	+	+	+	−	−	+	+	−	−	−
Z0 to Z5	−	−	−	+	−	+	+	+	+	−	−	−	+	−	−	−	−
II	−	+	−	−	−	4	−	2D	2	−	−	−	2L	−	−	−	−
III	−	+	−	−	−	3	−	2D	2	−	−	−	2L	1L	−	−	−
Semisynthetic																	
E 1	−	−	−	−	+	2	−	−	1	−	2	1	2	2	−	−	−
E 2	−	−	−	−	+	2	−	−	−	−	2	2	2	2	−	−	−
F 1	−	−	−	−	+	4	−	1	2	−	1	−	2	−	−	−	−
F 2	−	−	−	−	+	3	−	1	2	−	1	−	2	1	−	−	−
F 3	−	−	−	−	+	4	−	−	2	−	2	−	2	−	−	−	−
F 4	−	−	−	−	+	3	−	−	2	−	2	−	2	1	−	−	−

[a] Symbols: + = produced by organism; − = not produced by it.
[b] Symbols: + = amino acid present; − = not present. Wherever possible the plus sign is replaced by D or L (indicating configuration) and/or a numeral (indicating number of molecules of the amino acid in one of the polypeptide.

should be stressed that the hydroxy amino acid threonine is a constant component of these antibiotics. Although the complete structure of the actinomycins has not been wholly worked out for each one of them, they are all believed to be, in the main, similar to actinomycin C_3 (LIX). They all have a common chromophore, actinocinin, which will be discussed later on. It possesses two carboxylic groups (LXXV) which are each engaged in an amidic bond with an amino acid. The latter belongs to a pentapeptide which is cyclized through the formation of an ester bond between the carboxylic group of an amino acid and the alcohol group of threonine. The two cyclic peptides may or may not be identical.

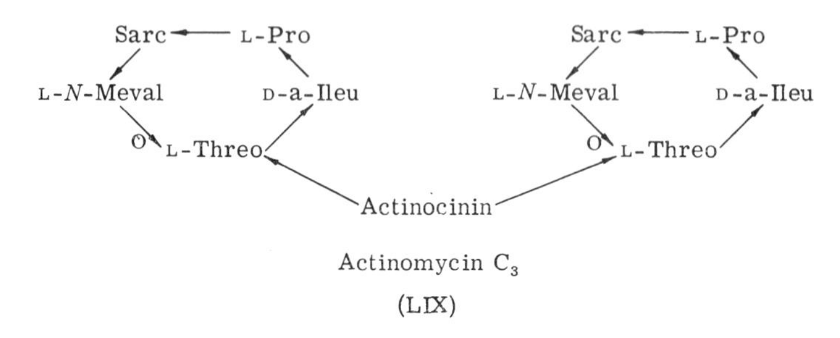

Actinomycin C_3

(LIX)

Actinomycin D, which differs from actinomycin C_3 only in that D-valine replaces D-alloisoleucine, has been rather extensively used as an anticancer agent. Its mode of action has therefore been especially studied. According to some authors, this antibiotic acts primarily on deoxyribonucleic acid (DNA), to which it can be specifically bound (*184a,b*), since it inhibits the production of a DNA-containing, but not of a RNA-containing, virus (*185*) and the DNA-dependent synthesis of RNA in a cell-free system, this effect being reversed by the addition of DNA (*186a,b*). However, according to others, its fundamental action would be the inhibition of RNA synthesis (*187*), more precisely of the incorporation of guanine nucleotides (*188a*). In any case, its long-known inhibitory effect upon protein biosynthesis might be explained as an indirect consequence of a biochemical lesion occurring on the metabolic pathway of either one of the nucleic acids. Actinomycin seems to inhibit the maturation of coliphage T2, but not the synthesis of its nucleic and protein moieties (*188b*).

Simpler derivatives (*189*) and synthetic analogs (*190*) of the actinomycins are actively investigated as potential anticancer agents.

A lactone ring similar to that of actinomycins occurs in echinomycin (LX), from S. *echinatus*, which is a typical representative of a group of streptomycete polypeptide antibiotics containing a quinoxaline moiety and comprising actinoleukin (S. *aureus*), levomycin, antibiotic F-43, the quinomycins, and the triostins (*191–193*).

It is also observed in other streptomycete-produced antibiotics: etamycin or viridogrisein (LXI), from S. *griseus*, S. *lavendulae*, S. *griseoviridus*, possibly the related pyridomycin (S. *pyridomyceticus*), and the B members of the staphylomycin complex, namely, staphylomycin S (LXII), from S. *virginiae*, ostreogrycins B, B_1, B_2, and B_3, from S. *ostreogriseus*, mikamycin B, from S. *mitakaensis*, antibiotics PA-114-B1 and PA-114-B3, from S. *olivaceus*.

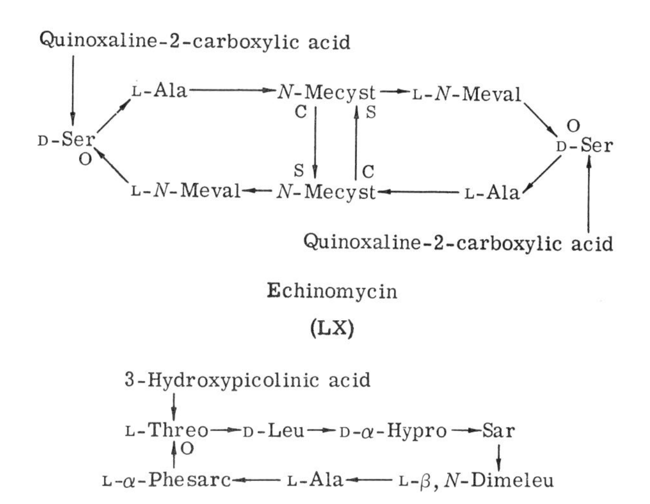

Echinomycin

(LX)

Etamycin

(LXI)

3-Hydroxypicolinic acid

L-Phegly —O→ L-Threo → D-α-aminobutyric acid

L-4-oxopipecolic acid ← L-N-Mephe ← L-Pro

Staphylomycin S[a]

(LXII)

[a] *p*-Dimethylamino-*N*-methylphenylalanine replaces *N*-methylphenylalanine in the ostreogrycins B, B_1, and B_3; in addition, D-alanine replaces D-α-amino-*n*-butyric acid in ostreogrycin B_1, and an unidentified compound replaces 4-oxopipecolic acid in ostreogrycin B_3.

p-Methylamino-*N*-methylphenylalanine probably replaces *N*-methylphenylalanine in ostreogrycin B_2.

p-Dimethylaminophenylalanine replaces *N*-methylphenylalanine in antibiotic PA-114-B1 which contains no 4-oxopipecolic acid but sarcosine and perhaps 5-hydroxymethylhydroxyproline. The same components occur in antibiotic PA-114-B3, except for sarcosine, which is replaced by another unidentified *N*-methylamino acid.

A minor component of the antibiotic complex streptogramin, from *S. graminofaciens,* also belongs in the staphylomycin family.

Antibiotics of this group, especially mikamycin (*194, 195*), appear to inhibit protein, but not nucleic acid, metabolism.

4. *Peptolide Antibiotics*

A lactone ring, in this case resulting from the combination of a hydroxy fatty acid and an amino acid, is observed in esperin (LXIII), a

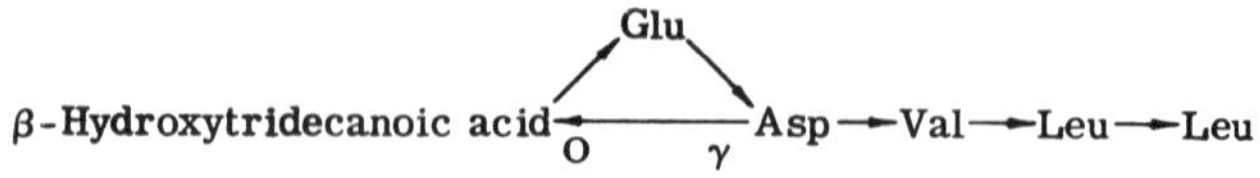

Glu
β-Hydroxytridecanoic acid ← O γ Asp → Val → Leu → Leu

Esperin

(LXIII)

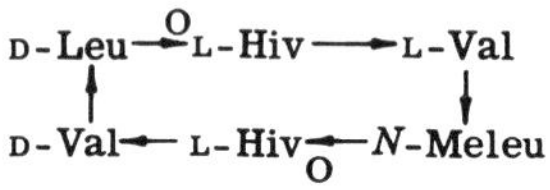

D-Leu →O L-Hiv → L-Val
D-Val ← L-Hiv ←O N-Meleu

Sporidesmolide I

(LXIV)

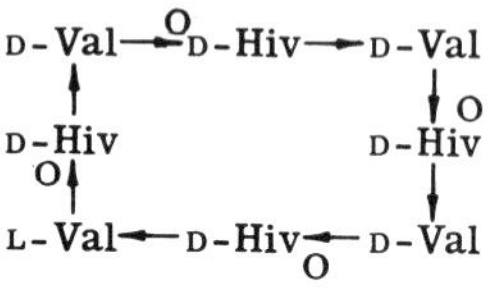

D-Val →O D-Hiv → D-Val
D-Hiv O D-Hiv
L-Val ← D-Hiv ←O D-Val

Amidomycin

(LXV)

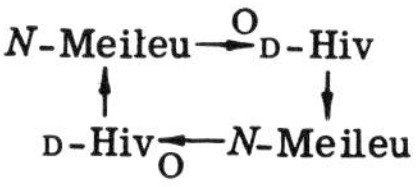

N-Meileu →O D-Hiv
D-Hiv ←O N-Meileu

Enniatin A

(LXVI)

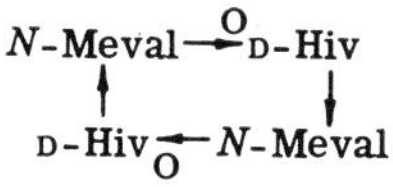

N-Meval →O D-Hiv
D-Hiv ←O N-Meval

Enniatin B

(LXVII)

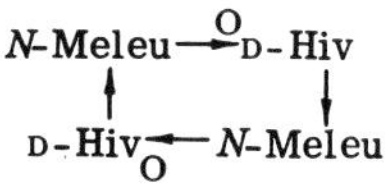

N-Meleu →O D-Hiv
D-Hiv ←O N-Meleu

Enniatin C

(LXVIII)

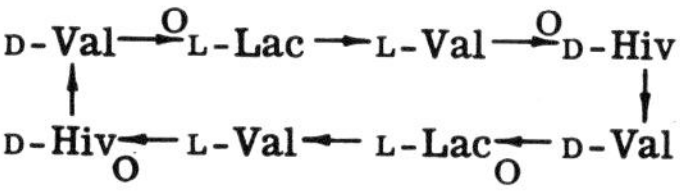

D-Val →O L-Lac → L-Val →O D-Hiv
D-Hiv ←O L-Val ← L-Lac ←O D-Val

Valinomycin

(LXIX)

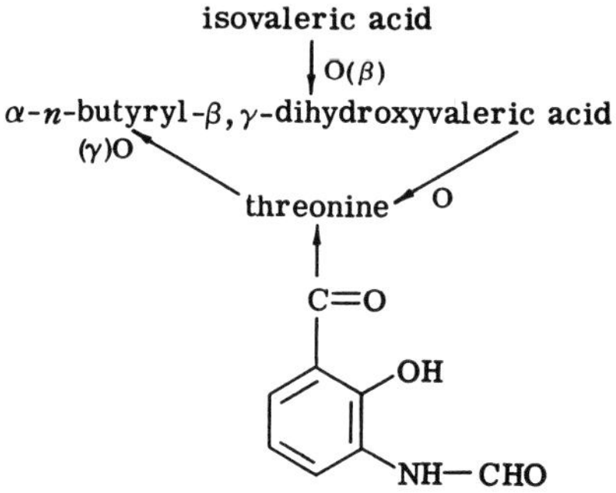

isovaleric acid
O(β)
α-*n*-butyryl-β,γ-dihydroxyvaleric acid
(γ)O O
threonine
C=O
OH
NH—CHO

Antimycin 3 or Blastmycin

(LXX)

metabolic product from *Bacillus mesentericus*. This type of oxygen bridge occurs in a number of cyclic antibiotic peptides containing, in addition to amino acids, α-hydroxyisovaleric acid (HIV), first discovered in sporidesmolide I (LXIV), a metabolic product from *Phytomyces chartarum* (*Sporidesmium bakeri*) (*196a,b*). Examples of those compounds, for which the names peptolides and depsipeptides were suggested, are amidomycin (LXV) from *Streptomyces* sp. and several antibiotics produced by species of the genera *Fusarium* and *Gibberella*: the enniatins A (LXVI) (*196c*), B (LXVII) (*196d*), and C (LXVIII) and the lateritiins (lateritiin II, avenacein, fructigenin, sambucinin).

In valinomycin (LXIX) or aminomycin from *S. fulvissimus* and other streptomycetes (*196e,f*), lactic acid (Lac) is present together with Hiv. In the antimycins (*197*) or antipiriculins, produced by several species of streptomycetes (*S. griseus, S. kitasawaensis, S. blastmyceticus*), the amino acid moiety becomes only a minor part of the whole structure (LXX). Antimycins are specific respiration inhibitors. They block electron transfer, some of them by preventing the oxidation by cytochrome c of reduced cytochrome b (*198, 199a–d*).

5. *Proteinaceous Antibiotics*

The colicins (*67*), and possibly other bacteriocins (*200a,b*) such as megacins (*200c, 201a,b*), pyocins (*202a,b*), pesticins (*203, 204*), vibriocins (*205*), are complex antibiotics generally considered to be proteins or at least to contain an important proteinaceous moiety. In fact, their chemistry has been investigated in but a few cases. Colicins K and V are considered as lipocarbohydrate-protein complexes identical with somatic O antigens (*206, 207a,b*), but megacin (*208*) appears to be a pure protein. Their biochemical mode of action is unknown, although, in the case of megacin, leakage of cell components following damage to the cytoplasmic membrane was reported (*209a*). Colicins, like the bacteriophage capsides, to which they have been likened, attach themselves to specific cell receptors and, once thus bound, inhibit further synthesis of nucleic acid (*209b*).

Several protein enzymes which are able to kill microorganisms, or even to dissolve (*210, 211*) living bacterial bodies, are undoubtedly to be included, on that account, among the antibiotics. The best known of them is lysozyme (*212, 213*), which not only is found in the tissues and secretions of various animal species, particularly in egg white, but is also produced by bacteria, for instance, *Bacillus subtilis* and *Staphylococcus aureus* (*126, 214*). This enzyme digests a universal component (*69a*) of the bacterial cell wall (*215a,b*), responsible for its mechanical strength, with the result that the wall-less protoplast or wall-deficient spheroplast explodes unless it is stabilized in a medium of high enough osmotic pressure (*102, 103a*).

The degree of bacterial sensitivity to lysozyme is widely different for different species. It is related to the chemical composition and anatomical (*216*) structure of their cell wall (*217*). In species where the specific substrate of the enzyme is not readily accessible, normally lysozyme-resistant cells can be made sensitive either by suitable pretreatments, such as lipid extraction or freeze drying followed by rehydration (*218*), or by the choice of particular experimental conditions, such as a high alkalinity, the presence of Versene (*219*), of glycine (*220*), etc. (*221*). Lysozyme-resistant mutants of the very sensitive species *Micrococcus lysodeikticus* appear to owe their peculiar properties to an increase of the O-acetyl content of their cell wall (*222*).

Several other bacteriolytic enzymes acting upon different sites of the basal structure of the bacterial cell wall have been described. They are found, notably, in cultures of streptomycetes (*223, 224*), where they constitute the actinomycetin complex (*9, 225, 226*), of bacilli (*227*), and of other microorganisms as well (*228, 229*). Some are associated with bacteriophages, either as an integral part of the virus (*230*) or as a free entity produced by the host cell alongside with, but independently of, the virus (*231–233*).

The mode of action of all these enzymes superficially recalls that of several antibiotics already reviewed: novobiocin, D-cycloserine, the penicillins, bacitracin, and vancomycin (*126, 234a*). However, although the final result is the same in all cases, the mechanisms involved are greatly different: the antibiotics in some way prevent the biosynthesis of the wall, whereas the enzymes destroy, or impair the mechanical resistance of, an already existing wall. As a consequence, the latter are able to dissolve resting, or even killed, bacteria, whereas the former act only upon metabolically active organisms, their effect resulting precisely from the unbalanced growth for which they are responsible.

Another enzyme which can exert antibiotic effects is notatin, a flavoprotein with glucose oxidase activity, produced by *Penicillium notatum*, *P. vitale* (*234b*), and other species. It is indirectly bactericidal through its ability to produce the toxic hydrogen peroxide. The same kind of antibiotic effect was reported for xanthine oxidase in the presence of xanthine.

Antagonistic relations observed between mouth microorganisms and the antibiotic activity of pneumococci have been explained by a similar mechanism.

In closing this section, it should be recalled that several proteins from animal tissues, e.g., phagocytin (*235*) and especially protamines (*236*) and histones (*237a*), are responsible for various antimicrobial effects.

6. *Diketopiperazine Antibiotics*

Echinulin, a metabolic product of *Aspergillus echinulatus, A. chevalieri,* and members of the *Aspergillus glaucus* group, contains a moiety which appears as a diketopiperazine formed from alanine and leucine. Similarly, mycelianamide (LXXI), from *Penicillium griseofulvum,* and gliotoxin (LXXII), produced by several species belonging in the genera *Trichoderma, Gliocladium, Aspergillus,* and *Penicillium,* are diketo-

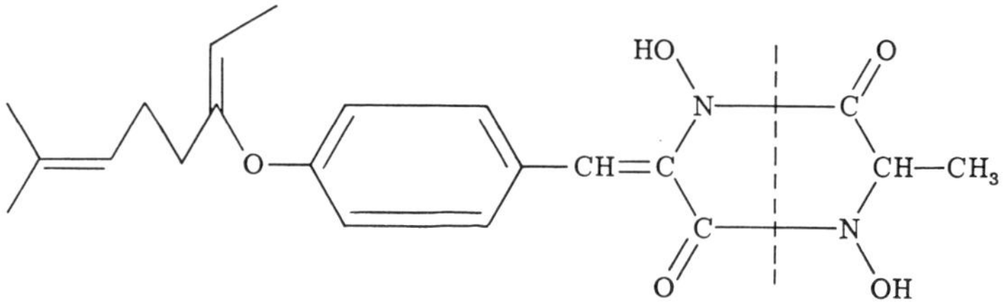

HO O N C O CH=C CH—CH_3 C N O OH

Mycelianamide

(LXXI)

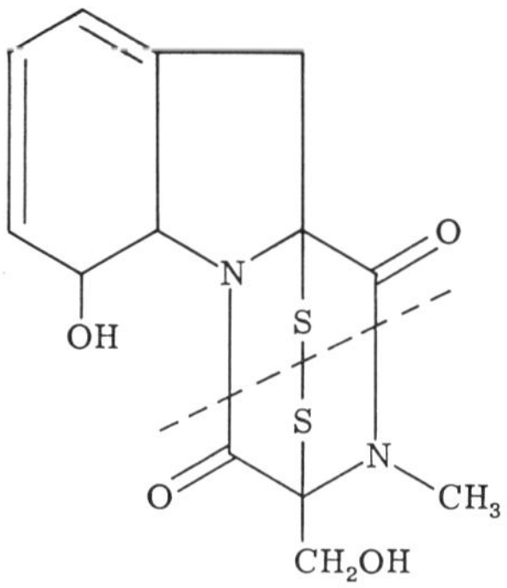

O N OH S S O N CH_3 CH_2OH

Gliotoxin

(LXXII)

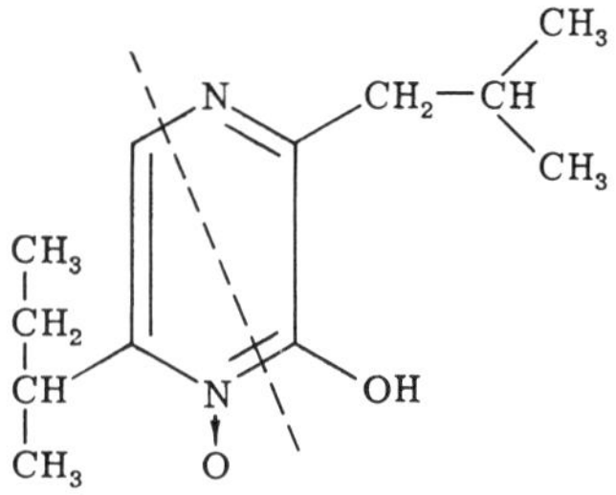

CH_3 N CH_2—CH CH_3 CH_3 CH_2 CH N OH CH_3 O

Aspergillic acid

(LXXIII)

piperazines formed, respectively, from tyrosine and alanine and from phenylalanine and serine. The latter antibiotic, which shows the additional feature of an —S—S— bridge across the heterocyclic ring, has been shown, by C^{14} labeling, to be effectively synthesized from the two amino acids cited and methionine.

Diketopiperazine formation, followed by oxidation to yield a dihydropiperazine, probably accounts for the biosynthesis (*237b*) of aspergillic acid (LXXIII), from leucine and isoleucine, by *Aspergillus flavus*. The same organism also produces flavacol, which arises through the same route from two molecules of leucine; further oxidation, however, results in aromatization to a pyrazine. It is worth noting that pulcherrimic acid, which, iron complexed, constitutes the red pigment pulcherrimin of *Candida pulcherrima*, is dioxyflavacol-*N*,*N'*-dioxide.

7. *Antibiotics Biogenetically Related to the Pathways of Biosynthesis of Aromatic Amino Acids*

Violacein (LXXIV), the antibiotic pigment of *Chromobacterium violaceum*, appears to be derived from two molecules of tryptophan, but is not a dipeptide.

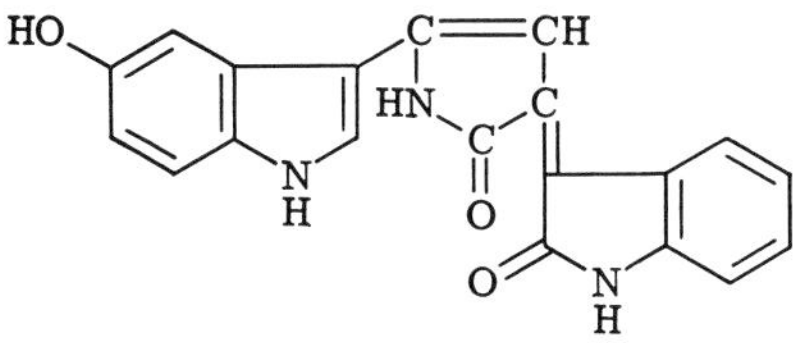

Violacein

(LXXIV)

Actinocinin (LXXV), the chromophore common to the actinomycins, red antibiotic pigments produced by streptomycetes (LIX) (Table V) is closely related to the cinnabarin (LXXVI) of *Coriolus sanguineus* and to the chromophore of the insect pigments called ommochromes. Feeding experiments with labeled tryptophan have shown that an ommo-

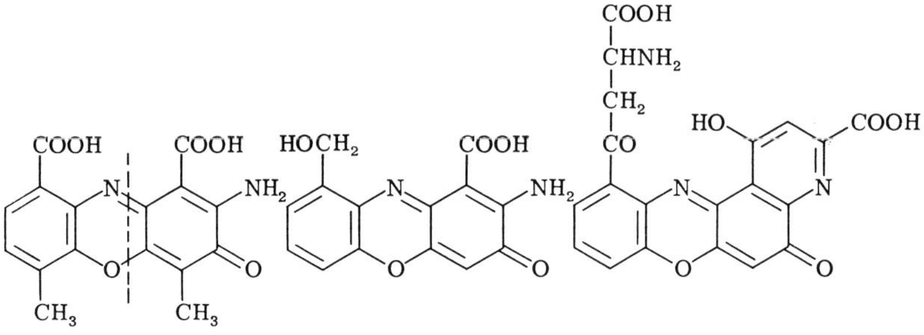

Actinocinin (LXXV)

Cinnabarin (LXXVI)

Xanthommatin (LXXVII)

chrome, xanthommatin (LXXVII), is derived from the amino acid via kynurenine. A similar origin was subsequently demonstrated for actinocinin (*238*, *239a*), the assumed intermediate being 3-oxy-4-methyl-anthranilic acid, which may stem from the normal biosynthetic route of tryptophan. It is probable that the peptide chains of the actinomycins are bound to the actinocinin precursors before their condensation to form the phenoxazone chromophore.

Although few experimental data are available, it is generally surmised, by analogy, that other phenazine and phenoxazone antibiotics also arise through the shikimic acid pathway (*239b*). Such would be the case for questiomycin A (LXXVIII), from *Streptomyces* sp., which appears to result from the condensation of two molecules of questiomycin B (LXXIX), itself identified as *o*-aminophenol,* and for a series of variously substituted phenazines (LXXX) including hemipyocyanin (1-hydroxyphenazine) from *Pseudomonas aeruginosa*, oxychlororaphine

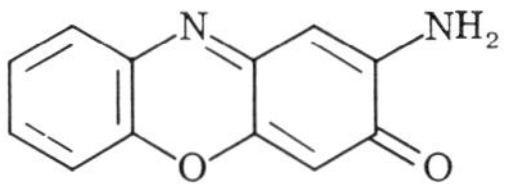

Questiomycin A

(LXXVIII)

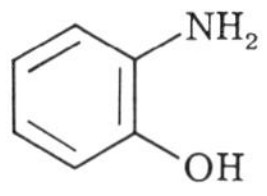

Questiomycin B

(LXXIX)

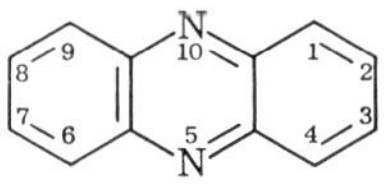

Phenazine

(LXXX)

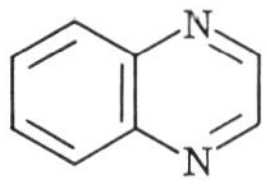

Quinoxaline

(LXXXI)

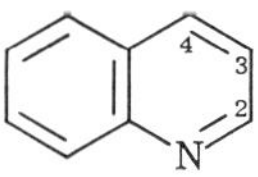

Quinoline

(LXXXII)

(1-carboxamidophenazine) and chlororaphine (a molecular compound of the former and its 5,10-dihydro derivative in the ratio 3:1), both from *P. chlororaphis*, 1-carboxyphenazine, which is produced by *P. aureofaciens*, *Streptomyces misakiensis*, and *Calonectria* sp., pyocyanine (5-methylphenazine 1-oxide), the blue pigment from *P. aeruginosa* and *Cyanococcus chromospirans* (*240, 241*), 1,6-dihydroxyphenazine, from *Streptomyces thioluteus*, and its 5,10-dioxide, iodinin, from *Chromobacterium iodinum*, the various metabolic products isolated from cultures of *Streptomyces griseoluteus:* 1-hydroxymethyl-6-carboxyphenazine, 1-methoxy-4-methyl-9-carboxyphenazine, 1-methoxy-4-hydroxymethyl-9-

* In a recent report, evidence was given for the production of *o*-aminophenol as a metabolic product from tryptophan. A human with multiple myeloma received DL-tryptophan-7a-C^{14}. The urine of the following 24 hours contained 14% of the radioactivity and small amounts of *o*-aminophenol-2-C^{14} were recovered [L. V. Hanks, M. Schmaeler, and K. Rai, *Proc. Soc. Exptl. Biol. Med.* **110**, 420–422 (1962)].

carboxyphenazine (or griseolutic acid), the griseoluteins A and B, which are 9-methoxy-1-carboxyphenazines bearing, respectively, in position 6, the side chain:

$$-CH_2—O—CO—CH_2OH \quad \text{and} \quad —CH_2—O—CHOH—CH_2OH$$

It should be stressed that, despite the great resemblance of the griseoluteins, only slight cross-resistance is observed between the two antibiotics, and also that, despite the similarity of 1,6-dihydroxyphenazine and iodinin, the former is specifically antifungal whereas the latter is antibacterial.

A relation with the shikimic acid route is also probable for the biosynthesis of the quinoxaline moiety (LXXXI) of antibiotics of the echinomycin (LX) family and for the quinoline nucleus (LXXXII) common to the pyo compounds of *Pseudomonas aeruginosa.* They include derivatives of 4-oxyquinoline [e.g., 2-*n*-heptyl, 2-*n*-nonyl (and their *N*-oxides), 2-*n*-Δ^1-nonenyl 2-*n*-undecyl-*N*-oxide] and the 2-*n*-heptyl-3-oxy-4-quinolone. These compounds may arise from the combination of anthranilic acid with a fatty acid followed by, first, oxidative decarboxylation, and next, reduction. The possibility of direct production from tryptophan, via kynurenine, has however not been ruled out.

According to Chambers *et al.* (*242*), the C_6–C_3 coumarin moiety of novobiocin (XVI), as well as the C_6–C_1 fragment to which it is linked by an amide bond, originate from tyrosine. The cinnamic acid moiety which, in homomycin (IX) and related antibiotics, is bound to an amino sugar by an amide linkage, is also likely to be formed via the shikimic acid pathway, and so is the *p*-aminobenzoic acid of the amicetin group of antibiotics (XV).

Little is known of the biosynthesis of chloramphenicol (LXXXIII) by *Streptomyces venezuelae.* Contrary to expectation, C^{14}-labeled *p*-nitrophenylserinol and dichloroacetic acid were found not to be incorporated into its molecule. The presence of the phenylpropane skeleton, however, suggests its relation to the common aromatic amino acids and the probability of its origin via the shikimic acid pathway.

The occurrence, in chloramphenicol, of the dichloroacetyl and aryl nitro groups are rather unusual features for a natural product. The latter, however, is also found in aureothin (LXXXIV) a by product found in the cultures of aureothricin-producing *S. thioluteus.* A nitro group is also present in azomycin (LXXXV), a heterocyclic antibiotic produced by *Nocardia mesenterica* and *Streptomyces eurocidicus,* and in the aliphatic antibiotic bovinocidin, $NO_2—CH_2—CH_2—COOH$, a substance, weakly active against *Mycobacterium tuberculosis,* which is produced by several green plants, fungi, and a *Streptomyces* sp.

Chloramphenicol is believed to act primarily as an inhibitor of protein synthesis (*243a–d*), since much higher concentrations are necessary to prevent RNA synthesis as well. In spite of its structural analogy with phenylalanine, chloramphenicol does not act as a specific antagonist of the particular amino acid. It interferes with a late stage of protein

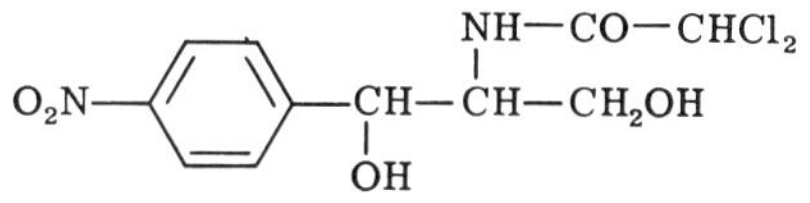

Chloramphenicol

(LXXXIII)

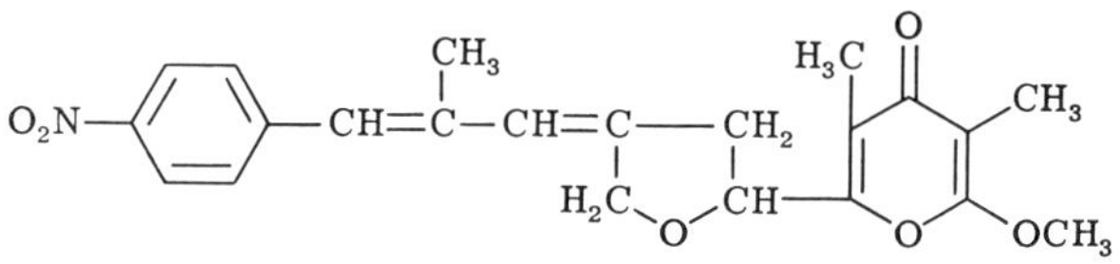

Aureothin

(LXXXIV)

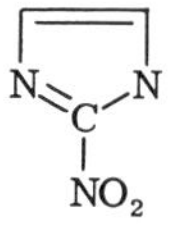

Azomycin

(LXXXV)

synthesis, as do also the tetracyclines, erythromycin, and puromycin. Chloramphenicol probably prevents the transfer of activated amino acids from their carrier, soluble RNA, to cytoplasmic proteins, but not to cell wall protein (mucopeptide) constituents (*122, 136, 138, 244a,b*). Evidence has been provided that RNA produced by cells in which protein synthesis is depressed by chloramphenicol is in an abnormal, unstable, and possibly nonfunctional state (*245, 246a,b*), also that its distribution within the cell is quite different from normal: it is found associated with DNA in the "chromatinic body" fraction separated from the cells by lipase treatment and in the "cell membrane-chromatinic body" fraction obtained from protoplasts by osmotic shock (*247*). However, according to Aronson and Spiegelman (*248a*), the abnormal distribution is an artifact resulting from the methods of extraction used, and the labile RNA recognized in chloramphenicol-treated cells represents a normal intermediate of ribonucleoprotein synthesis. It is found in small amount in normal cells, where it is stabilized by combination with a special protein, poor in sulfur-containing amino acids, the synthesis of which is less sensitive to chloramphenicol than that of other cell proteins.

The difficulty of assessing the primary biochemical lesion responsible for the antibacterial activity of chloramphenicol has been stressed by Hahn and collaborators (*248b*).

Chloramphenicol can be prepared by chemical synthesis and, of the four possible isomers, only the naturally occurring one, the D(—)-*threo* form, has appreciable antibiotic activity and inhibitory effect on most ordinary protein syntheses. But, on the contrary, as shown by Hahn, Wiseman, and Hopps, its antipode, the L(+)-*erythro* compound, is much more active as a specific inhibitor of the biosynthesis of the D-glutamyl polypeptide found in the capsular material of *Bacillus subtilis.* This interesting observation stresses the high degree of stereospecificity of the antibiotic. If the ring structure appears to be necessary for antibiotic activity, the position, and even the presence, of the aryl nitro group are not essential, since it can be shifted from the *para* to the *ortho* or *meta* positions or replaced by a halogen without much impairment of activity. On the contrary, even slight changes in the side chain are generally accompanied by an almost total loss of activity.

8. *Nitrogen-Containing Heterocyclic Moieties of Antibiotics*

The pyrrole ring occurs in netropsin (XXXIX) an antibiotic produced by several streptomycetes (*S. netropsis*, *S. ambofaciens*, *S. reticuli*), and in prodigiosin (LXXXVI), the red antibiotic pigment of *Serratia marcescens* (*249*). The presence in the latter of the rather uncommon 2,2′-

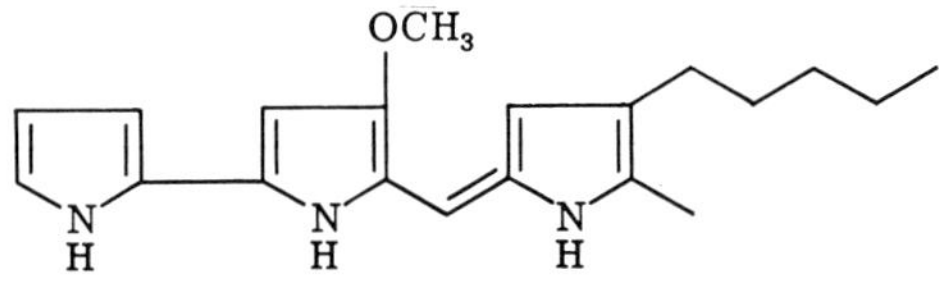

OCH_3

N N N
H H H

Prodigiosin
(LXXXVI)

dipyrrole skeleton should be stressed. Its biosynthesis, different from that of the porphyrins, appears to be linked to the metabolism of the 5-carbon atom amino acids: glutamic acid, proline, ornithine (*250*). It may not be out of place to recall here the well-known antibiotic activity of hematin against species of the genus *Bacillus* and the antibiotic properties of chlorophyll.

It has already been pointed out (p. 267) that the pyrimidine cytosine occurs in amicetin, plicacetin, and bamicetin (XV), and that 4-aminopyrrolo-(2,3-*d*)-pyrimidine occurs in tubercidin (XIII) and toyocamycin. The biosynthesis of these moieties is very likely related to that of normal pyrimidines, nucleosides, and nucleotides (*251*). The most favored pathway for the biosynthesis of cytosine is from L-glutamine amination of uracil, itself derived from decarboxylation of orotic acid which arises, through ureidosuccinic acid and L-dihydroorotic acid, from the condensation of L-aspartic acid and carbamyl phosphate.

The occurrence of antibiotics containing, as their basic ring system, the pyrimido-(5,4-*e*)-*as*-triazine nucleus should be mentioned here. They are toxoflavin (LXXXVII) from *Pseudomonas cocovenenans* (*252*) and fervenulin (LXXXVIII) from *Streptomyces fervens* (*253*).

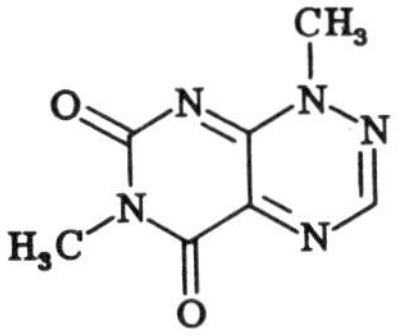

Toxoflavine

(LXXXVII)

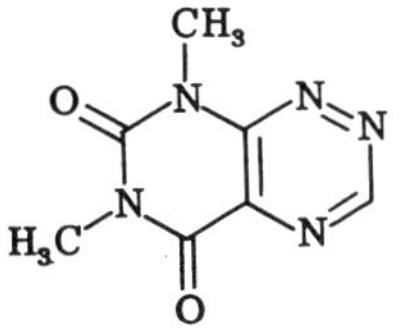

Fervenulin

(LXXXVIII)

The nucleosidic nature of several antibiotics has been reported above (p. 265): the purine-containing nebularine, the adenine-containing cordycepin, nucleocidin, angustmycins A and C, psicofuranine and antibiotic U-9586, the *N*-dimethyladenine-containing puromycin (XIV). Their purine moiety, again, is likely to arise through the normal routes of purine, nucleoside, and nucleotide synthesis, which involve, as starting materials, D-ribose, glycine, a formyl fragment, and the aminating agent glutamine (*254–256*).

It is interesting to note here that the recently discovered antifungal antibiotic pathocidin (*257*), produced by *Streptomyces* sp., is a naturally occurring analog of guanine (*258a*), identified as 8-azaguanine (LXXXIX).

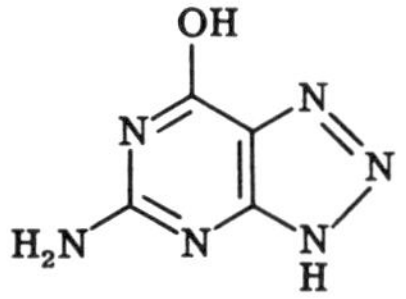

Pathocidin

(LXXXIX)

Mention should be made of actithiazic acid (XC), an S- and N-containing antibiotic produced by *Streptomyces virginiae, S. cinnamonensis,* and *S. lavendulae*. Its biosynthesis has not been worked out, but it shows a structural relationship to biotin (XCI) and appears to act as a specific inhibitor of the coenzyme.

Although nothing is known of their biosynthesis, antibiotics of the mitomycin group may also be conveniently mentioned here. They were

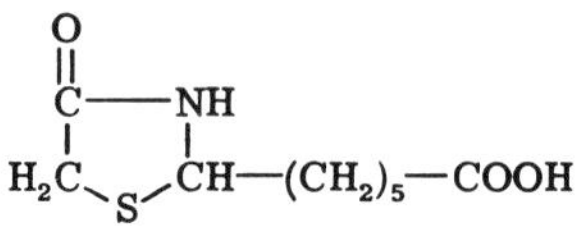

Actithiazic acid

(XC)

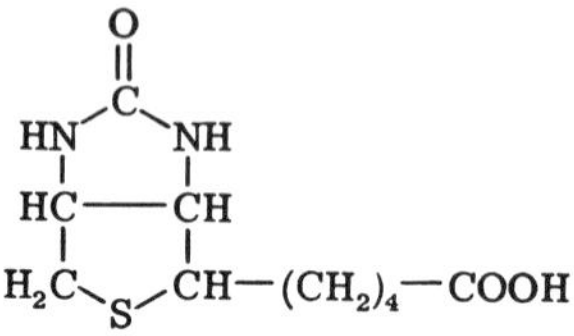

Biotin

(XCI)

recently attributed the curious structure shown in XCIb (*258b*). They comprise mitomycins A, B, and C, produced by *Streptomyces caespitosus* and S. *griseovinaceseus,* and porfiromycin (*258c,d*), from S. *ardus.* They

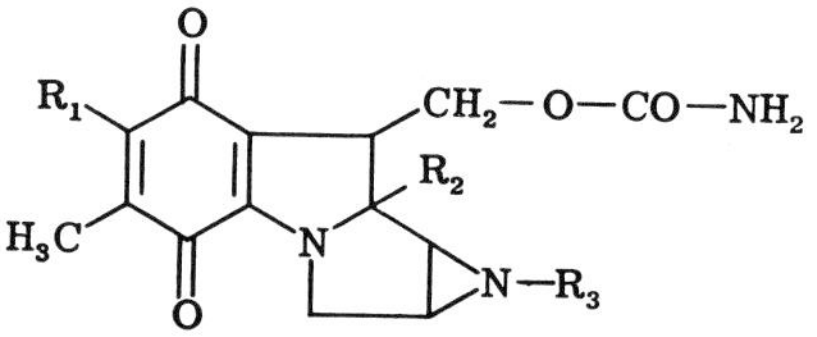

Mitomycins [a]

(XCIb)

[a] In "mitosane": $R_1 = H$; $R_2 = H$; $R_3 = H$.
In mitomycin A: $R_1 = OCH_3$; $R_2 = OCH_3$; $R_3 = H$.
In mitomycin B: $R_1 = OCH_3$; $R_2 = OH$; $R_3 = CH_3$.
In mitomycin C: $R_1 = NH_2$; $R_2 = OCH_3$; $R_3 = H$.
In porfiromycin: $R_1 = NH_2$; $R_2 = OCH_3$; $R_3 = CH_3$.

have antimicrobial as well as anticancer properties. Mitomycin C, which has been clinically used, was rather more studied than the others. It acts upon bacteria (*258e*), mammalian cells (*258f*), and plant cells (*258g,h*). Its primary effect appears to be the inhibition of DNA synthesis (*258i–l*).

C. Antibiotics Wholly or Partially Derivable from Acetate or Propionate

An acetate or propionate origin has been demonstrated for some antibiotics or antibiotic moieties. A similar biosynthesis is assumed, by analogy, for many more, ranging in complexity from simple aliphatic acids to macrocyclic lactones, steroids, aromatic and polycyclic compounds.

1. *Fatty Acids and Derivatives in Antibiotics*

Fatty acids, especially the unsaturated ones, have been reported as having antimicrobial properties (*259*) often ascribed to their lowering effect on surface tension. It is also worth while to recall that one of the first chemically defined substance isolated from a bacterial culture (*Bacillus mesentericus*) with a view to explaining its bactericidal and bacteriolytic activities was isovaleric acid (*260a*).

Many of the simpler aliphatic acids found in antibiotics are members of, or readily derived from, the citric acid cycle or related metabolic pathways. Longer-chain acids and derivatives are generally synthesized from acetate through a well-known route involving the participation of acetyl and malonyl units, coenzyme A, and biotin.

Actinomycin J_2 (or B), from *Streptomyces antibioticus,* was identified as the dodecyl ester of 5-oxostearic acid. Isovaleric acid, linked to the sugar mycarose (XXII), is found in carbomycins A and B (CXIV).

The occurrence of a fatty, or hydroxy fatty, acid moiety in glycolipid (V, VI), polypeptide (Table III, viscosine, LVI–LVIII), and depsipeptide (LXIII–LXX) antibiotics has been reported above. Similar moieties are also found in simpler substances partially derived from amino acids: fumarylylalanine, serratamic acid, antibiotics of the holothin-pyrrothin group (XLV), pyo compounds, cephalosporins N (XXXVIIb) and C (XXXVIII). The α-aminoadipoyl and acetoxy groups of the latter were shown, by isotope studies, to be acetate derived (*260b*).

A number of microorganisms are endowed with the ability to produce special types of acids, many of them antibiotic, as a result of the condensation of keto acids with long-chain fatty acids. Examples are roccellic (*260c*) (XCII), rangiformic (XCIII), and caperatic (XCIV)

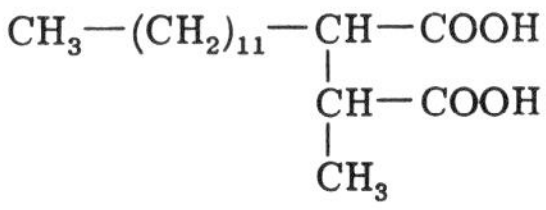

$$\begin{array}{l} CH_3-(CH_2)_{11}-CH-COOH \\ \qquad\qquad\qquad\quad | \\ \qquad\qquad\qquad\; CH-COOH \\ \qquad\qquad\qquad\quad | \\ \qquad\qquad\qquad\; CH_3 \end{array}$$

Roccellic acid

(XCII)

$$\begin{array}{l} CH_3-(CH_2)_{13}-CH-COOH \\ \qquad\qquad\qquad\quad | \\ \qquad\qquad\qquad\; CH-COOH \\ \qquad\qquad\qquad\quad | \\ \qquad\qquad\quad H-CH-COOH \end{array}$$

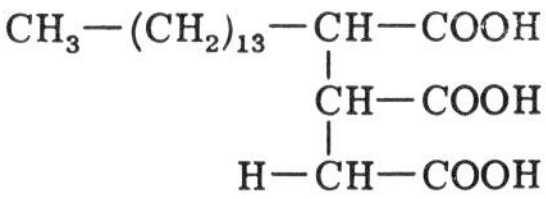

Rangiformic acid

(XCIII)

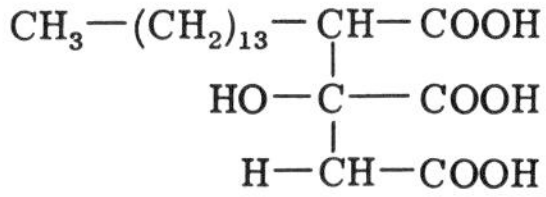

$$\begin{array}{l} CH_3-(CH_2)_{13}-CH-COOH \\ \qquad\qquad\qquad\quad | \\ \qquad\qquad\quad HO-C-COOH \\ \qquad\qquad\qquad\quad | \\ \qquad\qquad\quad H-CH-COOH \end{array}$$

Caperatic acid

(XCIV)

$$\begin{array}{l} CH_3-(CH_2)_{15}-CH-COOH \\ \qquad\qquad\qquad\quad | \\ \qquad\qquad\qquad\; CH-COOH \\ \qquad\qquad\qquad\quad | \\ \qquad\qquad\; HO-CH-COOH \end{array}$$

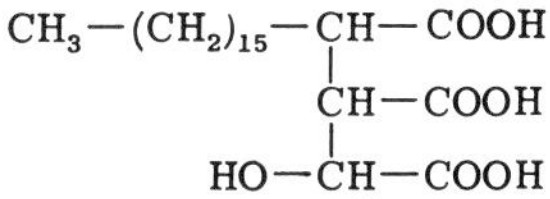

Ungulinic acid

(XCV)

acids, all produced by lichens, and ungulinic acid (XCV), from the basidiomycete *Polyporus betulinus.*

The mold-produced tetronic acids, carlosic (XCVI) and carolic (XCVII), have been shown, by isotope studies, to be formed from the condensation of a 6-carbon atom chain, derived from acetate, respectively, 3-ketohexanoic and 3-keto-6-hydroxyhexanoic acid, with an acid

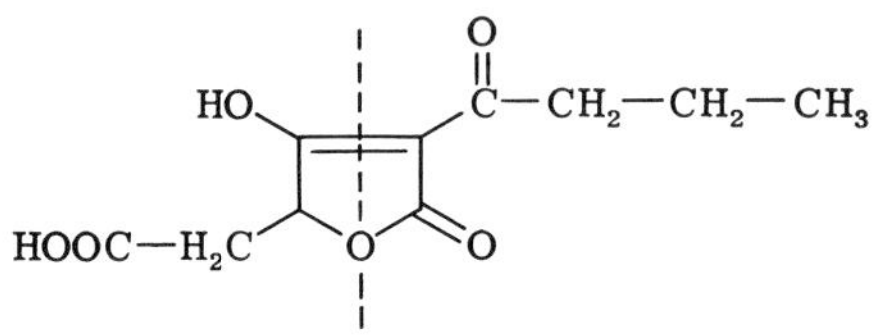

Carlosic acid
(XCVI)

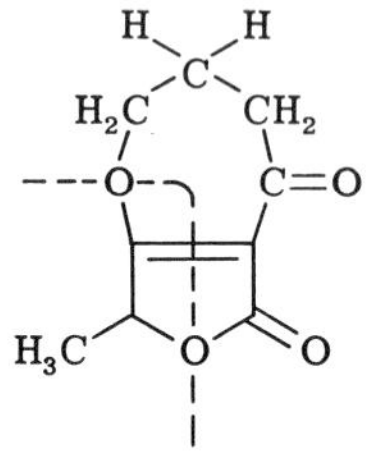

Carolic acid
(XCVII)

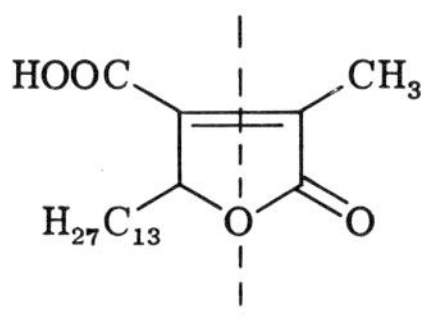

Lichesterinic acid
(XCVIII)

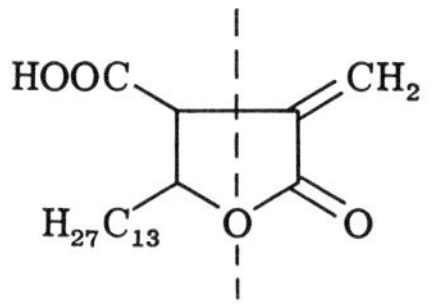

Protolichesterinic acid
(XCIX)

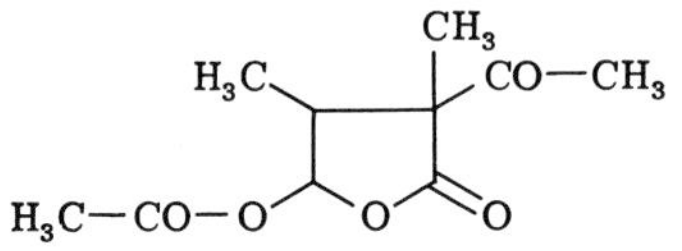

Acetomycin
(C)

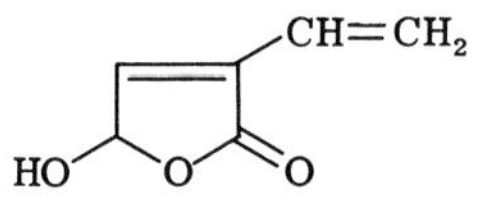

Antibiotic PA-147
(CI)

of the Krebs cycle, malic or oxaloacetic for the former, lactic or pyruvic for the latter (*261a*). By analogy, it is assumed that the lichen-produced *l*-lichesterinic (XCVIII) and protolichesterinic (XCIX) acid, of which the *d* and *l-allo* isomers are known, are formed from pyruvate and 3-oxypalmitate.

The mode of formation of two, obviously related, streptomycete antibiotics—acetomycin (C), from *S. ramulosus,* and PA-147 (CI) (*261b*) from *Streptomyces* sp., is possibly similar.

The same type of biosynthesis appears as a plausible hypothesis in the case of penicillic acid (*262a*), a product of several species of *Penicillium* and of *Aspergillus ochraceus.* However, it is not corroborated

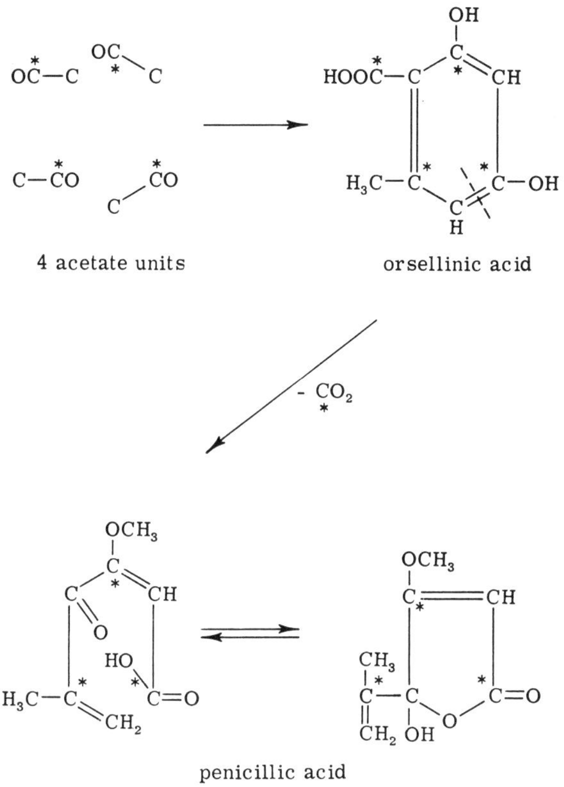

4 acetate units

orsellinic acid

$- CO_2$

penicillic acid

Biosynthesis of penicillic acid

(CII)

by experiments involving the use of labeled acetate. The antibiotic seems to arise from four acetate fragments via the aromatic orsellinic acid (CII).

It is well established that certain bacteria, especially in the genera *Corynebacterium* and *Mycobacterium,* are capable of coupling long aliphatic chains. A similar process is possibly involved in the biosynthesis of such antibiotics as alternaric acid (CIII), from *Alternaria solani,* and bongkrekic acid from *Pseudomonas cocovenenans.*

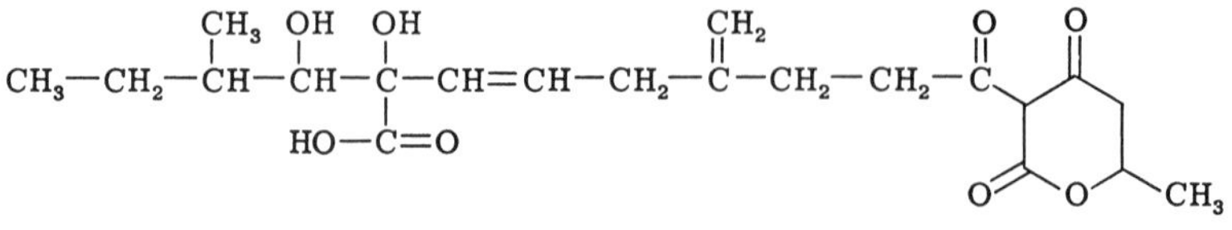

$$CH_3-CH_2-CH(CH_3)-CH(OH)-C(OH)(COOH)-CH=CH-CH_2-C(=CH_2)-CH_2-CH_2-C(=O)-[\text{ring: } C_5H_6O_3 \text{ lactone with } CH_3]$$

Alternaric acid

(CIII)

2. *Polyenes and Polyynes in Antibiotics*

A large number of antibiotics, very likely acetate derived, are characterized by the presence of several ethylenic or/and acetylenic bonds. They are often produced together with related substances devoid of antibiotic activity.

Polyynes, although they are found in higher plants (for instance, the antifungal capillin from *Artemisia capillaris*), lower fungi, and actinomycetes, are especially frequent as metabolic products of basidiomycetes. Examples are:

agrocybin from *Agrocybe dura,*

$$HOCH_2-C\equiv C-C\equiv C-C\equiv C-CONH_2$$

diatretyne 1 (inactive);

$$COOH-CH=CH-C\equiv C-C\equiv C-CONH_2$$

diatretyne 2 or nudic acid;

$$COOH-CH=CH-C\equiv C-C\equiv C-C\equiv N$$

diatretyne 3,

$$COOH-CH=CH-C\equiv C-C\equiv C-C\equiv C-CH_2OH$$

all from *Clitocybe diatreta.* It has been remarked that the latter substance bears some resemblance to the antibiotic principle of the royal jelly of bees:

$$COOH-CH=CH-(CH_2)_6-CH_2OH$$

The several quadrifidins, from *Coprinus quadrifidus,* and biformin, from *Polyporus biformis,* belong in the same category.

Nemotin,

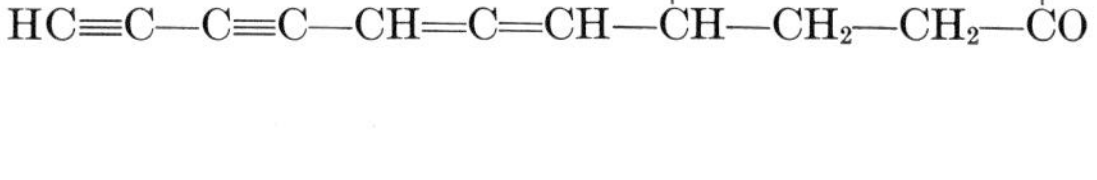

$$HC\equiv C-C\equiv C-CH=C=CH-CH-CH_2-CH_2-CO \quad (\text{CH and CO joined by } -O-)$$

nemotinic acid (also found as the xyloside, VII), odyssin,

$$\mathrm{H_3C{-}C{\equiv}C{-}C{\equiv}C{-}CH{=}C{=}CH{-}\underset{\lfloor\!\!-\!\!-\!\!-\!\!-\!\!-\!\!-\!\!-\!\!-\!\!-\!\!-\!\!-O-\!\!-\!\!-\!\!-\!\!-\!\!-\!\!-\!\!-\!\!-\!\!-\!\!-\!\!\rfloor}{CH{-}CH_2{-}CH_2{-}CO}}$$

and odyssic acid,

$$\mathrm{H_3C{-}C{\equiv}C{-}C{\equiv}C{-}CH{=}C{=}CH{-}CHOH{-}CH_2{-}CH_2{-}COOH}$$

all produced by *Poria corticola* and *Poria tenuis*, have been shown to be formed from the head-to-tail linkage of six molecules of an acetate derivative, the terminal methyl group being eliminated in the former two compounds, very likely by oxidation and decarboxylation, but retained in the latter two.

Grifolin, from *Grifola confluens*, is another example of a similar, yet more complex, antibiotic produced by a basidiomycete:

$$\mathrm{(H_3C)_2{=}C{=}CH{-}CH_2{-}CH_2{-}\underset{\displaystyle CH_3}{\underset{|}{C}}{=}CH{-}CH{=}CH{-}CHOH{-}\underset{\displaystyle CH_3}{\underset{|}{C}}OH{-}CH_2{-}CH_3}$$

It should be compared with variotin (*262b*), an antifungal antibiotic produced by the lower fungus *Paecilomyces variotis* var. *antibioticus*, in which a tetraene aliphatic acid is combined with the methyl ester of γ-aminobutyric acid:

$$\mathrm{H_3C{-}CH_2{-}CH_2{-}CH{=}COH{-}CH{=}\underset{\displaystyle CH_3}{\underset{|}{C}}{-}CH{=}CH{-}CH{=}CH{-}CO{-}NH{-}CH_2{-}CH_2{-}CH_2{-}CO{-}O{-}CH_3}$$

Similar polyene moieties are incorporated into other products of lower fungi such as fumagillin (CIV) (*263a*), from *Aspergillus fumigatus*,

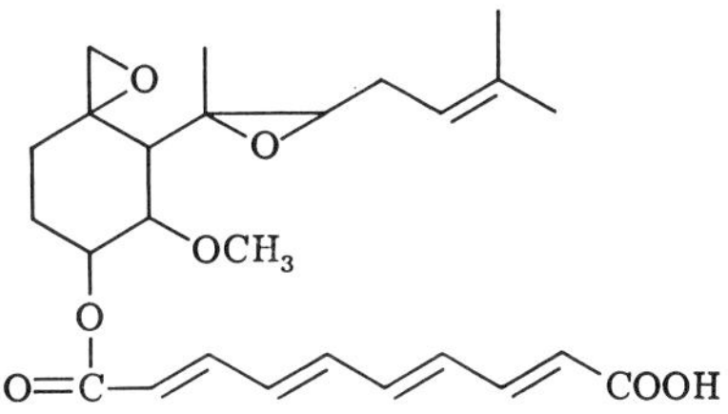

Fumagillin

(CIV)

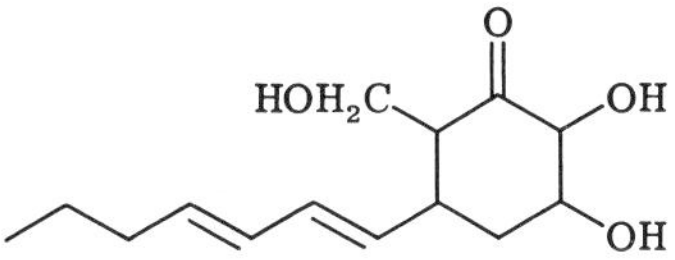

Palitantin

(CV)

and the two similar compounds (CV) frequentin (*Penicillium frequentans, P. cyclopium*) and palitantin (the same and *P. palitans*).

Examples of actinomycete antibiotics showing acetylenic bonds are mycomycin,

$$HC{\equiv}C{-}C{\equiv}C{-}CH{=}C{=}CH{-}CH{=}CH{-}CH{=}CH{-}CH_2{-}COOH$$

from *Nocardia acidophilus,* and cellocidin,

$$H_2NOC{-}C{\equiv}C{-}CONH_2$$

from *S. chibaensis* and *S. reticuli* var. *aquamyceticus.* To the latter substance is obviously related the ethylenic compound,

$$\begin{array}{l} H_2NOC{-}\underset{\displaystyle (O{-}C_2H_5)}{\underset{|}{C}}{=}CH{-}CONH_2 \end{array}$$

isolated from the culture of a *Streptomyces* sp.

However, polyene antibiotics from streptomycetes are more often found as cyclic compounds of the lactone type. They constitute the group of polyene macrolides which are typically antifungal agents. They are generally classified, according to the number of their conjugated olefinic bonds, as tetraenes, pentaenes, hexaenes, and heptaenes. Pentaenes, with few exceptions such as moldcidin A from *Streptomyces* sp., eurocidin, from *S. eurocidicus* and *S. albireticuli,* capacidin, from *Streptomyces* sp., antibiotic PA-153, from *Streptomyces* sp. and antibiotic 2814P, from *S. reticuli,* generally do not contain nitrogen. On the contrary, a nitrogen-containing moiety seems to be generally present in tetraenes and heptaenes. It is represented by mycosamine (XXVII) in most tetraenes and in some heptaenes such as amphotericin B, from *S. nodosus,* candidin, from *S. viridoflavus,* and candicidin, from *S. griseus.* In the latter case, *p*-aminoacetophenone is also found as a degradation product, which again is obtained from antibiotic PA-150, produced by *Streptomyces* sp., and from trichomycin (*263b*), produced by *S. hachijoensis.* The degradation of perimycin (*263c*), from *S. coelicolor* var. *aminophilus,* yields *p*-aminophenylacetone.

The fundamental mode of action of polyene antifungal antibiotics remains largely unknown. It has been likened to that of surface-active substances (*263d*). Among the tetraenes, nystatin, from *S. noursei,* has been the most studied on account of its therapeutic use. It is known to inhibit endogenous respiration and utilization, both aerobically and anaerobically, of glucose and other substrates. Its primary action appears to be an interference with some of the cell energy-yielding mechanisms (*264*). The amount of antibiotic taken up by the cells varies according to the nature of the microorganisms under study and the experimental conditions chosen, but this uptake, the first step of which requires energy, seems to be a critical factor (*265a,b*). Nystatin acts on the cell membrane and thus increases its permeability to small ions (*266a*). Its leishmanicidal activity is attributed to its action on the surface of the protozoan followed by lysis (*266b*). It has also been reported to inhibit the production of induced amylase, the step of the process which is blocked being the one immediately preceding protein synthesis (*267*). Another tetraene, etruscomycin, from *S. lucensis,* is supposed to inhibit sterol utilization by yeasts, an activity which was also suggested for the pentaene filipin, from *S. filipinensis,* and other polyenes (*268a,b*).

Heptaenes have also been the subject of some research. Amphotericin B was shown to inhibit protein synthesis (*264*) and energy-yielding mechanisms as an antagonist of riboflavin (*269*). Heptamycin from *Streptomyces* sp., inhibits the active transport of pyruvate, lactate, and trehalose into the cell. As do other heptaenes, it also prevents the uptake of phosphate. These effects are interpreted as the result of an action taking place at the cell surface (*270*). However, inhibition of phosphate uptake, observed with the heptaene ascosin, from *S. canescus,* was considered to be the consequence of the blocking of respiration, since this antibiotic was shown to inhibit the cytochrome-linked electron transfer in a way similar to that of antimycin A. The site of its action is located between coenzyme Q or cytochrome b and cytochrome c. Its ineffectiveness against bacteria, in contrast to its activity against fungi, is explained by the lack, in bacteria, of the specifically sensitive receptor system (*271a*).

3. *Terpenoids and Steroids in Antibiotics*

Although they do not show the isoprenoid structure, the polyenes have some resemblance to the carotenes, and it should be stressed that

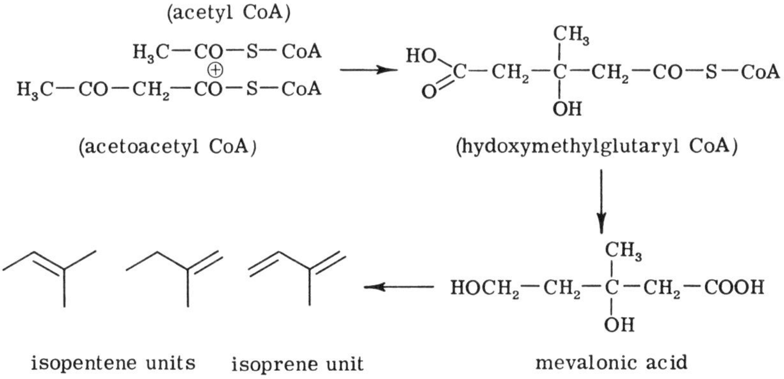

(acetyl CoA)

$H_3C-CO-S-CoA$ $\oplus$ $H_3C-CO-CH_2-CO-S-CoA$ $\longrightarrow$ $HOOC-CH_2-C(CH_3)(OH)-CH_2-CO-S-CoA$

(acetoacetyl CoA) (hydoxymethylglutaryl CoA)

$\downarrow$

$HOCH_2-CH_2-C(CH_3)(OH)-CH_2-COOH$

isopentene units isoprene unit $\longleftarrow$ mevalonic acid

Mevalonic acid

(CVI)

the production of several members of the group—for instance, antimycin, from *S. aureus*, antibiotics S-8, from *Streptomyces* 3832, and candidin—is stimulated by mevalonic acid (CVI), a common intermediate on the biosynthetic pathways of carotenoids, terpenoids, and steroids (*271b,c,d*).

A terpenoid moiety (*271e*) is observed in mycelianamide (LXXI). Lactaroviolin (CVII), from *Lactarius deliciosus*, may be considered as a sesquiterpenoid. Isotope studies indicate that the main skeleton of tri-

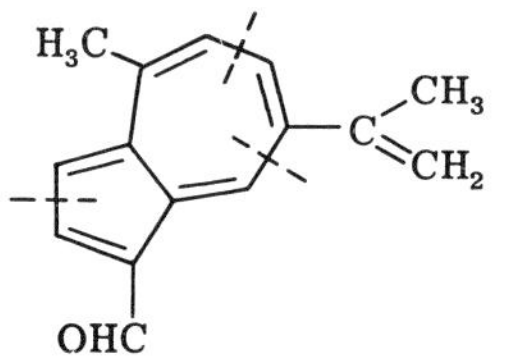

Lactaroviolin

(CVII)

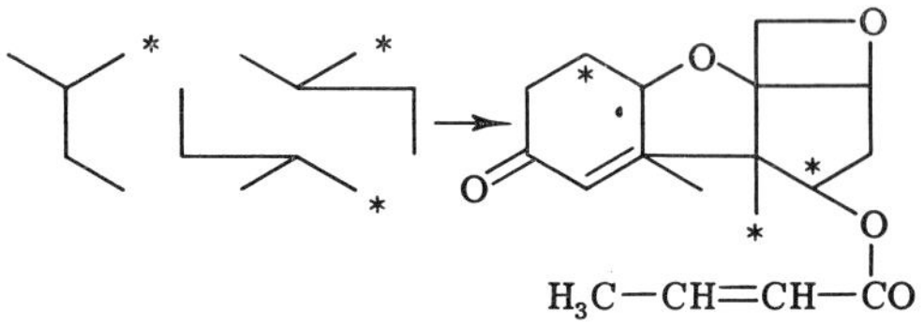

Trichothecin

(CVIII)

chothecin, from *Trichotecium roseum*, derives, with the shifting of two methyl groups, from a sesquiterpenoid intermediate (CVIII). A sesquiterpene constitution is attributed to verrucarol, $C_{15}H_{22}O_4$, one of the products obtained by hydrolysis of verrucarin A, an antibiotic produced, together with verrucarins B to G and roridins A and B, by *Myrothecium verrucaria* and *M. roridum* (*271f*). The other products of degradation are muconic acid, $C_6H_6O_6$ (configuration *cis-cis, trans-trans,* or *cis-trans*), and verrucarinolactone, the δ-lactone of verrucarinic acid (*trans-α,δ*-dihydroxy-*β*-methylvaleric acid), a new natural isomer of mevalonic acid (*272a*).

Antimicrobial terpenoid compounds were isolated from alcyonarians (coelenterates). Some of them were purified and crystallized. They were found to be terpenoid lactones and sesquiterpenes. They are believed to be synthesized by the associated flora of dinoflagellates (Zooxanthellae) and are supposed to prevent the invasion of polyps by microorganisms (*272b*).

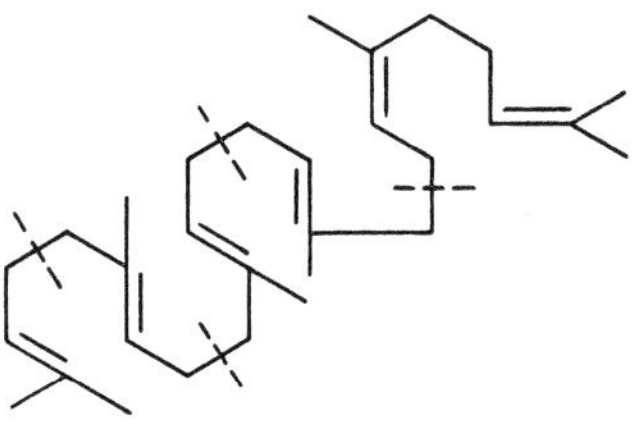

Squalene

(CIX)

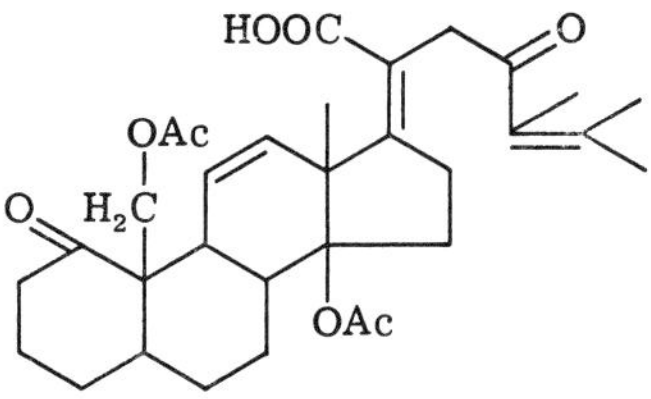

Helvolic acid

(CX)

Examples of steroid antibiotics very likely derived from acetate through mevalonic acid and squalene (CIX), are the cephalosporins P (*272c*), from *Cephalosporium salmosynnematum,* helvolic acid (CX,

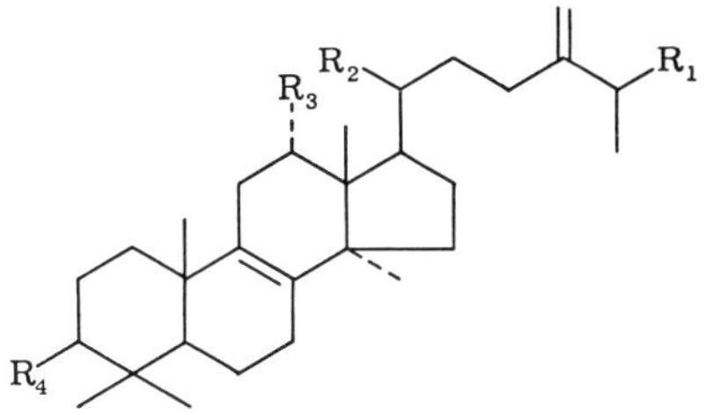

Polyporenic acids A and B[a]

(CXI)

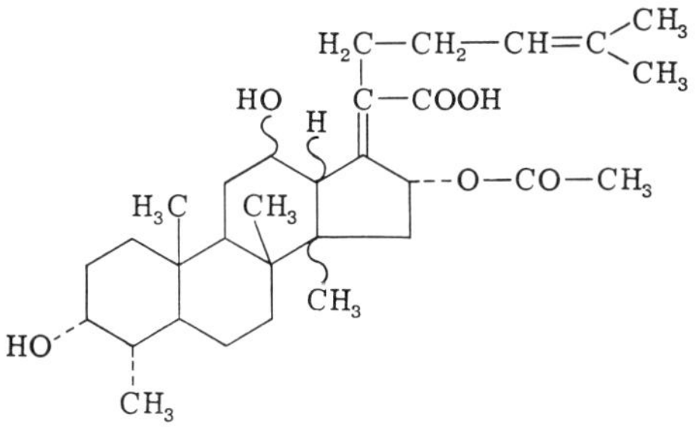

Fusidic acid

(CXIb)

[a] In A: $R_1 = COOH$; $R_2 = CH_3$; $R_3 = R_4 = OH$
In B: $R_1 = R_3 = H$; $R_2 = COOH$; $R_4 = O$

272d), from *Aspergillus fumigatus* var. *helvola,* the polyporenic acids (CXI) A and B, from *Polyporus betulinus, P. benzoinus,* and *P. pinicola* and fusidic acid (CXIb) from *Fusidium coccineum* (*272e,f*).

4. *Macrolide Antibiotics*

Besides the polyene macrolides, the complete structure of which is known in a few cases only, such as filipin (CXII), lagosin, from *Streptomyces* sp., fungichromin (*272g*), from *S. cellulosae,* and pimaricin (CXIII), from *S. natalensis,* there is an important class of streptomycete-produced antibiotics also characterized by a large lactone ring. These nonpolyene macrolides, in contrast to the antifungal polyene macrolides, exhibit a specifically antibacterial type of activity. In addition to

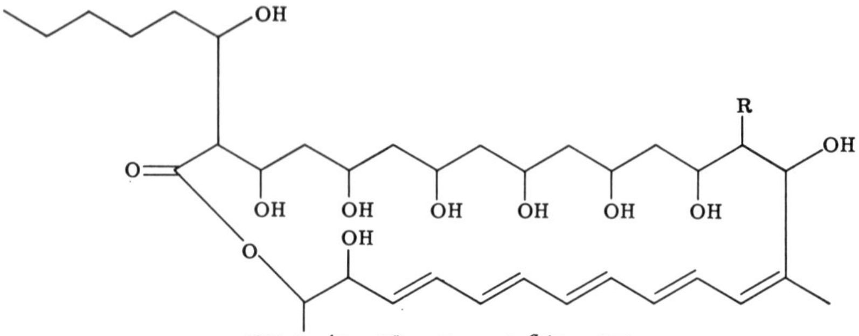

OH

R

OH

O

OH OH OH OH OH OH

OH

O

Filipin (R = H) Lagosin[a] (R = OH)

(CXII)

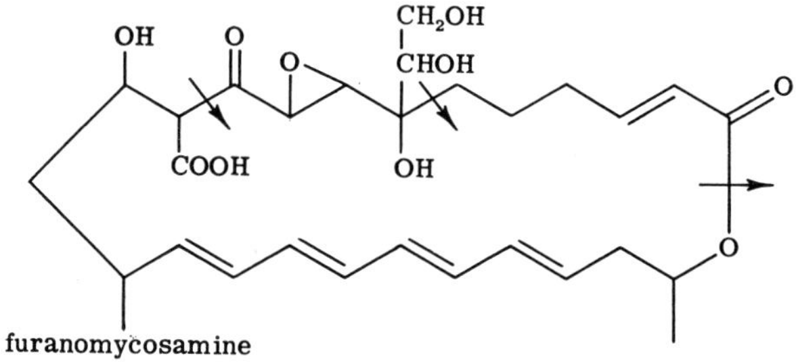

CH_2OH

OH O CHOH

O O

COOH OH

O

furanomycosamine

Pimaricin

(CXIII)

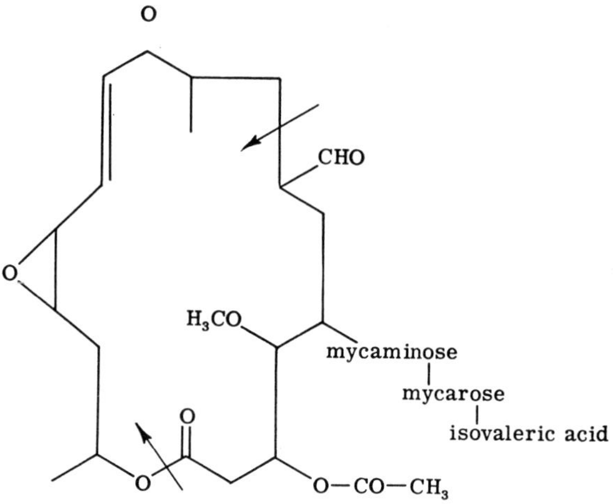

O

CHO

O

H_3CO

mycaminose

mycarose

O isovaleric acid

O O—CO—CH_3

Carbomycin A[b]

(CXIV)

[a] The structural identity of fungichromin and lagosin has been recently established (*272b*).

[b] In carbomycin B, the oxyethylene bridge is replaced by a double bond.

their macrolide moiety, they usually comprise one, two, or even three [in the foromacidins or spiramycins from *S. ambofaciens*] unusual sugars (XXII, XXV, XXVI, XXVIII, XXIX), of which one at least is an amino sugar (XXI, XXIII, XXIV, XXVII). Lankamycin (*272h*), from *S. violaceoniger*, is a conspicuous exception since it contains no nitrogen.

The complete structure of several macrolides has been established.

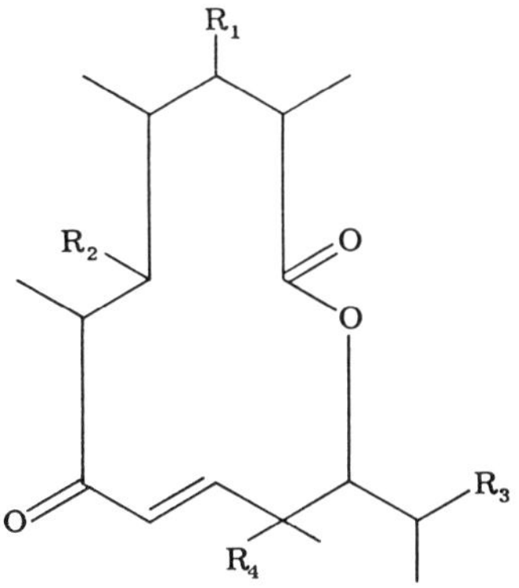

Methymycin Neomethymycin Picromycin[c]

(CXV)

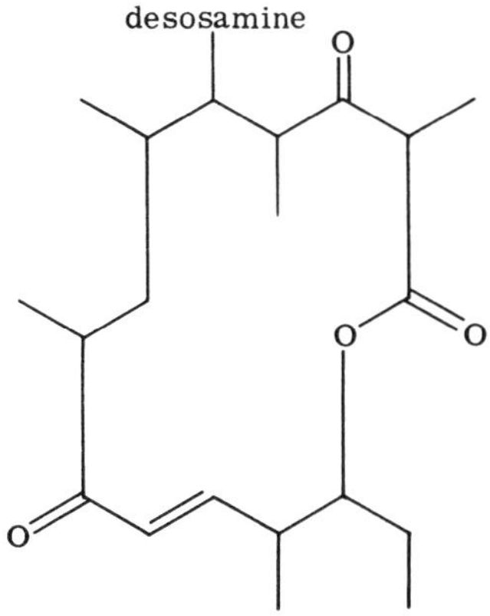

Narbomycin

(CXVI)

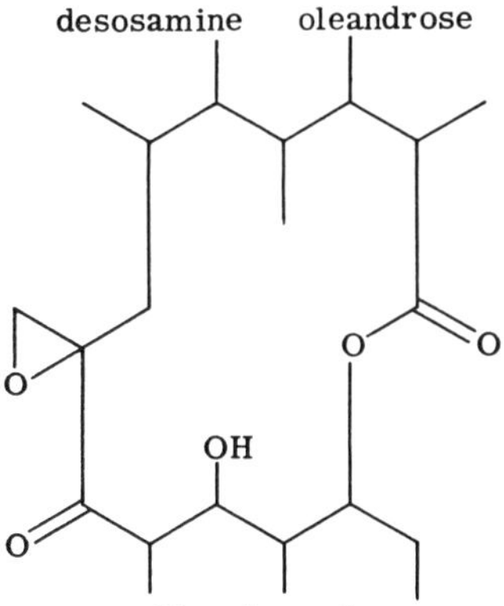

Oleandomycin

(CXVII)

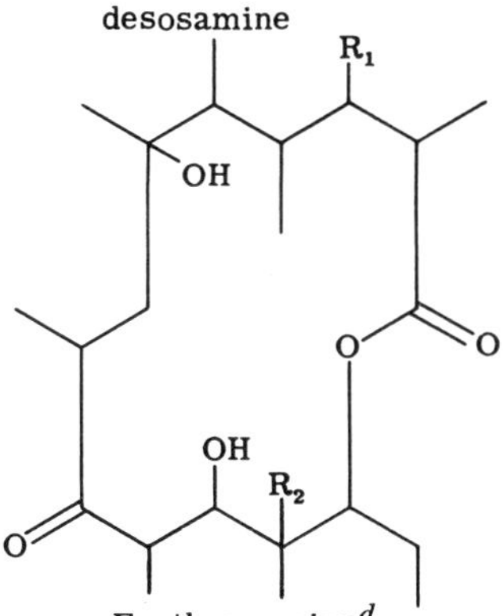

Erythromycins[d]

(CXVIII)

[c] In methymycin: R_1 = desosamine; $R_2 = R_3$ = H; R_4 = OH
In neomethymycin: R_1 = desosamine; $R_2 = R_4$ = H; R_3 = OH
In picromycin: R_2 = desosamine; $R_1 = R_3$ = H; R_4 = OH

[d] In erythromycin A: R_1 = cladinose; R_2 = OH.
In erythromycin B: R_1 = cladinose; R_2 = H.
In erythromycin C: R_1 = unidentified sugar; R_2 = OH.

Such is the case for carbomycins A and B (*272i*, CXIV), from S. *halstedii*, S. *hygroscopicus*, and S. *albireticuli;* the three related compounds (CXV) methymycin, from S. *eurocidicus*, neomethymycin, from *Streptomyces* sp., and picromycin, from S. *felleus;* narbomycin (CXVI), from S. *narbonensis* (*273*), oleandomycin (CXVII), from S. *antibioticus*, and erythromycins (*274a,b*) A, B, and C (CXVIII), from S. *erythreus*.

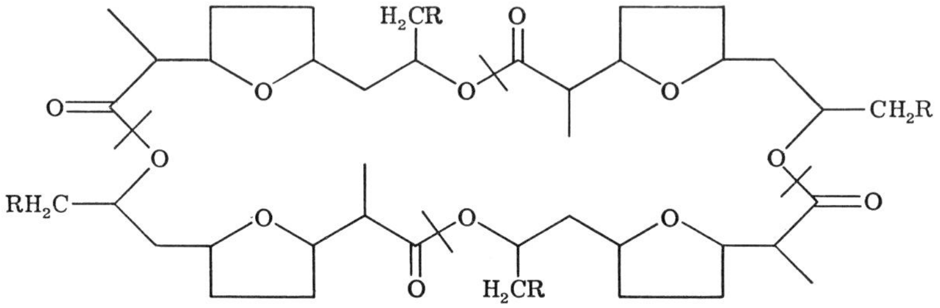

(nonactic acid: R = H) (homononactic acid: R = CH_3)

Macrotetrolides[e]

(CXIX)

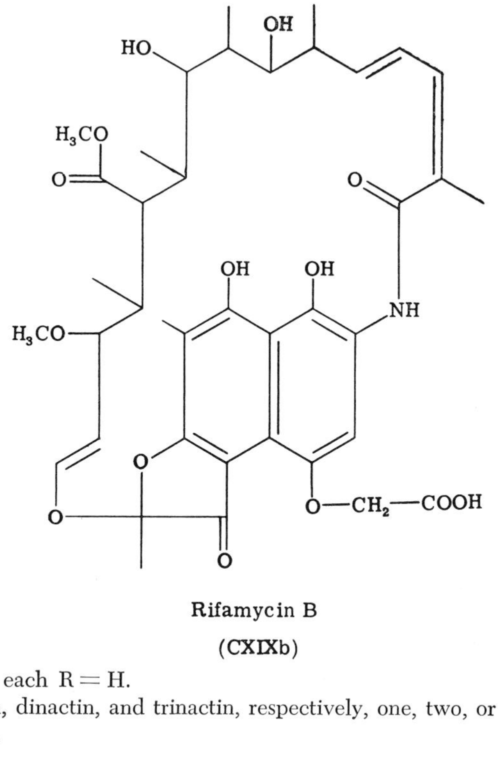

Rifamycin B

(CXIXb)

[e] In nonactin, each R = H.

In monoactin, dinactin, and trinactin, respectively, one, two, or three R's = CH_3, the other(s) = H.

It is worth noting that biologically inactive metabolites with a macrolide structure are also found in streptomycete cultures: an interesting example is given by the macrotetrolides (CXIX) nonactin (*275a*), monactin, dinactin, and trinactin (*275b*).

The structure of the rifamycins, a group of antibiotics comprising natural substances produced by *Streptomyces mediterranei* (*275c*) and semisynthetic derivatives (*275d*), was recently elucidated (*275e*). The structural formula of rifamycin B (CXIXb) shows that antibiotics of this family are macrocyclic lactones. However, in contradistinction to the other macrolides, they have a dibenzene nucleus and they contain no sugars nor sugar derivatives.

It is generally assumed that the lactone moiety of the macrolides is acetate derived. However, isotope studies have shown that, for erythromycin (*276, 277*) and methymycin, it is formed from propionate, in the latter case with the possible incorporation of one acetate fragment. At least part of carbomycin also appears to be propionate derived (*278a,b*).

The biogenesis, in most instances, is visualized as the result of a series of alternate oxidations on a single methylated straight-chain precursor (CXV–CXVIII), although in a few cases (see arrows in CXIII, CXIV), the possible coupling of two or three smaller precursor units has been suggested.

Various metabolic disturbances have been reported in bacteria submitted to the action of nonpolyene macrolides. Their fundamental mode of action remains, however, unknown.

5. *Alicyclic Antibiotics*

It was demonstrated that the shikimic acid pathway does not play any part in the biosynthesis of palitantin (CV), which is wholly acetate derived. A similar mode of formation is also likely for the nitrogen-free moiety of cycloheximide (*279a*) or actidione (CXX), from *Streptomyces griseus, S. noursei, S. albulus,* and a *Streptomyces* related to *S. viridochromogenes* or *S. olivochromogenes.* This antifungal, antiprotozoal, and antialgal (*279b*) antibiotic, which has the unexpected property of being very repellent to rats, is but one member of a family of closely related metabolites featuring a substituted cyclohexyl linked to glutarimide through an ethyl chain. Two of its possible isomers (*279c*) are known to occur in nature: naramycin B, from *Streptomyces* sp., and a diastereoisomer produced by *S. albulus.* They have very little antifungal activity. The streptovitacins, from *S. griseus,* mainly known as anticancer agents, are cycloheximides monohydroxylated, respectively, at position 5 (A), 4 (B), or 3 (C_2). They have some antifungal activity. The 5-acetoxy derivative of cycloheximide, antibiotic E-73, is an antitumor agent produced by *S. albulus*. It is highly toxic, but potentially useful derivatives are being studied (*280*). Inactone is a biologically inactive 1,6-dehydrocycloheximide produced by *S. griseus*. The equally inactive actiphenol, a closely related compound in which the cyclohexyl moiety is replaced by an aromatic ring (CXXI), was isolated from the cultures of a *Streptomyces* sp. The antifungal niromycin A and B, from *S. albus*, and

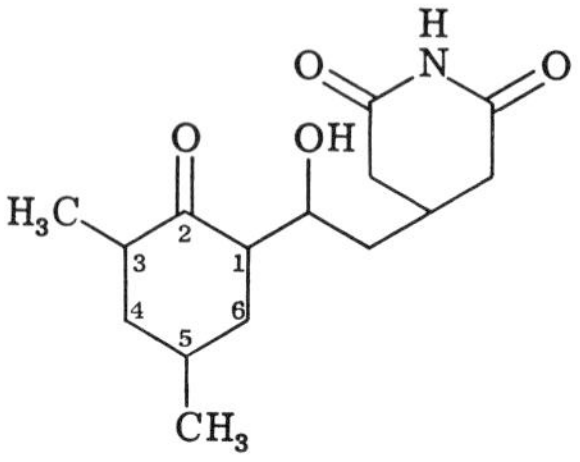

Cycloheximide

(CXX)

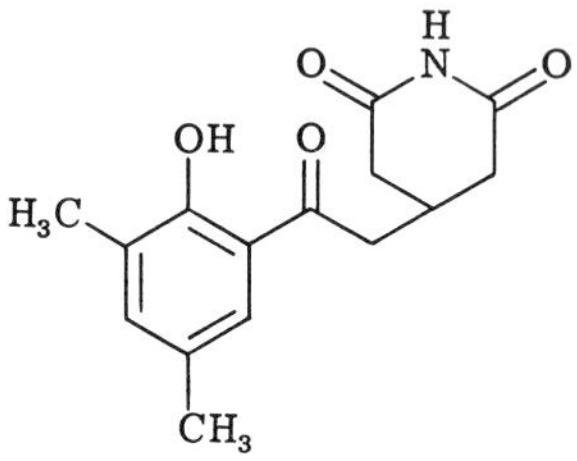

Actiphenol

(CXXI)

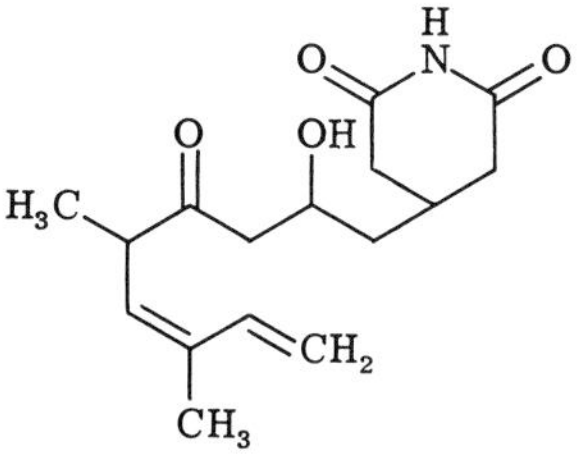

Streptimidone

(CXXII)

possibly fermicidin, from *S. griseolus*, belong in the same family. Streptimidone (CXXII), an antibiotic from *S. rimosus* f. *paromomycinus*, active against fungi and protozoa and weakly active against a few bacteria, should be mentioned here since it comprises a glutarimide moiety linked to a methylated 9-carbon unsaturated straight chain. It has also the unexpected property of being herbicidal.

Cycloheximide, at the minimal growth-inhibitory level, completely prevents protein and DNA synthesis in *Aspergillus nidulans* (*281*) and *Saccharomyces carlsbergensis;* slightly higher concentrations also block RNA synthesis (*282*).

According to Greig and collaborators (*283*), it inhibits fermentation by *Saccharomyces cerevisiae*, an effect which is not observed on cell-free extracts and is therefore attributed to an action at the cell surface.

However, Tsukada and co-workers (*284*), working with *Zygosaccharomyces sojae,* found that the growth inhibition could not be explained by the slight depression of respiration and glycolysis observed. They surmised that the antibiotic either uncouples ATP formation or prevents ATP uptake in the synthesis of protein and nucleic acids.

It has also been advanced that cycloheximide interferes with cell wall biosynthesis in such a way that an irreversible enlargement of that structure occurs and, as a consequence, formation of giant yeast cells (*285*).

The activity of cycloheximide on diverse fungi appears to be linked to their capacity to utilize sugars (*286*), and its primary action on many different sensitive cells seems to be the inhibition of DNA synthesis (*286a*).

The structural analogy of sarcomycin (XXXV) to antibiotics which are simple derivatives of amino acids has been stressed above. Sarcomycin, however, is probably acetate derived. Produced by *Streptomyces erythrochromogenes,* this compound, identified as 2-methylene-3-oxocyclopentanecarboxylic acid, shows moderate activity against some species of gram-positive bacteria and protozoa of the genus *Trichomonas.* Its main interest resides, however, practically, in its antitumor effects, and theoretically, in the differences of activity displayed by its many derivatives. Its hydrogenation yields the 2-methyl derivative, or dihydrosarcomycin, which has antitumor but no antimicrobial activity. Heating sarcomycin *in vacuo* gives a rearrangement product, 2-methyl-3-oxocyclopent-1,2-enecarboxylic acid, which is biologically inactive. So are the high molecular weight polymers that are formed from sarcomycin in the presence of peroxides. Sarcomycin B, which occurs spontaneously upon storage of the natural antibiotic at 37°C, is made up of two molecules of dihydrosarcomycin joined together through their respective methyl groups and through a 3,2′ oxygen bridge. It has some anticancer but no antimicrobial activity. In the presence of formic acid, sarcomycin or sarcomycin B are transformed into sarcomycin E, a compound in which one molecule of dihydrosarcomycin and one of 2-hydroxydihydrosarcomycin are joined through their methyl groups. This product is antitumoral and antimicrobial. Lyophilization of sarcomycin or sarcomycin E gives a crystalline product, M-crystal, biologically inactive. It differs from sarcomycin E only in that it has lost the 2-hydroxy group and therefore appears as made up of one molecule of dihydrosarcomycin and one of sarcomycin rearrangement product linked through their methyl groups. Treatment of sarcomycin with H_2S gives the sarcomycins S_1, S_2, and S_3. In the first and second compounds, the methyl groups of two molecules of dihydrosarcomycin are joined together, respectively, by a sulfur and disulfur bridge. The structure of the third one is not known.

Compared to sarcomycin, S_1 is much less active upon *Staphylococcus aureus* but equally upon *Micrococcus flavus,* has no action upon *Trichomonas,* and shows about 50% of the antitumor effect. S_2 is about one-half as active upon *M. flavus* and has only slight anticancer activity. S_3 is about twice as active upon bacteria, has only a moderate effect upon cancer cells and none upon *Trichomonas.* Sarcomycin can be prepared by synthesis as well as analogs (*286b*), such as 3-methylene-4-oxocyclopentanecarboxylic acid and its methyl ester, and derivatives, such as addition products with isoniazid or isonicotinic acid hydrazide. These analogs and derivatives have antimicrobial and anticancer activity.

The peculiar *Penicillium*-produced 7-membered cyclic acids, stipitatic (CXXIII) and stipitatonic (CXXIV) from *P. stipitatum,* puberulic (CXXIII) and puberulonic (CXXV), both from *P. puberulum, P. aurantiovirens, P. cyclopium-viridicatum,* and *P. johannioli,* have been shown, by isotope studies, to be built up from acetate and formate units.

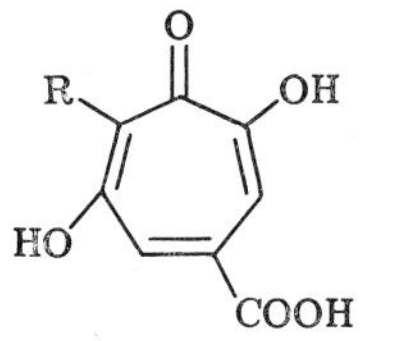

Stipitatic (R = H) and puberulic (R = OH) acids

(CXXIII)

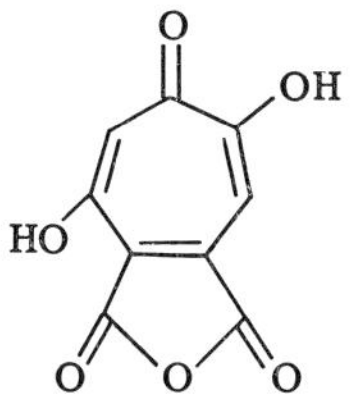

Stipitatonic acid

(CXXIV)

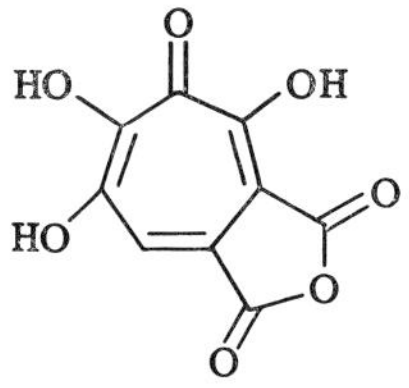

Puberulonic acid

(CXXV)

It still remains to know, however, whether they arise as the direct cyclization of a 7-carbon straight chain or as a secondary enlargement of an aromatic precursor (*286c*). The same tropolone structure is found in the plant antibiotics thujaplicins, from *Thuja plicata.*

6. *Aromatic Antibiotics*

The scheme proposed for the biosynthesis of penicillic acid from acetate via orsellinic acid (CII) shows the possible derivation of aromatic compounds from 2-carbon units. Extensive studies bearing on the biogenesis, mainly by fungi, of phenolic compounds and benzoquinones, which are clearly their oxidation products, has demonstrated the occurrence of two different routes. One is from acetate, the other via the shikimic acid pathway. It also appears that both mechanisms may operate simultaneously in a single microorganism. In some cases, experiments with labeled precursors have pointed out which is the actual route of biosynthesis, whereas in many other instances the question remains open.

In the case of acetate derivation, two main pathways have been suggested. One involves cyclic precursors of the orsellinic or 6-methyl-salicylic acid type. The other postulates an aliphatic polyketomethylene chain precursor which is susceptible of undergoing various types of molding on an appropriate enzyme surface.

Examples of compounds thus derived are: gentisic acid and alcohol (CXXVI), from several species of *Penicillium;* drosophilin A (CXXVII), from *Drosophila subatrata;* sparassol (CXXVIII), from *Sparassis ramosa* and *Evernia prunasti.* Fumigatin (CXXIX), from *Aspergillus fumigatus;* spinulosin, from *A. fumigatus, P. spinulosum* and *P. cinerascens;* aurantiogliocladin, which is produced, together with the corresponding quinhydrone and gliorosein (CXXX), by *Gliocladium* sp. and has been shown, by labeling experiments, to be acetate and formate derived, are benzoquinone antibiotics more or less related to the coenzymes Q.

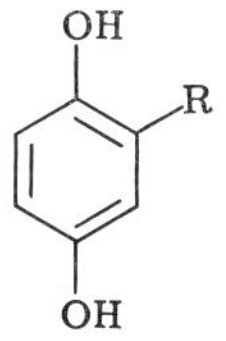

OH, R, OH

Gentisic acid (R = COOH) and gentisic alcohol (R = CH_2OH)

(CXXVI)

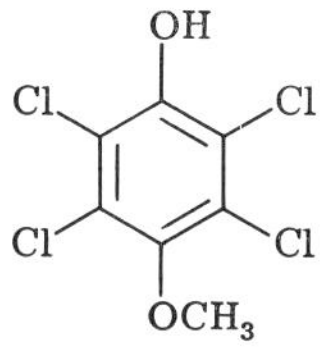

OH, Cl, Cl, Cl, Cl, OCH_3

Drosophilin A

(CXXVII)

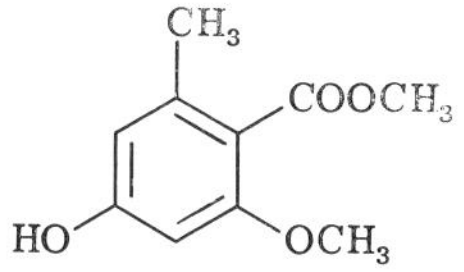

CH_3, $COOCH_3$, HO, OCH_3

Sparassol

(CXXVIII)

O, H_3C, R_1, R_2, OCH_3, O

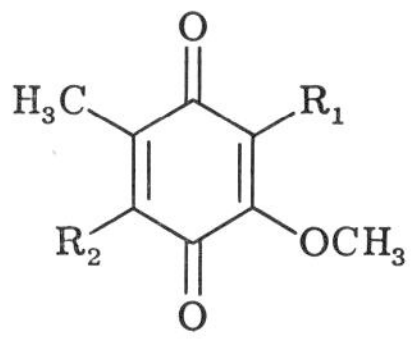

Fumigatin and related compounds [a]

(CXXIX)

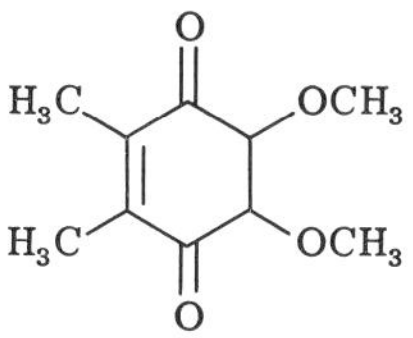

O, H_3C, OCH_3, H_3C, OCH_3, O

Gliorosein

(CXXX)

[a] In fumigatin: $R_1 = OH$; $R_2 = H$.
In spinulosin: $R_1 = R_2 = OH$.
In aurantiogliocladin: $R_1 = OCH_3$; $R_2 = CH_3$.
In coenzymes Q_n: $R_1 = OCH_3$; $R_2 = (CH_2—CH = C(CH_3)—CH_2)_nH$.

A number of plant antibiotics also belong in this group: for instance, the phenolic acids caffeic acid, from *Helichrysum italicum*, and anacardic acid from *Anacardium occidentale;* or the quinones thymoquinone, from *Tetraclinis articulata*, lupulon and lumulon, from *Humulus lupulus*.

The phenolic acids (CXXXI)—gladiolic and dihydrogladiolic, from *P. gladioli*, cyclopaldic and cyclopolic, from *P. cyclopium*—have some antibiotic activity and are related to mellein or ochracin (CXXXII), from *A. melleus* and *A. ochraceus*, a compound which is very similar to a substance extracted from carrots which, while stored in the cold, had

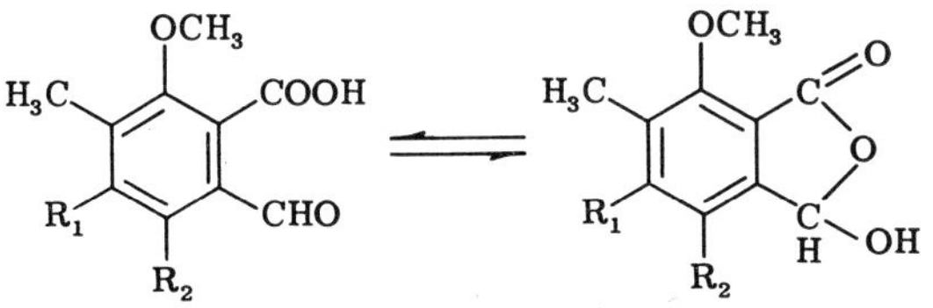

Gladiolic acid and related compounds [a]

(CXXXI)

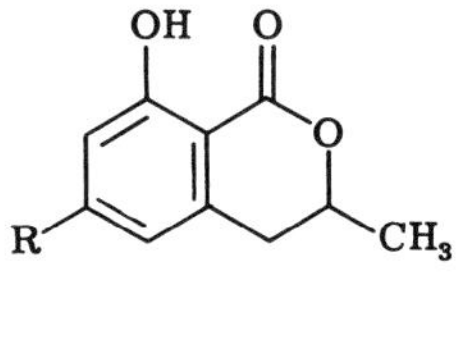

Mellein (R = H) [b]

(CXXXII)

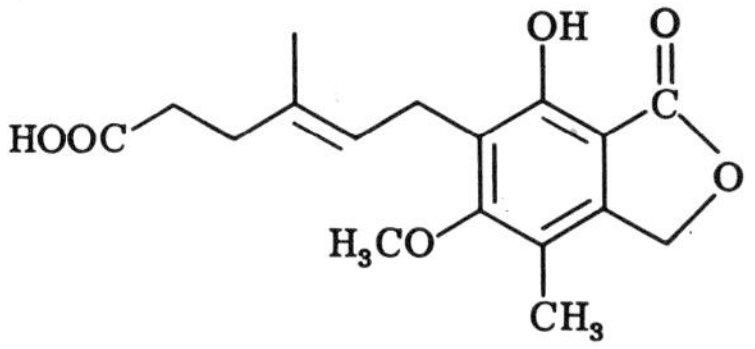

Mycophenolic acid

(CXXXIII)

[a] In gladiolic acid: $R_1 = H$; $R_2 = CHO$.
In dihydrogladiolic acid: $R_1 = H$; $R_2 = CH_2OH$.
In cyclopaldic acid: $R_1 = OH$; $R_2 = CHO$.
In cyclopolic acid: $R_1 = OH$; $R_2 = CH_2OH$.
[b] In a related compound, isolated from spoiled carrots, $R = OCH_3$.

developed a bitter taste. Mycophenolic acid (CXXXIII), from *P. brevicompactum*, is a related yet more complex antibiotic. Mevalonic acid, a precursor of its side chain, is not incorporated in its aromatic nucleus, which is derived from acetate, its methyl groups being furnished by methionine.

Patulin, an antibiotic produced by several species of *Penicillium, Aspergillus,* and *Gymnoascus,* is thought to be formed, by a route very similar to that of penicillic acid (CII), from acetate units through an aromatic precursor, possibly gentisaldehyde, which undergoes a ring cleavage followed by lactonization (CXXXIV).

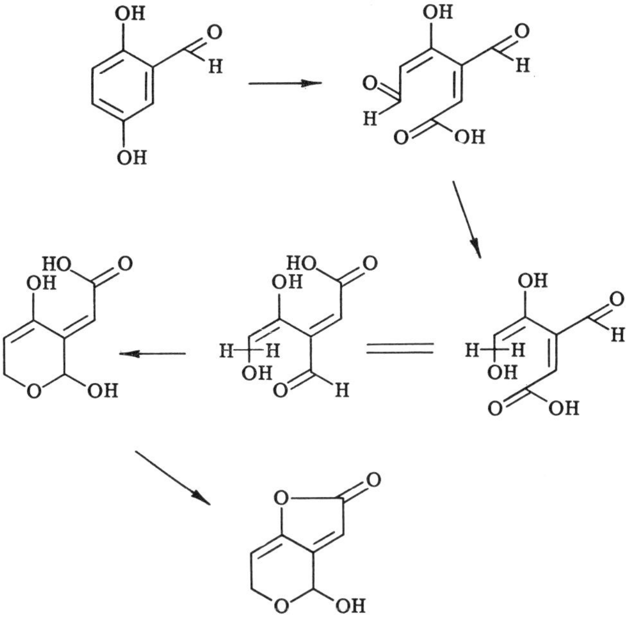

Biosynthesis of patulin

(CXXXIV)

The biosynthesis of many antibiotics seems to involve some kind of coupling of two or more phenolic units.

A first type of such coupling is seen in griseofulvin (CXXXV), an antifungal compound produced by several species of *Penicillium* and by *Carpentes brefeldianum*, in its natural analogs bromogriseofulvin and

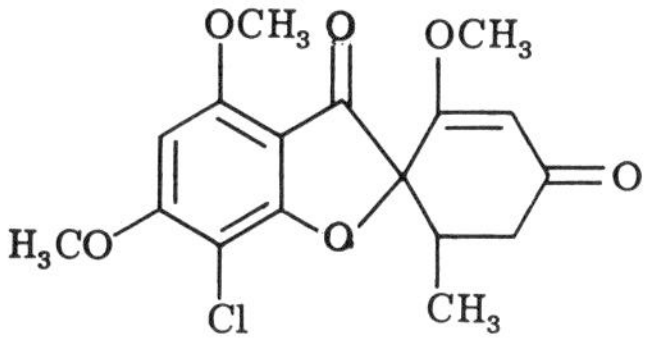

Griseofulvin

(CXXXV)

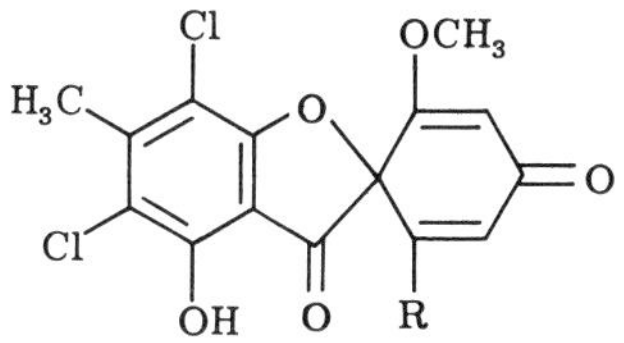

dl-Erdin (R = COOH) and *d*-geodin (R = $COOCH_3$)

(CXXXVI)

dechlorogriseofulvin, and in the very similar and closely related compounds, *d*-geodin and *d,l*-erdin (CXXXVI) from *A. terreus* (*287–289a*).

The wide use of griseofulvin as a therapeutic agent (*289b,c*) attracted attention to this antibiotic, and several derivatives have been prepared recently (*290–298*). The (+)-griseofulvin obtained synthetically has the same biological activity as the natural compound whereas the antifungal action of the (—)-isomer is negligible (*299*).

A highly characteristic type of phenol coupling occurs in a variety of lichen-produced metabolic products, many of which have antibiotic properties. They assume the general structure of depsides (CXXXVII)

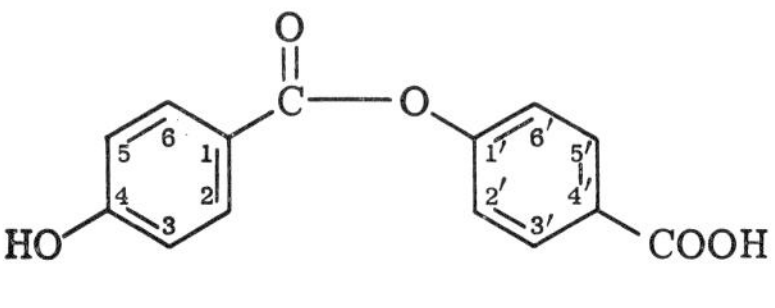

General structure
of the depsides (*PARA*)

(CXXXVII)

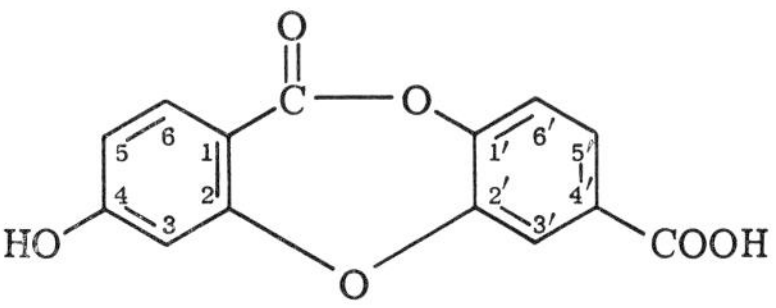

General structure
of the depsidones

(CXXXVIII)

and depsidones (CXXXVIII). Some of them, which have been reported to inhibit the growth of *Mycobacterium tuberculosis* or *Staphylococcus aureus* at concentrations varying from 1 to 200 μg./ml., are listed in Table VI. The biosynthesis of these substances cannot be achieved by either the isolated fungal or algal partner of the lichen association. The former appears to be responsible for the production of the phenolic precursors, and the latter is responsible for their coupling. However, a structure reminiscent of the depsides is found in chartreusin (CXXXIX),

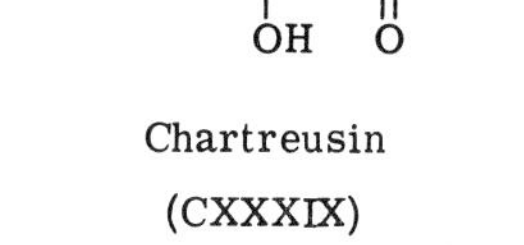

Chartreusin

(CXXXIX)

from *Streptomyces chartreusis,* and three related compounds, nidulin, nornidulin (or ustin), and dechlornidulin, are typical depsidones synthesized by *Aspergillus nidulans.*

The dibenzofurans, metabolites also characteristically produced by lichens, are probably formed by the coupling of two similar acetate-derived phenolic precursors. Examples of antibiotics belonging in that class are usnic acid (CXL), produced by a variety of yellow lichens, and didymic acid (CXLI), from *Cladonia* spp. (*300, 301*).

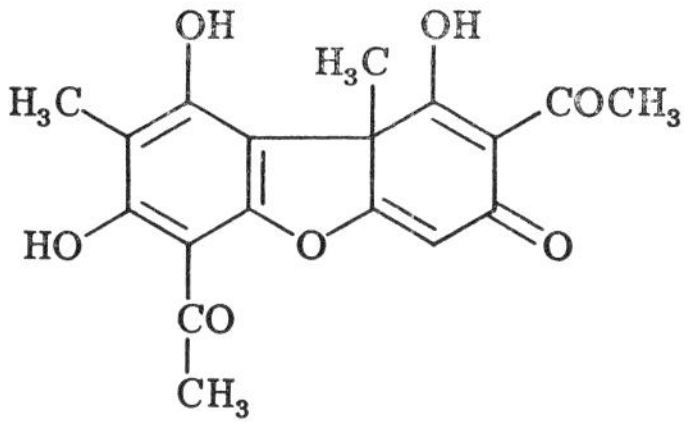

Usnic acid

(CXL)

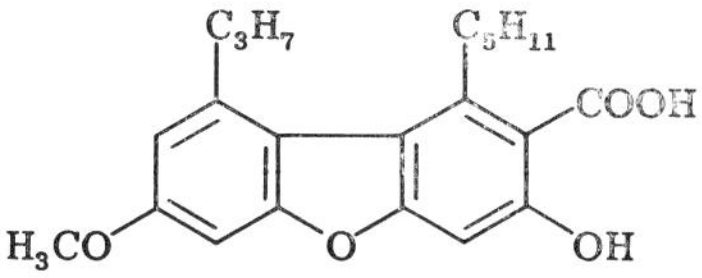

Didymic acid

(CXLI)

Vulpinic acid (CXLII) is an antibiotically active compound, representative of a group of lichen-produced curious metabolites the biosynthesis of which has not been investigated. A similar diphenylbutadiene skeleton is also observed in xanthocillin X (CXLIII) from *Penicillium notatum.* A number of plant antibiotics also feature the linkage of two

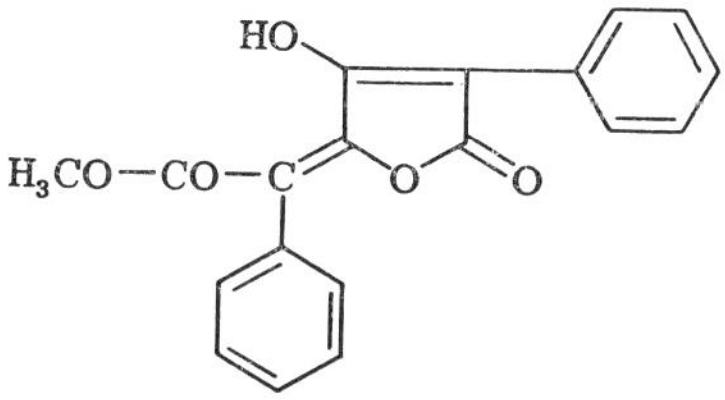

Vulpinic acid

(CXLII)

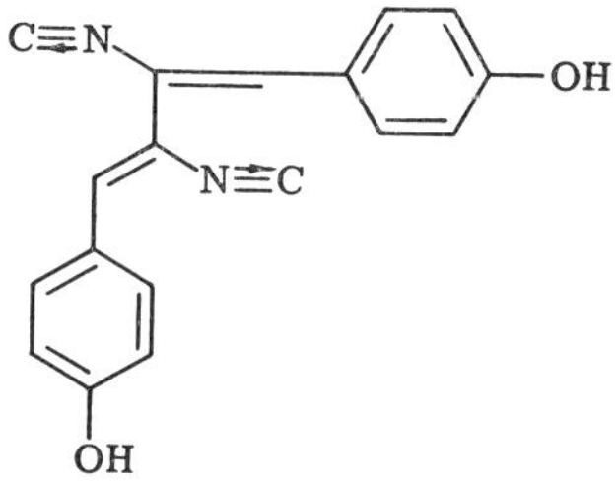

Xanthocillin X

(CXLIII)

phenolic radicals through a more or less complex aliphatic chain: chlorophorin, from *Chlorophora excelsa;* pinosylvin, from *Pinus sylvestris;* phloretin, found in apple leaves; guajaretic acid and its dihydro derivative, from *Larrea divaricata;* curcumin, from several species of *Curcuma.*

It was suggested that the symmetrical compound phoenicin (CXLIV), from *Penicillium phoeniceum* and *Penicillium rubrum,* is formed by the oxidative coupling of two identical benzoquinones; a similar mechanism was proposed for the biosynthesis, from two identical naphthoquinones, of the nucleus of protoactinorhodin (CXLV), an antibiotic from *Streptomyces coelicolor* (*302*). However, isotope labeling has shown that such a mechanism is not responsible for the biosynthesis of the dianthra-

TABLE VI
STRUCTURE OF DEPSIDE AND DEPSIDONE ANTIBIOTICS

Antibiotic	Producing microorganisms	Substitution on carbon number: 2	3	4	5	6
Depsides (see CXXXVII)						
Anziaic acid	*Anzia opuntiella, A. gracilis A. leucobatoides* f. *hypomelaena, Cetraria sanguinea*	OH	—	OH	—	C_5H_{11}
Atranorin	Many lichens	OH	CHO	OH	—	CH_3
Boninic acid	*Ramalina boninensis*	OCH_3	—	OCH_3	—	C_3H_7
Diffractaic acid	*Usnea diffracta, U. longissima, Alectoria ochroleuca*	OCH_3	CH_3	OCH_3	—	CH_3
Divaricatic acid	*Evernia divaricata, E. mesomorpha* f. *esorediosa*	OH	—	OCH_3	—	C_3H_7
Evernic acid	*Evernia prunastri, Ramalina pollinaria, Usnea jesoensis*	OH	—	OCH_3	—	CH_3
Lecanoric acid	*Parmelia tinctorum, P. borreri, P. scortea, P. latissima*	OH	—	OH	—	CH_3
Obtusatic acid	*Ramalina* spp., *R. pollinaria*	OH	CH_3	OCH_3	—	CH_3
Olivetoric acid	*Parmelia olivetorum, Cornicularia pseudosatoana, C. divergens*	OH	—	OH	—	CH_2—CO—C_5H_{11}
Perlatolic acid	*Parmelia perlata, Cladonia impexa, C. evansi, C. pseudoevansi*	OH	—	OCH_3	—	C_5H_{11}
Ramalinolic acid	*Ramalina intermediella, R. calicaris, R. geniculata, R. usneoides*	OH	—	OCH_3	—	C_3H_7
Sekikaic acid	*Ramalina geniculata, R. calicaris, R. intermediella*	OH	—	OCH_3	—	C_3H_7
Sphaerophorin	*Sphaerophorus fragilis, S. coralloides, S. melanocarpus*	OH	—	OCH_3	—	CH_3
Thamnolic acid	*Thamnolia vermicularis, Cladonia polydactyla, C. digitata, Cladonia, Parmeliopsis,* and *Pertusaria* spp.	OH	COOH	OCH_3	—	CH_3
Depsidones (see CXXXVIII)		2	3	4	5	6
Diploicin	*Buellia canescens*	—	Cl	OH	Cl	CH_3
Fumarprotocetraric acid	*Cetraria islandica, Cladonia rangiferina, C. sylvatica*	—	CHO	OH	—	CH_3
Lobaric acid	*Stereocaulon paschale, S. exutum*	—	—	OCH_3	—	CO—C_4H_9

Substitution on carbon number:				
2′	3′	4′	5′	6′
—	OH	COOH	C_5H_{11}	—
CH_3	OH	CO—O—CH_3	CH_3	—
OCH_3	—	C_5H_{11}	COOH	OH
CH_3	OH	COOH	CH_3	—
—	OH	COOH	C_3H_7	—
—	OH	COOH	CH_3	—
—	OH	COOH	CH_3	—
—	OH	COOH	CH_3	—
—	OH	COOH	C_5H_{11}	—
—	OH	COOH	C_5H_{11}	—
OH	—	C_5H_{11}	COOH	OH
OCH_3	—	C_3H_7	COOH	OH
—	OH	COOH	C_7H_{15}	—
OH	CHO	OH	COOH	CH_3

2′	3′	4′	5′	6′
—	CH_3	Cl	OCH_3	Cl
—	CH_3	COOH	OH	CH_2—O—CO—CH=CH—COOH
—	C_5H_{11}	COOH	OH	—

(Continued)

TABLE VI (*Continued*)

Antibiotic	Producing microorganisms	Substitution on carbon number: 2	3	4	5	6
Physodic acid	*Parmelia physodes, P. furfuracea*	—	—	OH	—	CH_2—CO—C_5H_{11}
Protocetraric acid	*Parmelia caperata, Ramalina farinacea, etc.*	—	CHO	OH	—	CH_3
Psoromic acid	*Psoroma crassum, Alectoria zopfi*	—	CHO	OH	—	CH_3
Salazinic acid	*Parmelia cetrata, P. conspersa, P. marmariza, P. saxatilis, P. abyssinica*	—	CHO	OH	—	CH_3
Nidulin	*Aspergillus nidulans*	—	Cl	OH	Cl	CH_3
Nornidulin	*Aspergillus nidulans*	—	Cl	OH	Cl	CH_3
Dechlornidulin	*Aspergillus nidulans*	—	—	OH	Cl	CH_3

quinone pigments skyrin, luteoskyrin, and iridoskyrin, from *P. islandicum,* which appear to derive directly from a common nonaromatic precursor.

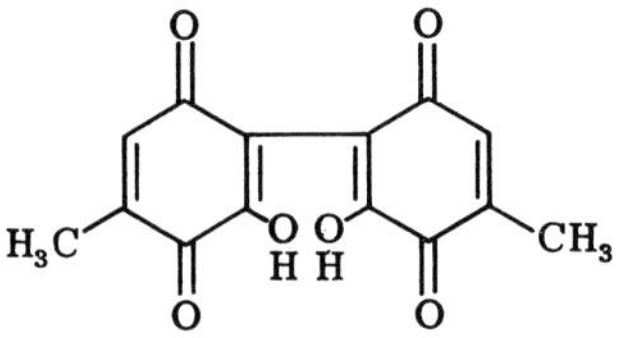

Phoenicin

(CXLIV)

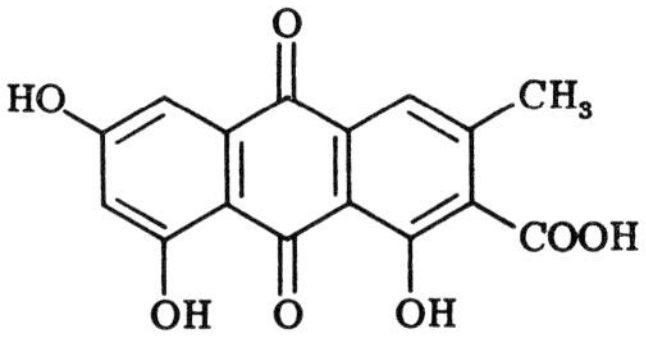

Endocrocin

(CXLVI)

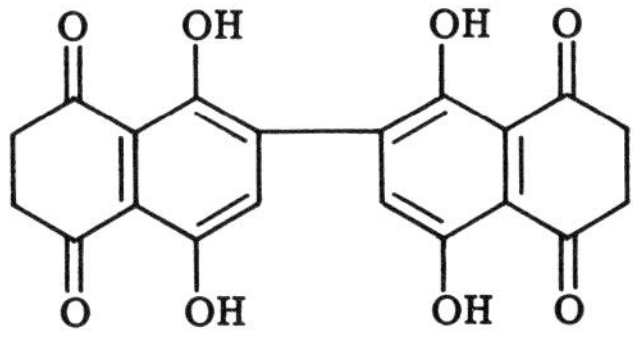

Nucleus of protoactinorhodin

(CXLV)

Substitution on carbon number:				
2′	3′	4′	5′	6′
—	C_5H_{11}	COOH	OH	—
—	CH_3	COOH	OH	CH_2OH
—	COOH	—	OCH_3	CH_3
—	HOHC—O—CO—		OH	CHOH
—	$H_3C—C{=}CH—CH_3$	Cl	OCH_3	CH_3
—	$H_3C—C{=}CH—CH_3$	Cl	OH	CH_3
—	$H_3C—C{=}CH—CH_3$	Cl	OH	CH_3

These experiments have established the acetate origin of the anthraquinones studied. By analogy, it can be surmised that a similar biosynthesis occurs in the case of endocrocin (CXLVI), from the lichen *Nephromopsis endocrocea,* and its decarboxylated analog, emodin, from *Cortinarius sanguineus* and *Chaetomium affine.* Whether they are formed from the coupling of 3,5-dihydroxyphthalic acid and 6-methylsalicylic acid, or from a straight-chain polyketomethylene precursor, remains to be known. They are closely related to the plant antibiotic rhein or cassic acid from *Cassia reticulata.*

The structure of javanicin (CXLVII), from *Fusarium javanicum* and *F. solani* (the latter also producing fusarubin or oxyjavanicin, CXLVIII),

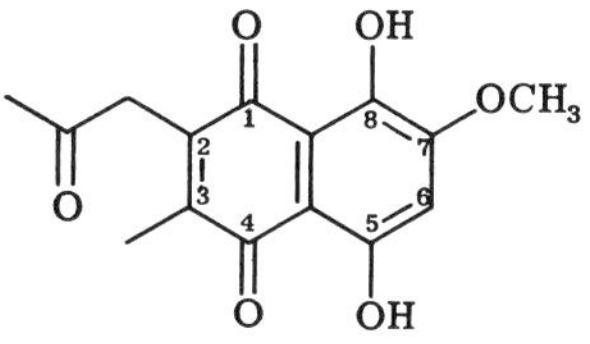

Javanicin
(CXLVII)

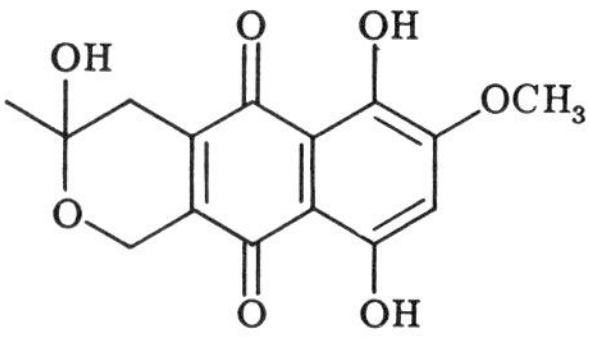

Fusarubin (oxyjavanicin)
(CXLVIII)

suggests that naphthoquinones (CXLIX) are acetate derived. Several antibiotics belonging to that class of compounds have been reported; for instance: 6-methyl-1,4-naphthoquinone, from *Marasmius gramineum;* phthiocol (2-methyl-3-oxy-1,4-naphthoquinone), from *Mycobacterium tuberculosis* var. *hominis* and *Corynebacterium diphtheriae.* Several

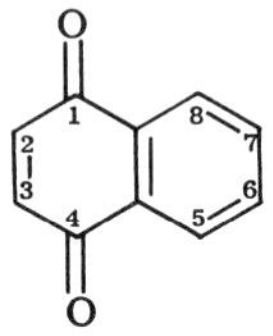

Naphthoquinone

(CXLIX)

plant antibiotics also belong in this category: plumbagol (2-methyl-5-oxy-1,4-naphthoquinone), from *Plumbago europaea;* juglone (5-oxy-1,4-naphthoquinone), from *Juglans nigra;* 2-methoxy-1,4-naphthoquinone, from *Impatiens balsamina;* pristimerin from *Pristimera indica* and *P. grahami.* All these compounds bear the same sort of structural relationship to the vitamins K, which are 2-methyl-1,4-naphthoquinones in which position 3 is occupied by

$$(CH_2—CH{=}\underset{\displaystyle (CH_3)}{C}—CH_2)_nH$$

as some benzoquinones to the coenzymes Q (CXXIX).

Labeling studies have shown that citrinin (CL), a product of several species of *Penicillium* and *Aspergillus* (*303, 304*) is formed from an acetate-derived polyketomethylene chain of 10-carbon atoms to which are added three 1-carbon units from methionine or formate. Sclerotiorin (CLI), from *P. sclerotiorum, P. multicolor,* and *P. implicatum,* is formed from acetate and three formate units. The use of acetate with the carboxylic carbon labeled has shown that citromycetin, which is produced by several species of the genera *Penicillium* and *Citromyces* and by *Corynebacterium diphtheriae,* is derived from 7 acetate units and exhibits the regular pattern of the label as shown in formula (CLII). A similar origin appears likely for fuscin (CLIII), an antibiotic produced by the lichen *Cidiodendron fuscum.*

Rutilantinone, or ϵ-pyrromycinone, is a metabolic product of several streptomycetes which also occurs as the chromophore of glycosidic antibiotics: η-pyrromycin from *Streptomyces* sp., which contains rhodosamine (XX); the cinerubins A and B, from *S. antibioticus, S. galilaeus,* and

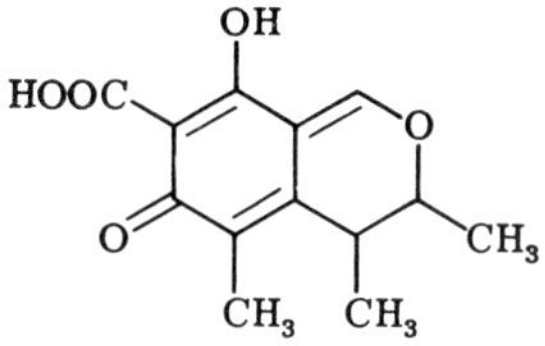

Citrinin

(CL)

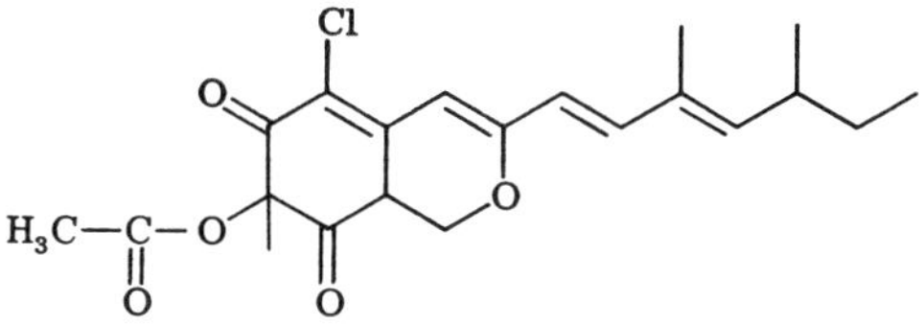

Sclerotiorin

(CLI)

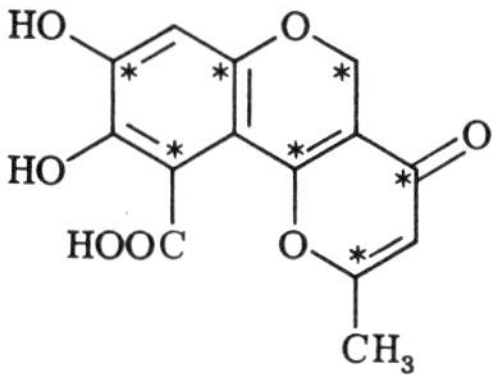

Citromycetin

(CLII)

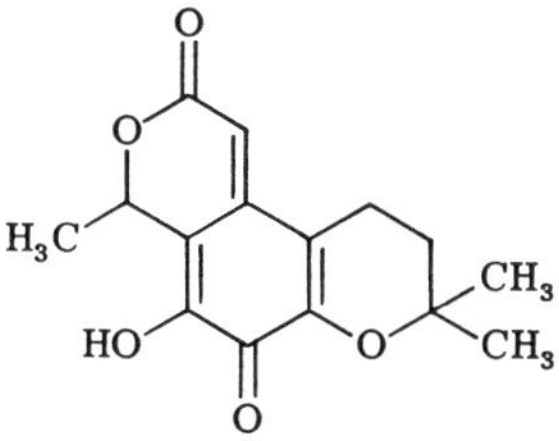

Fuscin

(CLIII)

S. *niveoruber*, which contain three sugars (p. 269). Rutilantinone (CLIV) appears to derive from nine acetate units and one propionate unit, the latter being incorporated into the C_2H_5 side chain and the ring C bearing it. Aklavinone, the chromophore of aklavin, from *Streptomyces* sp., differs from rutilantinone in that it lacks one hydroxyl group. It is also supposed to be formed from an acetate-derived polyketomethylene chain, a mecha-

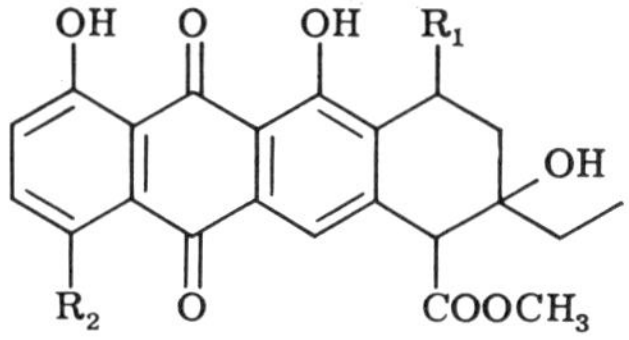

Rutilantinone ($R_1 = R_2 = OH$)
Aklavinone ($R_1 = OH$; $R_2 = H$)
ζ-Pyrromycinone ($R_1 = H$; $R_2 = OH$)

(CLIV)

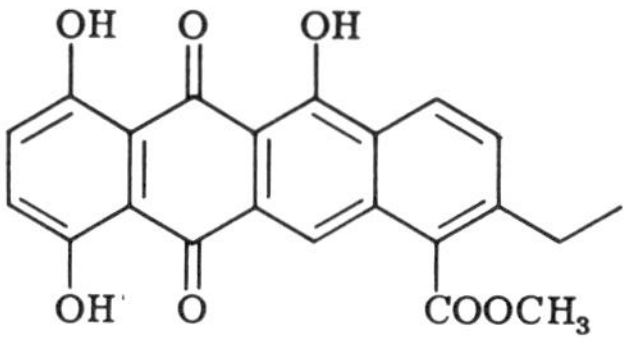

η-Pyrromycinone

(CLV)

nism also likely to be responsible for the biosynthesis of other pyrromycinones (CLV) and possibly of the chromophore of the quinocyclines, from *Streptomyces* sp., and of those, the rhodomycinones, of the rhodomycins and isorhodomycins from S. *purpurescens* (*305*).

All these substances are closely related to a group of streptomycete-produced antibiotics having in common a substituted naphthacene nucleus (CLVI), the tetracyclines (*306–311b*). They are believed to arise, at least in large part, from an acetate-derived polyketomethylene chain (CLVII), some fragments of the molecule, the C_6-methyl and the two N-methyl groups, being furnished by methionine (*312, 313*).

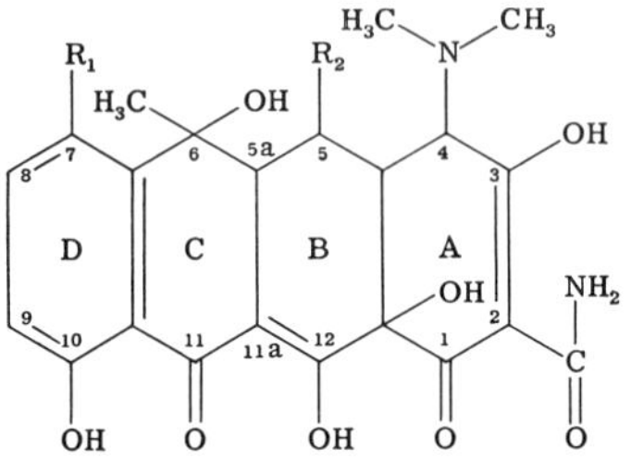

Tetracyclines [a]
(CLVI)

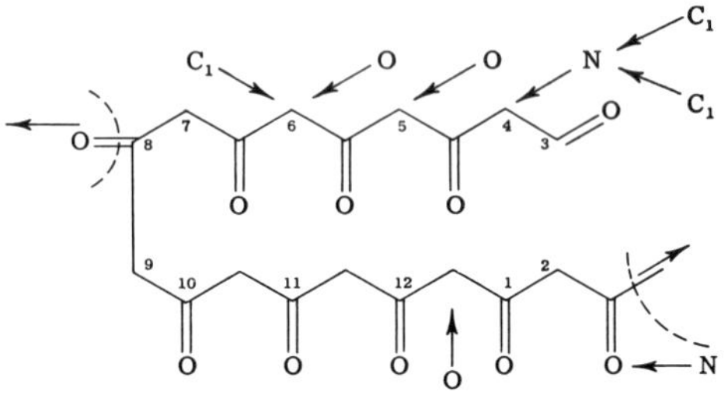

Biosynthesis of 5-oxytetracycline
(CLVII)

[a] In tetracycline: $R_1 = R_2 = H$.
In chlortetracycline (Aureomycin): $R_1 = Cl$; $R_2 = H$.
In bromtetracycline: $R_1 = Br$; $R_2 = H$.
In oxytetracycline (Terramycin); $R_1 = H$; $R_2 = OH$.

The biosynthesis of Terramycin (5-oxytetracycline), from *Streptomyces rimosus,* has been the most studied (*314*). Omission of the oxidative step at C-5, however, would yield tetracycline, a natural product of *Streptomyces* sp., or, coupled with chlorination or bromination at C-7, respectively, chlortetracycline and bromotetracycline, both produced, under suitable conditions, by *Streptomyces aureofaciens.* Similarly, omission of methylation at C-6 would yield the 6-demethyltetracyclines, of which 6-demethyltetracycline itself and 7-chloro-6-demethyltetracycline have been obtained from mutants of *S. aureofaciens,* whereas omission of oxidation at the same site would yield the 6-deoxytetracyclines (*315*) and omission of both steps, the 6-demethyl-6-deoxytetracyclines (*316*).

The discovery of 5a,11a-dehydrotetracyclines, such as 5a,11a-dehydrotetracycline itself, 7-chloro-5a,11a-dehydrotetracycline, and 7-bromo-5a, 11a-dehydrotetracycline, produced by mutants of *S. aureofaciens,* is in agreement with the acetate derivation theory, since these substances may be considered as precursors of the other antibiotics in which ring closure, by an aldol-type condensation, has not yet reached the final reduction stage. Similarly, the discovery of Terramycin-X (2-acetyl-2-decarboxamido-5-oxytetracycline), found in cultures of *S. rimosus,* gives additional support to the theory, since it can be regarded as a precursor directly derived from ten head-to-tail linked acetate residues. However, it is has not been demonstrated that Terramycin-X actually is a precursor of Terramycin. Further, it is known that, if acetate may well furnish the carbon atoms of the A ring, part of it, the carboxamide chain and carbon atoms 2,3,4,4a together with 4-amino nitrogen, may be synthesized from glutamic acid.

Among other tetracycline antibiotics recently studied (*317*), special mention should be made of N-methylethyloxytetracycline. This substance, synthesized by a mutant of *S. rimosus* in the presence of DL-ethionine (*318*), offers an example of transethylation similar to that which yields the 2′-ethoxy analog of griseofulvin (*297*).

Under suitable conditions, each tetracycline is transformed into the corresponding epitetracycline, and one obtains a mixture in equilibrium of the two compounds. Epitetracyclines are the result of racemization at C-4. They have a reduced antibiotic activity *in vitro* but not *in vivo*.

Many derivatives of the tetracyclines have been chemically prepared (*319*). The 5a,6-anhydrotetracyclines, obtained by acid degradation, can be biologically rehydrated (*320, 321*).

The modes of action of the tetracycline have been recently reviewed by Snell and Cheng (*322*). The authors insist on the fact that such antibiotics, with so many functional groups, must have many modes of action, the relative importance of each one of them being likely to vary with the biological or biochemical system considered and the experimental conditions chosen.

If the chemical differences existing between the several tetracyclines explain that they do not act exactly alike, their close similarity of general structure, on the other hand, accounts for the fact that they have many effects in common and for the frequent occurrence of cross-resistance.

The often-reported cross-resistance to the tetracyclines and chloramphenicol, despite the lack of any resemblance between these compounds, linked to the fact that their antibiotic effects are strictly additive, is interpreted as the consequence of their blocking different biochemical pathways leading, however, to the biosynthesis of the same final product, proteins.

At growth-inhibiting concentration, various tetracyclines depress, or completely abolish, the activity of many enzymatic systems, either in the cell or isolated, oxygen uptake, and biosynthesis of several substances.

In many instances, the effects of tetracyclines are reversed by divalent cations (*323*), which, conversely, were sometimes shown to be indispensable, in suitable concentration, for the manifestation of their activity. Tetracyclines are in fact known to chelate divalent cations, and it has been advanced that the biologically active substances might be the metal-complexed antibiotics rather than the free ones. The main forms of oxytetracycline occurring *in vivo* are believed to be calcium and magnesium complexes (*324*). Tetracycline inhibition of essential enzymatic reactions as a consequence of sequestration of necessary ions cannot be retained as a general explanation of their many observed effects. Thus, inhibition by chlortetracycline of leucine incorporation into proteins is not reversed by magnesium ions (*325*).

Interference of tetracyclines with essential metabolites is stressed by the fact that their antibiotic effects may be reversed by as yet unidentified substances present in culture filtrates from resistant microorganisms. Two metabolites of general importance are especially suspected of being the main targets responsible for tetracycline activity: flavoproteins and glutamic acid.

Riboflavin is able to reverse the antibacterial effects of chlortetracycline, which, possibly on account of structural analogy, competitively inhibits both the synthesis and the utilization of the vitamin. On the other hand, oxytetracycline has the capacity of strongly binding riboflavin (but also other biological compounds featuring similarly fused rings such as deoxyribonucleic acid and adenylic acid), and the inhibitory effect of chlortetracycline on D-amino acid oxidase appears as the result of a competition, for the same binding site of flavin adenine dinucleotide, between the antibiotic and the enzyme protein. Chlortetracycline is also supposed to interfere with the electron transport mechanism by preventing the reoxidation of reduced flavoprotein.

The analogy of the A ring of tetracyclines to glutamic acid, joined to the fact that integrity of that part of the molecule is necessary for its biological activity, has led to the suggestion that the antibiotics interfere with the metabolism of the amino acid. Oxytetracycline inhibits the incorporation of D-glutamic acid (*244a*), and also of lysine (*122*), into the bacterial cell wall.

III. Conclusions

It is obvious that the production of metabolites endowed with antibiotic activity is a widespread property of microorganisms.

These active substances comprise an infinite variety of widely different chemicals. Although they have been tentatively classified, on the basis of their structure and biosynthesis, within the classical categories of fundamental metabolites, of which they offer innumerable variations, they include many types of new compounds. Their occurrence as families of related substances, including antibiotically inert ones, and the frequent production of identical or closely similar compounds by very different organisms, should be stressed.

These general considerations raise a number of highly controversial questions: What is the significance—if any—of antibiotics in nature? In particular, what function do they play in the producing organism? What is their role in the physiology of complex ecosystems? Are there significant correlations between antibiotic production, or antibiotic sensitivity, and taxonomy? Finally, apart from obvious utilitarian reasons, is there any sound biological justification for grouping together certain natural compounds under the common and particular name antibiotics?

Antibiotics were initially, and *a priori,* considered to be the main agents responsible for microbial antagonism, an evident natural phenomenon. They were therefore regarded as important factors of evolution by virtue of the natural selection which they were supposed to exert in nature. Experiments on heterogeneous microbial populations *in vitro,* as well as the current selection of resistant species, naturally resistant races, and resistant mutants, as a consequence of chemotherapy and chemoprophylaxis (*326*), have clearly shown that under suitable conditions antibiotics do act in the postulated way. However, the question whether they do or do not act effectively so in nature, apart from their artificial introduction in ecosystems through human agency, remains open.

Against their role in nature, it has been argued that the production of antibiotics often requires very special conditions of environment (*44*) that are not likely to be met in natural surroundings and, further, that attempts to demonstrate their presence in natural habitats have most often given negative results, either because they are not actually produced or because they are rapidly inactivated by destruction or adsorption. Finally, it has been remarked that producers of antibiotics do not appear to have a selective advantage over other microorganisms, since species without any known antibiotic activity are often much more abundant in a given substrate than the former.

This argumentation, however, appears insufficient to rule out the possibility of a selective action of antibiotics under natural conditions. There certainly would be little justification in the inference that an organism producing an antibiotic in a suitably prepared and maintained artificial culture medium would behave similarly when growing, for instance, in the soil. But the converse is also true. If a microorganism does not produce any detectable antibiotic when artificially cultured, it does not follow that it is necessarily equally inactive when developing in its natural habitat. The fact that no antibiotic can be extracted from its natural surroundings is devoid of any absolute significance, since the important consideration here is the "microenvironment" (*327*), practically inaccessible to our means of investigation. It is also well known that some of the antibiotics are reasonably stable in soil and other natural media. Finally, it should be stressed that the production of a diffusible antibiotic by a given microorganism would confer some advantage not only to the producer itself but equally so, or even more so, under given circumstances to the resistant individuals living in his vicinity.

In fact, a few examples of microbiological competition occurring in nature can be attributed, beyond any reasonable doubt, to antibiotic production (*15, 328, 329a,b*). At any rate, the production of any kind of metabolite by one member of a complex microbial population is likely to modify its composition, if not on account of its direct and specific toxicity, then because it will make the surroundings more favorable to some microorganisms than to others, either by modifications of the physicochemical conditions, such as pH, rH, surface tension, or by being more or less readily utilized as nutrient or growth-enhancing factor. The dynamic equilibrium of mixed microbial populations (parabiosis) and the shifting of populations successively inhabiting a given, but chemically changing, microenvironment (metabiosis), are the result of an infinitely complex series of metabolic reactions, continuously leading to probiotic and antibiotic effects, in which the actual participation of antibiotics as such, although possible, is far from being the rule (*330*).

If antibiotics are not to be necessarily considered as the chemical agents of a struggle for life among microorganisms, what other role can they conceivably play?

They have sometimes been regarded as reserve materials, together with their biologically inactive close relatives which have also to be accounted for. But such an interpretation certainly has no general significance since it can hardly apply to external metabolites.

Products of "secondary metabolism," among which antibiotics may be included, were described as "shunt metabolites" (*331*), since they are formed from "normal" intermediates thanks to special mechanisms different from, but related to, those operating in general metabolism. These products, in many instances, are known to be mainly synthesized when cultural conditions have become such that growth has either completely stopped or been greatly reduced. In some cases, a relation between antibiotic production and formation of specialized resting cells, endospores or conidia, has even been demonstrated. Linking these considerations with the observation that enzymes are often stabilized by their specific substrate, Bu'Lock (*28*) proposed that secondary metabolites would "maintain mechanisms essential to cell multiplication in operative order when that cell multiplication is no longer possible."

Such a function, by preventing the progressive breakdown of biosynthetic mechanisms when the reactions of general metabolism are stopped or depressed, would ensure a rapid resumption of normal cell activities when suitable conditions do reappear. The capacity of synthesizing secondary metabolites, whether antibiotically active or not, would therefore be a definite advantage for the producer, inasmuch as it would thus continue to remove from its surroundings nutrient materials that would otherwise be at the disposal of its competitors. Bu'Lock's interpretation has the merit of explaining the role of antibiotics, as well as that of chemically related inactive compounds, without necessarily postulating an antimicrobial function of the former.

As pointed out above on several occasions, some classes of antibiotics and related substances are rather characteristic of certain taxonomic groups. However, one should be aware that such a situation may be more apparent than real and mainly due to the fact that some kinds of microorganisms have been more thoroughly explored from that point of view than others. Even in the present sketchy stage of our knowledge, there are generally conspicuous exceptions to any statement of a correlation between the production of a given antibiotic and the taxonomic position of the producing organisms.

Further, within the larger taxonomic groups, the capacity to produce a given antibiotic appears, generally, not as a property of species, but rather of strains. It is also a property which is often easily lost by mutation. These remarks apply equally to antibiotic sensitivity.

However, in the present-day rather confused situation with respect to the definition of most microbial species, at least in the case of bacteria and fungi imperfecti, production of and sensitivity to antibiotics are given very different weight as criteria of classification by different authors. Also, the intensive search for antibiotic production in some bacterial groups, the streptomycetes for instance, has led to the study of a large number of individual isolates, with the result that any one of the characters studied showed a continuous quantitative change throughout the series of specimens examined. Such observation rather blurs the concept itself of species.

The existence of some correlation between the ability to produce a given antibiotic and sensitivity of the producers to a definite bacterial virus was reported in a few instances. Waksman and co-workers (*332*) thus described an actinophage specifically lysing streptomycin-producing strains of *Streptomyces griseus*. Burkholder and collaborators (*333*) also described a virus acting upon streptomycin-, but not on grisein- or on viomycin-, producers. More recently, Kutzner (*334*) reported that heptaene-producing streptomycetes are specifically sensitive to a same actinophage. Welsch (*335*) described an actinophage, φ-17, which first appeared to act specifically upon actinomycin-producing strains. But further and more extensive studies, using several viruses, including some produced by lysogenic streptomycetes (*336*), showed that, in fact, there was no correlation between actinomycin production and phage sensitivity. Actinophage φ-17, in particular, acts upon all strains of the "*griseus*" group, whether they produce actinomycin or do not, but has no effect on actinomycin-producers belonging to other groups (*337*).

It therefore appears, and the fact is not surprising, that the evolution of biochemical mechanisms responsible for the biosynthesis of secondary metabolites has not been parallel to that of the various characters up to now preferentially chosen by taxonomists. Antibiotic production as well as lysogeny, and antibiotic sensitivity as well as phage-sensitivity, are not a sound basis for microbial classification; they may, however, be useful as accessory characteristics for that purpose (*338*).

From the foregoing, we are finally led to conclude that antibiotics appear as a highly artificial collection of most interesting natural substances, grouped together, for commendable practical reasons, on the basis of a common property—their specific toxicity. This property generally has but little biological significance and is rather fortuitous, albeit useful, in making of antibiotics not only drugs of value, but also invaluable tools for unraveling biochemical problems of fundamental importance.

References

1. S. A. Waksman, *Mycologia* **39,** 565–569 (1947).

2. M. Welsch, *Compt. rend. 3e Congr. nat. sci., Bruxelles, 1950,* Vol. 1, pp. 141–144 (1950).

3. P. R. Burkholder, *Am. Scientist* **40,** 601–631 (1952); **41,** 14–16 (1953).

4. S. A. Waksman, *Am. Scientist* **41,** 8–12 (1953).

5. G. M. Gould, "Gould's Medical Dictionary," p. 94. McGraw-Hill (Blakiston), New York, 1926.

6. P. Vuillemin, *Assoc. franc. avance. sci.* **2,** 525–542 (1889).

7. H. M. Ward, *Ann. Botany (London)* **13,** 549–562 (1899).

8. G. Papacostas and J. Gaté, "Les associations microbiennes. Leurs applications thérapeutiques." Doin, Paris, 1928.

9. M. Welsch, Phénomènes d'antibiose chez les Actinomycètes. *Rev. belge pathol. et méd. exptl.* **18,** Suppl. 2, 1–315 (1947).

10. A. de Bary, "Die Erscheinungen der Symbiose." K. J. Trübner, Strassburg, Germany, 1879.

11. R. Emmerich, *Arch. Hyg.* **6,** 442–501 (1886).

12. S. A. Waksman, "Microbial Antagonisms and Antibiotic Substances," 1st ed., p. 271. Commonwealth Fund, New York, 1945.

13. S. A. Waksman, "Microbial Antagonisms and Antibiotic Substances," 2nd ed., p. 331. Commonwealth Fund, New York, 1947.

14. S. A. Waksman, *Giorn. microbiol.* **2,** 1–14 (1956); The role of antibiotics in nature. *In* "Perspectives in Biology and Medicine," Vol. 4, pp. 271–287. Univ. of Chicago Press, Chicago, Illinois, 1961.

15. P. W. Brian, Ecological significance of antibiotic production. *In* "Microbial

Ecology" (R. E. O. Williams and C. C. Spicer, eds.), pp. 168–188. Cambridge Univ. Press, London and New York, 1957.
16. R. G. Benedict and A. F. Langlykke, *Ann. Rev. Microbiol.* **1**, 193–236 (1947).
17a. S. M. Wingo, *New Engl. J. Med.* **233**, 80 (1945).
17b. M. Welsch, Que peut-on espérer des antibiotiques dans la thérapeutique des infections à virus? *In* "Journées thérapeutiques de Paris 1955," pp. 455–474. Doin, Paris, 1957; *Rev. franç. études clin. et biol.* **1**, 958–965 (1956); *Chemotherapia* **1**, 4–18 (1959).
17c. M. Welsch, L'hypothèse virale du cancer et ses conséquences en chimiothérapie. *Colloq. C.N.R.S., Paris, 1957* pp. 327–333 (1958).
18. F. E. Hahn, *Proc. 4th Intern. Congr. Biochem., Vienna* Vol. 5, pp. 104–124 (1958); *Antimicrobial Agents Ann.* **1960**, pp. 310–319 (1961).
19. E. F. Gale, *Brit. Med. Bull.* **16**, 11–15 (1960).
20. M. Welsch, *Antibiotica et Chemotherapia* **2**, 34–90 (1955); *Giorn. ital. chemioterap.* **4**, 5–21 (1957); *Méd. et hyg.* **18**, 672–673 (1960).
21. R. J. Schnitzer and E. Grunberg, "Drug Resistance in Microorganisms." Academic Press, New York, 1957.
22. M. R. Pollock, *Brit. Med. Bull.* **16**, 16–22 (1960).
23. D. A. Mitchison, *Brit. Med. Bull.* **18**, 74–80 (1962).
24. E. B. Chain, *Ann. Rev. Biochem.* **27**, 167–222 (1958); *Proc. 4th Intern. Congr. Biochem., Vienna* Vol. 5, pp. 219–239 (1958).
25. P. P. Regna, *in* "Antibiotics, Their Chemistry and Non-Medical Uses" (H. S. Goldberg, ed.), pp. 58–172. Van Nostrand, Princeton, New Jersey, 1959.
26. E. P. Abraham and G. G. F. Newton, *Proc. 4th Intern. Congr. Biochem., Vienna* Vol. 5, pp. 42–60 (1959); *Brit. Med. Bull.* **16**, 3–10 (1960).
27. P. R. Burkholder, *Science* **129**, 1457–1465 (1959).
28. J. D. Bu'Lock, *Advances in Appl. Microbiol.* **3**, 293–342 (1961).
29. H. W. Florey, E. Chain, N. G. Heatley, M. A. Jennings, A. G. Sanders, E. P. Abraham, and M. E. Florey, "Antibiotics." Oxford Univ. Press, London and New York, 1949.
30. A. L. Baron, "Handbook of Antibiotics." Reinhold, New York, 1950.
31. L. Karel and E. S. Roach, "A Dictionary of Antibiosis." Columbia Univ. Press, New York, 1951.
32. T. Korzybski and W. Kurylowicz, "Antybiotyki." Panstwowy zaklad wydawnictw lekarslich, Warsaw, 1955.
33. "Merck Index," 7th ed. Merck and Co., Rahway, New Jersey, 1960.
34. M. W. Miller, "The Pfizer Handbook of Microbial Metabolites." McGraw-Hill, New York, 1961.
35. S. A. Waksman and H. A. Lechevalier, "The Actinomycetes," Vol. III: Antibiotics of Actinomycetes. Williams & Wilkins, Baltimore, Maryland, 1962.
36. L. Ettlinger, *Antibiotica et Chemotherapia* **4**, 46–68 (1957).
37. E. P. Abraham, "Biochemistry of Some Peptide and Steroid Antibiotics." Wiley, New York, 1957.
38. E. E. van Tamelen, *Fortschr. Chem. org. Naturstoffe* **16**, 90–138 (1958).
39. J. Büchi and X. Perlia, *Antibiotica et Chemotherapia* **5**, 1–164 (1958).
40. L. Mosonyi, *Antibiotica et Chemotherapia* **5**, 230–299 (1958).
41. R. E. Harman, *Trans. N. Y. Acad. Sci.* **21**, 469–483 (1959).
42. N. G. Brink and R. E. Harman, *Quart. Revs. (London)* **12**, 93–115 (1958).
43. P. Muller, *Antibiotica et Chemotherapia* **6**, 1–40 (1959).
44. H. B. Woodruff, Antibiotic production as an expression of environment. *In*

"Microbial Reaction to Environment" (G. G. Meynell and H. Gooder, eds.), pp. 317–342. Cambridge Univ. Press, London and New York, 1961.
45a. V. Bryson, *Survey Biol. Progr.* **4**, 345–440 (1962).
45b. S. Umezawa and T. Tsuchiya, *J. Antibiotics (Japan)* **15**, 51–52 (1962).
46. T. Erdös and A. Ullman, *Nature* **183**, 618–619 (1959).
47. T. Erdös, A. Ullman, A. Tomcsanyi, and M. Demeter, *Acta Physiol. Acad. Sci. Hung.* **17**, 229–239 (1960).
48. C. L. Rosano, R. A. Peabody, and C. Hurwitz, *Biochim. et Biophys. Acta* **37**, 380–382 (1960).
49. N. Anand, B. D. Davis, and K. A. Armitage, *Nature* **185**, 22–23, 23–24 (1960).
50a. H. Roth, H. Amos, and B. D. Davis, *Biochim. et Biophys. Acta* **37**, 398–405 (1960).
50b. P. H. Plotz and B. D. Davis, *J. Bacteriol.* **83**, 802–805 (1962).
51a. R. Hancock, *J. Gen. Microbiol.* **23**, 179–196 (1960); *Biochem. J.* **76**, 69P–70P (1960).
51b. R. Hancock, *Biochem. J.* **74**, 12P (1960); **78**, 7P (1961); *J. Gen. Microbiol.* **25**, 429–440 (1961); **28**, 493–502, 503–516 (1962).
51c. J. F. Speyer, P. Lengyel, and C. Basilio, *Proc. Natl. Acad. Sci. U. S.* **48**, 684–685 (1962).
51d. C. R. Spotts, *J. Gen. Microbiol.* **28**, 347–365 (1962).
51e. J. G. Flaks, E. C. Cox, M. L. Witting, and J. R. White, *Biochem. Biophys. Research Communs.* **7**, 385–389, 390–393 (1962).
51f. D. T. Dubin and B. D. Davis, *Biochim. et Biophys. Acta* **55**, 793–795 (1962); *J. Gen. Physiol.* **45**, 596 (1962).
51g. D. S. Feingold and B. D. Davis, *Biochim. et Biophys. Acta* **55**, 787–792 (1962).
51h. J. Mager, M. Benedict, and M. Artman, *Biochim. et Biophys. Acta* **62**, 202–204 (1962).
51i. M. O. Tirunarayanan, W. A. Vischer, and U. Rennen, *Antibiotics & Chemotherapy* **12**, 117–122 (1962).
51j. C. Hurwitz and C. L. Rosano, *J. Bacteriol.* **83**, 1193–1201, 1202–1209, 1210–1216 (1962).
51k. K. L. Rinehart, Jr., W. S. Chilton, M. Hichens, and W. von Phillipsborn, *J. Am. Chem. Soc.* **84**, 3216–3218 (1962).
51l. P. F. Wiley, M. V. Sigal, Jr., and O. Weaver, *J. Org. Chem.* **27**, 2793–2796 (1962).
51m. G. R. Allen, Jr., *J. Am. Chem. Soc.* **84**, 3128–3131 (1962).
51n. J. S. Brimacombe and M. J. How, *Chem. & Ind. (London)* pp. 1382–1385 (1962).
51p. A. P. MacLennan, *Biochim. et Biophys. Acta* **48**, 600–601 (1961).
51q. A. Markowitz, *J. Biol. Chem.* **237**, 1767–1771 (1962).
52. L. J. Hanka, *J. Bacteriol.* **80**, 30–36 (1960).
53a. R. E. Handschumacher and A. D. Welch, *in* "The Nucleic Acids" (E. Chargaff and J. N. Davidson, eds.), Vol. 3, pp. 453–526. Academic Press, New York, 1960.
53b. E. J. Reist, P. A. Hart, B. R. Baker, and L. Goodman, *J. Org. Chem.* **27**, 1722–1727 (1962).
54a. K. Ohkuma, *J. Antibiotics (Japan)* **14**, 343–352 (1961).
54b. J. Greenberg and H. A. Barker, *Biochim. et Biophys. Acta* **61**, 71–74 (1962).
55a. M. B. Yarmolinsky and G. L. de la Haba, *Proc. Natl. Acad. Sci. U. S.* **45**, 1721–1729 (1959); *Antimicrobial Agents Ann.* **1960**, pp. 320–325 (1961).

55b. J. Gorski, Y. Aizawa, and G. C. Mueller, *Arch. Biochem. Biophys.* **95,** 508–511 (1961).

55c. M. Rabinovitz and J. M. Fisher, *J. Biol. Chem.* **237,** 477–481 (1962).

55d. A. M. Nemeth and G. L. de la Haba, *J. Biol. Chem.* **237,** 1190–1193 (1962).

55e. E. F. Wheelock, *Proc. Natl. Acad. Sci. U. S.* **48,** 1358–1367 (1962).

56a. V. G. Allfrey, J. W. Hopkins, J. H. Frenster, and A. E. Mirsky, *Ann. N. Y. Acad. Sci.* **88,** 722–740 (1960).

56b. L. Bosch and H. Bloemendal, *Biochim. et Biophys. Acta* **51,** 613–615 (1961).

56c. L. Levintow, M. M. Thoren, J. E. Darnell, Jr., and J. L. Hooper, *Virology* **16,** 220–229 (1962).

56d. N. N. Gerber and H. A. Lechevalier, *J. Org. Chem.* **27,** 1731–1732 (1962).

56e. C. L. Stevens, K. Nagarajan, and T. H. Haskell, *J. Org. Chem.* **27,** 2991–3005 (1962).

57a. H. Hoeksema and C. G. Smith, *Progr. in Ind. Microbiol.* **3,** 91–139 (1961).

57b. A. J. Birch, P. W. Holloway, and R. W. Rickards, *Biochim. et Biophys. Acta* **57,** 143–145 (1962).

57c. R. B. Walton, L. E. McDaniel, and H. B. Woodruff, *Develop. Ind. Microbiol.* **3,** 370–375 (1962).

58. J. Frei, N. Canal, and E. Gori, *Experientia* **14,** 377–378 (1958).

59. J. L. Strominger, J. T. Park, and R. E. Thompson, *J. Biol. Chem.* **234,** 3263–3268 (1959).

60. J. L. Strominger, R. H. Threnn, and S. S. Scott, *J. Am. Chem. Soc.* **81,** 3803–3804 (1959).

61. T. D. Brock and M. L. Brock, *Arch. Biochem. Biophys.* **85,** 175–185 (1959).

62. T. D. Brock, *Science* **136,** 316–317 (1962).

62a. E. Simonitsch, W. Eisenhuth, O. A. Stamm, and H. Schmid, *Helv. Chim. Acta* **43,** 58–63 (1960).

62b. A. C. Richardson, *Proc. Chem. Soc.* p. 430 (1961); *J. Chem. Soc.* pp. 2758–2761 (1962).

62c. A. B. Foster, J. Lehman, and M. Stacey, *J. Chem. Soc.* pp. 1396–1401, 2116–2118 (1962); *Chem. & Ind. (London)* pp. 142–147 (1962).

62d. W. Hofheinz and H. Griesebach, *Z. Naturforsch.* **17b,** 355–358 (1962).

62e. H. Bickel, E. Gäumann, R. Hütter, W. Sackmann, E. Visscher, M. Voser, A. Wettstein, and H. Zähner, *Helv. Chim. Acta* **45,** 1396–1405 (1962).

62f. H. Griesebach and H. Achenbach, *Z. Naturforsch.* **17b,** 63 (1962).

62g. A. B. Foster, T. D. Inch, J. Lehman, L. F. Thomas, J. M. Webber, and J. A. Wyer, *Proc. Chem. Soc.* p. 254 (1962); *Chem. & Ind. (London)* pp. 1619–1620 (1962).

62h. C. H. Bolton, A. B. Foster, M. Stacey, and J. M. Webber, *J. Chem. Soc.* pp. 4831–4835 (1961).

62i. F. Korte, A. Bilow, and R. Heinz, *Tetrahedron* **18,** 657–666 (1962).

62j. W. Hofheinz and H. Griesebach, *Tetrahedron Letters* pp. 377–380 (1962).

62k. W. Keller-Schierlein and G. Roncari, *Helv. Chim. Acta* **45,** 138–152 (1962).

63. P. W. K. Woo, H. W. Dion, and L. F. Johnson, *J. Am. Chem. Soc.* **83,** 3352–3353 (1961); **84,** 1066–1071, 1512 (1962).

64. M. Stacey and S. A. Barker, "Polysaccharides of Microorganisms." Oxford Univ. Press (Clarendon), London and New York, 1960.

65a. M. R. J. Salton, "Microbial Cell Walls." Wiley, New York, 1960.

65b. P. F. Wiley, *J. Am. Chem. Soc.* **84,** 1514–1515 (1962).

65c. D. D. Chapman, R. L. Autrey, R. H. Gourlay, A. D. Johnson, J. Souto, and D. S. Tarbell, *Proc. Natl. Acad. Sci. U. S.* **48,** 1108–1112 (1962).

65d. D. J. Mason, A. Dietz, and R. M. Smith, *Antibiotics & Chemotherapy* **11,** 118–122, 123–126, 127–133 (1961).

65e. M. E. Bergy, T. E. Eble, and R. R. Herr, *Antibiotics & Chemotherapy* **11,** 661–664 (1961).

65f. H. Hoeksema, A. D. Argoudelis, and P. F. Wiley, *J. Am. Chem. Soc.* **84,** 3212–3213 (1962).

66a. S. K. Majumdar and H. J. Kutzner, *Science* **135,** 734; *Appl. Microbiol.* **10,** 157–168 (1962).

66b. A. Franck, L. Kelly, and S. Kelly, *Biochem. Biophys. Research Communs.* **7,** 204–209 (1962).

67. P. Fredericq, *Ann. Rev. Microbiol.* **11,** 7–22 (1957); *Ergeb. Mikrobiol. Immunitätsf. exptle. Therap.* **37,** 115–161 (1963).

68a. M. Welsch, *J. Bacteriol.* **53,** 101–102 (1947).

68b. Y. Okami, K. Maeda, H. Kondo, T. Tanaka, and H. Umezawa, *J. Antibiotics (Japan)* **15,** 147–151 (1962).

68c. W. A. Zygmunt, *J. Bacteriol.* **84,** 154–156 (1962).

68d. F. C. Neuhaus and J. L. Lynch, *Biochem. Biophys. Research Communs.* **8,** 377–382 (1962).

69a. E. Work, *Nature* **179,** 841–847 (1957); *J. Gen. Microbiol.* **25,** 167–189 (1961); *Biochem. J.* **82,** 35P–36P (1962).

69b. P. H. Clarke and M. D. Lilly, *Nature* **195,** 516 (1962).

70. M. F. Michel and W. Hijmans, *J. Gen. Microbiol.* **23,** 35–46 (1960).

71a. J. Ciak and F. E. Hahn, *Antibiotics & Chemotherapy* **9,** 47–54 (1959).

71b. R. K. Ledneva, E. D. Vishepan, and K. I. Ivanova, *Antibiotiki* **7,** 724–728 (1962).

71c. J. Michalský, J. Čtvrtník, Z. Horáková, and V. Bydžovský, *Experientia* **18,** 217 (1962); *Monatsh. Chem.* **93,** 618–631 (1962).

72. E. D. Weinberg, *Exptl. Cell Research* **13,** 175–177 (1957).

73. E. D. Weinberg, J. H. Billman, and D. Borders, *Exptl. Cell Research* **15,** 625–628 (1958).

74. E. D. Weinberg, A. K. Saz, and E. Y. Pilgren, *J. Gen. Microbiol.* **19,** 419–433 (1958).

75a. F. R. Judith and E. D. Weinberg, *J. Bacteriol.* **78,** 485–487 (1959).

75b. T. D. Brock and M. L. Brock, *J. Bacteriol.* **81,** 212–217 (1961).

75c. R. F. Pittillo, *Antimicrobial Agents Ann.* **1960,** pp. 276–287 (1961).

75d. R. K. Barclay, E. Garfinkel, and M. A. Phillipps, *Cancer Research* **22,** 809–814 (1962).

76. A. L. Demain, *Advances in Appl. Microbiol.* **1,** 23–47 (1959).

77a. D. Hockenhull, *Progr. in Ind. Microbiol.* **1,** 1–27 (1959).

77b. V. N. Deshpande, *J. Sci. Ind. Research (India)* **21,** 377–383 (1962).

78a. H. R. V. Arnstein, D. Morris, and E. Toms, *Biochim. et Biophys. Acta* **35,** 561–562 (1959).

78b. M. A. Pisano, A. I. Fleischman, M. L. Littman, J. D. Dutcher, and F. E. Pansy, *Antimicrobial Agents Ann.* **1960,** pp. 41–53 (1961).

78c. R. P. Elander, J. F. Stauffer, and M. P. Backus, *Antimicrobial Agents Ann.* **1960,** pp. 91–102 (1961).

79. H. R. V. Arnstein and D. Morris, *Biochem. J.* **76,** 323–327, 353–357, 357-361, 375–381 (1960).

80. R. T. Williams, "Detoxication Mechanisms." Chapman & Hall, London, 1947.

81. F. P. Doyle, G. R. Fosker, J. H. C. Nayler, and H. Smith, *J. Chem. Soc.* pp. 1440–1441 (1962).

82. E. G. Brain, F. P. Doyle, K. Hardy, A. A. W. Long, M. D. Mehta, D. Miller, J. H. C. Nayler, M. J. Soulal, E. R. Stove, and G. R. Thomas, *J. Chem. Soc.* pp. 1445–1452 (1962).
83. F. P. Doyle, K. Hardy, J. H. C. Nayler, S. J. Soulal, E. R. Stove, and H. R. J. Waddington, *J. Chem. Soc.* pp. 1453–1458 (1962).
84a. F. P. Doyle, *Mfg. Chemist* **32,** 533–535 (1961).
84b. T. A. Seto, H. T. Huang, J. M. Weaver, T. J. MacBride, A. R. English, and G. M. Shull, *Antimicrobial Agents Ann.* **1960,** pp. 85–90 (1961).
85a. F. R. Batchelor, F. P. Doyle, J. H. C. Nayler, and G. N. Rolinson, *Nature* **183,** 257–258 (1959); *Proc. Roy. Soc.* **B154,** 478–489, 490–497, 498–508, 509–513, 514–521 (1961).
85b. H. T. Huang, A. R. English, T. A. Seto, G. M. Shull, and B. A. Sobin, *J. Am. Chem. Soc.* **82,** 3790–3791 (1960); *Proc. Soc. Exptl. Biol. Med.* **104,** 547–549 (1960).
86a. G. N. Rolinson, *Chemotherapia* **2,** 52–59 (1961); *Brit. Med. J.* **2,** 880 (1959).
86b. G. N. Rolinson, F. R. Batchelor, D. Butterworth, J. Cameron-Wood, M. Cole, G. C. Eustace, M. V. Hart, M. Richards, and E. B. Chain, *Nature* **187,** 236–237 (1960); *Proc. Roy. Soc.* **B154,** 522–531 (1961).
86c. C. A. Claridge, A. Gourevitch, and J. Lein, *Nature* **187,** 237–238 (1960).
86d. W. Kaufman, K. Bauer, and H. A. Offe, *Antimicrobial Agents Ann.* **1960,** 1–5 (1961); *Naturwissenschaften* **47,** 474–475 (1960).
86e. E. Auhagen and A. M. Walter, *Arzneimittel-Forsch.* **12,** 733–735 (1962).
86f. K. Bauer, R. Dillenburg, H. B. Konig, T. Knott, W. Meiser, H. A. Offe, J. Schmid, J. Schwartz, and H. Timmler, *Arzneimittel-Forsch.* **12,** 736–740 (1962).
86g. J. C. Sheehan and K. R. Hennery-Logan, *J. Am. Chem. Soc.* **84,** 2983–2989 (1962).
87. A. Gourevitch, G. A. Hunt, and J. Lein, *Antibiotics & Chemotherapy* **10,** 121–127 (1960); *Antimicrobial Agents Ann.* **1960,** pp. 6–9 (1961).
88. L. P. Garrod, *Brit. Med. J.* **1,** 527–529; **2,** 1695–1696 (1960).
89. G. N. Rolinson, S. Stevens, F. R. Batchelor, J. C. Wood, and E. B. Chain, *Lancet* **2,** 564–567 (1960); *Brit. Med. J.* **1,** 191–196 (1961).
90. W. B. Hugo and A. D. Russell, *Nature* **188,** 875 (1960).
91. C. G. McCarthy, G. Wallmark, and M. Finland, *Am. J. Med. Sci.* **241,** 143–159 (1961).
92a. G. Tunevall and A. R. Frisk, *Chemotherapia* **3,** 449–461 (1961).
92b. M. Barber and P. M. Waterworth, *Brit. Med. J.* **1,** 1159–1164 (1962).
92c. J. A. P. Trafford, D. M. MacLaren, D. A. Lillicrap, R. D. S. Barnes, J. C. Houston, and R. Knox, *Lancet* **1,** 987–990 (1962).
92d. A. D. Russell, *J. Pharm. and Pharmacol.* **14,** 390–392 (1962).
93. F. P. Doyle, A. A. W. Long, J. H. C. Nayler, and E. R. Stove, *Nature* **192,** 1183–1184 (1961).
94. R. Knox, *Nature* **192,** 492–496 (1961); **195,** 1300–1302 (1962); *J. Gen. Microbiol* **28,** 471–480 (1962).
95. R. P. Novick, *Biochem. J.* **83,** 229–235 (1962).
96a. F. L. Jackson and K. K. Rao, *Lancet* **1,** 850–851 (1961).
96b. B. A. Waisbren and I. Brown, *Antibiotics & Chemotherapy* **12,** 97–102 (1962).
96c. H. G. Steinman, *Antimicrobial Agents Ann.* **1960,** pp. 256–262 (1961).
96d. D. L. Swallow and P. H. A. Sneath, *J. Gen. Microbiol.* **28,** 461–470 (1962).
96e. N. Garber and N. Citri, *Biochim. et Biophys. Acta* **62,** 385–396 (1962).

96f. A. Gourevitch, C. T. Holdrege, G. A. Hunt, W. F. Minor, C. C. Flanigan, L. C. Cheney, and J. Lein, *Antibiotics & Chemotherapy* **12**, 318–324 (1962).

96g. J. H. C. Nayler, A. A. W. Long, D. M. Brown, P. Acred, G. N. Rolinson, F. R. Batchelor, S. Stevens, and R. Sutherland, *Nature* **195**, 1264–1267 (1962).

96h. A. E. Kraushaar and E. E. Schmid, *Antimicrobial Agents Ann.* **1960**, pp. 264–270 (1961).

97. J. T. Park and J. L. Strominger, *Science* **125**, 99–101 (1957).

98. J. Lederberg, *Proc. Natl. Acad. Sci. U. S.* **42**, 574–577 (1956); *J. Bacteriol.* **73**, 144 (1957).

99. F. E. Hahn and J. Ciak, *Science* **125**, 119–120 (1957); **137**, 982–983 (1962).

100. K. Liebermeister and E. Kellenberger, *Z. Naturforsch.* **11b**, 200–206 (1956).

101. J. P. Duguid, *Edinburgh Med. J.* **53**, 401–412 (1946).

102. J. Tomcsik and S. Guex-Holzer, *Schweiz. Z. allgem. Pathol. u. Bakteriol.* **15**, 517–525 (1952).

103a. C. Weibull, *J. Bacteriol.* **66**, 688–695 (1953); *Ann. Rev. Microbiol.* **12**, 1–26 (1958).

103b. W. B. Hugo and A. D. Russell, *Biochem. Pharmacol.* **11**, 829–834 (1962).

104. S. Brenner, F. A. Dark, P. Gerhardt, M. H. Jeynes, O. Kandler, E. Kellenberger, E. Klieneberger-Nobel, K. McQuillen, M. Rubio-Huertos, M. R. J. Salton, R. E. Strange, J. Tomcsik, and C. Weibull, *Nature* **181**, 1713–1714 (1958).

105a. K. G. Lark, *Can. J. Microbiol.* **4**, 165–177, 179–189 (1958).

105b. J. Foldes and K. Meretey, *Acta Microbiol. Acad. Sci. Hung.* **7**, 43–49 (1960).

106. G. G. F. Newton, K. Crawford, and E. P. Abrams, *cited in:* E. P. Abraham, "Biochemistry of Some Peptide and Steroid Antibiotics," p. 81. Wiley, New York, 1957.

107a. P. E. Reynolds, *Biochim. et Biophys. Acta* **52**, 403–405 (1961); *Biochem. J.* **84**, 99P (1962).

107b. D. C. Jordan, *Biochem. Biophys. Research Communs.* **6**, 167–170 (1961).

108. J. L. Strominger, *J. Biol. Chem.* **234**, 1520–1524 (1959); *Antimicrobial Agents Ann.* **1960**, pp. 328–337 (1961).

109. C. Lark and K. G. Lark, *Can. J. Microbiol.* **5**, 369–379 (1959); *Biochim. et Biophys. Acta* **49**, 308–322 (1961).

110. A. L. Tuttle and H. Gest, *J. Bacteriol.* **79**, 213–216 (1960).

111. M. Welsch, *Compt. rend. soc. biol.* **151**, 1990–1993 (1957); *Schweiz. Z. allgem. Pathol. u. Bakteriol.* **21**, 741–768 (1958).

112. M. Welsch and P. Osterrieth, *Antonie van Leeuwenhoek, J. Microbiol. Serol.* **24**, 257–273 (1958).

113. Y. Takagi and N. Otsugi, *Biochim. et Biophys. Acta* **29**, 227–228 (1958).

114. N. Otsugi and Y. Takagi, *J. Biochem.* (*Tokyo*) **46**, 791–798 (1959).

115. H. J. Rogers and H. R. Perkins, *Biochem. J.* **74**, 6P; **77**, 448–459 (1960).

116a. M. Pitzura and W. Szybalski, *J. Bacteriol.* **77**, 614–620 (1959).

116b. T. Kawata, Th. Sall, and S. Mudd, *J. Bacteriol.* **79**, 459 (1960).

117. A. Bondi, J. Kornblum, and C. Forti, *Proc. Soc. Exptl. Biol. Med.* **96**, 270–272 (1957).

118. A. Buogo, A. di Marco, M. Ghione, A. Migliacci, and A. Sanfilippo, *Giorn. microbiol.* **6**, 131–145 (1958).

119. G. D. Shockman, *Proc. Soc. Exptl. Biol. Med.* **101**, 693–695 (1959).

120a. P. Barbieri, A. di Marco, L. Fuoco, and A. Rusconi, *Biochem. Pharmacol.* **3**, 101–109, 264–271 (1960).

120b. J. F. Collins and M. H. Richmond, *Nature* **195**, 142 (1962).
121. J. L. Strominger, *J. Biol. Chem.* **224**, 509–523, 525–532 (1957).
122. J. T. Park, *Biochem. J.* **70**, 2P; *Proc. 4th Intern. Congr. Biochem., Vienna, Abstr. Communs.* p. 136 (1958).
123a. E. Ito, N. Ishimoto, and M. Saito, *Nature* **181**, 906–907 (1958); *Arch. Biochem. Biophys.* **80**, 431–441 (1959).
123b. E. B. Wyllie and M. J. Johnson, *Biochim. et Biophys. Acta* **59**, 450–457 (1962).
123c. J. Roberts and M. J. Johnson, *Biochim. et Biophys. Acta* **59**, 458–466 (1962).
123d. P. Mandelstam, R. Loercher, and J. L. Strominger, *J. Biol. Chem.* **237**, 2683–2688 (1962).
123e. I. Eiji and J. L. Strominger, *J. Biol. Chem.* **237**, 2689–2695, 2696–2703 (1962).
124. J. G. Buchanan, G. R. Greenberg, B. Carss, J. J. Armstrong, and J. Baddiley, *Proc. 4th Intern. Congr. Biochem., Vienna, Abstr. Communs.* p. 7 (1958).
125. J. J. Saukkonen, *Nature* **192**, 816–818 (1961); *Acta Pathol. Microbiol. Scand.* **154** (Suppl.), 322–323 (1962).
126. M. Welsch, *Bull. acad. roy. méd. Belg.* **25**, 117–159 (1960).
127. J. Salmon, *Compt. rend. soc. biol.* **146**, 792–795 (1952).
128. J. Guillaume, G. Martin, and J. C. Derieux, *Ann. inst. Pasteur deLille* **10**, 159–178 (1958–1959); *Compt. rend. soc. biol.* **154**, 138–141 (1960).
129. M. Leyh-Bouille, *Compt. rend. soc. biol.* **154**, 1500–1502 (1960); **155**, 2457–2461 (1962).
130. P. Meadow, D. S. Hoare, and E. Work, *Biochem. J.* **66**, 270–282 (1957).
131. L. E. Rhuland, *J. Bacteriol.* **73**, 778–783 (1957).
132. J. L. Strominger and R. H. Threnn, *Biochim. et Biophys. Acta* **36**, 83–92 (1959).
133. T. Fukasawa and H. Nikaido, *Nature* **183**, 1131–1132 (1959); *Biochim. et Biophys. Acta* **48**, 470–483 (1961).
134. K. McQuillen, *J. Gen. Microbiol.* **18**, 498–512 (1958).
135. J. T. Park, Selective inhibition of bacterial cell wall synthesis. Its possible application in Chemotherapy. *In* "The Strategy of Chemotherapy" (T. S. Cowan and E. Rowatt, eds.), pp. 49–61. Cambridge Univ. Press, London and New York, 1958; *Antimicrobial Agents Ann.* **1960**, pp. 338–342 (1961).
136. R. Hancock and J. T. Park, *Nature* **181**, 1050–1052 (1958).
137. M. R. J. Salton and F. Shafa, *Nature* **181**, 1321–1324 (1958).
138a. J. Mandelstam and H. J. Rogers, *Nature* **181**, 956–957 (1958); *Biochem. J.* **72**, 654–662 (1959).
138b. I. D. Nestor, *Antibiotiki* **7**, 75–79, 296–305 (1962).
139a. R. Tulasne, R. Minck, A. Kirn, and J. Krembel, *Ann. inst. Pasteur* **99**, 859–874 (1960).
139b. B. M. Kagan, C. W. Molander, and H. J. Weinberger, *J. Bacteriol.* **83**, 1162–1163 (1962).
140. P. D. Cooper, *Bacteriol. Revs.* **20**, 28–48 (1956).
141. H. Doll, *Z. ges. inn. Med. u. ihre Grenzgebiete* **15**, 1021–1023 (1960).
142. K. F. J. Thatcher and E. R. Roberts, *Biochim. et Biophys. Acta* **49**, 411–450 (1961).
143. R. G. E. Murray, W. H. Francombe, and B. H. Mayall, *Can. J. Microbiol.* **5**, 641–648 (1959).
144. H. Gooder and W. R. Maxted, *Brit. Med. J.* **1**, 205 (1961).
145. H. G. Steinman, *Proc. Soc. Exptl. Biol. Med.* **106**, 227–231 (1961).

146. H. J. Rogers and J. Jeljaszewicz, *Biochem. J.* **80**, 6P; **81**, 576–584 (1961).
147. H. J. Rogers and J. Mandelstam, *Biochem. J.* **81**, 43P–44P (1961); **84**, 299–302 (1962).
148. A. Rau-Hund and O. Kandler, *Zentr. Bakteriol. Parasitenk. Abt. I Orig.* **184**, 272–278 (1962).
149. H. J. Rogers, Mode of action of the penicillins. *In* "Resistance of Bacteria to the Penicillins" (A. V. S. de Reuck and M. P. Cameron, eds.), pp. 25–43. Churchill, London, 1962.
150. R. Hancock, *Biochem. J.* **70**, 15P (1958).
151. R. E. Trucco and A. B. Pardee, *J. Biol. Chem.* **230**, 435–446 (1958).
152. M. H. Fusillo and D. L. Weiss, *Antibiotics & Chemotherapy* **8**, 21–26 (1958).
153. L. S. Prestidge and A. B. Pardee, *J. Bacteriol.* **74**, 48–49 (1957).
154. C. Hurwitz, J. M. Reiner, and J. V. Landau, *J. Bacteriol.* **76**, 612–617 (1958).
155. W. B. Hugo and A. D. Russell, *J. Bacteriol.* **80**, 436–440 (1960); **82**, 411–417 (1961); *J. Pharm. and Pharmacol.* **13**, 705–722 (1961).
156. E. P. Abraham and G. G. F. Newton, *Biochem. J.* **79**, 377–393 (1961).
157a. D. C. Hodgkin and E. N. Maslen, *Biochem. J.* **79**, 393–402 (1961).
157b. R. B. Morin, B. G. Jackson, E. H. Flynn, and R. W. Roeske, *J. Am. Chem. Soc.* **84**, 3400–3401 (1962).
158. B. Loder, G. G. F. Newton, and E. P. Abraham, *Biochem. J.* **79**, 408–416 (1961).
159. C. W. Hale, G. G. F. Newton, and E. P. Abraham, *Biochem. J.* **79**, 403–408 (1961).
160a. J. d'A. Jeffery, E. P. Abraham, and G. G. F. Newton, *Biochem. J.* **81**, 591–596 (1961).
160b. R. R. Chauvette, E. H. Flynn, B. G. Jackson, E. R. Lavagnino, R. B. Morin, R. A. Mueller, R. P. Pioch, R. W. Roeske, C. W. Ryan, J. L. Spencer, and E. Van Heyningen, *J. Am. Chem. Soc.* **84**, 3401–3402 (1962).
161. B. Crompton, M. Jago, K. Crawford, G. G. F. Newton, and E. P. Abraham, *Biochem. J.* **83**, 52–63 (1962).
162a. A. G. Moat, L. N. Ceci, and A. Bondi, *Proc. Soc. Exptl. Biol. Med.* **107**, 675–677 (1961).
162b. A. L. Demain and J. F. Newkirk, *Appl. Microbiol.* **10**, 321–325 (1962).
162c. P. A. Plattner, A. Boller, and H. H. Günthard, *Helv. Chim. Acta* **43**, 887–888 (1960).
163a. W. Keller-Schierlein and V. Prelog, *Helv. Chim. Acta* **44**, 1981–1985 (1961).
163b. U. Schmidt and F. Geiger, *Angew. Chem.* **74**, 328–329 (1962).
164. K. Mizuno, *Bull. Chem. Soc. Japan* **34**, 1419–1430, 1631–1639 (1961).
165a. J. M. Sieburth, *Science* **132**, 676–677 (1960); *J. Bacteriol.* **82**, 72–79 (1961).
165b. A. Delaunay, *Bull. schweiz. Akad. med. Wiss.* **17**, 455–476 (1962).
165c. W. Konigsberg and L. C. Craig, *J. Org. Chem.* **87**, 934–938 (1962).
165d. R. H. Adler and J. E. Snoke, *J. Bacteriol.* **83**, 1315–1317 (1962).
165e. J. L. Smith and E. D. Weinberg, *J. Gen. Microbiol.* **28**, 559–569 (1962).
165f. H. K. Kuramitsu and J. E. Snoke, *Biochim. et Biophys. Acta* **62**, 114–121 (1962).
166a. O. Mikes and F. Šorm, *Collection Czechoslov. Chem. Communs.* **27**, 581–590 (1962).
166b. E. P. Krysin and N. A. Poddubnaya, *Zhur. Obschei Khim.* **32**, 2102–2110 (1962).
167a. E. Bachmann and H. Zähner, *Arch. Mikrobiol.* **38**, 326–328 (1961).

167b. H. Bickel, E. Gaümann, G. Nussberger, P. Reusser, E. Visscher, W. Voser, A. Wettstein, and H. Zähner, *Helv. Chim. Acta* **43,** 2105–2118 (1960).

168. W. Sackmann, P. Reusser, L. Neipp, F. Kradolfer, and F. Gross, *Antibiotics & Chemotherapy* **12,** 34–45 (1962).

169. H. Bickel, E. Gaümann, W. Keller-Schierlein, V. Prelog, E. Visscher, A. Wettstein, and H. Zähner, *Experientia* **16,** 129–133 (1960).

170a. H. Zähner, R. Hütter, and E. Bachmann, *Arch. Mikrobiol.* **36,** 325–349 (1960).

170b. H. Bickel, R. Bosshardt, E. Gaümann, P. Reusser, E. Visscher, W. Voser, A. Wettstein, and H. Zähner, *Helv. Chim. Acta* **43,** 2118–2129, 2129–2138 (1960).

171. W. Keller-Schierlein and V. Prelog, *Helv. Chim. Acta* **44,** 709–713 (1961); **45,** 590–595 (1962).

172a. V. Prelog and A. Walser, *Helv. Chim. Acta* **45,** 631–637, 1732–1734 (1962).

172b. H. Bickel, B. Fechtig, G. E. Hall, W. Keller-Schierlein, V. Prelog, and E. Visscher, *Helv. Chim. Acta* **43,** 901–904 (1960).

172c. R. F. C. Brown, G. Büchi, W. Keller-Schierlein, V. Prelog, and J. Renz, *Helv. Chim. Acta* **43,** 1868–1871 (1960).

172d. J. Francis, H. M. Macturk, J. Madinaveitia, and G. A. Snow, *Biochem. J.* **55,** 596–607 (1953); *J. Chem. Soc.* pp. 2388–2396, 4080–4093 (1954).

172e. M. Inoue, *Bull. Chem. Soc. Japan* **35,** 1249–1254, 1255–1271 (1962).

172f. T. Morito, *J. Agr. Chem. Soc. Japan* **36,** 393–397, 398–402 (1962).

173a. M. Dautrevaux and G. Biserte, *Bull. soc. chim. biol.* **43,** 495–504 (1961).

173b. A. B. Silaev, G. S. Katrukha, and N. A. Kusmina, *Antibiotiki* **7,** 703–708 (1962).

174a. Z. T. Sinitsyna and S. M. Mamioff, *Uspekhi Khim.* **31,** 211–221 (1962).

174b. G. B. Chapman, *J. Bacteriol.* **84,** 169–179 (1962).

174c. B. A. Newton, *Bacteriol. Revs.* **20,** 14–27 (1956).

174d. D. Neubert and A. L. Lehinger, *Biochim. et Biophys. Acta* **62,** 556–565 (1962).

175. J. K. Spitznagel, *J. Exptl. Med.* **114,** 1063–1078, 1079–1091 (1961).

176. S. Shankman, V. Gold, and S. Higa, *Texas Repts. Biol. and Med.* **19,** 358–369 (1961).

177a. K. Vogler, *Experientia* **15,** 334–335 (1959).

177b. K. Vogler, P. Lanz, W. Lergier, and R. O. Studer, *Helv. Chim. Acta* **43,** 270–279, 279–286, 574–582, 1751–1759 (1960); **44,** 131-140 (1961); **45,** 819-826 (1962).

178. B. F. Erlanger and L. Goode, *Science* **131,** 669–670 (1960).

179. R. Schwyzer and P. Sieber, *Helv. Chim. Acta* **41,** 1582–1587 (1959); **43,** 1910–1915 (1960).

180. R. E. Winnick and T. Winnick, *Biochim. et Biophys. Acta* **53,** 461–468 (1961).

181. V. M. Stepanov and A. B. Silaev, *Zhur. Obschei Khim.* **31,** 3799–3804, 3804–3810, 3811–3814 (1961).

182. D. J. Buchanan-Davidson, M. A. Stahmann, C. A. Neeper, C. V. Seastone, and J. B. Wilson, *J. Bacteriol.* **80,** 595–599 (1960).

183. K. Kovacs, A. Kotai, and L. Szabo, *Nature* **185,** 266–267 (1960).

184a. W. Muller, *Naturwissenschaften* **49,** 156–157 (1962).

184b. W. Kersten and H. Kersten, *Z. Physiol. Chem. Hoppe-Seyler's* **327,** 234–242 (1962).

185. E. Reich, R. M. Franklin, A. J. Shatkin, and E. L. Tatum, *Science* **134,** 556–

557 (1961); *Biochim. et Biophys. Acta* **61**, 310–312 (1962); *Proc. Natl. Acad. Sci. U. S.* **48**, 1238–1244 (1962).

186a. I. H. Goldberg and M. Rabinowitz, *Science* **136**, 315–316 (1962).

186b. J. Hurwitz, J. J. Furth, M. Malamy, and M. Alexander, *Proc. Natl. Acad. Sci. U. S.* **48**, 1222–1229 (1962).

187. E. Harbers and W. Muller, *Biochem. Biophys. Research Communs.* **7**, 107–110 (1962).

188a. G. P. Wheeler and L. L. Bennett, Jr., *Biochem. Pharmacol.* **11**, 353–370 (1962).

188b. A. Nakata, *Biken's J.* **5**, 29–43 (1962).

189. B. Weinstein, O. P. Crews, M. A. Leaffer, B. R. Baker, and L. Goodman, *J. Org. Chem.* **27**, 1389–1394 (1962).

190. N. Takahayashi, Y. Mio, T. Oka, T. Shima, N. Shimahara, and M. Iki, *Chem. & Pharm. Bull. (Tokyo)* **10**, 147–151 (1962).

191. M. Kuroya, N. Ishida, K. Katagiri, J. I. Shoji, T. Yoshida, M. Mayama, K. Sato, S. Matsuura, Y. Niinome, and O. Shiratori, *J. Antibiotics (Japan)* **14**, 324–329 (1961).

192. T. Yoshida, K. Katagiri, and S. Yokozawa, *J. Antibiotics (Japan)* **14**, 330–334 (1961).

193. J. I. Shoji and K. Katagiri, *J. Antibiotics (Japan)* **14**, 335–339 (1961).

194. H. Yamaguchi, *J. Antibiotics (Japan)* **14**, 313–323 (1961).

195. K. Watanabe, *J. Antibiotics (Japan)* **14**, 1–13, 14–17 (1961).

196a. D. W. Russell, *J. Chem. Soc.* pp. 753–760 (1962).

196b. G. W. Butler, D. W. Russell, and R. T. J. Clarke, *Biochim. et Biophys. Acta* **58**, 507–513 (1962).

196c. Y. A. Ouchinnikov, V. T. Ivanov, A. A. Kiryushkin, and M. M. Shemyakin, *Izvest. Akad. Nauk. S.S.S.R.* p. 1497 (1962).

196d. M. M. Shemyakin, Y. A. Ouchinnikov, A. A. Kiryushkin, and V. T. Ivanov, *Tetrahedron Letters* pp. 301–306 (1962).

196e. J. C. MacDonald, *Can. J. Microbiol.* **6**, 27–34 (1960).

196f. R. Brown and C. Kelley, *Ann. Rept. Div. Lab. Research, N. Y. State Dept. Health* **1960**, p. 50; **1961**, p. 74.

197. A. J. Birch, D. W. Cameron, Y. Harada, and R. W. Rickards, *J. Chem. Soc.* pp. 303–306 (1962).

198. F. M. Strong, Antimycin, Coenzyme A, Kinetin and Kinins. *In* "Topics in Microbial Chemistry," p. 166. Wiley, New York, 1958.

199a. A. L. Tappell, *Biochem. Pharmacol.* **3**, 289–296 (1960).

199b. R. W. Estabrook, *Biochim. et Biophys. Acta* **60**, 236–248 (1962).

199c. A. M. Humphrey, *J. Biol. Chem.* **237**, 2384–2390 (1962).

199d. J. S. Rieske and W. S. Zaugg, *Biochem. Biophys. Research Communs.* **8**, 421–426 (1962).

200a. Y. Hamon and Y. Peron, *Compt. rend. acad. sci.* **253**, 1883–1885 (1961).

200b. G. Ivanovics, *Bacteriol. Revs.* **26**, 108–118 (1962).

200c. G. Ivanovics and L. Alföldi, *Nature* **174**, 465 (1954); *J. Gen. Microbiol.* **16**, 522–530 (1957).

201a. G. Ivanovics, L. Alföldi, and E. Abraham, *Zentr. Bakteriol. Parasitenk. Abt. I Orig.* **163**, 274–280 (1955).

201b. G. Ivanovics and E. Nagy, *J. Gen. Microbiol.* **19**, 407–418 (1958).

202a. F. Jacob, *Ann. inst. Pasteur* **86**, 149–160 (1954).

202b. M. Kageyama and F. Egami, *Life Sciences* **1**, 471–476 (1962).

203. R. Ben-Gurion and I. Hertman, *J. Gen. Microbiol.* **19,** 289–297 (1958); **21,** 135–153 (1959).
204. R. R. Brubaker and M. J. Surgalla, *J. Bacteriol.* **82,** 940–949 (1961); **84,** 539–545 (1962).
205. H. Farkas-Himsley and P. L. Seyfried, *Nature* **193,** 1193 (1962).
206. W. F. Goebel, G. T. Barry, M. A. Jesaitis, and E. M. Miller, *Nature* **176,** 700–701 (1955); *J. Exptl. Med.* **107,** 185–209 (1958).
207a. J. J. Hutton and W. F. Goebel, *J. Gen. Physiol.* **45,** (Suppl.), 125–141 (1962).
207b. E. Rude and W. F. Goebel, *J. Exptl. Med.* **116,** 73–100 (1962).
208. I. B. Holland, *Biochem. J.* **78,** 641–648 (1961).
209a. G. Ivanovics, L. Alföldi, and E. Nagy, *J. Gen. Microbiol.* **21,** 51–60 (1959).
209b. N. Masayatu and N. Masayoshi, *Biochem. Biophys. Research Communs.* **7,** 306–309 (1962).
210. M. Welsch, *Ergeb. Mikrobiol. Immunitätsforsch. Exptl. Therap.* **30,** 217–279 (1957).
211. M. Welsch, *J. Gen. Microbiol.* **18,** 491–497 (1958).
212. M. R. J. Salton, *Bacteriol. Revs.* **21,** 82–99 (1957).
213. J. Jolles and P. Jolles, *Compt. rend. acad. sci.* **253,** 2773–2775 (1961).
214. S. Kashiba, K. Niizu, S. Tanaka, H. Nozu, and T. Amano, *Biken's J.* **2,** 50–55 (1959).
215a. M. R. J. Salton, *J. Gen. Microbiol.* **18,** 481–490 (1958); **29,** 15–23 (1962).
215b. J. Mandelstam, *Biochem. J.* **84,** 294–298 (1962).
216. M. R. J. Salton and J. G. Pavlik, *Biochim. et Biophys. Acta* **39,** 398–407 (1960).
217. M. R. J. Salton, *Bacteriol. Revs.* **25,** 77–79 (1961).
218. A. Kohn and W. Szybalski, *Bacteriol. Proc.* (*Soc. Am. Bacteriologists*) p. 126 (1959); *J. Bacteriol.* **79,** 697–706 (1960).
219. W. C. Brown, W. E. Sandine, and P. R. Elliker, *J. Bacteriol.* **83,** 697–698 (1962).
220. D. J. Ralston and S. S. Elberg, *Proc. Soc. Exptl. Biol. Med.* **104,** 464–467 (1960); *J. Bacteriol.* **82,** 342–353 (1961).
221. E. C. Noller and S. E. Hartsell, *J. Bacteriol.* **81,** 482–491, 492–499 (1961).
222. W. Brumfitt, A. C. Wardlaw, and J. T. Park, *Nature* **181,** 1783–1784 (1958); *Brit. J. Exptl. Pathol.* **40,** 441–451 (1959).
223. Y. Mori, K. Kato, T. Matsubara, and S. Kotani, *Biken's J.* **3,** 139–150 (1960).
224. A. Furaya and Y. Ikeda, *J. Gen. Appl. Microbiol.* **6,** 40–48, 49–60 (1960).
225. J. M. Ghuysen, *Arch. intern. physiol. et biochem.* **65,** 173–305 (1957).
226. M. Welsch, *J. Gen. Physiol.* **45,** (Suppl.) 115–124 (1962).
227. T. Kawata, K. Asaki, and A. Tagagi, *J. Bacteriol.* **81,** 160–161 (1961).
228. S. Kotani, T. Hirano, K. Kitaura, K. Kato, and T. Matsubara, *Biken's J.* **2,** 143–150 (1959).
229. A. D. Brown, *Biochim. et Biophys. Acta* **48,** 352–361 (1961).
230. J. S. Murphy, *Virology* **11,** 510–513 (1960); *J. Gen. Physiol.* **45,** (Suppl.), 155–168 (1962).
231. D. J. Ralston, B. S. Baer, M. Lieberman, and A. P. Krueger, *J. Gen. Physiol.* **41,** 343–358 (1957); *J. Gen. Microbiol.* **24,** 313–325 (1961).
232. J. Panijel, *Ann. inst. Pasteur* **97,** 198–217 (1959).
233. E. Work, *Biochem. J.* **76,** 38P–39P (1960).
234a. W. Weidel and J. Primosigh, *J. Gen. Microbiol.* **18,** 513–517 (1958).
234b. N. K. Monakhov and S. A. Neufach, *Biokhimia* **27,** 495–501 (1962).

235. J. G. Hirsch, *J. Exptl. Med.* **103,** 589–611, 613–621 (1956); **111,** 323–337 (1960).

236. G. Moustardier, Ch. Dulong de Rosnay, P. du Pasquier, and J. Latrille, *Ann. inst. Pasteur* **101,** 192–202 (1961); **102,** 359–363 (1962).

237a. J. Guillaume, R. Osteux, and J. C. Derieux, *Compt. rend. soc. biol.* **155,** 85–90 (1961); *Compt. rend. acad. sci.* **254,** 2095–2097 (1962).

237b. J. C. Macdonald, *J. Biol. Chem.* **237,** 1977–1981 (1962).

238. A. Sivak, M. L. Meloni, F. Nobili, and E. Katz, *Biochim. et Biophys. Acta* **57,** 283–289; **62,** 80–90 (1962).

239a. E. Katz and H. Weissbach, *J. Biol. Chem.* **237,** 867–873 (1962).

239b. P. N. Morgan, M. I. Gibson, and F. Gibson, *Nature* **194,** 1239–1240 (1962).

240. R. C. Millican, *Biochim. et Biophys. Acta* **57,** 407–409 (1962).

241. J. M. Ingram and A. C. Blackwood, *Can. J. Microbiol.* **8,** 49–56 (1962).

242. K. Chambers, G. W. Kenner, M. J. Temple-Robinson, and B. R. Webster, *Proc. Chem. Soc.* pp. 291–292 (1960).

243a. T. D. Brock, *Bacteriol. Revs.* **25,** 32–48 (1961).

243b. P. S. Sypherd, N. Strauss, and H. P. Treffers, *Biochem. Biophys. Research Communs.* **7,** 477–481 (1962).

243c. E. Katz and H. Weissbach, *Biochem. Biophys. Research Communs.* **8,** 186–190 (1962).

243d. S. Okamoto and D. Mizuno, *Nature* **195,** 1022–1023 (1962).

244a. L. Cheng and J. F. Snell, *J. Bacteriol.* **83,** 711–719 (1962).

244b. C. G. Kurland, M. Nomura, and J. D. Watson, *J. Mol. Biol.* **4,** 388–394 (1962).

245. R. B. Yee, S. Pan, and H. M. Gezon, *J. Gen. Microbiol.* **27,** 521–527 (1962).

246a. T. Horiuchi, S. Horiuchi, and D. Mizuno, *Japan. J. Med. Sci. & Biol.* **12,** 99–107 (1959).

246b. F. E. Hahn and A. D. Wolfe, *Biochem. Biophys. Research Communs.* **6,** 464–468 (1962).

247. D. H. Ezekiel, *J. Bacteriol.* **81,** 319–326 (1961).

248a. A. I. Aronson and S. Spiegelman, *Biochim. et Biophys. Acta* **53,** 70–84, 84–95 (1961).

248b. J. L. Allison, R. E. Hartman, R. S. Hartman, A. D. Wolfe, J. Ciak, and F. E. Hahn, *J. Bacteriol.* **83,** 609–615 (1962).

249. H. Rapoport and K. G. Holden, *J. Am. Chem. Soc.* **82,** 5510–5511 (1960); **84,** 635–642 (1962).

250. D. Stavri and A. Marx, *Arch. roumaines pathol. exptl. microbiol.* **20,** 287–294 (1961).

251. P. Reichard, *Advances in Enzymol.* **21,** 263–294 (1959).

252. G. D. Daves, Jr., R. K. Robins, and C. C. Cheng, *J. Am. Chem. Soc.* **83,** 3904–3905 (1961); **84,** 1724–1728 (1962).

253. G. D. Daves, Jr., R. K. Robins, and C. C. Cheng, *J. Org. Chem.* **26,** 5256 (1961).

254. J. Baddiley and J. G. Buchanan, *Quart. Revs.* (*London*) **12,** 152–172 (1958).

255. S. C. Hartman and J. M. Buchanan, *Advances in Enzymol.* **21,** 199–261 (1959).

256. J. L. Strominger, *Physiol. Revs.* **40,** 55–111 (1960).

257. K. Anzai, J. Nagatsu, and S. Suzuki, *J. Antibiotics* (*Japan*) **14,** 340–342 (1961); **15,** 103–105 (1962).

258a. K. Anzai and S. Suzuki, *J. Antibiotics* (*Japan*) **14,** 253 (1961).

258b. J. S. Webb, D. B. Cosulich, J. H. Mowat, J. B. Patrick, R. W. Broschard,

W. E. Meyer, R. P. Williams, C. F. Wolf, W. Fulmor, C. Pidacks, and J. E. Lancaster, *J. Am. Chem. Soc.* **84,** 3185–3187, 3187–3188, 3188–3190 (1962).

258c. J. E. Evans, E. A. Musser, and J. E. Gray, *Antibiotics & Chemotherapy* **11,** 445–453 (1961).

258d. R. F. Pittillo and B. G. Quinnelly, *Antibiotics & Chemotherapy* **12,** 55–64 (1962).

258e. E. Reich, A. J. Shatkin, and E. L. Tatum, *Biochim. et Biophys. Acta* **53,** 132–149 (1961).

258f. A. J. Shatkin, E. Reich, R. M. Franklin, and E. L. Tatum, *Biochim. et Biophys. Acta* **55,** 277–289 (1962).

258g. R. Truhaut and G. Deysson, *Compt. rend. soc. biol.* **154,** 718–719 (1960).

258h. T. Merz, *Science* **133,** 329–330 (1961).

258i. S. Shiba, A. Terawaki, T. Taguchi, and J. Kawamata, *Nature* **183,** 1056–1057 (1959).

258j. Y. Nakata, K. Nakata, and Y. Sakamoto, *Biochem. Biophys. Research Commns.* **6,** 339–343 (1961).

258k. H. Kersten, *Biochim. et Biophys. Acta* **55,** 556–557 (1962); *Z. physiol. Chem. Hoppe-Seyler's* **329,** 31–39 (1962).

258l. G. Balassa, *Ann. inst. Pasteur* **102,** 547–555 (1962).

259. M. Welsch, *J. Bacteriol.* **42,** 801–814 (1942).

260a. H. O. Hettche and B. Weber, *Arch. Hyg.* **123,** 69–80 (1939).

260b. P. W. Trown, E. P. Abraham, G. G. F. Newton, C. W. Hale, and G. A. Miller, *Biochem. J.* **84,** 157–166 (1962).

260c. B. Akermark, *Acta Chim. Scand.* **16,** 599–606 (1962).

261a. R. Bentley, D. S. Bhate, and J. G. Keil, *J. Biol. Chem.* **237,** 859–866 (1962).

261b. E. Akita, Y. Okami, M. Suzuki, K. Maeda, T. Takeuchi, and H. Umezawa, *J. Antibiotics (Japan)* **15,** 130–136 (1962).

262a. R. Bentley and J. G. Keil, *J. Biol. Chem.* **237,** 867–873 (1962).

262b. N. Tanaka and H. Umezawa, *J. Gen. Appl. Microbiol.* **8,** 149–159, 160–164 (1962); *J. Antibiotics (Japan)* **15,** 189–190 (1962).

263a. J. R. Turner and D. S. Tarbell, *Science* **134,** 1435–1436 (1961); *Proc. Natl. Acad. Sci. U. S.* **48,** 733–735 (1962).

263b. T. Azuma, K. Kojo, and T. Koibuchi, *J. Fermentation Technol.* **40,** 290–296, 297–302, 332–335, 336–341 (1962).

263c. E. Borowski, C. P. Schaffner, H. Lechevalier, and B. S. Schwartz, *Antimicrobial Agents Ann.* **1960,** pp. 532–538 (1961).

263d. S. G. Bradley, P. J. Farber, and L. A. Jones, *Antimicrobial Agents Ann.* **1960,** pp. 558–569 (1961).

264. R. A. Steggle, F. L. Jackson, V. Moses, and M. J. H. Smith, *Biochem. J.* **78,** 7P (1961).

265a. J. O. Lampen, E. R. Morgan, A. Slocum, and P. Arnow, *J. Bacteriol.* **78,** 282–289; *Proc. Soc. Exptl. Biol. Med.* **101,** 792–797 (1959).

265b. S. C. Kinsky, *Proc. Natl. Acad. Sci. U. S.* **48,** 1049–1056 (1962).

266a. F. Marini, P. Arnow, and J. O. Lampen, *J. Gen. Microbiol.* **24,** 51–62 (1961).

266b. B. K. Ghosh and A. N. Chatterjee, *Antibiotics & Chemotherapy* **12,** 204–206; 221–224 (1962).

267. L. Horvath and A. Szentirmai, *Antibiotics & Chemotherapy* **10,** 303–305 (1960).

268a. M. Ghione, A. Sanfilippo, R. Mazzoleni, and A. Migliacci, *Giorn. microbiol.* **9,** 73–82 (1961).

268b. C. V. Pichappa, T. S. Raman, and E. R. B. Shanmugasundaram, *Experientia* **18**, 269 (1962).
269. T. Tsukahara, *Japan. J. Microbiol.* **5**, 41–50 (1961).
270. Y. Henis and N. Grossowicz, *J. Gen. Microbiol.* **23**, 345–355 (1960).
271a. D. Gottlieb and S. Ramachandrian, *Biochim. et Biophys. Acta* **53**, 391–396, 396–402 (1961).
271b. M. C. Khosla, *J. Sci. Ind. Research (India)* **21**, 327–330 (1962).
271c. J. D. Brodie, G. W. Watson, and J. W. Porter, *Biochem. Biophys. Research Communs.* **8**, 76–80 (1962).
271d. M. A. Siddiqui and W. Rodwell, *Biochem. Biophys. Research Communs.* **8**, 110–113 (1962).
271e. A. J. Birch, M. Kocor, N. Sheppard, and J. Winter, *J. Chem. Soc.* pp. 1502–1504 (1962).
271f. E. Härri, W. Loeffler, H. P. Sigg, H. Stähelin, C. Stoll, C. Tamm, and D. Wiesinger, *Helv. Chim. Acta* **45**, 839–853 (1962).
272a. C. Tamm and J. Gutzwiller, *Helv. Chim. Acta* **45**, 1726–1731 (1962).
272b. L. S. Ciereszko, *Trans. N. Y. Acad. Sci.* **24**, 502–503 (1962).
272c. B. M. Baird, T. G. Halsall, E. R. H. Jones and G. Lowe, *Proc. Chem. Soc.* p. 257 (1961).
272d. N. L. Allinger and J. L. Coke, *J. Org. Chem.* **26**, 4522–4529 (1961).
272e. W. O. Godtfredsen, K. Roholt, and L. Tybring, *Lancet* **1**, 928–931 (1962).
272f. W. O. Godtfredsen and S. Vangedal, *Tetrahedron* **18**, 1029–1049 (1962).
272g. A. C. Cope, R. K. Bly, E. P. Burrows, O. J. Ceder, E. Ciganek, B. T. Gillis, R. F. Porter, and H. E. Johnson, *J. Am. Chem. Soc.* **84**, 2170–2178 (1962).
272h. E. Gaümann, R. Hütter, W. Keller-Schierlein, L. Neipp, V. Prelog, and H. Zähner, *Helv. Chim. Acta* **43**, 601–606 (1960).
272i. H. Griesebach and H. A. Achenbach, *Tetrahedron Letters* 569–572 (1962).
273. V. Prelog, A. M. Gold, G. Talbot, and A. Zamojski, *Helv. Chim. Acta* **45**, 4–21 (1962).
274a. W. M. Stark and R. L. Smith, *Progr. Ind. Microbiol.* **3**, 211–230 (1961); *Appl. Microbiol.* **10**, 293–296 (1962).
274b. S. L. Brinberg, A. P. Skvortsova, and S. S. Krivobokava, *Antibiotiki* **7**, 689–692 (1962).
275a. J. Dominguez, J. D. Dunitz, H. Gerlach, and V. Prelog, *Helv. Chim. Acta* **45**, 129–138 (1962).
275b. J. Beck, H. Gerlach, V. Prelog, and W. Voser, *Helv. Chim. Acta* **45**, 620–631 (1962).
275c. P. Sensi, A. M. Greco, and R. Ballotta, *Antibiot. Ann.* **1959–1960**, 262–270 (1960).
275d. P. Sensi, N. Maggi, and R. Ballotta, *Chemotherapia* **7**, 137–144 (1963).
275e. V. Prelog, *Chemotherapia* **7**, 133–136 (1963).
276. T. Kaneda, J. C. Butte, S. B. Taubman, and J. W. Corcoran, *J. Biol. Chem.* **237**, 322–328 (1962).
277. H. Griesebach, H. Hofheinz, and H. Achenbach, *Z. Naturforsch.* **17b**, 64 (1962).
278a. H. Griesebach and H. Achenbach, *Z. Naturforsch.* **17b**, 6–8 (1962).
278b. D. Gilner and P. R. Srinivasan, *Biochem. Biophys. Research Communs.* **8**, 299–304 (1962).
279a. T. Okuda and M. Suzuki, *Chem. & Pharm. Bull.* **9**, 1014–1015 (1961).
279b. A. Zehnder and E. O. Hughes, *Can. J. Microbiol.* **4**, 399–408 (1958).

279c. T. Okuda, M. Suzuki, T. Furumai, and H. Takahashi, *Chem. & Pharm. Bull.* **10,** 639–640 (1962).
280. K. V. Rao, *Antibiotics & Chemotherapy* **12,** 123–127 (1962).
281. C. J. Shepard, *J. Gen. Microbiol.* **18,** iv (1958).
282. D. Kerridge, *J. Gen. Microbiol.* **19,** 497–506 (1958).
283. M. E. Greig, R. A. Walk, and A. J. Gibbons, *J. Bacteriol.* **75,** 489–491 (1958).
284. Y. Tsukada, T. Sugimori, K. Imai, and M. Katagiri, *J. Bacteriol.* **83,** 70–75 (1962).
285. K. Gundersen and T. Wadstein, *J. Gen. Microbiol.* **28,** 325–332 (1962).
286. S. G. Bradley, *Nature* **194,** 315–316 (1962).
286a. W. J. Cooney and S. G. Bradley, *Antimicrobial Agents and Chemotherapy* 237–244 (1961).
286b. A. Ermili, R. Giuliano, and P. Tafaro, *Ann. chim.* (*Rome*) **52,** 332–339, 404–408, 641–651 (1962).
286c. S. W. Tanenbaum and E. W. Bassett, *Biochim. et Biophys. Acta* **59,** 524–526 (1962).
287. G. Stork and M. Tomasz, *J. Am. Chem. Soc.* **84,** 310–313 (1962).
288. A. Rhodes, B. Boothroyd, M. P. McGonagle, and G. A. Somerfield, *Biochem. J.* **81,** 28–37 (1961).
289a. A. Rhodes, M. P. McGonagle, and G. A. Somerfield, *Chem. & Ind.* (*London*) pp. 611–612 (1962).
289b. O. von Lofferer and G. Riehl, *Antibiotica et Chemotherapia* **10,** 335–397 (1962).
289c. J. F. Grove, *Quart. Revs.* **17,** 1–19 (1963).
290. B. Boothroyd, E. J. Napier, and G. A. Somerfield, *Biochem. J.* **80,** 34–37 (1961).
291. A. C. Day, J. Nabney, and A. I. Scott, *Proc. Chem. Soc.* p. 284 (1960).
292. A. Brossi, M. Baumann, M. Gerecke and E. Kyburz, *Helv. Chim. Acta* **43,** 1444–1447, 2071–2082, 2082–2087 (1960); **45,** 813–819, 2241–2256 (1962).
293. V. Arkley, J. Attenburrow, G. I. Gregory, and T. Walker, *J. Chem. Soc.* pp. 1260–1268, 1269–1276, 1277–1281, 1282–1291 (1962); pp. 1603–1609, 1610–1618 (1963).
294. J. E. Page and S. E. Staniforth, *J. Chem. Soc.* pp. 1292–1303 (1962).
295. D. Taub, C. H. Kuo, and N. L. Wendler, *Chem. & Ind.* (*London*) pp. 557, 1617–1618 (1962); *Tetrahedron* **19,** 1–18 (1963).
296. Z. Vaněk and M. Souček, *Folia microbiol.* (*Prague*), **7,** 262–268 (1962).
297. M. Jackson, E. L. Dulaney, I. Putter, H. M. Schaffer, F. J. Wolf, and H. B. Woodruff, *Biochim. et Biophys. Acta* **62,** 616–619 (1962).
298. H. Auterhoff, H. Frauendorff, W. Liesenklas, and C. Schwandt, *Angew. Chem.* **74,** 586–587 (1962).
299. A. Brossi, M. Baumann, and F. Burckhardt, *Helv. Chim. Acta* **45,** 1292–1297 (1962).
300. K. Takahashi and S. Miyashita, *Chem. & Pharm. Bull.* (*Tokyo*), **10,** 603–606, 607–611 (1962).
301. J-I. Shoji, *Chem. & Pharm. Bull.* (*Tokyo*) **10,** 483–491 (1962).
302. S. G. Bradley, *Develop. Ind. Microbiol.* **3,** 362–369 (1962).
303. A. Jabbar and A. Rahim, *J. Pharm. Sci.* **51,** 595–596 (1962).
304. H. H. Warren, M. Finkelstein, and D. A. Scola, *J. Am. Chem. Soc.* **84,** 1926–1927 (1962).
305. H. Brockmann, Jr. and M. Legrand, *Naturwissenschaften* **49,** 374 (1962).

306. A. di Marco and P. Pennella, *Progr. in Ind. Microbiol.* **1**, 45–92 (1959).
307. T. L. Fields, A. S. Kende, and J. H. Boothe, *J. Am. Chem. Soc.* **83**, 4612–4618 (1961).
308. I. Gado and I. Horvath, *Acta Microbiol. Acad. Sci. Hung.* **9**, 1–10 (1962).
309. V. N. Shaposhnikov, N. S. Egorov, and I. P. Baranova, *Izvest. Akad. Nauk S.S.S.R.* **144**, 1387–1389 (1962).
310. G. Kobrich, *Angew. Chem.* **74**, 443–452 (1962).
311a. E. Stempel, *Am. J. pharm.* (*Suppl. Public Health*) **134**, 114–132 (1962).
311b. K. H. Spitzy, *Antibiotica et Chemotherapia* **10**, 193–334 (1962).
312. S. Gatenbeck, *Biochem. Biophys. Research Communs.* **6**, 422–426 (1962).
313. D. Hendlin, E. L. Dulaney, D. Drescher, T. Cook, and L. Chaiet, *Biochim. et Biophys. Acta* **58**, 635–636 (1962).
314. A. J. Birch, J. F. Snell, and P. J. Thomson, *J. Chem. Soc.* pp. 425–429 (1962).
315. M. Schach von Wittenau, J. J. Beereboom, R. K. Blackwood, and C. R. Stephens, *J. Am. Chem. Soc.* **84**, 2645–2647 (1962).
316. L. H. Conover, K. Butter, J. D. Johnston, J. J. Korst, and R. B. Woodward, *J. Am. Chem. Soc.* **84**, 3222–3223 (1962).
317. M. W. Miller and F. A. Hochstein, *J. Org. Chem.* **27**, 2525–2528 (1962).
318. E. L. Dulaney, I. Putter, D. Drescher, L. Chaiet, W. J. Miller, F. J. Wolf, and D. Hendlin, *Biochim. et Biophys. Acta* **60**, 447–449 (1962).
319. H. Muxfeldt, *Angew. Chem.* (*Intern. Ed.*) **1**, 372–381 (1962).
320. A. I. Scott and C. T. Bedford, *J. Am. Chem. Soc.* **84**, 2271–2272 (1962).
321. J. R. D. McCormick, P. A. Miller, J. Johnson, W. Arnold, and N. O. Sjolander, *J. Am. Chem. Soc.* **84**, 3023–3025 (1962).
322. J. F. Snell and L. Cheng, *Develop. Ind. Microbiol.* **2**, 107–132 (1961).
323. S. Banic, *Zentr. Bakteriol. Parasitenk. Abt. I Orig.* **186**, 219–223 (1962).
324. K. H. Ibsen and M. R. Urist, *Proc. Soc. Exptl. Biol. Med.* **109**, 797–801 (1962).
325. T. J. Franklin, *Biochem. J.* **84**, 110P (1962).
326. M. Welsch, *Rev. franç. études clin. biol.* **7**, 870–876 (1962).
327. R. Y. Stainer, Adaptation, evolutionary and physiological: or Darwinism among micro-organisms. *In* "Adaptation in Microorganisms" (R. Davies and E. F. Gale, eds.), pp. 1–14. Cambridge Univ. Press, London and New York, 1953.
328. P. W. Brian, The production of antibiotics by micro-organisms in relation to biological equilibria in soil. *In* "Selective Toxicity and Antibiotics" (J. F. Danielli and R. Brown, eds.), pp. 357–372. Cambridge Univ. Press, London and New York, 1949.
329a. R. F. Nigrelli, *Trans. N. Y. Acad. Sci.* **24**, 496–497 (1962).
329b. J. McN. Sieburth and D. M. Pratt, *Trans. N. Y. Acad. Sci.* **24**, 498–501 (1962).
330. C. E. Lucas, External metabolites and ecological adaptation. *In* "Selective Toxicity and Antibiotics" (J. F. Danielli and R. Brown, eds.), pp. 336–356. Cambridge Univ. Press, London and New York, 1949; On the significance of external metabolites in ecology. *In* "Mechanisms in Biological Competition (F. L. Milthorpe, ed.), pp. 190–206. Cambridge Univ. Press, London and New York, 1961.
331. J. W. Foster, "Chemical Activities of Fungi." Academic Press, New York, 1949.
332. S. A. Waksman, H. S. Reilly, and D. A. Harris, *Proc. Soc. Exptl. Biol. Med.* **66**, 617–619; *J. Bacteriol.* **54**, 451–466 (1947).

333. P. R. Burkholder, S. H. Sun, J. Ehrlich, and J. L. Anderson, *Ann. N. Y. Acad. Sci.* **60,** 102–123 (1954); *Bull. Torrey Botan. Club* **82,** 108–117 (1955).
334. H. J. Kutzner, *Pathol. et Microbiol.* **24,** 170–191 (1961).
335. M. Welsch, *Giorn. microbiol.* **1,** 339–348 (1956).
336. M. Welsch, *Virology* **2,** 703–704 (1956); *Bull. Research Council Israel* **7E,** 141–154 (1958); *Ann. N. Y. Acad. Sci.* **81,** 974–993 (1959).
337. M. Welsch, R. Corbaz, and L. Ettlinger, *Schweiz. Z. allgem. Pathol. u. Bakteriol.* **20,** 454–458 (1957).
338. M. Welsch, *Intern. Bull. Bacteriol. Nomencl. Taxon.* **9,** 27–29 (1959); *Mikrobiologiya* **28,** 451–459 (1959).

AUTHOR INDEX

Numbers in parentheses are reference numbers and indicate that an author's work is referred to although his name is not cited in the text. Numbers in italic show the page on which the complete reference is listed.

A

C

D

E

F

G

H

L

N

O

P

T

U

V

W

SUBJECT INDEX

Bold face figures following names of organisms indicate mention of antibiotic(s) produced by them; following names of compounds, their structure.

A

B

D

E

G

H

M

O

Q

R

U

TOPICAL SUBJECT INDEX—VOLUMES I–VII

B

C

H

I

J

K

L

O

S

U

X

Y

Z